# Fundamentals of
# FORESTRY ECONOMICS

# The American Forestry Series

HENRY J. VAUX, *Consulting Editor*

---

Walter Mulford was Consulting Editor of this series from its inception in 1931 until
January 1, 1952.

# Fundamentals of
# FORESTRY ECONOMICS

## WILLIAM A. DUERR

*Professor of Forestry Economics*
*and Chairman of Department*
*State University of New York*
*College of Forestry at Syracuse University*

McGRAW-HILL BOOK COMPANY, INC.

New York   Toronto   London   1960

To
Jean Barnes Duerr

# PREFACE

A LL OVER the world, new interest in forest culture and utilization is demanding that new attention be given their economic aspects. In the United States, just since World War II, industrial forestry has taken a tremendous leap ahead. Public forestry has become more intensive and also more attentive to the multiple uses of the resource. Consumers are being offered wider choices of everything, including wood products and the services of forest land. The nation is seeking ways to supply the ravenous demands of a steeply rising population. In such an environment, forestry economics is thrust upon our attention. We are compelled to understand as clearly as we can the economic question of forestry: How far may the forest owner reasonably carry his land-management efforts and outlays? What should guide the management decisions of the timber-processing and the timber-marketing firm? What are the consumer's alternatives? How does the forest economy carry out its function of getting forest goods and services into people's hands? What are its defects, and how mend them? One must understand such questions in order to be an intelligent participant in the mounting events of forestry or even to be an intelligent witness to these events.

Out of such experience as I have with the economic questions of forestry, I have tried in this book to sift the fundamentals, sort them into principles, and illustrate them with cases, mostly from American forestry.

I have written the book to students of forestry economics—those who are out of college as well as those who are in. I hope, indeed, that many of the chapters will be useful as a reference for resource managers in industry and other branches of private forestry and in public service, for research foresters and economists, and for anyone who is making a serious study of resource conservation.

As for the college student, I assume that by the time he gets to this book he has had at least an introduction to silviculture, forest products, and forest engineering and measurements. I assume that he knows something about algebra and geometry, but not calculus. And I suppose that he has taken one or two terms of general introductory economics and retained the customary amount of it.

The book is meant for use as a whole or in part. As a whole, it represents perhaps three hours of course work for an academic year. For shorter programs, the instructor may assign reading from selected chapters. Some illustrative selections are listed below.

| General survey of forestry economics | | Production economics of forestry | | Financial aspects of forestry | | Marketing and prices of forest products | | Macro-economics of forestry | |
|---|---|---|---|---|---|---|---|---|---|
| 1 | *17* | 1 | 11 | 1 | 16 | 1 | 14 | 1 | *17* |
| 5 | 18 | *3* | 12 | 5 | *17* | 2 | 17 | 5 | 18 |
| 6 | 19 | 4 | 13 | 6 | 18 | 3 | 18 | 6 | 24 |
| *8* | *20* | 5 | 14 | 8 | 19 | 5 | 19 | *8* | 25 |
| 9 | 21 | 6 | 15 | 9 | *20* | 6 | 20 | 9 | 29 |
| 11 | 26 | 7 | 16 | 10 | 23 | *8* | 21 | 10 | 30 |
| 13 | 28 | 8 | 26 | *13* | 26 | 9 | 22 | *13* | 31 |
| 14 | *30* | 9 | *27* | 14 | 27 | *11* | 23 | 14 | 32 |
| 15 | 31 | *10* | *28* | *15* | 28 | *13* | *28* | *15* | 33 |

For still further shortening, the instructor may wish to cover a few of the chapters by working them into his talks and omitting formal assignment of the reading. Chapters that may lend themselves to such treatment are listed in italics.

Whatever the program, the text can well be supplemented by outside reading. The student will find it helpful to refer at times to his introductory economics text. Among other suitable outside readings are the references cited in the footnotes.

Many of the special terms used in the book are set in distinctive type at the place where they are first defined or explained. In this way the terms can be located readily during review. They can also be found through the boldface numbers in the index, which thus doubles as a glossary. The student, especially the one who is covering selected chapters, should make use of this glossary in the course of reading.

Whereas many texts list questions for study and discussion at the ends of chapters, this one brings them up within chapters, at the points where they arise. The questions are marked by square brackets so that the reader may, if he prefers, pass over them and return later. The purpose of the questions is to provoke reflection and original thinking and not to send the student scurrying to some adjacent paragraph for a pat answer.

In the College of Forestry at Syracuse, one of our three weekly meetings in undergraduate forestry economics is a sectional laboratory in which small groups of men carry out experiments, work practice problems, and discuss questions such as the bracketed ones in the text. Some of the materials used in these highly productive sessions are being assembled into a manual. As an aid to the student in grasping otherwise elusive ideas, the instructor may find the laboratory approach a useful one, or at least the assignment of practice problems of the take-home variety.

A number of persons have been responsible for getting me into this venture and keeping me at it. Henry Vaux of the University of California suggested that we write a book together, but then he was made a dean and had to bow out of our project for want of time. Otherwise this would be a much better book. Professor Ronald Beazley of the University of Minnesota read some of the chapters when they were in the formative stage of "talks on forestry economics," and encouraged me to go ahead at a time when I was very much in doubt. My wife, Jean, has given me constant help and support. A good conspirator has been Dr. Marion Clawson of Resources for the Future, who in 1953 proposed the idea of my writing a textbook, and later suggested that I seek financial help from that foundation.

A generous grant from Resources for the Future enabled me to meet the out-of-pocket costs of preparing the book.

While I was doing the work, I was continually nudged and prompted by the men from whom I have learned about forestry and economics, personally and through their writings. This is their book, though I am not sure enough of their approval, or even, always, of their identity, to charge them with it. Some of my most obvious debts I have acknowledged in the course of the text.

In processed form, copies of the manuscript have knocked about the country and in other corners of the world for the past two or three years. I am grateful to the teachers and students of forestry economics and forest management who used the manuscript in class and gave me their criticism, and to my many other critics at the schools and in the United States Forest Service and forest industry. If I had taken all their suggestions for deletion, there would be no book left. And if I had accepted all their other proposals, I should have a finer book in view, but finishing it would be beyond me. As it is, I have picked and chosen the ideas I thought I could handle, and have no one but myself to blame for the outcome.

I shall not try to name all these good friends and colleagues who helped me. However, I want to mention my first four Ph.D. students—Wallace Christensen, Hans Brandes, Frederick Hopkins, and Robert Seale—who argued my ideas with me as a new teacher and helped me put them across to undergraduates. I should like also to thank two hardy and generous critics who sifted the entire manuscript with special care: Professors John Zivnuska of the University of California and Joseph Zaremba of the College of Forestry at Syracuse.

*William A. Duerr*

# CONTENTS

## Part Four. Institutions of the Forest Economy

## Part Five. Operation and Planning of the Forest Economy

# Part One

# INTRODUCTION

**Chapter 1**

**SUBJECT
OF FORESTRY
ECONOMICS**

E CONOMICS, as you know, is the study of how we manage our resources to help satisfy our wants. The *economics of forestry* centers on the questions of resource management that especially involve forests. Its hub is forest-land management,[1] and from there its spokes extend into the management of forest-products conversion, distribution, and consumption. It considers these subjects individually, and it considers them collectively in the form of the forest economy and its workings.

Some foresters have the notion that the economics of forestry means the dollars and cents of forestry. This notion is misleading. It is like defining forest surveying as the feet and inches of forestry. Feet and inches are simply units of measure used for precision in surveying. They are a tool, not the subject, of surveying. And so dollars and cents are just a measuring unit—a tool, not the subject—of economics.

Actually, the subject of economics is people. Thus the subject at once claims our special interest. Economics is the study of certain aspects of our own behavior—our behavior, it has been said, "in the ordinary business of life."[2] Now if we take this study of human behavior and apply it to the cases where forest resources are significantly involved, we have our present field.

But if the field is simply the application of economics to forestry problems, is there really any need for it as a special study? Why not just learn general economics, to be applied when and as required? Dr. Henry

[1] Duerr, William A., and Henry J. Vaux (eds.): *Research in the Economics of Forestry*, Charles Lathrop Pack Forestry Foundation, Washington, 1953, p. 209.

[2] Marshall, Alfred: *Principles of Economics*, 8th ed., Macmillan and Co., Limited, London, 1930, p. 1.

3

Vaux of the University of California has commented on this question.[3] He believes that forestry has three characteristics that distinguish it from much of the remaining economy and call for economic analysis different from most in emphasis and method. These characteristics are, first, the long period of production in timber growing; second, the fact that much timber is, at one and the same time, both capital plant and finished product; third, the fact that many forest values are not directly measured by existing markets. We shall be studying these three economic features of forestry. Dr. Vaux adds that, even in the absence of such features, the special field would still emerge because of the great importance of the forest industry and because of its peculiarities in respect to organization, institutions, techniques, and terminology. This point too we shall understand better as we work our way into the economics of forestry.

Economics of forestry, or forestry economics—these are the field's formal names. The commoner, shorthand term is *forest economics.* Surely our rose by this easier name smells as sweet, though one should remember that he is speaking not just of the economics of the forest but of the whole process of creating and converting and using the products of forest land.

However termed, our field abounds in fascination and excitement, for (permitting ourselves some unreasonable biases) it is a study of man, the most interesting creature, in relation to forestry, the most interesting profession.

Let us take some sample questions in the economics of forestry—not mainly to answer them but rather to illustrate our brief definition and point up some of the characteristics of the field. Thus, we can introduce the chapters to come, which are really our main definition of the subject.

### PRICE AND CONSERVATION

If you will leaf through past volumes of the *Journal of Forestry*—or, for that matter, talk to members of the forestry faculty—you will discover a widespread belief within our profession that the general arrival of intensive timber management in the United States waits upon a higher level of prices for timber, presumably in relation to costs of production. In other words, we tend to feel that most forest owners need high prices as an incentive to practice "good forestry." Is this belief correct? What role *does* the price of wood play in forest conservation? Here is a question in the economics of forestry.

Interestingly, the answer to the question is different from what we might expect. The answer is that price level has a variable influence

[3] Vaux, Henry J.: "Content of Forest Economics," in Duerr and Vaux: Work cited, pp. 17–18.

upon the intensity of forestry: Often the influence is minor or even negligible. In other cases a high price tends to induce owners to practice "poor forestry"!

In many businesses, it's true, a rise in product price while costs are lagging normally leads to expansion of output and more intensive management. Thus sawmills tend to intensify their operations if lumber values have gone up. But in timber growing, when the price of the product rises, the cost of producing it invariably increases also, because the two are hitched together, in ways that we shall explore later on. Indeed, the two—prices and costs—may rise equally, leaving the economic position of the forest owner as a timber grower not a whit changed! Or the rise in price may make timber merchantable that formerly was not, and thus heighten the incentives for liquidation on the part of the owner who inclines in this direction. Then again, for other owners, high price may encourage certain forestry investments such as in planting.

Thus a general answer to how the timber-price level affects forestry is, "That depends." Forestry economics endeavors to explain *on what it depends*. Later in this book, we shall give a lot of thought to the question.

But where does one get the idea that high timber prices generally favor the practice of forestry? Perhaps in part the idea is rather instinctive. A rise in returns calls forth heavier investments: What could be more obvious? Perhaps in part the idea comes from a common-sense interpretation of European forestry. There, intensive silviculture has attended high prices. And so one jumps to the conclusion that it will do so always and everywhere.

At any rate, the inference that this example seems to urge upon us is that although forestry economics does deal with the behavior of common people like ourselves, the solution of its problems is not always just a matter of common sense. In fact, the exercise of common sense and the ready endorsement of the obvious may be bear traps, and foresters can get caught in them.

### GUIDING SOCIAL POLICY

Studying the economics of forestry helps a forester in two ways: First, it helps him better to perceive and appreciate and explain what goes on around him: to be an intelligent *witness* at forestry events. Second, it helps him to make better recommendations and judgments: to be an intelligent *participant* in forestry events. The first of these two parts played by forestry economics is illustrated in the question just discussed: the role of price in conservation. If one grasps this role, he can better understand the condition of the wooded properties that he observes along the countryside and explain why their owners have put them into this condition. Now take a corollary question that illustrates the second part played by our studies, the part that leads to someone's taking action. If product price is not significant in forest conservation, then what *is?* That is to say, what conditions will bring people to "practice forestry"?

What *will* induce people to practice forestry? Here is a broad and complex question. It is a question typical of forestry economics in two respects especially: For one, it clearly involves forest products other than simply timber. Surely owners are often motivated in forestry by their interest in water or recreation or other forest resources. And society as a whole is concerned with managing all these resources and can hardly manage any of them independently, considering that they come jointly from the same land. In other words, the question has its setting in multipurpose forestry, and this is typical of forestry economics, though at times it may seem to dwell upon timber matters.

The second respect in which the question is typical is that it clearly reaches beyond money values. For surely people are motivated in forestry by many other values. They may, for example, be motivated by religious values. And as we look around us we cannot escape noticing a certain proportion of human behavior that is hard to account for under any common rationale. As one pursues the economics of forestry, he tends to become continuously less certain of the dominant role of dollars in human affairs generally. And he may become ever more impressed with the fascinating complexity of questions involving human action. He may learn to approach such questions with less assurance, more humility, and fuller comprehension.

What does the student of forestry economics do when he finds himself faced with a complex question of broad scope? He applies a rule of reason, the main feature of which is the method of abstraction, or *partial analysis.* He may, for example, begin by assuming that people manage forest tracts solely to make the greatest possible net revenue from wildlife—although he knows this is not true. He studies examples of forest tracts—although he can find none that quite satisfies his assumption—and from these data and his own deductions he lists and describes the influences upon management practice. Next he may repeat the process for each of the other products of the forest. Then he may attempt to put these observations together in terms of multipurpose management, meanwhile studying cases where such management is in effect and deducing how the fact of multiple products modifies his first approximations. Lastly he may try to analyze some of the human motives other than to produce the most net revenue. In these later stages of his thinking he is drawing the parts of the question together and perhaps discovering some unifying and simplifying principles. For example, he may conclude, as we ourselves shall find later on, that the practice of forestry is strongly controlled by the relative importance that people attach to the near as against the distant future. In this line of reasoning, what will induce people to practice forestry is anything that will increase the relative importance of the farther future in their minds.

Thus one need not attempt to attack a complex problem in its entirety: He may break off what he can handle and work with this separately. In the end he may put some of the pieces back together. This sort of approach to the study of problems is familiar to you, because it is taken in all academic subjects. Every such subject is an abstraction—from the sum total of experience. Economics shares this characteristic of being an abstraction.

Speaking of abstractions, let's bow to the issue between theory and practice. No doubt you have heard the old saw "Good in theory but not in practice." What can this mean? The theories that are no good in practice are no good anyhow. This book that you are now starting to read is primarily a book of theory—or principles. There will be examples of the use of principles to solve major forestry questions of an economic sort, yet this is not a book of facts. Facts are fine—but there are so many of them! In the economic world, they are highly practical, but not very practicable. Principles are fewer. They are the master keys to a world of facts, and they are carried easily in one's pocket. However, it takes skill to select and use them. The hard thing about principles is not learning them but learning to apply them with results that are good in practice as well as in theory. Each principle implies an abstraction, and each abstraction implies the process of partial analysis.

### STEERING INDIVIDUAL POLICY

Now consider a question that has implications mainly for individual policy. The last question, concerning conservation and what makes it go, had implications chiefly for public, or social, policy. That is to say, the big issue implied was what the community, or society, should do to promote forestry. Now let us take a question concerning what an individual firm should do to meet *its* objectives.

Suppose you belong to a company of consulting foresters and are summoned by a forest-land owner who seeks advice on a prospective lumbering operation. The landowner wants your company to make a plan covering the acreage and quantity of timber to be logged annually; the road system, machinery, and labor force; the type and location of the mill; the marketing of products; and kindred matters. Setting to work, you first inquire about the objectives of the firm which are to guide your plan. What does the firm want to accomplish? You learn that there are certain objectives for the permanency and stability of the community and for preservation of scenic and other values, and that within these limitations the general goal is to earn profits. Here again is a question in the economics of forestry.

Notice particularly three things about this question:

Notice, first, that the question centers around what amounts of various things shall be used to turn out what quantities of products. About how much land, labor, timber, machinery, and so on shall be combined in what ways to produce approximately what output from year to year? The alternatives are almost limitless, but only one can be chosen. Presumably one can be proposed that meets the firm's objectives best, or at least satisfactorily. Here is a sort of cake-baking problem, like the problem of the cook who has to decide on the kind and size and quality of cake, the kinds and amounts of ingredients, and the cooking devices and procedures. All through the producing segment of our economy, at every moment, these cake-baking questions are being decided. The decisions determine, for individual firms, the combinations of the agents of production. In the aggregate they determine society's allocation of resources. The problem of combining agents, or allocating resources, will constitute the main theme in our study of forestry economics.

Concerning cake baking, it is well to remark that every cake worth its salt has a dual aspect: one presented to the cook and one to the hungry man. By the same token, every complete economic act entails not only production, in which resources are used to create something, but also consumption, in which resources are given up in exchange for the use of the thing created. The consumer—who, like the producer, is organized into a sort of firm—is also confronted by decisions among alternatives that may be complex. As the economic sovereign, his decisions rule the economy, ultimately swaying resource use, including the use of forest products and forest land. Forestry economics is therefore concerned with the consumer, often indirectly but always vitally. The fact that there are consumers, human beings with tastes and preferences to be satisfied, is in the last analysis the forestry profession's sole reason for existence.

Notice, second, that our planning question is concerned to a very great extent with biological and engineering matters, such as how trees and machines may be expected to perform in service. This material stuff of forestry is in the province of silviculture, logging engineering, and other such specialties. Where, then, does the economics of forestry fit in? The answer is that it has no material stuff as its special province, although it is intimately concerned with all the material stuff of forestry. Its special province is a *viewpoint*—that is, the significance of this material stuff to people in pursuit of their aims in life's business. Forestry economics is therefore a sort of transverse slice through all the tissues and bundles and ducts that make up the stem of forestry. If you take the subject of forestry economics and remove from it one by one the pieces of biology, engineering, and human relations, you have Lewis Carroll's Cheshire-Cat, which slowly vanished until only the grin remained.

Notice, third, that our question (planning the firm's lumbering operation) treats of the future. It entails prediction. This fact is characteristic of questions in the economics of forestry. Of course, forecasting is not peculiar to forestry economics, and, indeed, as one reflects about other areas of science and practice, it grows on him that few are concerned with much except forecasting. "I hold that man is in the right," wrote Henrik Ibsen, "who is most closely in league with the future." Take silviculture, for instance. Is it not essentially the forecasting of forest-stand development? Perhaps you can name many other parts of forestry which similarly may be defined in terms of prediction. But in forestry economics the look ahead is peculiarly long and, alas, particularly hazardous. Both the length and the hazard are the fault of human beings, who are now the subject and who complicate things immensely. However, since we cannot get along without people, we must bear up—even when asked to consider such enterprises as "sustained-yield" forest operation, which, being ageless, is in the last analysis the pawn of the whole universe of variables that conceivably influence human behavior! But then, again, there is consolation—as in the fact that only part of the future is relevant, and the nearest is the most relevant.

## FORESTER AND FOREST ECONOMIST

Obviously the economics of forestry is a big subject, drawing together a staggering number of specialties. What, then, of the "forest economist," that superman who presumably rules these vast domains? Ideally, he is someone who is both broadly and deeply conversant with forestry, with economics, and with the application of the latter to the former, a specialist of many parts and a generalist to boot. In reality, no such person exists—and the likelihood of his appearing on the scene becomes more remote with every passing advance in forestry and in economic science. A few men who have specialized upon economic problems of forestry have acquired the name of forest economist. These men make their contributions as best they can, often working only in a small segment of the field, and often collaborating with technologists or economists or both. It is worth observing that the very person who approaches most closely the ideal forest economist at the same time qualifies excellently for the honorable and more ancient title of forester.

This book is a general introduction to the elements of the economics of forestry. Its immediate object is to help knit your forestry curriculum;

to show that silviculture, forest measurements, logging engineering, forest products, range management, forest wildlife, . . . are not isolated strands of knowledge, but are threaded together into the same cloth: man's behavior in the ordinary business of life. Its further object, and the prime function of forestry economics, is to help you make a better educated man and a better forester of yourself.

## ARRANGEMENT OF THIS BOOK

The book is arranged in five parts, comprising thirty-three chapters altogether.

The remaining three chapters of Part One introduce the subject of forestry economics by outlining briefly the operations and characteristics of the economy at large and describing two features of special interest: the resources that propel economic activity, and the relations between society and the individual which partly govern its course.

In Part Two, twelve chapters are devoted to fundamental building blocks of the forest economy, the firms that supply forest goods and services. Principles governing these firms' combining of resources are studied. Special attention is given to their use of forest labor, capital, and land, and to their supply responses to the influence of price and cost. Part Two closes with the subject of planning for the firm's resource use and product supply.

Part Three, made up of seven chapters, considers first the demand side of the forest economy. It then analyzes the meeting of demand and supply in the market, and the outcome in terms of quantity, price, and appraised value of commodities produced and consumed.

The five chapters of Part Four turn from the relatively automatic features of the forest economy that are stressed in Parts Two and Three to take up the human institutions that sway economic activity: centers of influence in business, labor, and government; the institution of tenure; and taxation, credit, and insurance.

Finally Part Five, in five chapters, depicts the operation and planning of the forest economy as a whole. It sketches the forest economy of the world and United States, and talks about social planning and problem analysis in forestry.

## SUMMARY

Forestry economics considers how forest lands and related human and industrial resources are allocated, or managed, to help satisfy people's wants. It considers the question from two points of view: first, that of the witness trying to describe, and if possible explain, human behavior;

second, that of the consultant offering guides to social or individual policy.

Economics is complicated, because people are complicated. Being people ourselves, we have a head start in the study of economics. Yet there are pitfalls that even we must watch out for. The obvious answer is not always right, and common sense (except in an uncommon sense) not always reliable.

Our approach to the economics of forestry in this book will be characterized partly as follows: We shall deal with principles in preference to events, and hence with reasoning more than memory. We shall take the biological, engineering, and human relationships of forestry as given and build on them to analyze how economic goals are reached. We shall continually abstract parts of problems as a simplifying device, using the method of partial analysis. We shall be oriented to the future, and often to the far future. We shall be oriented to the consumer, who provides the forestry profession's sole reason for existence. And we shall try to use our subject primarily as a means of becoming better professional foresters in a broad sense.

The book is organized in five parts: (1) introductory ideas, (2) production firms and their supply, (3) demand and its meeting with supply, (4) institutions, and (5) the forest economy at large.

# Chapter 2

# ECONOMY AND
# FOREST
# ECONOMY

CHAPTER 1 hinted that the student of forestry economics must be prepared to delve into a fair range of topics. To carry through, let us begin now with the subject of *ants*. Briefly, and as philosophers rather than entomologists, we shall examine the behavior of these creatures, thus readying ourselves to view the apparently more complex economic life of our fellow men. Then we shall focus upon that part of man's economic life which especially concerns forests.

## ANT ECONOMY

Perhaps sometime in your career as an outdoorsman you have had occasion to poke into an anthill. Whether you did so through scientific curiosity or in a spirit of devilment, surely you were arrested by the seething activity you had exposed. Nursemaids scurried devotedly to get eggs and undeveloped progeny out of harm's way. Hod carriers ran up and down, hopefully and doggedly, a grain at a time, to mend the damage. Fighters sallied, ready to take on without question any enemy.

Or perhaps you have lingered near a hill of ants to watch their ordinary comings and goings: foragers packing chunks of food; soldiers on patrol; everyone hurrying. What is the meaning and aim of such diligent, untiring effort? Here, evidently, is a well-ordered society. It drives without cease or humor toward some all-absorbing goal. What is its goal?

Let us cast the ant in something of a human mold, and at the same time side-step the genetic and spiritual issues that our question may seem to imply. Here, then, is an answer that we can propose:

The goal of the ants is to satisfy their wants. These wants, listed in no particular order, are of the following goods and services: food, shelter, security, and progeny. To meet their wants, they call into use the resources at their disposal, i.e., the *agents of production:* land, consisting of

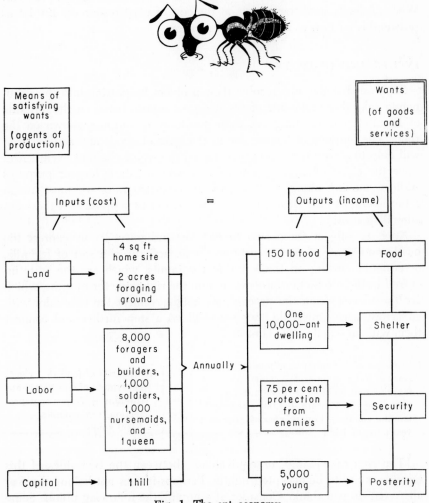

Fig. 1. The ant economy.

the home site and its tributary foraging ground; labor, for the foraging, for building the home, for fighting to defend it, and for rearing the young; capital, the durable, productive fruits of labor upon the land, consisting of the hill home with its marvelous tunnels and rooms. With this concept of wants and the means for satisfying them, we have the makings of an *ant economy,* such as pictured in Figure 1.

With means at their disposal and a general goal in view, the ant community is confronted with a cake-baking problem, a *production* problem:
What agents shall they combine, to turn out what products, and in what
amounts? They are of course, at the same time—to look at the identical
matter from the converse viewpoint—faced with a *consumption* problem:
What products shall they enjoy, at the cost of what resources? But let us
pursue this for now as a production question.

### INPUTS AND OUTPUTS

Suppose that the ants resolve their problem by putting into their economic cake those amounts of resources, or *inputs,* listed on the left side
of Figure 1, and turning out those products, or *outputs,* shown on the
right. The outputs, of course, are in the form of goods and services that
will help to satisfy the wants that started the whole chain of events. And
since the chain of wanting and of satisfying wants is for our purposes
endless, moving along continuously at a certain rate, we must assign
a time period to the quantities in Figure 1. Let us suppose that these are
annual quantities.

Now, to subject these ants to one last indignity, let us express the
hustle and drive of their yearly economic activity in a sort of formula,
or equation, listing on the left side the inputs, which are the costs incurred in the production process, and on the right side the outputs, which
are the income from the process. We might connect the two sides with
an arrow, as chemists do. But we shall go a step further and connect
them with an equals sign. Thus

| | | |
|---|---|---|
| 1 year's use of 4 square feet of homesite and 2 acres of foraging ground + 8,000 ant-years' foraging and building + 1,000 ant-years' patrolling and fighting + 1,000 ant-years' tending young + 1 queen-year of labor + 1 year's use of 1 hill | = | 150 pounds of food + 1 year's enjoyment of one 10,000-ant dwelling + 75 per cent pro-tection from enemies + 5,000 young |

[The sign of equality, or equivalence, between the two sides of this
formula is not to be accepted lightly. Perhaps it does not belong there at
all. What do you think? Consider, if you will, the following points. Some
careful thought devoted to these and other questions that may occur to
you should help you to understand the workings of an economy. If any
of them merely contributes to your confusion, it should be insisted in all
seriousness that confusion is a valid ticket of admission to our subject,
and we will get the ticket punched as we go along.

[Do inputs equal outputs?

[1. Surely the two sides of the formula are not literally equal. For example, labor and the use of foraging ground are not literally equal to food. Are they then equal in some figurative sense? In what sense?

[2. The economy that we have here is apparently communistic. Further, it is a subsistence economy, consisting of one family, or tribe, that is completely self-sufficient. No money is needed for the working of the economy. In this circumstance, we are faced with the odd problem of whether various quantities of unlike things (acreage, ants, and so on), if added together, equal other combined quantities of unlike things. And we have apparently no common denominator. How could one ever demonstrate equivalence or the lack of it under these circumstances?

[3. This economy is surely not perfectly successful in all its undertakings. Even an ant may occasionally rest in the shade of a leaf when he might be out working. The most conscientious ant will often be frustrated in his labors, as when he struggles all day to bear home a big chunk of food, only to have it stolen in the end by some stronger creature. Ants die, disappear, leave home not to return. Small boys play havoc with the hill. Even if we suppose that this little economy is on some sort of sustained-yield basis over the years, maintaining its resources and its flow of products, are there not a great many unaccounted loose ends and gaps that destroy such equivalence as we might otherwise demonstrate between inputs and outputs—between cost and income?

[4. But suppose that the economy is *not* on sustained yield. Suppose that it is a dynamic and changing economy. Let us imagine, for example, that the inputs and outputs in the formula are occurring while heavy new net savings and investments are being made: A great many ants that might otherwise be gathering food for this year's consumption have been set upon the task of enlarging the hill, so that in years to come the labor force may be expanded and the colony enjoy so much the greater consumption of food and other things. But now, in the meantime, more stomachs are going empty. Many ant-years of effort being crammed into the production hopper, and listed on the left side of our formula, are not yet emerging as finished goods and services for listing on the right side. Certainly under these circumstances the two sides, as now listed, are not equivalent. Or are they?]

## HUMAN ECONOMY AT LARGE

Now it is an obvious and not too difficult step from the little world of the ants to the somewhat vaster vale of tears in which we ourselves are the inhabitants. Let us find a vantage point, some high knoll, from which we can look out across the hills and foraging grounds of the human economy. Much the same frenzied coming and going meets our view. Inquiring into the purposes of it all, we can distinguish much the same existence of wants, existence of resources, and conversion of resources into the goods and services that will help satisfy the wants. We can identify much the same problem in cake baking by which resources are allocated toward their most satisfying uses.

Although the sound and fury of this larger vale force the impression upon us that it is different from the simple and quiet economy of the ants, we may well ask how basic the difference is, whether of kind or merely of degree. [Is the human economy basically different from the ant economy by virtue of the institution of property? The institution of money? The manner in which the economy is regulated and controlled? The human power of reason, innovation, and enterprise? The greater variety of human wants and resources? The greater prominence of capital among man's resources? What other differences do you recognize between the two economies? How basic are these differences?]

We have used the terms *society* and *economy*. By *society* is meant a group of individuals whose lives are interrelated in some respect. The identity of the group is often determined by family ties, as with the ants; or by geographic lines, such as those bounding a human neighborhood; or by political lines, as in the case of a nation; or by cultural lines, as with "Western society" or "Western civilization"; or by economic or other lines. The concept of a society is flexible, adjustable to the purpose at hand. One may conceive of different kinds and sizes of societies, one within another or overlapping others.

By an *economy* is meant the economic aspect of a society's environment and activity. Like the society, the economy is an abstraction. The material evidence of its existence is people, farms, forests, roads, factories, stores, consumables, smoke, talk—in fact, nearly everything that one can name. Nearly everything is in the economy, since nearly everything has an economic aspect. But again, the economy has no material stuff exclusively its own. A forest, for example, has a geographic, a political, an engineering, an artistic identity, as well as being part of an economy. Just as economics is a viewpoint, so the economy is in a sense a product, a creature, of this viewpoint.

Bearing in mind, then, the abstract character of our economy, let us define it now as a mechanism—a mechanism for putting goods and services into consumers' hands, more or less in response to the consumers' wants. For this purpose, resources are used—natural, cultural, and human. These resources are the agents of production. They are scarce in relation to the wants they are used to satisfy. The ideal economy (implying the central problem of economics) is one which uses its resources in such a way as to maximize human satisfaction.

## ECONOMIC CAROUSEL

The dominant figure in this economy is man. The figure has, like Janus, two faces: One is the wanter, the consumer. The other is the satisfier of wants, the controller of resources, the agent of production. In each of us these two faces are embodied. With one, money in hand, we receive goods and services. With the other we pass on the goods or services that we ourselves have helped create, our hand outstretched for the money reward which soon, in our consumer guise, we shall pay out again. Thus

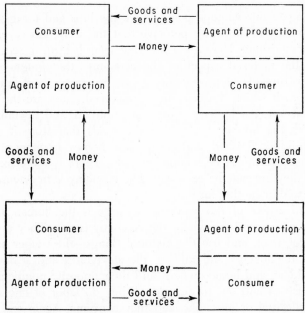

Fig. 2. The economic carousel. We work for one another and the income goes around.

goods and services pass through the economy, as it were, in one direction, while money in corresponding amounts flows in the opposite direction. This movement and flow, essentially circular, is represented in Figure 2 as a carousel. If the chart's four Janus-like consumer-producers were multiplied by millions, all connected up with thickly interlacing arrows, we should have a sort of picture of our national economy. Of course, besides the flows there represented, one would have to picture the vast sums of consumables created and used by the same individuals or families and not entering into the scheme of exchange.

[The subtitle of Figure 2 refers to income going around on the carousel. What do you interpret this income to be—the goods and services or the money?]

No doubt, if one were immensely ambitious, he might set about representing our national economy, or some other economy, by a formula of inputs and outputs, or perhaps several formulas, such as we used to describe the doings of the ants. In summary form, such formulas would help one to understand the composition and the working of the economy. Spelled out in full, they would be unbelievably complex and probably not very rewarding in their maze of detail.

## ASPECTS OF THE ECONOMY

Returning to our vantage point above the hills and foraging grounds of the economy at large, we perceive that the scene has several aspects worth distinguishing. Here are a few that seem helpful to recognize:

One is the material aspect of the economy: the *things*—natural resources, instruments of production, goods in process, and finished commodities—with which the economy is involved. Such are the timber on yonder seacoast; the logging equipment, railroad, and sawmill; the ship that carries the lumber to market; the sheds that store it; the frame houses abuilding, finished, and occupied as homes. Looking at these material things, we might be inclined to say, "There is the economy." But of course they are not the economy. The economy is in a sense far more than that, and in another far less.

A second aspect of the economy at large is the human aspect—the *people* by whom and for whom the economy is run. They are the ones who control, man, and use the material things—the timber owners and managers, the loggers and millers, the stevedores and seamen, wholesalers, builders, and home owners, and their opposite numbers in all the other industries laid out to our view. They do labor of one sort or another, intellectual or muscular, and they consume. Again one must suppress the conclusion that these people are the economy, though this is more nearly a sound conclusion than identifying materials with the economy.

A third aspect of the economy at large is the geographic aspect. Every one of the materials and persons and events of the economy occurs at some *place*. Yonder seacoast is a place, and if we fix our attention there, we can observe its economy, which is a thing peculiar to its resources, wants, and external influences. Among these influences are the wants of the home owners across the water. The geographic relationship of these two places therefore becomes important. As we study the economics of forestry, we will come to emphasize the importance of place, distance, terrain, and other geographic circumstances in their influence upon the role of forests in economic life.

A fourth aspect is the temporal aspect. Every economic event occurs at some *time*. Furthermore, the passage of time reveals a prominent characteristic of economies as we know them—change and fluctuation. Still further, some recognition of the time element is essential in measuring economic activity. We have referred to this activity as a flow. To measure a flow calls for the use of a rate: quantity per unit of time. With a river, it may be so many cubic feet per second; with an economy, so many dollars per year.

Finally, the economy at large has a functional aspect, by which is meant that we can view it in terms of the functions or services that it performs for society. Or we can view any one function or *industry* within the economy. Thus we can view the raw-material industry of an economy, or the transportation industry, or manufacturing, or the wholesale or retail trades, each of which represents an economic function. Or we may slice the economic loaf lengthwise and study the steel economy—i.e., steelmaking, steel fabrication, and steel distribution as an economic function—or the fisheries economy, or the agricultural economy, or the forest economy.

## FOREST ECONOMY

Let's take the functional approach and have a look at this thing called the forest economy. What is it? How does one describe and measure it?

The *forest economy* is that part of the general economy which is concerned with making, distributing, and consuming the goods and services of the forest. These goods and services are primarily recreation, wildlife, forage, water and watershed regulation, trees, and the products into which they may be converted.

Now it is easy enough to talk about "that part" of an economy which is concerned with a certain function, but essentially impossible in practice to identify it, because all the various parts of an economy are so closely interwoven. Think, for instance, of the forest land underlain by coal mines. If we ascribe this land to the forest economy, how do we account for its role in the coal economy? Or if we divide it two ways, on what basis is the division made? Going on to commoner and more difficult cases of interweaving, think of the farmer who has a woods as part of his business. To what extent shall his labor and enterprise be considered as within the forest economy? Or the factory where upholstered wooden furniture is made—can this somehow be attributed partly to the forest economy and partly to other economies concerned with textiles, glue, metal fastenings, and so on? Does the forest economy extend into the work of the electrician because he uses a hammer with a wooden handle? Or into the work of the hotel manager because his secretary is more efficient by virtue of having enjoyed a forest vacation?

One forest product is forage, and therefore livestock. Does the forest economy include packing plants? Retail meat counters? The stove industry, which surely depends for its existence partly upon the meat that people want cooked?

As one pursues such questions to more and more ridiculous lengths, he comes to realize that everything in the economy depends, in the last analysis, upon everything else, and that therefore such a concept as the forest economy is an abstraction of a high order. In practical light, any boundary that we set up within the economy at large, saying, "Inside this line is the forest economy; outside is something else," is an arbitrary boundary.

Let us therefore adopt two useful rules:

The first is to accept the idea of the forest economy as an arbitrary, but nevertheless very helpful idea. Let us delimit the forest economy as suits the problem at hand. Sometimes we may wish to consider the forest economy broadly conceived to include the activities surrounding all the products of the forest, carried on toward the consumer just as far as they still bear significantly upon forest-land management. At other times we may wish to narrow our view to one kind of product—say, the timber economy—carried only to the point of remanufacture, or even of the first processing, or of logging.

The second rule is to be always conscious of the weighty influences that bear upon the forest economy from the outside, avoiding the naïve error of studying the forest economy in a vacuum. For example, the management of the farm woods is determined largely by the circumstances of the whole farm business: The farmer aiming to maximize his net returns will do so on the basis of all his resources, and the woods will receive much or little attention according to the attractiveness of the farmer's other alternatives. Again, the wage rates of forest labor will be governed mainly by labor supplies and demands outside forestry. And the value of forest wildlife and other forest products will stem in part from consumers' alternatives, most of which lie outside the forest economy.

## DESCRIBING THE FOREST ECONOMY

Edward Crafts and Martha Dietz, of the Federal Forest Service, attempted the difficult job of describing the forest economy of the United States.[1] They described it in terms of the stock of resources and the flow of products—timber, water, forage, wildlife, and spiritual strength—in

[1] Crafts, Edward C., and Martha A. Dietz: "Forest Resources and the Nation's Economy," in *Trees: The Yearbook of Agriculture, 1949,* U.S. Government Printing Office, Washington, pp. 721–730.

a year just following World War II. They emphasized the high value in our national life of these resources and products, some of which are measurable in dollars and some of which are not. In the timber branch of the forest economy, they enumerated the quantities or numbers of, and in some cases the investments in, timber lands, growing stock, and improvements; sawmills, pulp and paper mills, and other wood-processing establishments; and transportation and marketing installations. And they listed the lumber, firewood, pulp and paper, furniture, and other goods, valued in all at no less than $15 billion, pouring forth during the year.

If we were to take this picture of the United States timber economy in an immediate postwar year and condense it into the sort of input-output formula that we have used before, the result might be somewhat as follows, with inputs (costs) on the left and outputs (income) on the right:

1 year's use of:
    461 million acres of commercial forest land and 470 billion cubic feet of standing timber,
    Administrative and protective installations,
    Logging installations,
    60,000 sawmills, 250 pulp mills, and other wood-processing plants,
    Transportation and marketing installations +
Planting stock and other timber-management supplies +
Administrative and protective supplies +
Processing, transportation, marketing supplies +
3.3 million man-years of labor

Lumber, firewood, paper, furniture, plywood, posts, poles, and other products, worth $15 billion

[What sort of symbol should be used to connect the two sides of the formula? Would it be correct to insert an equals sign? You should consider carefully why, or why not. And if you find yourself coming to the conclusion that the two sides are unequal, then you should back up your reasoning with a list of the items that would have to be added to, or subtracted from, each of the sides in order to make them equal.]

From the input-output formula one can derive various measures of the timber economy as defined. In terms of output, one may express the size as an annual flow of 15 billion postwar dollars, and perhaps add for comparative purposes that this represents about 5 per cent of yearly national income of the period. Or, if inputs and outputs are equal, one may derive his measure, a $15-billion economy, from the inputs. Alternatively, one may select a single item or group of outputs or inputs as a measure. Thus he may establish the size of the timber economy by saying that it employed the full-time equivalent of 3.3 million persons, roughly 6 per cent of all employment. Or he may say that the timber economy involved 461 million acres of commercial forest land, some three-fourths of the forest land and one-fourth of all the land in the United States. Each of these measures is satisfactory, provided one clearly understands—and, where necessary, explains—what it means and what its uses and limitations are. Above all, one should not forget the primary limitation stemming from the concept of the timber economy itself—the fact that any definition of it will be arbitrary, taking in components that others, with their own particular objectives in view, may want to leave out.

[Under what circumstances would you wish to describe the timber economy in terms of forest-land acreage? Numbers of processing plants? Expenditures (inputs) for timber management? Employment? Total output?]

## SUMMARY

The economy is one way of looking at human life. It stresses the activities concerned with satisfying wants through use of resources. Its workings may be described and measured as a flow of resources, or agents of production, or inputs into the economic mechanism and an outflow of products (goods and services), or outputs. The inputs are the costs of the process; the outputs are the income from it.

There are several ways of viewing an economy: We may fix upon its material aspect, or upon the people by and for whom it is run, or upon its geography, or its time element, or the functions it performs. That is, in studying an economy, one may ask the questions "What?" "Who?" "Where?" "When?" "Why?"

The forest economy radiates from the central activity of forest-land management. Its boundaries are arbitrary or are fixed to suit the problem at hand. Never complete in itself, or closed, the forest economy must be studied in relation to the whole economy of which it is a functional part.

**Chapter 3**

**RESOURCES
OF THE FOREST
ECONOMY**

I N SPEAKING of economics and the economy, we have had occasion to mention *resources,* which are the means for satisfying wants, both individual wants and social objectives. We have pointed out that resources are scarce in relation to the wants they help satisfy, and we have identified the management of these scarce resources with the subject of economics. We have referred to the agents of production as resources, and alluded to the classical triumvirate, labor, capital, and land—that is, human, cultural, and natural resources. Considering our basic interest in resources, we may well devote a little time to pointed study of them. What, specifically, are they? What are their characteristics? How does one assess them?

Later on, when we get into the subject of combining the agents of production, we will define in detail the major classes of agents and emphasize distinctions. Here let us emphasize rather the common traits of resources. Much of what follows draws inspiration from the work of Prof. Erich Zimmermann[1] of the University of Texas.

### ECONOMIC DEVELOPMENT—EXAMPLE

In the southern yellow pine region of the United States,[2] the decades following the Great Depression saw a dramatic surge in economic ac-

[1] Zimmermann, Erich W.: *World Resources and Industries,* Harper & Brothers, New York, 1951, especially chaps. 1–3.

[2] A 12-state region is considered here, extending from Virginia through eastern Texas, including also Alabama, Arkansas, Florida, Georgia, Louisiana, Mississippi, North Carolina, eastern Oklahoma, South Carolina, and Tennessee.

tivity. This general development was shared by the forest economy in greater degree than in any other major region of the country. Within the forest economy of the South, the pulp and paper industry showed outstanding growth. In 1935, there were twenty-four pulp-manufacturing concerns in the region, operating thirty-seven plants with a total twenty-four-hour capacity of about 5,000 tons of pulp.[3] By 1956, the number of concerns had grown to fifty; there were ninety-four plants operating or going up; and the total daily capacity of these plants was 36,000 tons,[4] or seven times what it had been two decades before. Much new plant capacity was abuilding during the 1930s, although business generally

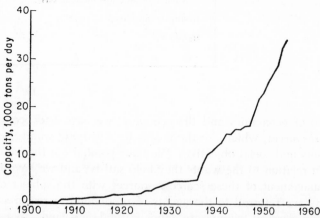

Fig. 3. Wood-pulp mill capacity in the South, 1900 to 1955. (*Sources: Stover, William S.: Pulpwood Production and Use in Southern Forest Survey Territory, 1946, New Orleans, Southern Forest Experiment Station Forest Survey Release 56, 1948, p. 7; also subsequent annual pulpwood-production releases of Southern and Southeastern Forest Experiment Stations.*)

was then sorely depressed. During World War II, development was in abeyance while the nation turned its resources into the fighting machine. But immediately thereafter the pulp and paper industry resumed its growth at a faster pace than ever (Figs. 3 and 4). In 1936, the South had 22 per cent of the nation's total wood-pulping capacity; in 1955, it had 55 per cent.[5]

[3] Lockwood Trade Journal Co., Inc.: *Lockwood's Directory of the Paper and Allied Trades, 1936*, New York, 1935.

[4] Lockwood Trade Journal Co., Inc.: *Lockwood's Directory of the Paper and Allied Trades, 1956*, New York, 1955.

Cruikshank, James W., and J. F. McCormack: *1955 Pulpwood Production in the South*, Southeastern Forest Experiment Station Forest Survey Release 47, Asheville, N.C., 1956, pp. 27–29.

[5] U.S. Pulp Producers Association: *World Wood Pulp Statistics 1927–1937*, New York, 1938, p. 20.

Stover, William S.: *Pulpwood Production and Use in Southern Forest Survey Ter-*

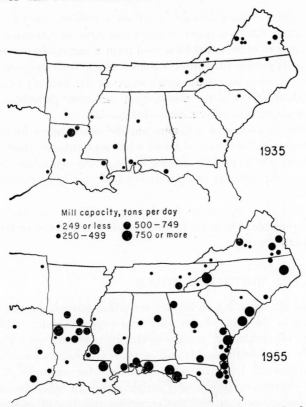

Fig. 4. Wood-pulp mills in the South, 1935 and 1955. (*Sources: Lockwood Trade Journal Co., Inc.: Lockwood's Directory of the Paper and Allied Trades, 1936, New York, 1935; Cruikshank, James W., and J. F. McCormack: 1955 Pulpwood Production in the South, Southeastern Forest Experiment Station Forest Survey Release 47, Asheville, N.C., 1956.*)

The swift rise of the Southern pulp and paper industry between the mid-1930s and mid-1950s is evidenced by expansion in every phase of its activity. The region's output of pulpwood increased thirteenfold, to a total of some 18 million cords annually. Hardwood pulpwood shared in this expanding harvest. By the end of the period the region was turning out six-tenths of the pulpwood produced in the United States.[6] The industry's ownership and long-term leasing of forest land was pushed up

---

*ritory, 1946,* Southern Forest Experiment Station Forest Survey Release 56, New Orleans, 1948, p. 7.

Carey, Charles: "A Decade of Progress in the Southern Pulp Industry," *Southern Pulp and Paper Manufacturer,* Oct. 1, 1955, p. 50.

[6] U.S. Department of Agriculture, Forest Service and Commodity Stabilization Service: *The Demand and Price Situation for Forest Products 1956,* Washington, 1955, p. 23.

Cruikshank and McCormack: Work cited, p. 2.

by acquisition from probably less than a million acres to some fifteen million acres. Its total plant employment rose an estimated sixfold, and its employment of foresters increased from a negligible number to several hundred. Its output of products soared along with its plant capacity, so that it came to produce the lion's share of the nation's kraft paper and substantial fractions of the corrugating and other paperboard, dissolving pulp, newsprint, and other such useful goods.

Thus in the course of a generation the means were found within the communities of the South to build what was virtually new industry and to direct its genius and its driving force to the central economic goal of furnishing to people at comparatively low cost big quantities of things they want.

Now how does economic development of this sort take place? What makes it possible? On what foundations is it built? Let us try to describe the foundations.

### WANT—THE MOTIVATING FORCE

First of all, there is a necessary condition to such growth as the South witnessed in the case of the pulp and paper industry, and that is the existence of unsatisfied wants—probably new and growing wants. An insatiable appetite for goods and services is not, as we might suppose, a universal human trait. In some societies—for example, the American Indians—wants are simple and rather static. In other societies, such as that of India, one can find the conscious practice of asceticism and its ennoblement as a moral virtue. But in our society and many others where self-denial is not normally necessary to survival, wants are free to grow and are commonly thought of as insatiable. These wants represent latent demands, more and more of which are unleashed when society's income goes up—that is to say, when its output of goods and services goes up. The individual industry shares in these social events to the extent that it holds or enhances its product's position in the esteem of consumers and to the extent that it economizes its use of the agents of production.

The southern pulp and paper industry encounters people's new and growing wants for paper bags and cartons, news and advertising, rayon and wallboard; and these wants are relayed back through the layers of the industry to the producers forming each of the layers—the retailers, wholesalers, converters, paper and pulp makers, timber owners, and foresters. These Janus-like producers respond by enlarging their capacity and output, for they are consumers too, in search of satisfaction for their insatiable wants. And so the system lumbers along, with many a pause and a setback, so long as there are resources to keep it going.

But one cannot take for granted the circumstances in which wants arise and are communicated to the economy. These circumstances are peculiar to each society, and are vital to the working of the system. What, for example, are the circumstances of our society's want for newsprint paper, such as comes in part from southern mills? This want is so closely imbedded in our culture that we seldom question its whys and wherefores. We want newsprint because we want newspapers and comic books and "penny pulps," an old-fashioned name that has long ceased to describe the price accurately. We want these things partly because we know how to read—at least after a fashion, and especially with the help of pictures—and are curious about people, both in fiction and in the events of the world around us. The fiction is interesting partly because it brightens our complicated and somewhat regimented lives. The events are interesting partly because as individuals we may have at least a small hand in them, through our work or through our votes, and these privileges in turn arise in the democratic organization of our society.

The want for newsprint paper is also the result of the position of advertising in our economy. Some 60 per cent of all newspaper space is given to advertising. The reason for this is a story in itself, but the most apparent factor is the kind of competition, or quasi competition, that prevails in most of our commodity markets, and another is our income-tax laws and postal regulations, which have the effect of setting a cut-rate price upon advertising space.

And then in the want for newsprint there are those elements that are common to most of our wants—society's customs and ways of life; the pressure upon the individual to conform and to keep up, even to the matter of owning the latest comic books; the allotment of the family's time to such things as reading the news and studying the ads; and finally the great freedom accorded the consumer under our laws to direct resources into trivial as well as vital uses.

This sketch of the circumstances of the want for newsprint paper will suffice at least to illustrate how far-flung the influences are. Perhaps in the last analysis they include everything under the sun. But the direct influences are comparatively few. [Take the case of kraft bags or wrapping paper or the case of rayon or some other product of the pulp and paper industry in your own region, and see if you can describe how wants arise and are translated into demands.]

Now that we have had a look at the motivating force in resource use, we can get on to our main point, the resources themselves. What were the resources that made it possible for the South's pulp and paper industry to rise to the occasion of wants?

## NATURAL RESOURCES

We may as well begin with timber, this being our tendency as foresters. In doing so, we don't claim that timber is the most important, whatever that might mean; and anyway it will soon become clear that it doesn't matter where we start, since our attention will be drawn at once across the whole resource board. There were some 180 million acres of commercial forest land in the twelve-state region, including about 80 million acres of pine-forest types. And among other essential natural resources were water, which the industry uses at a rate several times greater than all the region's municipalities put together, and minerals such as sulfur, salt, limestone, and natural gas, which are made over into chemicals and energy required by the industry. In the absence of any of these natural resources, pulp and paper manufacture could not have proceeded as it did.

And yet the significant thing about the natural resources was the human and cultural resources used with them. The natural resources were there—partly as unused "neutral stuff," partly as the base for other industry—for generations and ages prior to the mid-1930s, but no surge of papermaking occurred. Something else was needed, and this was not simply human want, for wants existed before and were satisfied in other ways.

### KNOWLEDGE

One of the chief ingredients required to make natural resources out of neutral stuff is knowledge, based upon man's inquisitiveness and inventiveness. Francis Bacon wrote, "The sovereignty of man lieth hid in knowledge; wherein many things are reserved that kings with their treasure cannot buy, nor with their force command." Knowledge is itself a resource, and the greatest one of all. Or at least this is evidently the view taken by society, for upon no other resource do we lavish such attention, consecrating years of our lives to the precious labor of receiving and passing along the facts and arts of the past, and other years to extending the boundaries of what we know. You yourself are now sharing in this labor, and you have been at it for a long while already. Here's hoping that as a graduate forester you will long continue.

For it was foresters who contributed one share of the knowledge that sparked the southern pulp and paper industry into new life in the mid-1930s. One thing they did was find out the extent and quantity and location of southern timber, forecast its growth and the demands upon it from existing industry, and make known its potentialities as raw material. This work was begun in the United States Forest Service, as part of the nationwide forest survey authorized by the McSweeney-McNary Forest Research Act of 1928. By the early 1930s, under the direction of Inman F. Eldredge, the Southern Forest Survey had already revealed the outlines of the timber situation. These were new outlines, new facts, for the South was in the last stages of its great lumbering boom, its woods were cut over, and most people were disinclined to be optimistic about the future of the forest economy. But Mr. Eldredge was saying, "The pulp and paper industry can be expanded and at the same time the growing stock can be built up."[7] Later he was pointing to the surprisingly vast hardwood resources, making up half of the timber volume and only a small fraction of the cut, and exclaiming, "Our industrialists, the most progressive in the world today, have in our southern hardwoods a new, intriguing, and almost unlimited field. . . . "[8] These were clear visions.

We may need to remind ourselves of the scientific and professional heritage that made such fact finding and prediction possible. Units of measure were needed, units that could be widely understood and accepted, and men were needed capable of planning the measurement work and of organizing it and carrying it out. These men had to call upon their inherited and acquired knowledge of such divers fields as personnel administration, trigonometry, and ecology. It was necessary for them to operate complex calculating devices and machines to summarize the data from forest sample plots numbering in the hundred thousands. They had to call upon their talents in speaking and writing to convey the information they gathered. And they were required to *interpret* this information in terms of industrial potentialities, in which process they made use of an indefinable professional optimism and faith in the capacity of soil and growing trees. This optimism came down to them through the professional generations in Europe and America.

And so it was with each of the professional and scientific groups that contributed their knowledge to building the Southern pulp and paper industry. Consider the history of the chemical and engineering development that was a necessary forerunner to what happened in the South in the decades after 1935. The invention of a continuous paper machine by Nicolas-Louis Robert about the turn of the nineteenth century and its early improvement by John Gamble; Friedrich Keller's and Henry Voelter's devising of the first wood-pulping machine at mid-century; the introduction of chemical wood pulping by Hugh Burgess and Charles Watt in the 1850s and of the kraft process by C. F. Dahl in the 1880s; the work of Carl Carlson which led to the South's first kraft mill in 1909; the studies of the United States Forest Products Laboratory during the 1920s on cooking sulfate pulps from southern pines; W. H. Mason's invention of the masonite process in 1924; the promotional work

[7] Eldredge, I. F., A. R. Spillers, and M. S. Kahler: *The Expansion of the Pulp and Paper Industry in the South,* Southern Forest Experiment Station, New Orleans, 1935.

[8] Eldredge, I. F.: *What Are We Going to Do with Our Hardwoods?* Southern Forest Experiment Station, New Orleans, 1939, p. 9.

of Charles Herty and the realization of his dreams in such developments as the first southern newsprint mill, completed in 1940—these are mere highlights, giving no hint of the long toil, the trial, failure, and retrial, that were exerted upon almost every significant advance in mill machines, materials, and procedures.

## TECHNOLOGICAL ARTS

The knowledge and ingenuity of which we have been speaking, the machines and methods of doing things, the "know-how" and "think-how" of production are collectively termed *technology*. This precious social possession is the charmed ingredient of economic life. Without it, other resources are sterile—neutral stuff. With it, other resources can be made to bloom in seemingly limitless profusion. "Knowledge," J. M. Clark once wrote, "is the only instrument of production that is not subject to diminishing returns."[9]

In 1565, when Menéndez founded St. Augustine, the whole region that became the southern states had a native population of probably less than a hundred thousand. These Indians roamed in poverty and fear over their wide domain that was so rich in soils, forests, water, minerals, and other natural gifts. After nearly four hundred years and the dissipation of much of the original gift, the region supported a population of more than forty-one million in what we incline to believe was comparative prosperity and security.

Obviously the change did not come about through any increase in the quantity or size of society's natural base. Quite the contrary. But the change did come as a result of an increase in resources, paced by the development of technology. Today's comparatively sparse forest stands contribute immeasurably more to satisfying human want than did the dense and widespread forests of Menéndez's time. The resource has grown —has proved to be renewable—not in the puny sense that trees put on annual rings and reproduce themselves, but in the sense that knowledge grows. The growth of knowledge, which continues so long as a society holds its intellectual heritage and its inquisitiveness, makes new resources where there was nothing before, adds to the quantity of existing resources, and mitigates or reverses the influence of physical depletion.

Or then again, advancing technology may diminish or even extinguish certain resources. Look how the same wave of progress that made pulpwood resources in the South wiped out a great share of the firewood resource. What happened mainly was that most consumers switched their

---

[9] Clark, John Maurice: "Overhead Costs in Modern Industry," *Journal of Political Economy*, October, 1923, p. 621.

votes from wood to other heat sources created by technology. These other sources thus became resources.

At any rate, resources are highly dynamic. They change, grow, and shrink. Each resource, depending as it does upon man's wants and upon all the other resources with which it is joined, comes into being and finds its role determined in accordance with these wants and other resources, and not in accordance merely with its own state of existence. "Resources," as Professor Zimmermann says, "*are* not; they *become.*"[10]

## NATURE'S RESOURCES AND MAN'S RESOURCEFULNESS

Having said something about knowledge and technology as resources and having considered an example of resource growth in the face of physical depletion, we must at least introduce an issue to which we shall return later from time to time. This is the issue between natural resources and technology.

You will remember about Thomas Robert Malthus, whose *Essay on Population* first appeared in 1798. He argued that population, which is necessarily limited by food supply, tends to increase faster than this supply, and that the inevitable checks upon population can all be resolved into moral restraint, vice, and misery: Take your choice. There is today a school of thought, termed **Neo-Malthusian,** which points to the steep rise in population over much of the world and views with great alarm the depleted and supposedly limited physical means of subsistence, the material resources such as soils, watersheds, minerals, and forests. Books have been published with frightening titles such as *Our Plundered Planet,* and with only slightly reassuring titles such as *Road to Survival.* In the latter,[11] for instance, one finds

One common denominator controls [our] lives: the ratio between human populations and the supply of natural resources, with which they live, such as soil, water, plants, and animals. . . . Without the new world on which to draw, the Industrial Revolution would have been a stunted dwarf. For, although the work of man became more efficient and less workers were needed on the farm to raise food, thus releasing a surplus of labor to work the machine, *the amount of land* did not increase. Actually, it shrank. . . . A large part of American prosperity . . . was bought by permanent destruction of one-third of our topsoil. . . . Much [agricultural land] achieved a temporary, high carrying capacity only by being worn out. We have produced a waster's psychology that would have appalled our frugal forebears and that is regarded

[10] Zimmerman: Work cited, p. 15. Quoted by permission.

[11] Vogt, William: *Road to Survival,* William Sloane Associates, Inc., New York, 1948, pp. 14, 21, 22, 59, 66–67, 146. Reprinted by permission of the author; copyright 1948 by William Vogt.

as lunacy—even criminal lunacy—by people in other parts of the world. . . .
Each piece of land has its own unique carrying capacity. . . . This productive capacity—*the biotic potential*—varies as to the quantity of vegetation
it can produce, and as to its nutritive and other *qualities*. The biotic potential
of any piece of cultivated land has an absolute or *theoretical ceiling*. . . .
At varying distances below the theoretical ceiling of production lie a very
large number of *practical* ceilings. And it is the practical ceilings, in most
of the world dropping lower every year, with which man must concern himself; for it is these that determine the amount of food . . . that man is
able to make available to his rapidly increasing populations. Whether man
likes it or not, he must live within his means, and these are shrinking. . . .
In terms of what we like to think of as American standards, . . . we are now
probably overpopulated. In the opinion of one of our foremost population
students, our optimum would be 100,000,000.

While the Neo-Malthusians seek the road to survival, the opposing
school of thought sees society traveling the highway to opulence. This,
the argument runs, society does by virtue of technological progress, man's
ingenuity outrunning the devil of physical depletion. *Time* magazine[12]
has reported the position of the "real scientists" in such terms as these:

It simply is not true that land is static. Virgin soils vary widely in fertility
and character, but once under cultivation they are subject to the will of modern
man. . . . The well-kept farms of New York State, Pennsylvania and Ohio
are now far more fertile than they were when the pioneers . . . first felled the
forest. . . . The soil men laugh at the Neo-Malthusian doctrine that man must
adapt himself to soil, and live with it as helplessly as wildlife. Man is not the
servant of the soil. . . . He is its master. . . . Man is master not only of the
soil, but of the plants that grow in it, molding them plastically to suit human
purposes. . . . A few years ago the U.S. Department of Agriculture began
breeding special hybrid corns. . . . [The] results reduce to gibberish [the]
theory of "biotic potential." Output per farm worker in the U.S. has been
multiplied 2½ times in the past 50 years. . . . How quickly the practice of
conservation will spread throughout the world, U.S. soil men cannot say. But
they do say that the obstacles are economic and social, not technical. Science
can stop most kinds of soil deterioration and will surely lick the rest. . . . If
the world wants to make the great effort, it can, by applying present-day
techniques, provide food for more than twice its present population. . . . By
the time population has increased that much, man may (and probably will)
have discovered new ways of increasing his food supply. . . . If he uses his
head he can eat hearty—indefinitely.

The controversy between Neo-Malthusians and their opponents goes
on pretty heatedly within the field of forestry. One of the hottest arguments concerns the significance of timber-stand depletion in terms of
tree stocking, size, soundness, quality, and species. The Neo-Malthusians,

---

[12] *Time*, Nov. 8, 1948, pp. 27–31. Quoted by permission.

who in this instance include probably the majority of foresters and whose greatest spokesman is our Federal Forest Service, tend to attach an absolute significance to depletion. You are familiar with this thesis, and we needn't elaborate on it. The opposing school, with organized wood-using industry as the chief spokesman, wants to temper the interpretation of the decline with the thought that timber quantity and quality are relative and are governed in part by the state of technological arts. One of the policy leaders of big industry, a Westerner, has been heard to state the case somewhat as follows:

Rapid advances in wood technology and utilization are materially expanding the wood supply. Take as examples—(1) Lamination of arches, beams, ship decking, doors, and thousands of other finished products. (2) Manufacture of plywood from new species and from smaller and lower-grade logs. Douglas-fir plywood is now being made from second-growth trees under 75 years of age. (3) Rapidly expanding manufacture of fiber boards of many different types, from mill wastes and logging slash. Composition boards have largely replaced sawn lumber in the sheathing of buildings. Wood is being molded with synthetic resins under heat and pressure into constantly new structural forms which are given almost any density and strength desired. (4) Expansion of pulp and paper manufacture based on many more tree species and commercial products. There are no more "weed" trees, even in western virgin forests. I know of many cases where, within the last 20 years, estimates of standing timber have increased 25 percent because of closer utilization.

These are live issues, immensely significant for the future. [What is your position? What merit do you see in the other fellow's position?]

Surely it is quite clear already that resources include much more than just tangible things, material objects. Soil, water, wood, and wildlife are material objects. But knowledge isn't. Nor are the resources next to be mentioned. Indeed, as we continue it will appear that none of our resources properly speaking is tangible—that a resource is *"a function which a thing or substance may perform or . . . an operation in which it may take part,* namely, the function or operation of attaining a given end such as satisfying a want."[13]

## ENTERPRISE

Somewhat allied to knowledge is foresight. We have spoken of foresters' foresight respecting the South's timber potentialities. However, the decisive foresight in the industrial expansion was that of the enterprisers, the decision makers in the corporations that built the new pulp and paper mills. Their foresight was perhaps a combination of faith with carefully reasoned and calculated optimism. They considered the prob-

[13] Zimmermann: Work cited, p. 7. Quoted by permission.

able future demands for their product and the probable difficulties of establishment and operation, and they considered the risks, and came to the conclusion that the venture was promising enough to warrant investing altogether more than a billion dollars. The decision makers exercised a function of labor, mainly labor of the mind. They were part of the human resources. And now let us go back of them to the cultural resources that made their decisions feasible and effective.

In order for the capital to be invested, society had to save, to abstain, to postpone fulfillment of some of its wants. This it did on a grand scale. So much saving implies a high level of living and of corporate and individual incomes. Now the southern states in the mid-thirties, and even in later years, were not by themselves in best position to furnish all this saving. The fact that they were one nation with other states which possessed great centers of capital accumulation and which were capable of drawing upon and redirecting the resources of many lands made the southern development possible. In other words, it was necessary for society to have institutions capable of bringing savings together and making them available for the industrial investments in the South.

## SOCIETAL ARTS

It is only in the presence of highly developed societal arts that such a saving-investment phenomenon can happen. If the thing is voluntary, there must be a tremendous social sense of security and confidence in an orderly future, and this must come through institutions in which people have faith. They must, for instance, be quite sure that the Armed Forces will defend them, the police protect them, the courts make consistent and just decisions, and communities and people continue friendly and trustworthy. They must foresee freedom from confiscatory taxation, and in general they must see the promise of sufficient freedom of action to carry out their designs. Obviously the relation of the individual and corporation to the government is here crucial—down to such specific governmental aids as local tax concessions and the Federal tax benefits and materials priorities that counted so much in the years immediately after World War II, when public policies were aimed at averting a dreaded depression.

The patterns and institutions of land ownership were also material to the expansion of the pulp and paper industry in the South, for they determined that wood raw material could be had. To safeguard its wood supply, each company normally sets out to acquire substantial forest acreages. In the southern states, where about six-tenths of the privately owned forest is in holdings, such as farm woods, smaller than 500 acres, acquisition of parcels and their consolidation for management can be extremely costly. Some acquisition of this sort was done, and more will undoubtedly be undertaken. But the core of industry-acquired lands came in big chunks, many of which were available from lumbering concerns that had recently completed their liquidation cuttings. One of the South's biggest pulp mills is at the abandoned site of one of its biggest sawmills, surrounded by the old cutovers which have now been converted to the most extensive private forest plantation in the world. Here and in many locations the historical setting was just right for the one industry to succeed the other.

However, southern pulpmakers generally don't attempt to be self-sufficient in wood. It is out of the question, and is not necessary anyhow. The woodlands that are so hard to acquire promise a continuing open market for raw material for the very reason that they *do* present such obstacles to consolidation. Leasing arrangements may give rise to problems and contests in the future, but that is another story. The gist of the present story is that the institutions of land ownership favored the industrial development.

## MUSCULAR AND MECHANICAL ENERGY

We have spoken here and there about the human resource—about the labor of enterprise and management, of inventing things and of knowing things. It is high time to recognize the role of labor in the more ordinary sense, whose sweat comes from physical work. For the comparative abundance of labor in this sense within the South was surely a big element in the expanding pulp and paper production. In their 1935 bulletin on the potentialities of southern forests, Mr. Eldredge and his associates wrote of the "abundant labor supply" and the "surplus of common labor," and underscored their assertions by referring to wage rates of 1 to 2 dollars per day![14] No other major region of the country could offer such an inducement to profit-seeking firms with manual work to be done. Here was a plentiful resource. The resource was the product of the culture in which it was created, and its quality was as good as that of the culture— the outcome of its standards of health, education, and morality, and its standards of work, leisure, and life.

Yet over our economic history, industry has grown by combining with labor more and more machines and the inanimate power to drive them. History may be interpreted as a story of man's mastery of energy. Through immense ages, virtually all the world's reasoned output of energy was muscular. In the United States as late as 1890, most of it still came from this source. But since then, while animate power output has stayed about constant, the output of inanimate power in the United

---

[14] Eldredge, Spillers, and Kahler: Work cited.

States has been raised more than twentyfold, so that it now equals the muscular effort which might be produced by a population several times greater than that of the entire world. In all this sweep of events, the most vital was Watt's discovery of the steam engine, whereupon "the earth became pregnant with new earths."[15]

Machines powered by water or minerals, and made possible by man's abstinence, were largely instrumental in making both the plants and the products during the South's pulp and paper boom. We have mentioned some of the mill machines. In the woods, and on the road, mechanization came more slowly. The old heave-ho, with main strength and awkwardness, in mid-1950s was still an accepted way to put pulp sticks on a truck or car. However, the power saw, the tractor, the mechanical loader, and other such devices were playing an ever larger part in the growth of the industry. They made labor increasingly more productive, and also less "common."

Indeed, each resource serves to overcome the limitations or resistances in the other resources with which it is combined for production. Every resource is accompanied by resistances. It is a gross amount accompanied by a subtraction, and only the net remainder is effective. Every acre of timber resource imposes resistances to man's use, varying greatly from case to case, in the form of its location and the difficulties of culture and logging. Every man's output of labor is limited by the resistances of his body and mind. The greatest surmounter of resistances is, in the last analysis, knowledge—though even knowledge, as you well appreciate, has its resistances.

## RESOURCE APPRAISAL

Now with this case of the southern pulp and paper industry and its resources in mind, let us consider in the abstract the interesting problem of resource appraisal—assessing the significance of a resource to mankind. This is a problem to which we shall return from time to time. Here let us deal with it summarily. We can do so, having now the main points in hand. We will take the economics of the matter—that is, consider it as a problem in management toward satisfying man's wants.

What is the significance of an even-aged stand of pine, 50 years old, 70 feet total height of the tallest trees, 12 inches average tree diameter, 100 stems per acre? You can elaborate on these specifications with your own mind's eye, filling in the species, site quality, terrain, volume per acre (watch out!), stand structure, and so on. The question is, what is the *value* of this stand—to people, in the ordinary business of their lives?

[15] Sombart, Werner: *Der Moderne Kapitalismus*, Duncker and Humblot, Munchen and Leipsig, 1921.

Well, surely that depends! For here we are up against, not the absolutes of natural science, but the relatives of the study of man. Conceivably, the stand is worthless. Or it may be exceedingly valuable. If we can see clearly the kinds of things this depends on, we shall have gone far enough for now.

It comes to mind almost at once that the location of the stand is im-·portant. How accessible is it, to users having what kinds and intensities of demand? A thousand cubic feet of timber back of the mountain may be quite a different thing from the timber that is identical except that it is situated a stone's throw from town. But accessibility is not just a matter of distance or of transportation cost either. We need to know how much timber there is altogether in this location. Who owns it is another vital question, and what are the owner's policies with respect to it. Other questions will occur to you, related to accessibility.

Concerning the use of the timber, one would need to know the status of industrial development in the area, or in areas to which this one has access. Questions of labor supply, degree of mechanization, and in fact the whole situation of the technological arts now come in view. A thousand cubic feet of timber in a comparatively undeveloped economy has a quite different meaning from the same timber in a highly industrialized economy. And then again, an acre of timber in Denmark, where the silvicultural arts can be used to wring the last ounces of growth from the stand, is wholly different from an acre in some country where management is extensive or exploitive and the time view short.

As we consider nations, still other and more abstract thoughts may cross our minds. The freedom of the individual, the political institutions under which he lives—don't these matters bear on the value of our timber stand? [Would an acre of it be likely to have the same significance in a capitalistic democracy as in a communistic dictatorship? What differences would you expect?]

To make a long story short, the value of our pine forest depends upon all the same kinds of influences that we considered as bearing on the southern pulp and paper development—individual wants, social aims, and all man's resources and the context in which he puts them to use. It seems inescapable that the value of a thing depends in the last analysis upon almost everything else, and therefore that individual resource appraisal ideally must consider the whole economy. That is to say, there is no such thing as individual resource appraisal! It will do you no harm to linger over this thought now, because later, when we return to the subject, we shall have less patience for philosophizing and will be looking for practical short cuts.

Surely it is clear that resources are not single assets. They are clusters —timber-plus-technology-plus-human-freedom—and often complex clusters. Rather early in this chapter the term "natural resources" cropped up. It is a convenient term to apply to such items as soil, water, trees, and wildlife that include large gifts of nature. But the gifts of nature alone are seldom resources in our sense of the word. A natural resource, like any other resource, is a combination of the works of nature and those of man.

## SUMMARY

Resources are the scarce means for satisfying individual wants and social objectives. They are created by man out of the neutral stuff of nature. Always accompanied by resistances, resources are the net remainder after these resistances have been overcome.

Resources are not material objects; rather, they are functions performed by tangible and intangible things in the process of want satisfaction. They are not single assets but clusters of assets performing together. They are not static but, like the people and societies that make them, are living and changing.

To appraise resources in their significance to man, it is necessary to use relative rather than absolute measures—to assess them in their setting rather than in themselves. Resource appraisal considers individual wants, social aims, and all man's material assets in the context of his technological and societal arts.

# Chapter 4

# SOCIETY
# AND THE
# INDIVIDUAL

PAST CHAPTERS have introduced the subject of forestry economics mainly from the social view of resources and their management. Now in the chapters just ahead the view will be primarily that of the individual. And so let us try here to smooth the transition. It will be especially helpful to have a look at two matters: first, the relation of the individual to the social interest; second, the relation of individual accounting to that of the group.

Remember how we have defined society, as a group of individuals whose lives are interrelated in some respect. Turn back to page 16 and review the comments on this definition, which emphasize the flexibility of the concept. Societies may be small and overlapping groups. Or society may be the people of one national state or a larger body of mankind.

## ROLE OF THE STATE

The central problem of state policy through the ages has been the issue between divergent goals within the state. The most general issue is that between the desires of the individual or interest group and the aims conceived to be those of the state's society at large. In Chapter 3 we spoke in a breath of individual wants and social objectives. This was not to imply that the two are the same. In some cases they are; in others, not. It was to imply only that, through the devices for expressing want, a will is established. The devices are political and economic. In each state in each era they incorporate that blend of state, other social, and individual control which the leaders believe is effective and which they find feasible. The devices of each state in each period thus have their characteristic biases in the expression of wants.

Western society within the last few centuries has witnessed something of a cycle in the degree of state control over want expression. In the *sixteenth century*, the prevailing view and practice was that of mercantilism, which, in all its schemes, "looked to a benevolently paternal government, assumed wise enough to interfere everywhere. Mercantilism was a policy of ubiquitous and perpetual governmental activity. There was nothing the Government might not do; there was nothing it ought not to do, if thereby its activity was calculated to promote the general well-being."[1]

*Eighteenth-century* liberalism, founded upon belief in the natural order, was in the economic sphere a doctrine of the social interest fostered by individuals' free pursuit of their wants. According to this optimistic doctrine of sweetness and light, an invisible hand guides selfish individuals to serve society's aims. This is not the hand of the state, but the automatic working of a competitive economy. Generally indeed, as Adam Smith wrote in 1776, the individual "neither intends to promote the public interest, nor knows how much he is promoting it. . . . He intends only his own gain, and he is in this . . . led by an invisible hand to promote an end which was no part of his intention."[2]

But Adam Smith's ideal competitive economy has not materialized. Many of its features, latent in his time, have been replaced by monopolistic forces. And other features of his own economy have proved unequal to the work of reconciling individual with social wants. Among economists, such leaders as Alfred Marshall, A. C. Pigou, and John Maynard Keynes have explored the implications of the fact that all is not necessarily for the best in this somewhat less than best of all possible worlds.

*Twentieth-century* liberalism advocates freedom under the state rather than from it. It seeks freedom for the individual from superfluous state control, but, more pointedly, from unbridled private initiative. The brand of liberalism so labeled today in the United States is thus a quite different idea from the liberalism of revolutionary times and frontier days. Our current liberalism sounds at best only a faint echo of Adam Smith, as in this statement by President Dwight D. Eisenhower: "We still believe that, in the aggregate, the initiative of the individual, his aspirations and his hope of bettering himself and his family—his ambitions—

[1] Gray, Alexander: *The Development of Economic Doctrine*, Longmans, Green & Co., Ltd., London, 1931, p. 77.

[2] Smith, Adam: *The Wealth of Nations*, Random House, Inc., New York, 1937, p. 423.

if directed equally toward the common good as toward his own betterment, will produce the greatest good for all of us."[3] [What do you think
is the essential difference between this point of view and the one quoted
just earlier?]

## SOCIAL INTEREST

But the important thing to understand here about these schools of
thought is their point of agreement—that the interest of the whole society must be served. None of them questions this. In fact, it is the accepted necessity for promoting the general good that gives rise to these
philosophies in the first place. Of course, the reasoning runs, if the individual and general good may differ, then the latter needs championing—
and by whom may this be done except government? Thus among the
eighteenth-century liberals of today are those who feel themselves ripest
for government control.

[You may think of individual wants as clearly expressed and of expressed wants as undebatable, at least to the degree that the individual
knows best what is in his mind. If in your home you want a fireplace that
will burn wood, no one is in position to tell you that you are misinter-
preting your desires. People may think them foolish or contrary to your
own good, but unless your mind is changed, your want remains a fact.
Is it so, too, with society's objectives? Who knows the mind of society
and states it? Is the statement clear and undebatable? What do you
think?] We shall return in Chapters 24 and 30 to the difficult question of
defining the social interest.

The terms *want* and *interest* have been used here nearly interchange-
ably. Of course we know very well they do not mean the same thing.
Let us, however, continue for the time being to bypass the issue between
the two, so as to keep after the issue between the individual and society.
We will assume, in effect, that persons and groups want what is in their
interest. This is partial analysis.

## ORIGINS OF SOCIAL CONFLICT

The characteristic of all cases where the individual and social interests
differ is that the attainment of the two involves using resources in different amounts or at different rates. For example, there is a lake with
wooded shores, a unique recreation ground within a section where several hundred thousand people live. The social interest as viewed by the
Park Commission lies in public acquisition of at least part of the shore

[3] *Time,* May 16, 1955, p. 21.

line and its development for various types of recreation which will effectively serve tens of thousands of people each year. On the other hand, there are many families who want to buy shore lots and build cottages for their own private use—many more families, indeed, than can be accommodated, for there is room for only a thousand families at the most without imposing seriously upon their interest as property owners. Thus, to the extent the social interest is satisfied, the private interest is thwarted. And the private interest equally conflicts with the social.[4] Here we have a resource, in this case land of a certain kind, which would be used at different rates in the attainment of individual and social aims.

It may seem that the scarcity of the resource in this example is a crucial point—and of course it is. But then all resources are scarce.

[The social interest, in this case, lies in more intensive resource use—per acre and per year. Is it always this way, or can you think of examples where the private interest calls for more intensive use than does the social?]

The conflict between society and the individual may be viewed as conflict between one group of persons and another. One group wants, and can afford, to own recreation ground as individuals and to enjoy it in privacy. The other group wants, or will be satisfied with, public development. The aims of these two interest groups are incompatible. So it is with virtually all conflicts to which society is party, that they may be interpreted as conflicts between interest groups. We shall come back to this subject in Chapter 24.

Disputing interest groups may be variously composed. The issue may be between labor and management, or between high- and low-income families, or between the residents of one area and those of another. Or it may be between present generations and the unborn, who may or may not have spokesmen among the living. Or it may be between producers and consumers, in which case a man may be turned against himself.

In fact, the conflict between society and the individual may be viewed as one manifestation of conflict within individuals. Each of us in his social relationships is a multiple being. He may identify himself partly with the interests of his family and partly with those of his employer, his profession, his church, his community, and even society at large irrespective of place or time. His social consciousness is determined by the mix. But in any case there is inward strife. Social issues are drawn on functional and not personal lines.

Let us, therefore, adopt a functional concept of society—that it consists of objectives, or wants, and ideas for meeting them. With such a

---

[4] The example represents a live issue respecting ownership and use of shore and coast lines. See, e.g., U.S. Department of Interior, National Park Service: *Our Vanishing Shoreline*, Washington, 1956.

concept, it will be easier for us—later on, when we return to the macro-economics of forestry—to understand how it is that the sum of all an action's benefits to individuals generally does not equal its social benefit (which sounds as though the sum of the parts is not equal to the whole), and how it is that the social interest may be contrary to that of every individual within the society.

Now the difference in amount or rate of resource use that gives rise to conflict between society and the individual may itself arise in various ways. Let us name three ways that are important in forestry.

## LENGTH OF VIEW

For one, there is the greater life span of society than of individuals and therefore the heavier emphasis placed by society on the values of the future and its greater freedom from concern over the uncertainties of the future. Because of its longer-run view, society generally differs from the individual in wanting more indirect processes of production and a slower rate of use of material assets. It is more content to incur resource expenditures which promise only distant returns. A business civilization emphasizing the short term may use its forests at a rate which, in the eyes of most groups, is wasteful. Some firms, of course, have a longer view than others. The lengthier a firm's process of production, the more its interest tends to coincide with society's.

Just as the individual is more conscious of uncertainty, so he is more apt at taking risks. His short-term view is well designed to accommodate change and promote innovation. Society in this sense is conservative and individuals progressive. It is at least partly by virtue of individual progressiveness that society can afford to be conservative. For example, the revenues earned in wood-using industry from short-term investments are part of the high national income which makes it possible for our national forest system to be managed for "the greatest good to the greatest number in the long run." Poor nations, like poor persons, can achieve conservatism—conservation—only with extreme difficulty. Man cannot live by bread alone, but he can't subsist on the spirit either.

## OWNERSHIP OF RESOURCES

A second cause of differences between society and individuals in the rate of resource use arises from the institution of ownership. This institution permits the capturing of certain resources. Site can be captured, by either private or public interests, as in the case of the lake-shore property. Minerals, soil, and soil cover can be captured. So, even, can some of the relatively foot-loose assets of the forest, such as wildlife and water

—at least to a degree. The urban sportsman finds himself party to one of society's conflicts when he discovers that private landowners have posted his likeliest hunting or fishing grounds. Again society enters the issue when the people who live at lower elevations suffer water shortage because of heavy use by upstreamers who get first call, or when they suffer from an overabundance of damaging waters released indiscriminately by neighbors at higher elevations.

Not only material assets, but also some of the most essential intangible ingredients of resources, can be captured. Under our laws, rights in the use of knowledge can be owned, as through patents and copyrights. Trademarks can be registered against infringement and firm names protected from damaging use by others, thus permitting ownership of good will. The most significant outcome of such ownership of material and intangible things is the appearance of monopoly elements in the economy. Adam Smith made it clear that the invisible hand would be stayed by monopoly. Monopoly of forest assets leads to reduction in the rate of their use and an exaggeration of their value, so that society at large is obliged to allocate more of its resources than otherwise to its wants for forest goods and services. Under such circumstances it would be possible for the forest manager following intensive and conservative practices to find himself in conflict with the social interest.

Clearly, however, private ownership *need* not lead to discord with society. Our American belief, in utter contrast to that of communists, is that this institution is on balance one of our cardinal and basic social assets. For special cases of conflict, our society, through government, reserves the right itself to own or regulate resources. The public owns more than a fourth of the forest land and close to a half of the standing saw timber in the United States—the outstanding instance of social resource ownership in our country.

### MARKETS AND MONEY

Thirdly, akin to our ownership institutions are those of the market and of money, which put sharp biases into our economic system. For example, there is a market for timber that enables this forest asset to be capitalized and to be converted to money income for individuals, but there is no comparable market for the accompanying recreational assets of the forest. As a result, recreational assets of great social value may be dissipated by private forest owners in their search for money income. These owners may similarly dissipate watershed values. In an economy strongly drawn toward commercial affairs, all those economic values which are non-commercial, and which to society are exceedingly great, tend to be slighted, to be deemphasized. Even timber, which we think of as the most commercial of forest products, may lose out in this running. There is no "futures market" for timber, which fact abets overcutting (by social standards) on the part of risk-conscious owners. In some sections of the country, as here and there in the farm-woodland areas of the East, current markets for timber are poorly developed. At the same time the markets for milk and other livestock products may be exceedingly efficient. The result may be that the farmer doubly emphasizes the forage product of his wooded land in preference to timber, though society could well benefit directly and indirectly from a reversal of emphasis.

Meanwhile the institution of money in itself does strange things to man's concepts of value and to his orientation in life. Perhaps our profession's finest heritage from European forestry is an appreciation for the essential beauty of the forest—the stand and the landscape—and an appreciation for those indefinable gifts of nature bestowed through the medium of the forest—human strength, dignity, and kinship of generations. These concepts of value are easily put aside in a money-directed society. Yet to the extent the economy neglects them it fails in its sole purpose: to satisfy both social and individual wants.

With these glimpses of the macroeconomics of forestry to hold in mind until we can return to the subject later, let us begin considering the units that make up the macroeconomy: the individual firms. If we first understand the parts, we may learn to understand the whole better. So now, while not entirely forgetting that in a sense, because of maladjustments to the social interest, the parts do not add up to the whole, let us consider a sense in which they do add up.

## GROUP AND INDIVIDUAL ACCOUNTS

Intermediate between the economy at large and the individual firm is the *industry,* the group of firms concerned with making a particular product or closely related products. From the viewpoint of the industry, one may look in one direction toward society at large and in the other toward the individual.

Consider the income statement of United States wood-manufacturing corporations for the year 1955 (Table 1). The statement says that these corporations during 1955 turned out products (other than those intended for remanufacture within the industry) that sold for about $13.1 billion. From this revenue, the corporations paid out nearly $12.2 billion for labor, raw materials purchased outside the industry, replacement of old equipment (here assumed to equal depreciation), rent to property owners, and other costs incurred in production, and for taxes. They had left about $0.9 billion, their net revenue, part of which they distributed to stockholders and part of which they retained as surplus.

*Table 1. Estimated revenue and costs of all United States wood-manufacturing corporations, 1955*

| Item | Revenue or cost |
|---|---|
| | *Million dollars* |
| Gross revenue | 13,050 |
| Costs: | |
|     Wages and salaries | 4,420 |
|     Raw materials and power | 4,060 |
|     Taxes | 1,010 |
|     Rent on property | 50 |
|     Other costs | 2,650 |
|       Total cost | 12,190 |
| Net revenue | 860 |

SOURCE: Estimates, based on data from Census of Manufactures and from *Quarterly Financial Report for Manufacturing Corporations*, Federal Trade Commission and Securities and Exchange Commission. "Gross revenue" and "raw materials" items are meant to exclude sales to remanufacturers within the industry.

Now we can take this income statement and view it, as we did in Chapter 2, in terms of inputs (cost) and outputs (revenue):

$4.42 billion of labor + $4.06 billion of raw materials and power + $1.01 billion of government services + $0.05 billion of use of property + $0.86 billion of enterprise + $2.65 billion of other inputs = Marketed pulp, paper, paper products, lumber, millwork, veneer, plywood, cooperage, and other wood products valued at $13.05 billion

The two sides are equal. Note that the left side includes as an input what is called "net revenue" in Table 1—that is, the value of the enterprisers' inputs. Note also that government services are included as an input, valued at the amount of the tax bill. [How do you account for the probable difference between the taxes paid by these corporations and the cost of services they themselves received in the form of police protection, roads, and so on? Can it be that all the social costs of manufacturing wood products are covered in the "government services" item?]

If the input-output equation is multiplied some thirty times and appropriately elaborated, it comes to represent the entire national economy. On the left side, each of the inputs represents materials or services poured into the hopper of the productive machine. On the right side, the outputs listed represent the real income of those who controlled the resources entering at the left. Goods and services are thus shown as flowing from left to right. At the same time, money is represented as moving from right to left: each of the dollar amounts on the left is the money income of one class of producers.

Next, looking in the other direction, toward the individual firm, let us begin to subdivide the totals of Table 1. A two-way subdivision into pulp and paper corporations and lumber and other wood-products corporations is estimated in Table 2. Differences within the sum-total of the

Table 2. Estimated revenue and costs of pulp and paper and other wood-manufacturing corporations in the United States, 1955

| Item | Pulp and paper | Lumber and wood products |
|------|------|------|
| | Million dollars | Million dollars |
| Gross revenue | 8,430 | 4,620 |
| Costs: | | |
| Wages and salaries | 2,620 | 1,800 |
| Raw materials and power | 2,910 | 1,150 |
| Taxes | 790 | 220 |
| Rent on property | 40 | 10 |
| Other costs | 1,500 | 1,150 |
| Total cost | 7,860 | 4,330 |
| Net revenue | 570 | 290 |

SOURCE: See Table 1.

Table 3. Estimated revenue and costs of Firm A, a wood-manufacturing corporation, 1955

| Item | Revenue or cost |
|------|------|
| | Thousand dollars |
| Gross revenue | 15,790 |
| Costs: | |
| Wages and salaries | 6,710 |
| Raw materials and power | 4,800 |
| Taxes | 660 |
| Rent on property | — |
| Other costs | 2,640 |
| Total cost | 14,810 |
| Net revenue | 980 |

wood-manufacturing economy now begin to appear. For instance, it seems that the mechanical-conversion industries on the right lay out a higher proportion of their sales revenue for the services of labor and a lower proportion for raw materials and power than do the chemical-conversion industries. However, these and all the other outlays represent at the same time the industries' costs and the actual money income of people, just as was true of the account for the whole economy.

The process of subdivision can be carried on until one reaches the individual firm. In Table 3, one such firm, a wood-processing corporation that operates plants in the Pacific Northwest, is pulled out of Table 2 as a case in point. You can observe here still further differences in the way resources were used. But it is still the case, as before, that those who controlled the resources received in return for their use the sums shown as the firm's costs and net revenue, in total equal to the value of the firm's product. The firm could conceivably have rewarded its agents of production by paying them in kind, as is done in effect by the economy at large. But few of the agents would have had use for all the lumber they were responsible for producing. And so the firm did the sensible thing, exchanging its product for money before paying its agents.

To the doings of individual firms such as this one we turn now as we move into Part Two of this book.

## SUMMARY

A central social problem is the divergence of individual interest from that of society. This problem may be interpreted in terms of conflict between interest groups or even conflict within individuals. It is here interpreted so as to stress the functional rather than personal concept of society—that is, as a conflict of wants. Solution to the problem of divergent interests is sought in each society according to the spirit of the time.

Conflict between individual and social wants may be traced to differences in the amount or rate of resource use required to fulfill the wants. These differences, in turn, are traceable to such fundamentals as the longer-range view of society, the institution of ownership, and the role of markets and money in the economy.

We turn now to the individual producing firm. This firm is the unit of economic activity that converts resources into things that will satisfy wants and then uses these things or their money equivalent to reward its agents for their efforts.

Part Two

# THE FIRM'S SUPPLY
# OF FOREST PRODUCTS

# Chapter 5

# MARGINAL APPROACH TO THE FIRM'S OBJECTIVES

WE HAVE taken, in Part One, a fleeting look at the economy at large. Now to our first main subject, to be pursued throughout Part Two: the individual producing firm and its doings. The economy at large is the context in which the firm exists. Let us keep this context, this environment with its weighty influences, closely in mind as we study the firm's life.

The purpose of this first chapter is to review the objectives of producing firms and to outline a method—the so-called marginal approach—for studying the firm's use of resources in pursuit of its objectives. Labor resources will be used as the case in point here and in the next two chapters.

By the *firm* is meant the unit of economic activity, under one management, which makes and carries out decisions. Almost every adult, at least as a consumer and as the impresario of his own labor and other resources, is a firm. But most of the firms we shall discuss include more than one person. A case in point is the family, which often acts as a unit in consumption, and in production too. Then there are the firms more formally and popularly speaking: partnerships and corporations. And finally, government is in its economic role a firm or firms, as are other organizations for social action.

Our interest at this stage centers on the producing, rather than the consuming, firm. Thus we shall be thinking about the tie cutter, the backwoods guide, the consulting forester, the farmer who owns woodland, the pulp and paper company, the lumber retailer, the city water department with its forest developments, the National Park Service. . . . These

**51**

are the units whose individual inputs and outputs add up to the totals of the forest economy. Their separate actions determine the whole economic hubbub.

Let us distinguish clearly between firm and industry. The latter is a collective term: the group of firms engaged in the same line—lumber industry, recreation industry, and so on. Our subject now is the firm, not the industry.

### PRODUCING FIRM: PROBLEMS

Consider the economic problem that the producing firm faces. What is the gist of it? In summary, it is to choose among alternatives, to make decisions, in such a way as to meet the objectives of the firm. Such choice and decision is called *management*. The firm has agents of production constituting its share of social resources, the opportunity to convert them into goods and services, and objectives that will guide its conduct. Management now consists in forecasting how the agents—labor, trees, machines, and so on—will perform in service, forecasting the consequences of their performance in terms relevant to the firm's objectives, and reaching and giving effect to decisions among the alternatives presented. Here is the cake-baking problem of Chapter 1 (p. 8). Its solution by firms— what we shall call the combination of the agents of production—determines the use of society's resources and the outflow of products. That is to say, management is the process of determining inputs and outputs.

For example, suppose that some years from now you consider giving up your job and going into business for yourself as a consulting forester. How would the two careers compare, you ask yourself. What are your personal and professional qualifications for consulting forestry? What are the opportunities in the territory where you would work, and how well are you known there? How might your earnings compare with those in prospect in your present connection? How highly do you value the greater independence that you might gain, and what weight do you attach to the worries, uncertainties, and headaches that you would also acquire? Do you have the capital to carry you during the period of getting established? Are you and your family willing to face the risks? These are some of the questions that might lie behind your first decision— whether to take the plunge.

Suppose that you do set up your own consulting firm. Your job thereafter may be principally to weigh alternatives, so as to make decisions for your firm and recommendations for your clients. How should you organize? Will you take a partner? Will your business yet warrant hiring full-time professional help, setting up an office outside your home, relieving your wife of the secretarial work? What changes are needed in your territory, your field of specialization, your fees, your advertising policy? How many laborers will you attempt to hire on the stand-improvement job coming up in the fall? Will you supervise them yourself or find someone else? How heavily will you mark the Jones tract for cutting? Will you advise Jones to set up a sawmill, and if so, what sort of mill, and where should it be placed?

Such questions could go on to traverse the whole range of economic decisions in forestry. The point is that they are many and highly diverse, that they all involve forecasting the performance of somebody or something in service and then placing an economic interpretation upon this forecast, and that they are all concerned, in essence, with the combination of the agents of production. They are all management questions.

The purpose of Part Two of this book is to help you understand the economics of such questions—the economics of decisions by the individual forestry firm in regard to the combination of the agents of production: labor, capital, land, and enterprise in their various forms. In pursuing this theme, bear in mind the twofold aim of our studies: first, to help you become a more sophisticated witness of the forestry scene and, second, to add a little to your equipment for making intelligent professional decisions.

## OBJECTIVES

Clearly, the beginning point in our study of any firm's behavior is its objectives, its goals. We begin with the ends that the firm wishes to reach. It would be nice from the standpoint of studying people if their goals were simple, clear-cut, and built-in, like those we imagined for the ants in Chapter 2 (pp. 12–13). But we may as well face the fact that human beings are not so orderly as that. Different firms have different goals, and often a single firm has various, changing, and possibly conflicting goals.

We need to distinguish among successive levels of goals, ranging from the most general to the most specific. For example, a firm may have the objective of making the greatest money profit. This is its very general goal, though you will perceive that in the background lie even broader aims that the firm is attempting to meet by means of profit making. In the last analysis, these broader aims are those of consumers. They are the consumer aims of the persons who make up the firm (what the persons want profits *for*). And socially speaking, they are the aims of consumers in general (what consumers want the firm's products for).

At any rate, for the purpose of making a profit the firm, let us say, grows timber on its forest land. Presumably it does so because it thinks timber growing is its most profitable alternative. Timber growing, then, is a means to an end. At the same time, however, it is an end in its own right, coordinate with other forest-product objectives that firms may have, such as to grow forage or to propagate game. In order to grow timber, the firm, let's suppose, must do some planting, which is a means, and simultaneously an end toward which the purchase of planting stock, and the like, is directed. Thus primary means are also secondary ends, which in turn have means that are tertiary ends, and so on, in a long chain. Since ends cannot well be weighed independently of means, every link in a firm's chain may affect, and be affected by, every other—another aspect of the universal interdependence with which we were confronted in Chapter 3 (p. 37).

Let us look into the objectives of the producing firm. Let us examine the aims that are situated above product goals in the chain. Later we shall have a great deal to say about the lower parts of the chain: product objectives and operational aims. Indeed, these make up most of our entire story. For now, let us ask what it is that producing firms intend to get out of life.

The persons who constitute the firm may wish to make the greatest possible net revenue: the largest excess of revenue over cost. Or they may want to make simply a customary revenue, or to avoid incurring a loss. Aside from the goods and services over which they gain control by means of their net revenues, they may seek personal security, continuity, social standing, satisfaction through service and accomplishment, the pleasure of combat and intrigue, publicity, freedom from publicity, or innumerable other benefits. Producers' aims are not a single, timeless complex but are a personal product, molded by contemporary life and institutions in the nation and community where they do business.

We shall begin our study of this varied and variable firm by resorting to the method of abstraction. First, we shall assume that the firm is *rational:* that what it wants to do with its net revenues is to maximize them. Second, *we shall regard **revenue** and **cost** as including not only the material outputs and inputs of production but also such other considerations (things either aimed at or avoided) as the firm may put value upon.*

As we have observed, revenue is a flow, with a time dimension. When we speak of maximizing revenue, we mean maximizing it *per unit of time* —for example, per year. Furthermore, we may recognize a *principle of unity of the firm:* The rational firm aiming to maximize yearly revenue will seek this maximum for its business as a whole, and not necessarily for any one part of its business or for any one of its inputs. For instance, the farmer who is rational by our definition will not want to maximize the annual revenue from his woodland if this would require neglecting his other land to the extent of reducing his total income. What he wants is the greatest annual net revenue from the farm at large. By the same token, the rational forest owner may not aim to get the highest return per acre or per dollar of investment. On 10,000 acres, his maximum annual net revenue per acre would be, let us say, $1. But if he has the alternative of acquiring another thousand acres and of netting 95 cents per acre on the 11,000 acres, this is better. To maximize annual net revenue per unit of land or other input is rational only if the input cannot be varied. In the last analysis, the firm itself is the only invariable unit, and maximizing net revenue *per firm*, per time unit, is the only sure rule.

That combination of productive agents which will maximize the firm's total net revenue per unit of time we will term the *best combination*.

## DIMINISHING RETURNS: EXAMPLE

There is a certain fact of economic life which commonly governs the firm's pursuit of its best combination, and therefore the running of the economy. This is the fact of diminishing returns.

The workings of the principle are so universal in the business of life that you take them for granted and adapt yourself to them almost automatically. You are, let's suppose, preparing for a big final exam. Your first half hour is spent, say, hitting the highlights of the textbook, and your second and third half hours likewise, by which time you have covered the ground once in barest summary and readied yourself for digging into the topics on which you need to spend more time. These first few intervals of study are tremendously productive, serving as they do to refresh your memory after some absence and to reconstruct in your mind the framework of the course, upon which you can now place its parts.

The specific parts of the course are your next concern as you start back through the book, working on the important topics first. Your fourth half hour adds a good deal to your command of the subject. However, it is not so productive as was the third. You have entered the stage of diminishing returns. Thereafter, each successive half hour continues to yield a smaller gain than the one preceding, as you delve into less and less fruitful detail. Your total preparation for the exam is increasing all the while, but the successive increases come harder. You could actually carry this process to the point where, in the limited time available, you could not better yourself any further. You would be crammed full, and the attempt to cram more might actually worsen your chances in the exam because of fatigue and confusion.

It is important to note that ordinarily you will not stop your efforts at the point where diminishing returns begin. In ordinary situations you will always be wise to go beyond this point. How far beyond will depend on your alternatives: how good a use you can make of your time elsewhere—in other work, recreation, or rest. Surely, however, you will not continue your work beyond the point of greatest total return. Defining the actual point where you stop is a job that we will tackle soon. [But at this stage it will help if you try your own hand at defining the point where the rational student leaves off studying for an exam.]

### RETURNS FROM TIMBER-STAND IMPROVEMENT

Consider now an example of diminishing returns in the practice of forestry.

A forester, let us call him Hubert Hawkins, acts as manager of a large timber property where mixed pine and hardwood is the principal forest type. A while ago he was making plans for extensive timber-stand-improvement operations, which were to consist of releasing the crop trees, mainly pine, from competing trees by harvesting or killing the latter. The areas where he would work and the procedure he would follow were pretty well decided in his mind. His main question at the moment was how many laborers he would hire for the job, to work with him as the foreman. The laborers would be hired from the pool available to the firm: its own force of more or less regular workers, and neighboring part-time farmers fairly familiar with woods tasks.

Hawkins at the time set down an estimate (forecast), based upon his experience, of what he could accomplish in an average working day with various numbers of men helping him. He would do the planning, marking, and supervising, and the men would do the cutting and poisoning. He estimated the accomplishment in terms of numbers of trees that would be released per day, by sizes of crew ranging from 0 up to 12 laborers. His result appears in columns 2 and 3 of Table 4. The other columns are added for us to analyze.

The first two columns in Table 4 tell about the firm's inputs into the hopper of production. There is one foreman (Hawkins) and varying numbers of laborers, plus, of course, the equipment and supplies they use, such as axes and saws. The men (with their materials) are those resources of the firm that concern us here. They are the agents of production that are to be combined. Thirteen possible combinations are shown. Observe that these inputs are *rates*—in this case, per day.

The last three columns in Table 4 tell about the output of the firm— that is, the product, expressed in numbers of crop trees released per day. Column 3 is the total output estimated to be obtainable with each number of laborers. With no laborers, the output is zero, since we assume that the foreman does no actual release work. With increasing labor input, total output rises, but not indefinitely. As in your preparation for an exam, it reaches a peak and falls off beyond. Notice that output, like input, is a rate per time unit.

Column 4 of Table 4 is the additional output that comes with each enlargement of the crew. It is the extra product per man-day—that is, per unit of variable input. Since the figures apply to the whole intervals between successive labor inputs, they are entered on the lines intermediate between these inputs. One laborer (with foreman) can release 15 trees (col. 3), which is 15 more (col. 4) than could be produced in his ab-

*Table 4. Estimated daily output in timber stand improvement,*
*Hawkins property*

| Fixed input (1) | Variable input (2) | Total output (3) | Additional output per laborer (4) | Average output per laborer (5) |
|---|---|---|---|---|
| *Foreman* | *Laborers* | *Trees released* | *Trees released* | *Trees released* |
| 1 | 0 | 0 | | — |
| | | | 15 | |
| 1 | 1 | 15 | | 15.0 |
| | | | 35 | |
| 1 | 2 | 50 | | 25.0 |
| | | | 60 | |
| 1 | 3 | 110 | | 36.7 |
| | | | 50 | |
| 1 | 4 | 160 | | 40.0 |
| | | | 43 | |
| 1 | 5 | 203 | | 40.6 |
| | | | 34 | |
| 1 | 6 | 237 | | 39.5 |
| | | | 23 | |
| 1 | 7 | 260 | | 37.1 |
| | | | 15 | |
| 1 | 8 | 275 | | 34.4 |
| | | | 10 | |
| 1 | 9 | 285 | | 31.7 |
| | | | 5 | |
| 1 | 10 | 290 | | 29.0 |
| | | | 0 | |
| 1 | 11 | 290 | | 26.4 |
| | | | −5 | |
| 1 | 12 | 285 | | 23.8 |

sence. Addition of the second laborer brings the total output to 50 (col. 3), an extra product, above the previous total of 15, amounting to 35 trees. The third laborer, in his turn, accounts for an additional output of 60 (110 minus 50). Here a peak is reached corresponding to your third half hour of exam preparation: With the next increase in crew size, the additional output falls, and *diminishing returns have begun*. Note that additional returns diminish continuously thereafter, reaching zero at maximum total output and negative values beyond. You should study columns

3 and 4 and familiarize yourself with the relationships between them. Observe that, just as the additional output may be derived from the total by successive subtractions, so the total may be figured from the additional output by cumulative addition.

Finally, column 5 is the average output per unit of variable input: column 3 divided by column 2. This average output per laborer rises at first, then comes to a peak. This peak is lower and further along than the peak in additional output. [Why so? And is it necessarily so?] Beyond the peak, average output falls continuously. [It does not reach zero in this illustration. Would it hit zero if the experiment were continued far enough?]

## CIRCUMSTANCES OF DIMINISHING RETURNS

Here, then, is an example of diminishing returns in timber-stand improvement. One might, if he liked, state a general *principle of diminishing returns* in forestry: In forestry production, so long as organization, methods, and equipment are unchanged, if the firm increases any input beyond a certain rate per unit of time, the total rate of output will rise, but by ever smaller amounts with each successive unit increase in the rate of input. In other words, every new rise in accomplishment is won at the cost of greater additional effort. Let us emphasize the main circumstances under which this principle works:

First, a firm is combining agents of production, or inputs, in order to produce an output.

Second, some of the inputs are variable, but *some are fixed.* In the exam preparation, the fixed input was you. In the Hawkins case, it is mainly the foreman.

Third, the methods and conditions of production are also fixed. In our statement of the principle we said, "so long as organization, methods, and equipment are unchanged"—that is, so long as Hawkins does all the supervising alone, regardless of crew size; so long as he continues to use handsaws, not power saws; and so on. Let us caption this proviso in these terms: *Technology is fixed.*

The condition of there being some fixed inputs and a fixed technology is termed *short run.* Later we shall be probing the issue of short run, long run, and so on in detail, but for now let us stick to the short run and take it to signify the existence of these two fixed elements in the problem. The assumption of some fixed inputs and a fixed technology may seem unrealistic—unrepresentative of economic life as we generally find it. In Chapter 3 we laid great stress on the fact that knowledge liberates man from the refractory and restrictive forces of nature—lets him, in our present terms, subdue diminishing returns. Our whole economic history is one of forestalling diminishing returns—of enjoying, in most cases, increasing returns. Why make the limiting assumption that technology is fixed, or some of the inputs either? The answer is that though most anything may be possible in the long run, there *is* the short run always to be contended with, where diminishing returns *do* exist, shaping the firm's decisions from day to day and even from year to year. Furthermore, we shall learn that in forest production there are in the environment rather fixed elements that impose diminishing returns even over great periods of time, so that they are the cardinal fact with which the manager continuously deals. Finally, our later analysis of the many cases in the forest economy where diminishing returns can be escaped will be more meaningful if we first see clearly the nature of the forces from which escape is sought.

Outputs (returns) can be thought of in various ways—total, additional, average—any of which may diminish at some stage of production. But when we speak of *diminishing returns,* let us always mean diminishing additional output per unit of input. The *point of diminishing returns* is the point where additional output culminates.

[We have managed somehow to escape what may be the most important point about diminishing returns—the why of it. Why, in the Hawkins case, did the additional output, after rising briefly, proceed to turn around and head for the cellar as the crew was enlarged? See if you can explain this illustration of diminishing returns, drawing on your own experience and imagination.]

### ECONOMIC INFERENCE

Here we have been talking about a forecast of inputs and outputs, and about diminishing returns, pointing out that in the short run extra output is harder to get, the more output the firm is getting already. Now these observations have economic significance on two counts: (1) Input-output data, supplemented by certain value information, can be used to draw a conclusion or make a decision about the best amount of input and output. This is the decision, regarding the combination of agents, that constitutes the core of management. Hence input-output data are of central significance in the economy. (2) What makes it possible to determine a best combination is the existence of diminishing returns.

Our next step, therefore, will be to draw an economic inference from input-output data, using the Hawkins data as an example. These data in their present form have engineering significance but are quite neutral otherwise. Let us lend them a bias of an economic sort, so that we may say, "This one combination out of the thirteen is best; the other twelve are inferior."

**Table 5. Best combination of productive agents and best output per day in timber-stand improvement, Hawkins property**

| Fixed input | Variable input | Total output | Average output per laborer | Marginal output or productivity | Total cost of inputs | | |
|---|---|---|---|---|---|---|---|
| | | | | | Fixed | Variable | Aggregate |
| a | b | c | d (c/b) | e (c) | f (40a) | g (10b) | h (f + g) |
| Foreman | Laborers | Trees | Trees | Trees | Dollars | Dollars | Dollars |
| 1 | 0 | 0 | — | | 40 | 0 | 40 |
| | | | | 15 | | | |
| 1 | 1 | 15 | 15.0 | | 40 | 10 | 50 |
| | | | | 35 | | | |
| 1 | 2 | 50 | 25.0 | | 40 | 20 | 60 |
| | | | | 60 | | | |
| 1 | 3 | 110 | 36.7 | | 40 | 30 | 70 |
| | | | | 50 | | | |
| 1 | 4 | 160 | 40.0 | | 40 | 40 | 80 |
| | | | | 43 | | | |
| 1 | 5 | 203 | 40.6 | | 40 | 50 | 90 |
| | | | | 34 | | | |
| 1 | 6 | 237 | 39.5 | | 40 | 60 | 100 |
| | | | | 23 | | | |
| 1 | 7 | 260 | 37.1 | | 40 | 70 | 110 |
| | | | | 15 | | | |
| 1 | 8 | 275 | 34.4 | | 40 | 80 | 120 |
| | | | | 10 | | | |
| 1 | 9 | 285 | 31.7 | | 40 | 90 | 130 |
| | | | | 5 | | | |
| 1 | 10 | 290 | 29.0 | | 40 | 100 | 140 |

| Variable input | Average cost per tree released | | | Marginal unit cost | Marginal unit revenue | Total gross revenue | Total net revenue |
|---|---|---|---|---|---|---|---|
| | Fixed | Variable | Aggregate | | | | |
| b | i (f/c) | j (g/c) | k (h/c) (i + j) | l (10/e) | m | n (0.70c) | o (n − h) |
| Laborers | Dollars | Dollars | Dollars | Dollars | Dollars | Dollars | Dollars |
| 0 | — | — | — | | | 0.00 | −40.00 |
| | | | | 0.667 | 0.70 | | |
| 1 | 2.666 | 0.667 | 3.333 | | | 10.50 | −39.50 |
| | | | | 0.286 | 0.70 | | |
| 2 | 0.800 | 0.400 | 1.200 | | | 35.00 | −25.00 |
| | | | | 0.167 | 0.70 | | |
| 3 | 0.363 | 0.273 | 0.636 | | | 77.00 | 7.00 |
| | | | | 0.200 | 0.70 | | |
| 4 | 0.250 | 0.250 | 0.500 | | | 112.00 | 32.00 |
| | | | | 0.233 | 0.70 | | |
| 5 | 0.197 | 0.246 | 0.443 | | | 142.10 | 52.10 |
| | | | | 0.294 | 0.70 | | |
| 6 | 0.169 | 0.253 | 0.422 | | | 165.90 | 65.90 |
| | | | | 0.435 | 0.70 | | |
| 7 | 0.154 | 0.269 | 0.423 | | | 182.00 | 72.00 |
| | | | | 0.667 | 0.70 | | |
| 8 | 0.145 | 0.291 | 0.436 | | | 192.50 | 72.50 |
| | | | | 1.000 | 0.70 | | |
| 9 | 0.140 | 0.316 | 0.456 | | | 199.50 | 69.50 |
| | | | | 2.000 | 0.70 | | |
| 10 | 0.138 | 0.345 | 0.483 | | | 203.00 | 63.00 |

Our assumptions will be as follows: First, Hawkins's firm has as its immediate goal to make the greatest possible net revenue per day from its stand-improvement operations. Second, Hawkins's own time, considering the alternatives open to him at the period when the work is to be done, is worth $40 per day. Third, Hawkins can hire all the labor he may need for $10 per man-day, including the cost of equipment and supplies that the laborer will use. Fourth, the revenue from releasing one crop tree is 70 cents, which is the estimated increase in present worth of the property as a result of the release, and this per-tree value of 70 cents will hold good, on the average, for any amount of stand improvement that the firm may undertake.

Our purpose, now, is to find what size of stand-improvement crew is "best," in the sense of producing the highest net return per day.

### BEST CREW SIZE

Consider Table 5, where inputs and outputs are analyzed in light of the values just assumed. The columns are lettered, and the derivation of each calculated column is shown in parentheses.

Columns a through e of Table 5 are copied from Table 4. However, data for 11- and 12-man crews are left off because crews of this size, beyond the point of maximum total output, are surely uneconomical and of no relevance to the problem at hand. What was called "additional" output in Table 4 is here called "marginal" output, which means precisely the same thing and is just a little harder to understand. *Marginal output* is the added output that comes with extra input. More precisely, it is the difference between total rates of output with and without the extra input. Usually it is expressed per unit of input—as in this case, per man-day. Another term for marginal output is marginal product, or "marginal productivity," as it is called in column e.

Columns f through h are the total daily costs of operating crews of from 0 to 10 men. Column f, fixed cost, is the result of assigning the assumed $40 value to the input of column a. Thus *fixed cost* is the cost of *fixed input*, that which does not change with output or with whatever alternative is being studied. Similarly column g, variable cost, is derived from column b, and the assumed $10 value. *Variable cost* is the cost of *variable input*, that which does change with output or with whatever alternative is being studied. Column h, the total aggregate cost, is the sum of the total fixed and variable costs in the two preceding columns.

Let us turn next to columns i, j, and k. These three columns are the average costs per tree released and are derived from the three preceding columns—f, g, and h, respectively—by dividing the total costs in those columns by the total output, trees released, as shown in column c. Note that the average fixed cost (col. i) falls continuously, though by smaller amounts all the while, reaching a minimum at the crew size where total output peaks. Note that average variable cost—labor cost per tree, col. $j$ —is least for a 5-man crew, the same size of crew for which average output per laborer (col. $d$) is most. [Why is this, or is it merely a coincidence? Can you discover a complete parallel between the relation of columns $j$ and $d$, on the one hand, and columns $i$ and $c$, on the other? That is to say, since $i$ and $j$ are both average costs, would you not expect each of them to be related to some kind of average output? Now column $d$ is an average output, but how about column $c$? Although it is labeled "total," is it actually an average also, in some sense?] Finally, note that average aggregate cost, column $k$, is the sum of the average fixed and variable costs, and that it is least at a crew size intermediate between minimum fixed and minimum variable cost. [Why does the least average aggregate cost occur where it does?]

Now for column $l$. This is the *marginal unit cost*, which means the additional cost per unit—in this case, per unit of output. It is computed in three steps as follows (take the fourth figure in the column, 20 cents, as an easy example): First, the total extra cost of the fourth increase in crew size is—referring to either column $g$ or column $h$, or going back to our assumption about labor value per man-day—$10. Second, the total extra output resulting from the fourth increase in crew size is—referring to column $c$, or to the figure already computed in column $e$—50 trees. Third, the extra cost per tree, marginal unit cost, is $10 divided by 50— i.e., 20 cents. Note that marginal unit cost is least where marginal output is greatest—that is, at the point of diminishing returns—and that marginal unit cost rises throughout the range of crew sizes where diminishing returns are in effect.

The marginal unit revenue of column $m$ is the exact counterpart of the marginal unit cost. *Marginal unit revenue* is the additional revenue per unit—here again, of output. How much is added to the firm's total revenue by releasing one more tree? The answer, by assumption, is 70 cents. This answer, which holds regardless of crew size or output, could be found by a three-step process analogous to the one we followed in getting the marginal unit cost. [It may help you to understand what we are doing if you will attempt to discover the three steps and follow them, even though they may turn out to be obvious and unnecessary.]

At this point we have in hand all the information we need to answer the opening question—i.e., what is the best size of crew, the size that will maximize net revenue. In fact, we have immediate need for only columns $l$ and $m$, the marginal unit cost and revenue, to answer the question. Run your eye down the two columns and find the point within the region of diminishing returns where marginal unit cost and revenue are equated. This point is found to occur at about a crew size of 8 men. The

8-man crew, therefore, is the best crew for this particular job: the best combination of the agents of production.

The reasoning is as follows:

## EQUATING MARGINAL UNIT REVENUE AND COST

1. So long as marginal unit revenue exceeds marginal unit cost, it means that increasing the output is economically worthwhile, since each extra tree released is more than paying its way. If, to take the 4-man crew as an example, Hawkins can increase his revenue 70 cents and his cost only 20 cents by releasing another tree, he will want to release that tree, and the next one and the next, so long as the total revenue is rising faster than the total cost. Therefore, if marginal unit revenue is higher than marginal unit cost, as is the case up through 7 men, it will pay to enlarge the crew.

2. On the other hand, if within the area of diminishing returns marginal unit revenue is less than cost, it means that each extra tree is being released at a loss—i.e., at a reduction in total net revenue. Under this circumstance, which obtains for 9-man and larger crews, it will pay to reduce the crew.

3. Therefore, the only crew size that cannot be improved upon, which is to say the "best" crew size, is the one where marginal unit revenue is neither greater nor less than marginal unit cost, but equal to it. This is the 8-man crew. If you will look at the top of columns $l$ and $m$, you will find another point where marginal unit revenue and cost are about equal. Here marginal cost is on the way down. The firm has as yet done nothing but accumulate net costs; it has not entered the range of production where extra output will contribute to net revenue. Consequently this is the point where net revenue is not maximized but minimized. It is for this reason that we look for the best crew size within the range of diminishing returns, where marginal unit cost has come from *beneath* marginal revenue to reach their point of equating.

We can verify this conclusion very simply by actually computing the total net revenue, which is the difference between total gross revenue and total cost. Total gross revenue is entered in column $n$ of Table 5 as the product of total trees released (col. $c$) times the value per tree, 70 cents. Total cost has already been figured, in column $h$. The difference, the total net revenue, is in column $o$, which, in exhibiting a maximum of $72.50 at the 8-man point, checks our previous result. The total net revenue per day *is* highest with the 8-man crew. [Under what circumstances do you suppose a net revenue of this order could be earned through forestry operations? Would it necessarily represent a failure in the competitive system?]

It may be helpful to regard the difference, marginal unit revenue minus marginal unit cost, as a fund contributed by the unit of product toward the payment of fixed cost and the accumulation of net revenue. Thus, in our example, with a 4-man crew, there is a fund of 50 cents (0.70 − 0.200) contributed in this manner by each tree released. Since there are 50 extra trees released (col. e), the total fund contributed by the addition of a fourth man to the crew is 50 times 50 cents, or $25. It is this $25 which accounts for the increase of total net revenue in column o from $7 at the 3-man level to $32 at the 4-man level. It follows that so long as there is a positive difference between marginal unit revenue and cost, total net revenue can be raised by increasing the output—i.e., the input. And it further follows that the best input-output level is at the point where this difference just disappears. Which is another way of stating our earlier conclusion.

### MARGINAL VALUES PER UNIT OF INPUT

In our thinking about diminishing returns and their economic meaning, we have from the beginning used the idea of marginal product per unit of input. This was what we did in column 4 of Table 4 and in column e of Table 5. However, we have yet to take the next logical step of expressing this marginal product as marginal revenue per unit of input. Our marginal unit revenue so far has been only per unit of output, and marginal unit cost likewise. But marginal unit revenue and cost can just as well be expressed per unit of input and used in this form to determine the best combination of productive agents. Let us see how this works. Our purpose here is not to make life more complicated, but to make our economic tools more flexible and versatile, capable of solving more varied problems. One can do better work with a shovel if he learns to hold it left-handed as well as right-handed.

Continuing with the Hawkins example, let us consider the three pairs of columns in Table 6: first, total input and output in physical terms; second, marginal input and output in physical terms; third, marginal input and output in value terms—i.e., marginal cost and revenue. The first pair is the same as those we have begun with before.

The second pair, columns 3 and 4, is derived from the first by successive subtractions. *Marginal input*, a new term for us, is simply the physical counterpart of marginal cost. Note that both marginal input and marginal output derived in this manner are, in effect, per unit of input.

The third pair, columns 5 and 6, is derived from the second by converting to value terms at the rate of $10 per laborer and 70 cents per tree. When marginal cost and revenue were expressed per unit of output, the cost showed ultimately a rising trend (because of diminishing returns), and the revenue was constant. Now, with marginal cost and revenue on a per-unit-of-input basis, the cost is constant, and the revenue falls throughout the region of diminishing returns. In either case there is within this region a point of equating, which occurs approximately with the addition of the eighth man to the crew. Thus our finding with respect to the best combination is the same whether we use the unit of

*Table 6. Marginal cost and revenue per unit of input,*
*timber-stand improvement, Hawkins property*

| Total variable input | Total output | Marginal input | Marginal output | Marginal unit cost | Marginal unit revenue |
|---|---|---|---|---|---|
| (1) | (2) | (3) | (4) | (5) | (6) |
| *Laborers* | *Trees* | *Laborers* | *Trees* | *Dollars* | *Dollars* |
| 0 | 0 | | | | |
| | | 1 | 15 | 10 | 10.50 |
| 1 | 15 | | | | |
| | | 1 | 35 | 10 | 24.50 |
| 2 | 50 | | | | |
| | | 1 | 60 | 10 | 42.00 |
| 3 | 110 | | | | |
| | | 1 | 50 | 10 | 35.00 |
| 4 | 160 | | | | |
| | | 1 | 43 | 10 | 30.10 |
| 5 | 203 | | | | |
| | | 1 | 34 | 10 | 23.80 |
| 6 | 237 | | | | |
| | | 1 | 23 | 10 | 16.10 |
| 7 | 260 | | | | |
| | | 1 | 15 | 10 | 10.50 |
| 8 | 275 | | | | |
| | | 1 | 10 | 10 | 7.00 |
| 9 | 285 | | | | |
| | | 1 | 5 | 10 | 3.50 |
| 10 | 290 | | | | |

output or the unit of input as the basis for expressing marginal cost and revenue.

[In order to draw a parallel clearly in your own mind and in order to see the workings of the margin, try setting up a six-column table which will be the counterpart of Table 6, but with marginal input and output in the terms we used first—per unit of output.]

The reasoning by which the best combination is discovered in Table 6 is simple and straightforward, being exactly what the business manager may use to make his decision in such a case. The reasoning runs as follows: With labor at $10 and the product worth 70 cents, a man must be able to increase output by 10/0.70, or 14.3 units, in order to pay his way. The eighth man, by releasing an extra 15 trees, pays his way with 50 cents to spare. But the ninth man cannot do so.

However, our major concern just now isn't with a procedure for making forest-management decisions. Nor are we especially trying to illustrate business practice. Our purpose runs deeper than procedure. It is to become familiar with a rule regarding the best combination of productive agents. The rule will prove valuable to you as an astute observer. It will serve you also, in various ways that we shall discover, in decision making. This *rule for the best combination,* in summary, is as follows: The firm's short-run best combination, where its total net revenue per unit of time is greatest, occurs at that level of input-output, within the range of diminishing returns, where marginal cost and revenue are equal. Marginal cost and revenue may be figured either per unit of input or per unit of output.

## SIGNIFICANCE OF THE MARGIN

You should firmly grasp the marginal concept, the concept of the increment (or decrement) in a total. This increment is a sure guide to the various points of maximum and minimum that require recognition in weighing alternatives. The marginal amount is very often the easiest quantity to recognize, and in our everyday experience we may compute and use it more commonly than other amounts such as the total and average. What is more familiar than decisions on the use of one's personal time, which is ordinarily reckoned not in sums or quotients but in terms such as "five minutes more"? Or as Horace wrote, "In the midst of hope and care, in the midst of fears and disquietudes, think every day that shines upon you is the last. Thus the hour, which shall not be expected, will come upon you an agreeable addition." If you will search your own experience in weighing the rewards against the penalties of each day's ordinary pursuits, you will be surprised to discover how commonly you focus upon the additional rewards and penalties in prospect. And when the latter come to exceed the former, the chances are you will judge it time to quit.

One must draw a clear distinction between the marginal and the average, and of course between the marginal and the total. The best combination is not the one where average output is highest, nor where total output is highest. In fact, we shall soon discover that it necessarily occurs somewhere in between these two points. It occurs at the point where the marginal output equals the marginal input—speaking in terms of value, rather than physical, units.

The best combination is sometimes called the highest-profit combination, using profit to mean what we term net revenue. It would be more accurate to say, "highest-profit or least-loss combination." Looking for the best combination does not assure finding one that is profitable. If, in the Hawkins illustration, Hawkins's time were valued at $120 per day instead of $40, the 8-man crew would still be the best combination, though it would show a net loss of $7.50 per day. It would be best in the sense that any other combination would show a higher loss. Of course if Hawkins's time were worth $120 per day, presumably on the basis of his alternatives, he would better put his time on the alternatives and not on the stand improvement.

Apparently we have just run onto an interesting principle, worth pausing upon. Let us term it the *principle of irrelevance of fixed factors:* Fixed cost has no part in determining the best combination of the agents of production. (It does, of course, help determine the absolute amount of net revenue or loss at this combination.) Or, to put the same thing differently, fixed cost has no effect upon marginal cost—and certainly none upon marginal revenue. Indeed, we found it possible in Table 6 to work out the best combination without any reference whatever to fixed cost. It becomes clear after a little thought that no factor that is fixed in the production equation—i.e., that is common to all the alternatives being weighed—can possibly affect the choice among the alternatives. Such a factor disappears because it is canceled out of both sides of the equation. Now we begin to see the unique value of the marginal concept. The marginal amount is the amount that changes with alternatives, and it contains no element that does not change. It is therefore the simplest complete expression of all the cost or revenue factors that are relevant to the production decision.

## USING THE MARGINAL APPROACH

If fixed costs do not affect the best combination, then what does affect it? Basically, what does one need to know in order to choose rationally among alternative combinations on the grounds of cost and revenue? One needs to know three things: (1) outputs in relation to variable inputs, (2) the unit value of the outputs, and (3) the unit value of the variable inputs. In our illustration, this means knowing the input-output relationship of crew size to trees released, the wage rate, and the value of a released tree. Everything else is irrelevant. But if any of these three items should turn out to be different from the estimate, then the best combination will need to be refigured.

Now put the marginal concept to work by considering some practical questions concerning the Hawkins case. These are the sorts of question that confront one very frequently in economic matters: How will the firm's program be affected if this or that underlying change takes place, or if forecasts prove faulty? The technique for answering such questions is as follows:

First, identify the relevant variables in the situation—the independent variables, or "causes," and the dependent variables, or "effects"—and determine how each independent variable affects the dependent ones, in direction, and if necessary in degree. This step is called *model* building. Tables 5 and 6 are models for analyzing stand improvement on the Hawkins property. The gist of the models is, "Best crew size is determined by the equating of marginal labor cost and marginal revenue from released trees." If you like, you may follow certain systematic steps to derive such cost-revenue models. Let us put the steps in the form of six questions, with illustrative answers from the Hawkins case:

1. What are the variable inputs? The answer in our example is laborers, or man-days of labor per day. To decide which are the variable inputs requires recognizing the fixed inputs and setting them aside.

2. What are the outputs? Trees released per day.

3. What shall be chosen as the *unit* for marginal unit cost and revenue? The choice may be made on the grounds of convenience. In Table 5, the unit of output was chosen; in Table 6, the unit of input.

4. What is the marginal unit cost? See Tables 5 and 6, columns *l* and 5, respectively.

5. What is the marginal unit revenue? See columns *m* and 6.

6. What is the best combination? Eight laborers, releasing 275 trees per day.

Second, determine if the change in question is a change in any of the relevant independent variables or will produce such a change. If it is, or will, then use the model to estimate the effect of the change. If the change has truly a negligible bearing on any of the independent variables, then it can be judged irrelevant.

[What will be the effect upon best crew size if wage rates rise, other things remaining the same?

[What will be the effect upon best crew size, other things remaining the same, if the value of the foreman's time decreases?

[What will it be if land values go up?

[What will it be if the value of releasing a tree increases?

[What if the laborers become 10 per cent more productive at the same pay?

[What if the foreman finds that he is spending much more time than he expected in keeping after the men and arguing with them?

[What if wage rates fall and the value of a released tree rises simultaneously?

[What if wage rates and the value of a released tree rise simultaneously? (You will need more information to answer this one. Exactly what information will you need?)]

## SUMMARY

A firm's actions are guided by its objectives. Let us study the actions of the producing firm whose objective is to maximize its net revenue per unit of time.

In the short run, when the firm's technology and some of its inputs are fixed, its efforts, beyond a point, to increase output run into diminishing returns. That is to say, successive inputs of the agents of production add less and less to total output.

Under these circumstances the firm's best combination of the agents of production—the one that will maximize net revenue or minimize net loss—is determinable. The best combination is that one, within the region of diminishing returns, which equates marginal cost and marginal revenue per unit of output—or per unit of input.

The firm's best combination is determined basically by three factors: (1) the relation of output to variable inputs, (2) the unit cost of variable inputs, and (3) the unit price of the output. Factors independent of these are irrelevant to the best combination. Notably, fixed cost has no bearing on the best combination.

# Chapter 6

## LABOR

## PRODUCTION

## FUNCTIONS

$\mathbf{M}$ANY OF the problems that we shall meet in the economics of forestry lend themselves best to simple graphic study. By way of introduction to such study, let us sketch with the use of graphs, the ground covered in Chapter 5.

Thus we shall continue to work with the relationships between output and input, in physical and in value terms: output as a function of input, or vice versa. Such a function, expressing as it does the cardinal process in production, is called a *production function*. As in Chapter 5, we shall take labor as our prime example of inputs. Toward the end of the chapter, we shall use our graphic analysis of the production function to determine the upper and lower limits of input-output within which the firm operates.

### BASIC GEOMETRY

As a preliminary, we need to consider the geometry of the total, the average, and the marginal output. The same principles will apply to input, to revenue, and to cost. Let us plot and curve a production function, laying out variable input per unit of time on the horizontal axis and output per time unit on the vertical axis (Fig. 5). This total output-over-input curve is S-shaped, as shown, if the onset of diminishing returns is delayed beyond the first inputs or shaped like an inverted J if diminishing returns set in at once.

First, the total: With 25 units of input, total output is, let us suppose, 60 units, as represented by point E (Fig. 5a). Total output at an input of 25 is the height of point $E$ above the horizontal axis. Or in general, we have the **geometric rule for the total:** The total output represented by any point on an output-over-input curve is the vertical distance of this point from the $X$ axis, measured on the scale of the $Y$ axis.

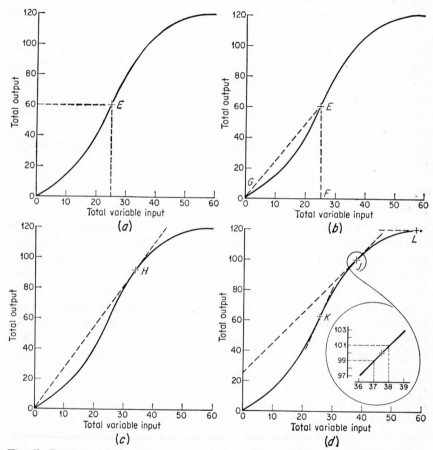

Fig. 5. Geometry of the input-output relationship. ($a$) Total output. ($b$) and ($c$) Average output per unit of variable input. ($d$) Marginal output per unit of variable input. (*Production function is hypothetical. It is given the general shape of familiar forestry production functions, such as timber yield over stand age, mill output over power input, and work accomplished over crew size.*)

Second, the average (mean): Average output per unit of variable input at any point on the production function is equal to total output divided by total variable input at this point. For point $E$, it is equal to $^{60}\!/_{25}$, or 2.4. Or in Figure 5b, average output at $E$ is equal to $FE/GF$. This, in turn, is the same thing as the slope of the line $GE$, connecting point $E$ with the origin. The slope of this line is measured in just the same way as one may measure the grade of a road: the vertical rise per unit of horizontal distance. The "road" *GE* rises 60 units in 25, or 2.4 units per unit of horizontal distance. In general, the *geometric rule for the average* is: The average output at any point on a total output-over-input curve is the slope of the line drawn to this point from the origin.

It follows that the slope of the steepest line that can be drawn from the origin to any point on the curve is equal to the maximum average output. Such a line is drawn in Figure 5c. The point *H*, where it meets the curve, is the point of maximum average output. Actually, as you can see, the line is tangent to the curve at this point, for any steeper line, by our terms, would not touch the curve at all. And so we have the *geometric rule for the maximum average:* Average output is a maximum at that point on a total output-over-input curve through which a tangent may be drawn that passes also through the origin. We are speaking, of course, of the steepest such tangent.

Third, the margin: Let us take any point on the curve, such as *J* in Figure 5d, and work out the marginal output per unit of variable input at this point. Since the marginal output is equal to the increase in total output per unit of input, it is equal to the rise in the curve per unit of horizontal distance—what we have already defined as slope. To view more clearly the slope of the curve at point *J*, let us magnify this section of the curve so that it becomes essentially a straight line, as in the inset. Now we can see what the slope, the marginal output, amounts to: It is 2 —i.e., 2 units of output per unit of input. In practice, however, it is not necessary to magnify the curve in order to measure marginal output. All one needs to do is draw the tangent to the curve at point *J*, which is simply an extension of the straight line in the inset, and measure its slope. Notice that this tangent cuts the *Y* axis at 25. That is, the tangent line rises from 25 to 100, or 75 units, in a horizontal distance of $37\frac{1}{2}$: Its slope is 2. In general, the *geometric rule for the marginal* is: The marginal unit output at any point on a total output-over-input curve is the slope of the line drawn tangent to the curve at this point—i.e., the slope of the curve at this point.

It follows that at point *L* (Fig. 5d), the point of maximum total output, where the tangent to the curve is horizontal (zero slope), marginal output is zero. And the steepest tangent that can be drawn at any point along the rising section of the curve—in our case at *K*, the point of inflection—determines and measures the maximum marginal output and marks the point of diminishing returns. It also follows that where average output peaks, as at point *H*, average and marginal output are the same, since both are equal to the slope of the same line.

Now if you have managed to digest these fairly sticky propositions, which may call for going back over them a bit, then we are ready to have a look at the graphics of the Hawkins stand-improvement problem. The graphs are laid out in Figure 6. They may be thought of as simply the plotting and curving of the data in Tables 5 and 6. However, we will begin with the physical production function and derive by geometry the various other pertinent relationships, including that of marginal unit revenue and of marginal unit cost to output and to input, and the best combination of the agents of production.

## PHYSICAL RELATIONSHIPS

Figure 6a shows the relation of total output to variable input. The three tangents that have been drafted mark, from left to right, the points of maximum marginal, maximum average (equal to marginal), and maximum total (zero marginal) output. You should check the occurrence of these points against Table 5 (p. 60), bearing in mind that the curve represents a continuous series of inputs and outputs and thus permits locating maximum *points*, whereas the table deals in discrete chunks of inputs and outputs and so reveals only the maximum *chunks*.

Our next steps are to derive Figures 6b, 6c, and 6d each from the one preceding. These three graphs all have output, not input, on the horizontal axis, for our first object will be to state the best combination in terms of output, just as we did in Table 5.

Figure 6b comes from 6a simply by reversing the axes. What was in 6a the maximum marginal output is now the point of minimum marginal input (i.e., cost), where the slope of the curve is least. And what was maximum average output is minimum average variable input or cost (per unit of output), where the slope of a line from the origin is least. The finely broken lines trace the location of these points from graph to graph.

## VALUES PER UNIT OF OUTPUT

Figure 6c, derived from 6b, introduces dollar units for the first time, showing total cost and revenue as related to output. First, total fixed cost is drawn as a horizontal line on the $40 abscissa. The height of this line above the X axis is the total fixed cost. Next, the total variable cost is drawn in above the fixed cost as the base. This curve is merely a redrafting of the curve in 6b, with the input scale converted from physical to dollar units at the rate of $10 per man-day. The height of the curve above the fixed-cost line is the total variable cost as related to output. Its height above the X axis is total aggregate cost. Note the derivation, on the curve, of a new point, the point of minimum average aggregate cost.

We come now to the revenue side of the story in Figure 6c. Total gross revenue as related to output is constructed as a straight line from the

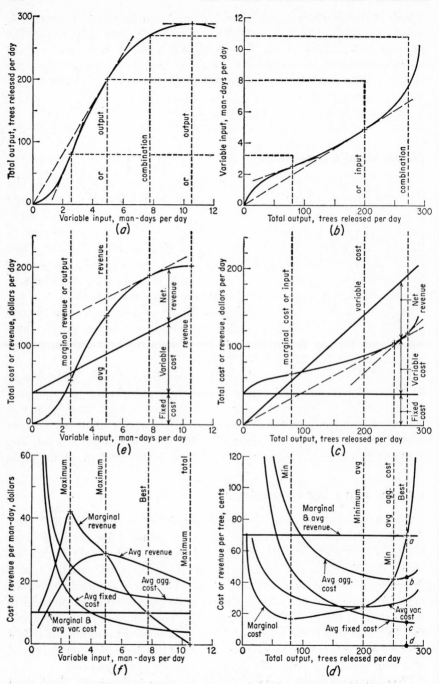

Fig. 6. Production functions, stand improvement, Hawkins property.

origin, with a slope of 0.7. That is, total gross revenue is directly proportional to the number of trees released, and accrues at the rate of 70 cents per tree. The height of the line above total aggregate cost is equal to total net revenue, which moves from the red into the black at an output of about 100 trees per day. You should check each of our findings against Table 5 as we go along.

Now what is the best combination? At what output is total net revenue the greatest? Let us see if we can derive the answer from Figure 6c. We want to find the point where the total-gross-revenue line lies at the greatest vertical distance above the total-aggregate-cost curve. Studying the latter curve as it moves toward the right, we see that for a while it is falling farther and farther below the revenue line (net revenue is growing), because the curve is rising less steeply than this line; its slope is less. On the other hand, we can easily observe that somewhere near the right end aggregate cost begins to rise at a steeper slope than gross revenue, so that it approaches the latter and net revenue shrinks. To catch aggregate cost just before it takes this fatal turn, we need to find the point where its slope is the *same* as that of the revenue line—i.e., 0.7. The point of tangency with some line of this slope is the point we want, as shown in the graph. Here, at an output of about 275 trees, is the best combination.

Do you perceive that, since the slope of the revenue line is the marginal unit revenue and the cost slope is the marginal unit cost, we have in effect taken the marginal approach to the best combination? Our approach, however, was indirect. Let us now work out the marginal values directly and also bring in the various averages that were first introduced in Table 5. For this purpose we turn to graph d in Figure 6.

The average and marginal curves in Figure 6d are all derived from the totals in 6c by the rules of geometry that we studied earlier. For example, the average variable cost is the slope of lines drawn from the $40 point on the Y axis to successive points along the cost curve. And the marginal cost is the slope of successive tangents to this curve. Note that fixed cost has a constant zero slope and thus has no bearing on marginal cost. Marginal unit revenue and cost intersect at point a, situated at the same output that we found for the best combination in graph c (and, with allowance for the difference between points and chunks, in Table 5).

We need to take special note of the relation between the marginal and average values. The rules as we observe them in graph d are as follows: (1) Where the marginal lies below the average, the average is always falling. (2) Where the marginal lies above the average, the average is always rising. That is, the average value moves toward the marginal. (3) Where the marginal and average are equal, the average is neither falling nor rising, but is constant, either as a horizontal line or (so far as graph *d* goes) as a minimum point on a curve. Furthermore, if the average is constant, even momentarily, we know that the marginal value must then be equal to it. [Can you figure out why these rules hold good?] Note that they do not apply to the average fixed cost, which, as we have seen, bears no relation to marginal cost.

Finally, before leaving graph *d*, observe that at the best combination the total revenue is represented by the area of the rectangle that extends between the *Y* axis on the left and the line *ad* on the right. Also observe that the total-fixed-cost rectangle is similarly determined by the line *cd*, total variable cost by *bc*, total aggregate cost by *bd*, and total net revenue by *ab*. The point *b* is that point at which the average-aggregate-cost curve just begins to rise so steeply that any further rise will produce a greater percentage narrowing than percentage lengthening of the net-revenue rectangle. In other words, the slope of the curve at *b* is equal to that of the diagonal of the net-revenue rectangle through *a*.

### VALUES PER UNIT OF INPUT

So far we have been studying that part of Figure 6 that ties back to Table 5, where everything is related to output. Now let us go on to graphs *e* and *f* of the figure, where values are related to input, as in Table 6 (p. 65).

Graph *e* shows total cost and revenue in reference to total variable input. It comes directly from graph *a*. It is analogous to graph *c* in every respect, the only basic difference being in the horizontal scale. Total revenue, now, is a curved line, following the path of the original production function in the ratio of 70 cents per tree. All the cost lines, on the other hand, are straight, since cost in this case is directly proportional to input. The best combination occurs where total revenue rises the furthest above cost: at an input of about 8 man-days, corresponding to the 275-tree output of earlier graphs.

In Figure 6f, derived from 6e by our rules of geometry, we have the counterpart, per unit of variable input, of 6d. Marginal revenue per unit of input peaks at the point of diminishing returns, where marginal cost per unit of output is least. It intersects average revenue at the latter's maximum point, intersects marginal (average variable) cost at the best combination, and reaches zero at the peak of total output and revenue.

If you will study the marginal- and average-revenue (value-output) curves in graph *f*, you may be struck by their resemblance to curves of current and mean annual timber growth over time, or stand age. The points of culmination and intersection all follow the same pattern. Indeed, current annual growth is the same thing as marginal output per unit of time, and mean annual growth is the average output per time unit. Both are derivable from the master curve of total yield over age, which is analogous to our total output-over-input curve.

As we observed (pp. 64–65) in contrasting Tables 5 and 6, marginal cost per unit of output rises (because of diminishing returns) to meet marginal revenue, whereas when the two are expressed per unit of input, marginal revenue falls (again because of diminishing returns) to meet cost.

## GRAPHS AS MODELS

It will help you to compare the graphs with the data in Tables 5 and 6 (pp. 61, 65). Remember that most of the curves may be thought of as the result of plotting those data, even though we did not derive the curves in that way. The important thing is to understand graphs $d$ and $f$ and their derivation, both by arithmetic and by geometry.

Now Figures $6d$ and $6f$ and their parent graphs are simply other models for analyzing the production economics of the firm. They are highly versatile models. They apply in principle not only to the use of labor in stand improvement on the Hawkins property but also to any other stand-improvement operation, and indeed to any productive operation of any sort where diminishing returns obtain and the other conditions of the problem are generally similar to those assumed here. This, as we shall see, covers a wide territory in forestry economics.

Remember that these graphs are not an end in themselves. They are just tools. One has to get out the tools, sharpen them up, and practice with them a bit before he can start the real job. This is the position we are in now, and will be for a while: getting set.

[Try turning back to the questions posed near the end of Chapter 5 (pp. 68–69) and see if you can answer them with the use of each of the graphic models. And then concentrate upon the curves of marginal unit cost and marginal unit revenue and ask yourself what are the various circumstances that can cause these curves, and thus the point of best combination, to shift one way or the other. Try tracing this effect back through the curves from which the marginal cost and revenue curves are derived.]

## ECONOMIC RANGE OF PRODUCTION

In Chapter 5, when we were talking about diminishing returns in exam preparation (p. 55), and again (p. 61) when we were setting up Table 5, we took it as self-evident that the rational firm will never employ more inputs than those which will maximize total output. In effect, we took maximum total output as an upper economic limit in the short run.

Now with Figure 6 at hand, we are in position to check our judgment about the upper economic limit. We can also explore the question whether there may be a corresponding lower limit, so that we may define an *economic range of production:* that within which the rational firm will always operate.

We will confine our attention and our conclusions to firms of the sort that our friend Hawkins manages: firms whose scale of operations does not affect the prices of their inputs or outputs. That is to say, in Hawkins's case, he can hire all the labor he is likely to want at $10, and the 70-cent value of the average released tree applies no matter how many of his acres are given stand improvement in a year.

To verify the upper economic limit, let us have a look at the intersection of marginal revenue and cost in Figure 6f. This intersection cannot very well occur to the right of the point where marginal revenue strikes zero, because then marginal cost also would be negative: The variable agents would be earning less than nothing and could better themselves by quitting. Zero marginal revenue—that is, maximum total output— therefore marks the upper limit of the best combination.

To spot the lower economic limit of production most readily, let us turn to graph *d* in Figure 6 and again eye the intersection of marginal revenue and cost. This intersection cannot very well occur (at least for long) to the left of the point where average variable cost is a minimum, because that would happen only if marginal (*and average*) revenue were less than average variable cost, and that in turn would mean that the fixed agents would be earning less than nothing and could better themselves by quitting: The firm would shut down and lay off its variable agents. Minimum average variable cost—that is, maximum average output—therefore marks the lower limit of the best combination.

To summarize the *rule for economic limits of production:* In the short run, for the rational firm whose scale does not affect its markets, the economic range of production lies between the points of maximum average and maximum total output. At the former, lower, limit, the return to the fixed agents of production just vanishes, all the revenue going to pay the variable agents. At the latter, upper, limit, the return to the variable agents is just extinguished, and all the revenue goes to the fixed agents. Only within these limits can some return be provided to both classes of agents.

### ECONOMIC RANGE IN GRAPHIC TERMS

The gist of the foregoing summary is given in the graphs of Figure 7. In both graphs, the X axis is scaled in physical units of variable input; the Y axis measures both total output and total revenue. This dual scal-

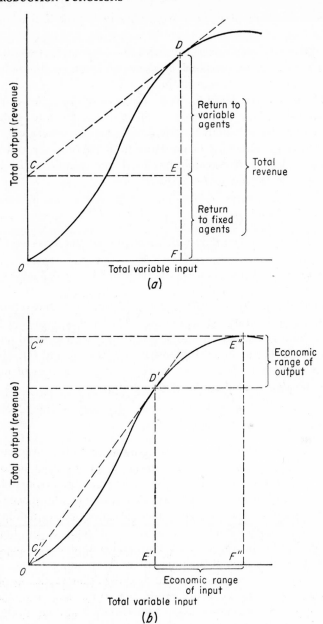

Fig. 7. The firm's economic range of production. (*Hypothetical production function; see Fig. 5, p. 71, for illustrations.*)

ing of the $Y$ axis is possible since we are analyzing the firm whose prices (as well as cost rates) are unaffected by its output.

Suppose that $D$ (graph $a$) is the point of best combination on the production function. Total variable input at the best combination is $OF$. Marginal output per unit of variable input is equal to the slope of the tangent at $D$—that is, $DE/CE$. With the dual scaling, this is the same thing as the marginal unit revenue. Since $D$ is the best combination, marginal unit revenue equals marginal unit cost. And marginal unit cost equals average variable cost (compare Fig. 6$f$). Average variable cost— that is, the return to the variable input—therefore is $DE/CE$. The total return to the variable agents thus equals

$$\frac{DE}{CE} \cdot OF = \frac{DE}{CE} \cdot CE = DE$$

And since the total revenue is $DF$, the return to the fixed agents is $DF$ minus $DE$, or $EF$.

Now at inputs just less than $OF$, $C$ descends toward $O$, and $E$ toward $F$, so that at the point of maximum average output, the triangle $CDE$ has assumed the position $C'D'E'$ (Fig. 7$b$), and $EF$, the return to the fixed agents, is just extinguished. On the other hand, at inputs just greater than $OF$, $C$ and $E$ rise, so that at the point of maximum total output the rectangle $OCEF$ has assumed the position $OC''E''F''$; and $DE$, the return to the variable agents, just vanishes. The economic ranges of input and of output thus determined are labeled in graph $b$.

*SUMMARY*

Considering production functions in graphic form, the basic one is that which shows in physical terms the relation of total output to total variable input per unit of time. From this basic production function, others may be derived by geometry, showing total, average, and marginal input and output, cost and revenue. Thus average output corresponding to any point on a total output-over-input curve is the slope of the line drawn to this point from the origin. And marginal output is the slope of the curve itself (i.e., the slope of the tangent) at this point.

Through such constructions one can derive graphic models of the firm's best combination of the agents of production in the short run: the equating of marginal cost and revenue per unit of output and per unit of input.

The firm's best combination in the short run lies within the economic range of production, extending from the point of maximum average output to the point of maximum total output.

Chapter 7

# COMBINING
# MULTIPLE
# LABOR INPUTS

I N CHAPTERS 5 and 6 we studied the firm's best combination in the short run, taking as our example the simplest of problems: a single type of variable agent (laborers) to be combined with the fixed inputs. The only decision to be made was how many laborers to employ. Frequently, however, a firm's decision is more complex than this, involving more than one set of alternatives at the same time.

For example, in forest planting and plantation management, there is a question not only of the effort to devote to site preparation but at the same time of the spacing of seedlings and the inputs for subsequent cultural treatment. The logging firm must decide both road spacing and the number of tractors for skidding. The lumber merchant has to make decisions simultaneously about his volume of advertising and his sales force.

Notice that all the foregoing examples have certain features in common: (1) In each case, there is a single kind of output to be produced; the firms are not weighing different products. (2) What the firms are weighing are different combinations of variable input. (3) In each case, there is more than one kind of variable input to be weighed. (4) In each case, the different kinds of variable input are interrelated; the use of one kind can be expected to affect the use of the other kinds. For instance, in the logging case, more tractors will *supplement* closer road spacing in raising the rate of output. At the same time tractors may within limits *substitute* for roads in achieving a given rate of output; the two are rivals for the attention of the firm. Hence the firm cannot decide on its tractor inputs independently of its road inputs, and vice versa, but must make

**81**

the decisions together. What produces an interrelationship among variable inputs is their use, in common, of some of the same fixed agents.

Were the different kinds of input not interrelated, each could be analyzed separately by the methods we have already studied. For example, it might be possible to weigh the size of planting crew independently of site preparation, spacing, and subsequent culture, since the crew is combined largely with its own fixed agents, primarily its supervisor.

Our purpose in this chapter is to analyze the more difficult case of multiple variable inputs that are interrelated through their common connection with some of the same fixed inputs. We shall continue to use labor inputs to illustrate the problem, and at the close of the chapter, to complete our discussion of labor in the firm, we shall have a look at the factors that determine production functions involving labor.

## PRODUCTION FUNCTION

Our friend Hubert Hawkins, planning his timber-stand improvement, has an alternative approach to the work that we must now explore. Instead of staffing his crew solely with woods laborers and handling all the job preparation and supervision directly and alone, he can supplement the crew with some forestry technicians. The technicians are men fresh from school, green on the job, but with a good understanding of principles. They are capable not only of doing release work along with the laborers but also of helping Hawkins with the day-to-day planning, the marking, and supervision. The presence of this flexible element in the crew therefore promises to lighten the load for Hawkins, increase his capacity for directing the job, and raise the productivity of the laborers.

Hawkins makes an estimate, or forecast, of his daily accomplishment in terms of numbers of trees released, with crews composed of varying numbers of laborers and technicians. His data, smoothed out and expanded for our use here, are given in Table 7. Outputs are shown for 91 combinations: 0 to 12 laborers supplemented by 0 to 6 technicians. Let's study this three-dimensional production function.

We are already familiar with the first two columns in Table 7, showing what Hawkins can accomplish with varying numbers of laborers alone. (The columns have been turned upside down so that their arrangement will key in with a graph that we shall use.) The third column, however, introduces a new element: an estimate of what will happen with one technician on the job in addition to the laborers. The output estimates in this third column represent a considerable upward jump, especially toward the top of the column. In fact, the technician working alone accomplishes but a modest output—less than the more experienced laborer working alone. The technician's contribution shows up after a few laborers have been added to the crew, when more of his time comes to be used in helping Hawkins with the supervision.

Compare each of the figures in the 1-technician column of Table 7 with the figure one line above it in the 0-technician column, representing the output of the same total number of men. The comparison suggests that the marginal productivity of forestry training in this case is high when well diluted; a little goes a long way! The consequence is to reduce very greatly the impact of diminishing returns. The technician has this

Table 7. *Estimated daily output by laborers and technicians in timber-stand improvement, Hawkins property*

| Laborers | Technicians | | | | | | |
|---|---|---|---|---|---|---|---|
| | 0 | 1 | 2 | 3 | 4 | 5 | 6 |
| | *Trees released* | *Trees released* | *Trees released* | *Trees released* | *Trees released* | *Trees released* | *Trees released* |
| 12 | 285 | 378 | 431 | 480 | 508 | 535 | 558 |
| 11 | 290 | 371 | 422 | 466 | 492 | 516 | 538 |
| 10 | 290 | 361 | 410 | 449 | 474 | 496 | 517 |
| 9 | 285 | 348 | 395 | 430 | 454 | 475 | 495 |
| 8 | 275 | 332 | 377 | 410 | 433 | 453 | 472 |
| 7 | 260 | 313 | 356 | 388 | 411 | 430 | 448 |
| 6 | 237 | 289 | 332 | 363 | 386 | 405 | 422 |
| 5 | 203 | 259 | 303 | 334 | 358 | 378 | 395 |
| 4 | 160 | 223 | 270 | 303 | 327 | 349 | 367 |
| 3 | 110 | 176 | 230 | 266 | 293 | 318 | 338 |
| 2 | 50 | 117 | 181 | 226 | 257 | 284 | 307 |
| 1 | 15 | 52 | 116 | 173 | 212 | 244 | 273 |
| 0 | 0 | 13 | 46 | 104 | 153 | 199 | 237 |

effect because he keeps Hawkins from being so much of a bottleneck on the job. It is, of course, the existence of the fixed agents, which become crowded or spread thin, that produces diminishing returns in the short run.

Considering the comparison between the 0 and 1 columns in Table 7, it certainly looks as though the firm should put on at least 1 technician, unless his services come very high. [Taking the crew of 8 laborers, how much could 1 technician contribute to the firm's daily revenue, at 70 cents per tree released? How much could the firm afford to pay him? Why would he probably not, in actual fact, be paid so much as that? Such questions are of great moment to you as a forester, for it is by virtue of your contribution to output that a salary can be paid to you.]

Now just as we have analyzed the 0 and 1 columns in Table 7, so you should study the remaining columns yourself, comparing the output estimates within the columns and across, and trying to explain what you observe. Notice the last line of output figures in the table—the estimates of trees released per day by technicians alone, with no laborers. Compare this line with the 0 column. Evidently the technicians are not expected to be at their best when working as laborers, though their handicap shrinks as the crew size is increased, since they are capable of working more independently than the laborers and of putting less burden on the fixed agent, Hawkins.

## ISO-OUTPUT CURVES

Let us go on now to the economic inference. Of the 91 combinations estimated in Table 7, which one is best? We need revenue and cost data, and these are assumed to be as follows: The value of a released tree is 70 cents. The laborers, with their equipment, cost the firm $10 per man-day; the technicians, $20. Hawkins's time is valued at $40 per day. We know now that this last figure has no bearing on the best combination. But it does affect the absolute amount of the total net revenue, which will be of interest to us.

As you studied Table 7, it perhaps struck you that what the table depicts is various ways of producing a given output. For instance, an output of about 290 to 300 or so trees can be produced, alternatively, with

> 10 laborers alone, or
> 6 laborers and 1 technician, or
> 5 laborers and 2 technicians, or
> 4 laborers and 3 technicians, or
> 3 laborers and 4 technicians, or
> 2 laborers and 6 technicians.

We could mark these six combinations in the table, and if we connected them all with a pencil line, we should have a sort of contour line that would trace out not, in this case, points of equal elevation but points of equal output. The result would be an *iso-output curve:* the locus of combinations that all yield the same output. The curve would designate roughly the 300-trees-per-day contour.

Similarly, we could trace out other contour lines on Table 7, as many as we wished, for other levels of output between 0 and 558. Indeed, we have in Table 7 an excellent basis for a whole contour map, such as you might develop in the field with a level and rod on a rectangular grid of bench marks, with the object of interpolating the contour lines.

A map based on Table 7 is worked out in Figure 8a (disregard for now the extra lines in the northwest part of the map). Arbitrarily, a contour interval of 50 trees per day has been selected. Because it would not have been accurate to use straight-line interpolation in setting the contour locations, Figure 8*b* was constructed from the columns in Table 7, breaking the 3-dimensional production function down into seven 2-dimensional functions. The exact location of the contour lines where they intersect the seven principal ordinates in graph *a* were read from the seven curves in *b*. In other words, the curves in graphs *a* and *b* are "harmonized." We could just as well have interpolated the other way, from a sheaf of thirteen curves, one for each number of laborers, in a graph showing output over the number of technicians; but the way chosen was simpler.

Now what we have in Figure 8*a* is a map of the southwest slope of a rather smoothly rounded hill that rises from "sea level" at the southwest corner. [Notice that the slope of the hill is steepest near the base, gentler at the very foot, and increasingly gentle toward the summit. What is the cause of this?]

### RATES OF SUBSTITUTION

Why is the hill rounded? Why are the iso-output curves bent, and concave toward the northeast? The answer lies in the rate at which technicians may be substituted for laborers, and vice versa, at the different combinations. Take the 300-tree line for example, and return for a moment to our list of alternatives on page 84. Notice that the first technician can replace 4 laborers. In the interval between 0 and 1 technician, the *marginal rate of substitution* of laborers for technicians—the rate at which laborers can be substituted for technicians without affecting output—is 4. This is because the technician's contribution to the job is still in the stage of increasing returns, whereas the laborers are well into diminishing returns. His marginal output is four times as great as theirs, per man. Study Table 7 to verify this fact for yourself. In general, we can state a *rule for the marginal rate of substitution:* The marginal rate of substitution of agent A for agent B at any combination equals the ratio of the marginal output per unit of agent B to that per unit of agent A at this combination.

Continuing down the list on page 84, we find that in the next three intervals (up to 4 technicians) the marginal rate of substitution of laborers for technicians has slumped to about 1, and beyond it has fallen to 0.5; the technicians are relatively bogged down in diminishing returns. We are speaking of the substitution of laborers for technicians because it suits the way Figure 8*a* is plotted. We could, however, analyze the reciprocal, the marginal rate of substitution of technicians for laborers, in which case our three measurements would become 0.25, 1, and 2, respectively.

Now if you will bear in mind our review of the basic geometry in Chapter 6 (p. 72) and draw the necessary analogy, you will grasp the *geometric rule for the marginal rate of substitution:* The marginal rate of substitution of agent A for agent B at any combination equals the slope

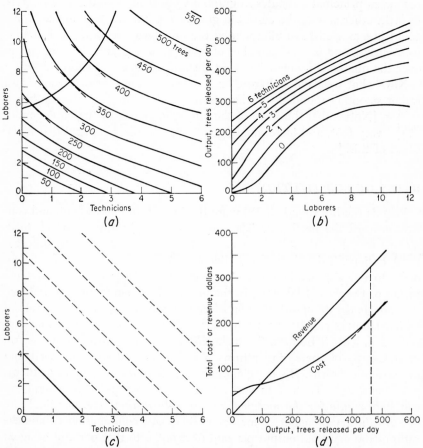

Fig. 8. Best combination of two variable inputs, technicians and laborers, in timber-stand improvement, Hawkins property. (*a*) Iso-revenue (-output) curves and expansion path. (*b*) Harmonized curves for interpolation in *a*. (*c*) Iso-cost curves. (*d*) Best combination.

of the iso-output curve at this combination, when inputs of agent A are plotted over those of agent B. The marginal rate of substitution and the slope of the curve are both negative: the quotient of a minus quantity and a plus quantity. [Try laying a straight edge tangent to a curve at various points in Figure 8*a* and compare Table 7 to see if you can test the foregoing proposition. Remember that you will be working with the marginal rate at a *point* instead of the discrete interval in the table.]

The iso-output curves, therefore, are concave from above because the marginal rate of substitution of laborers for technicians falls with increasing input of technicians. The rate falls because the marginal output per technician is decreasing relative to the marginal output per laborer. And this decrease, in turn, stems from the fact of diminishing returns, both the fixed inputs and the laborers in this case acting as the limiting agents.

## LEAST-COST COMBINATIONS

Continuing in pursuit of the best combination, let us next introduce the elements of revenue and cost. Clearly the iso-output curves of Figure 8a are at the same time *iso-revenue curves:* the locus of combinations that yield identical total gross revenue. Thus all combinations along the 300-tree curve will gross 300 times 70 cents, or $210, per day. So far as revenue is concerned, it is a matter of indifference to the firm which of the combinations is chosen. However, so far as cost is concerned, the choice is by no means indifferent. Some of the combinations are considerably more expensive than others. Referring again to the list on page 84 and bearing in mind the cost rates we have assumed, we observe that

> 10 laborers alone would cost $100 per day;
> 6 laborers and 1 technician, $80;
> 5 laborers and 2 technicians, $90;
> 4 laborers and 3 technicians, $100;
> 3 laborers and 4 technicians, $110;
> 2 laborers and 6 technicians, $140.

A little thought suggests what makes these costs fall and then rise as they do. The ratio of the marginal cost of a technician to the marginal cost of a laborer is $20/$10, or 2. So long as the firm can substitute a technician for more than 2 laborers, it can reduce total cost. But when it reaches the stage where the marginal rate of substitution is less than 2 laborers per technician, cost will start to rise again. The least-cost combination is the one where the marginal rate of substitution (laborers per technician) is just equal to the ratio of marginal costs (technicians to laborers). Using this principle, let us find the least-cost point on each of the iso-revenue curves in Figure 8a. This will be the point where total net revenue per day is maximized for the amount of output in question, and thus the point on the curve that is most desirable for the firm.

Graph c in Figure 8 is marked off with the same scales as graph a. Let us draw on graph *c* a line—any line—whose slope is equal to the ratio of marginal costs, technicians to laborers. (The ratio, being also a rate of substitution—in terms of cost—has a negative sign.) Such a line is the solid line in graph *c*. The broken lines are drawn parallel to it (same slope), in such a position that they will be tangent to the curves in graph *a*. The portions of them near the points of tangency are shown in graph *a*. These points of tangency, where all the slopes of tangents and curves (all cost ratios and substitution rates) are the same, mark the least-cost combinations. The locus of least-cost combinations, called an *expansion path*, is drawn through the points of tangency. It strikes the *Y* axis at about a 220-tree contour. We know that the firm's best combination must lie somewhere along the expansion path.

Note the distinction between the least-cost combination and the best combination. The *least-cost combination* is, among *combinations that produce a given gross revenue*, the one where total cost is the least and total net revenue therefore the highest. But the best combination is the highest among *all combinations* in respect to total net revenue: it is the best among all possible least-cost combinations. Thus the best combination is necessarily a least-cost combination, but there are many least-cost combinations besides the best combination. It is these many least-cost combinations that trace out the expansion path.

### ISO-COST CURVES

Before working out the best combination, let us check our derivation of the expansion path by going at it in a little different way. This will help us to understand more clearly this key step in our analysis of multiple inputs, the step of narrowing down the alternatives to a single series.

Returning to graph *c*, let us have a fresh look at the solid line drawn from 4 on the *Y* axis (0 technician, 4 laborers) to 2 on the *X* axis (2 technicians, 0 laborer). What are the amounts of total cost represented along this line? At the upper end, the cost is $(0 \times 20) + (4 \times 10)$, or \$40. At the lower end, it is $(2 \times 20) + (0 \times 10)$, or \$40. In the middle, with 1 technician and 2 laborers, it is \$40. And everywhere else it is \$40. In other words, this line is an *iso-cost curve*, the locus of combinations that all cost the same. This is so because we made the slope of the curve equal to the ratio of the two cost rates, technicians and laborers. Consequently, whenever one moves any distance in either direction along the curve, he subtracts just as much of one kind of cost as he adds of the other.

All the other lines drawn in graph *c*, being parallel to the first, are also iso-cost curves. Indeed, one can imagine an infinitely great number of such curves, all parallel, and differing only in the magnitude of the total cost they represent; the further southwest, the lower the cost.

Now look again at any curve in graph *a*—say, the 300-tree curve. This curve lies on a great many iso-cost curves. What we want to find is the least-cost point on the 300-tree curve, the one lying on the most south-westerly iso-cost curve. This must be the point of tangency, since any iso-cost curve more southwesterly than the tangent would not touch at all. The point of tangency is also that point on the iso-cost curve which lies at the highest "elevation" (output, revenue). Thus the expansion path that we proceed to draw is not only the locus of least-cost points on iso-revenue curves; it is at the same time the locus of maximum-revenue points on iso-cost curves.

We can now see where the expansion path goes from the place where it runs into the *Y* axis. We can continue to pick it up on each of the iso-output lines from 220 down, at the most southwesterly point. This is the point of intersection with the *Y* axis; the expansion path follows the axis below 220 trees. This means that with fewer than six laborers, technicians drop out of the least-cost combination entirely. The crew is too small to take advantage of them; they are too expensive; their marginal productivity is not great enough in these circumstances—however you want to look at it.

And so it becomes apparent that the expansion path is situated further down and to the right—in our example, more technicians, fewer laborers, in the least-cost combination—the steeper the iso-revenue curves and the flatter the iso-cost curves. Or, in general and dynamic terms, we have a *principle of economizing productive agents:* The firm tends to increase its use of those agents that become more cheap or productive and to reduce its input of those that become less.

### BEST COMBINATION

It remains for us now to find the firm's best combination from among the least-cost points traced by the expansion path. This we accomplish by plotting and curving over output, the total cost and revenue represented on the path. The result is Figure 8*d*, constructed with the help of Table 8, where the necessary data are computed. To take the 300-tree line of Table 8 as an example, the least-cost combination at this level of output involves 1 foreman and (reading at the intersection of the expansion path with the 300-tree contour in graph *a*) 1.0 technician and 6.5 laborers. The next three figures in the line attach values to these three inputs at the assumed rates. The three parts of total cost thus computed are added to get the total aggregate cost of $125. Total gross revenue at 70 cents per tree is $210, and net revenue, after subtracting cost, is $85. Graph *d* is the counterpart of Figure 6*c* (p. 74), and the best combination is determined there by the same method as in 6*c*. Best output is found to be 465 trees per day, and best input (reading graph $a$ with the help of graph $b$) 11 laborers and 3 technicians.

At the best combination, total net revenue is $115.50 per day. Compare this figure with net revenue at the best combination in Table 5 (p. 60), where Hawkins planned to use laborers alone: $72.50. Clearly the present form of organization is preferable. A place is found for three foresters (we can surely approve of this!) and for three more laborers,

*Table 8. Estimated daily gross revenue, minimum cost, and maximum net revenue at alternative levels of output in timber-stand improvement, Hawkins property*

| Output (Trees released) | Input | | | Total cost | | | | Total revenue | |
|---|---|---|---|---|---|---|---|---|---|
| | Fore-man | Tech-nicians* | Labor-ers* | Fore-man | Tech-nicians | Labor-ers | Aggre-gate | Gross | Net |
| | Number | Number | Number | Dollars | Dollars | Dollars | Dollars | Dollars | Dollars |
| 0 | 1 | 0.0 | 0.0 | 40 | 0 | 0 | 40 | 0 | −40 |
| 50 | 1 | 0.0 | 2.0 | 40 | 0 | 20 | 60 | 35 | −25 |
| 100 | 1 | 0.0 | 2.8 | 40 | 0 | 28 | 68 | 70 | 2 |
| 150 | 1 | 0.0 | 3.8 | 40 | 0 | 38 | 78 | 105 | 27 |
| 200 | 1 | 0.0 | 4.9 | 40 | 0 | 49 | 89 | 140 | 51 |
| 250 | 1 | 0.4 | 5.8 | 40 | 8 | 58 | 106 | 175 | 69 |
| 300 | 1 | 1.0 | 6.5 | 40 | 20 | 65 | 125 | 210 | 85 |
| 350 | 1 | 1.7 | 7.4 | 40 | 34 | 74 | 148 | 245 | 97 |
| 400 | 1 | 2.3 | 8.7 | 40 | 46 | 87 | 173 | 280 | 107 |
| 450 | 1 | 2.8 | 10.4 | 40 | 56 | 104 | 200 | 315 | 115 |
| 500 | 1 | 3.4 | 12.9 | 40 | 68 | 129 | 237 | 350 | 113 |

* Numbers taken from expansion path, Fig. 8a, p. 86.

raising costs altogether by $90 per day—but at the same time raising gross revenue $133 per day.

To summarize the procedure we have followed to find the best combination of multiple variable inputs, there were essentially two steps: (1) We worked out the least-cost combination for producing each of a wide range of outputs. (2) We then determined which of the least-cost combinations (which level of output) was the best in terms of its total net revenue per unit of time. Perhaps we should add a third point suggested by our comparison, just above, of the multiple-input with the single-input results: (3) One may similarly determine the best combination under any number of different forms of organization or other technological arrangements for making the same product and then select the best of all best combinations on the basis of net revenue.

## CONDITIONS FOR BEST COMBINATION

Before we leave our present problem, let us summarize the conditions that prevail at the best combination:

1. The ratio of marginal output (revenue) per technician to marginal output (revenue) per laborer equals the marginal rate of substitution of laborers for technicians. This condition, as we have seen, holds for any combination whatever.

2. The marginal rate of substitution of laborers for technicians equals the ratio of marginal cost per technician to marginal cost per laborer. This condition holds for any combination on the expansion path that includes both laborers and technicians.

3. The ratio of marginal cost per technician to marginal cost per laborer equals the ratio of marginal revenue per technician to marginal revenue per laborer. This third condition, which follows from the first two, applies, like the second, to any combination on the expansion path that includes both laborers and technicians.

4. The ratio of marginal revenue per technician to marginal cost per technician equals the ratio of marginal revenue per laborer to marginal cost per laborer. That is to say, the firm gets the same return from the marginal dollar spent on either technicians or laborers. This fourth condition is simply a restatement of the third and applies to the same combinations.

5. Marginal revenue per laborer equals marginal cost per laborer; and marginal revenue per technician equals marginal cost per technician. That is, both laborers and technicians are paid their marginal product; the marginal unit of input just pays its way; the firm gets a dollar's worth from the marginal dollar spent on either laborers or technicians. This condition is unique with the best combination; it obtains nowhere else within the area of diminishing returns. What it means in our example is that at the best combination, the laborer's marginal output must be 10/0.70, or 14.3 trees (compare Chap. 5, p. 66), and the technician's marginal output must be 20/0.70, or 28.6 trees. [Check this as well as you can in Table 7, remembering that our proposition relates to the *point* of best combination, whereas the table deals in comparatively big *intervals*. Can you tell from Table 7 whether it would pay the firm to add a twelfth laborer? A fourth technician?]

6. Marginal revenue per unit of output (unit value of product) equals marginal cost of laborers per unit of output equals marginal cost of technicians per unit of output equals aggregate marginal cost per unit of output. This sixth and last condition follows from the fifth and, like it, is uniquely true of the best combination. We state the condition as a reminder of the fact, first brought out in Chapter 5, that the best combina-

tion is determined by the equation of marginal revenue and cost per unit of either input or output. [Does it seem to you that marginal cost of laborers or of technicians could not possibly equal the marginal cost of both? Try reasoning this out for yourself, remembering that we are speaking of marginal cost *per unit of output*.]

## DETERMINANTS OF PRODUCTION FUNCTION

In Chapter 5 (p. 67) we concluded that marginal cost and revenue, which determine the firm's best combination, are in turn determined by three things—the basic production function, or physical input-output relationship, the unit value of variable inputs, and the unit value of outputs. It is time now that we began digging back into the determinants of these determinants.

The why of unit values of inputs and outputs is a question that we must postpone for a while, until we get more background for it. In general, these values are determined by the forces of supply and demand. But the basic production function we can explore now. Let us take the first two columns in Table 7 for example. What factors are responsible for this particular response of output to input?

| Input of laborers | Output of trees | Input of laborers | Output of trees |
|---|---|---|---|
| 1 | 15 | 7 | 260 |
| 2 | 50 | 8 | 275 |
| 3 | 110 | 9 | 285 |
| 4 | 160 | 10 | 290 |
| 5 | 203 | 11 | 290 |
| 6 | 237 | 12 | 285 |

Let us try to uncover the principles, with the thought that they will prove applicable to other input-output relationships that we may need to analyze.

Three elements in the relationship may surely be isolated. One is the foreman; second is the men; third is the whole web of conditions and circumstances within which they do the job, what may be called the production context.

## QUALITY OF FIXED INPUTS

We have all observed how vastly persons differ in the quality of their supervisory performance. The able supervisor may inspire his workers by example. He may exercise not only physical but also spiritual leadership. He may be subtle and imaginative, and gain his ends by joking and good humor. He usually succeeds in attracting productive workers and in holding them, but he may well have a faculty for training and developing personnel and thus making the most of whoever is assigned to him. By comparison with the high output of such a man, the lacks and faults of the less able supervisor show up in lower quality or quantity of product—perhaps at all times, perhaps only in the longer pull.

Cardinal rules aside, what is effective supervision and what isn't may often depend upon who is being supervised, and upon the production context. Quality of supervision, therefore, is not an absolute thing inherent in the supervisor. It varies with external circumstances. For example, a teacher may be highly effective with upperclassmen or graduate students but relatively ineffective with underclassmen. Or vice versa. He may do a good job of leading students in the classroom and a poor job in the laboratory. On the other hand, some persons are highly adaptable, able to perform well under a variety of circumstances.

You should think through such personal factors as age, appearance, intellect, strength, stamina, mental and bodily health, speech, personal character, and general personality—and such underlying influences as inheritance, upbringing, training, and experience—as affecting a person's quality as a supervisor. It will become apparent that everything, the whole complex of conditions and events, that goes to make the man is what goes to make the supervisor.

Now when it comes to other kinds of fixed inputs, the principle also holds that whatever goes to make the thing in question is what goes to determine its quality as an input. And even where the input is inanimate, the determinants may be equally complex with those of our supervisor. The quality of the engine that runs the sawmill is governed in the first instance by its materials and construction, but beyond that by whatever human genius and skills are in its design, its fuel, and its maintenance and operation.

The outcome of all the many factors determining the fixed agent's quality may be summarized in three measures: productivity, capacity, and efficiency.

## PRODUCTIVITY, CAPACITY, EFFICIENCY

*Productivity* is output. Thus, with a crew of 6 laborers, Hawkins's productivity is 237 trees per day, or with 8 laborers, 275. These are gross measures, including the contribution of the laborers as well as the foreman. For net measures, we can use the principle illustrated in Figure 7 (p. 79): With an 8-man crew, the net contribution of a laborer is his marginal output of 14.3 trees. The net productivity, then, of the whole crew is 14.3 times 8, or about 114 trees, and since the total output is 275, the net productivity of the foreman is the difference, 161 trees per day. One should always state whether he is talking about gross productivity or net and, if the latter, on what basis it was figured. Let us speak here of gross productivity.

Hawkins's gross productivity is 237 with 6 men, 275 with 8. But surely we need a single measure of it. For the best single measure in the economic context, one logically should turn to the point of central interest, the point of *best combination*. Thus we may say that Hawkins's gross productivity using laborers alone is 275 trees per day.

Now behind productivity, and accounting for it, are the other two measures of quality: capacity and efficiency.

*Capacity* is the quantity of variable agents with which the fixed agent can be combined. It is the measure of what the fixed agent can "hold," just as the capacity of a gas tank is the measure—say, 15 gallons—of what the tank can hold. An engine's capacity may be stated as the amount of fuel which it can consume efficiently per hour. A foreman's capacity may be expressed as the number of men he can supervise effectively. Again, in economic problems, it is necessary to find some one point at which to measure capacity, and the point to choose is generally that of the best combination, since our interest usually centers on a fixed agent's capacity to combine with other agents and still maximize the net return. Thus Hawkins's capacity as a foreman, without the use of technicians, is 8 men.

Earlier we made the point that the quality of the supervisor is not absolute and inherent. This point is well illustrated in our example of putting technicians in the crew. Look how this move increased the foreman's capacity: from 8 to 11 laborers, and 3 technicans besides! At the same time, it increased his gross productivity from 275 to 465 trees per day. The supervisor of high quality is always searching for such means to improve his quality.

*Efficiency* is a measure of the effectiveness of operation—effectiveness of use of the agents of production. This term, like the other two, has a technical meaning much the same as its popular meaning. We speak of an efficient worker as one who makes good use of his time or his tools, with a large accomplishment to show from them. Efficiency is always a rate: output per unit of something. The efficiency of an engine may be stated as its output in horsepower-hours per gallon of fuel consumed. The efficiency of a supervisor may be put in terms of the product he obtains per man supervised. Thus Hawkins's efficiency when he uses only laborers, measured gross at the best combination, is 34.4 trees released per laborer per day. This is what we have called average output (Table 5, col. *d*—

p. 60). His net efficiency, figured from net productivity, is $16\frac{1}{8}$, or 20.1 trees per laborer per day. Note that for consistency efficiency is expressed per unit of the same agent chosen for measuring capacity.

If we multiply Hawkins's capacity, 8 laborers, by his gross efficiency, 34.4 trees per laborer, the result is his gross productivity, 275 trees. Or his net efficiency, 20.1, times his capacity, 8, equals his net productivity, 161. The following relationships hold among productivity ($P$), capacity ($C$), and efficiency ($E$):

$$P = CE$$
$$C = P/E$$
$$E = P/C$$

In other words, the productivity of an agent of production is the amount of other agents with which it is capable of working without going beyond the point of best combination, multiplied by the product that it can win through each unit of these other agents.

Capacity and efficiency may be independent qualities in an agent of production, stemming from quite different fundamental attributes. High capacity may be associated with either high or low efficiency, and low capacity likewise. The foreman of low capacity may be a stickler for detail, a man who works well alone, who believes that if one wants a job done best one must do it oneself. His stamina may be low and his personality drab. But working with one or two helpers he may be highly efficient and as a consequence moderately productive. The highly productive foreman, of course, is the one who can stave off the pressures of diminishing returns in a large labor force, retaining command of both the detail and the aggregate sufficiently to achieve a high output per man.

We must not, however, dwell too heavily upon the inherent qualities of the agent as determining its capacity and efficiency. We must stress that, like everything in economic life, capacity and efficiency are the result of both internal and external forces. Capacity of the fixed agent is increased by any of the things that tend to push the point of best combination further to the right on the production function: higher product value, lower variable-cost rates, or higher marginal output of variable agents. Efficiency of the fixed agent may also be affected by these things. [Can you figure out what the effect would be?]

[Give some thought also to productivity, capacity, and efficiency of various examples of agents with which you are familiar in the forest economy. For instance, how would you define these three measures as applied to forest land? Are good sites—i.e., lands of high productivity —good because of high capacity, or high efficiency, or both? Can you think of any examples of land with high efficiency but low capacity? Or with high capacity but low efficiency?]

## QUALITY OF VARIABLE INPUTS

Since we have dealt at length with the quality of fixed inputs, we can now deal rather briefly with the variable inputs, because the principles involved are all essentially the same. What determines the productivity of Hawkins's men? For the laborers, aside from the external conditions under which they work, we should probably put strength and stamina high on the list, along with skill in getting about in the woods and in the handling of tools. And then we should want to stress those intangible qualities of the worker—spirit, pride in accomplishment, initiative, loyalty to the boss—qualities which the boss himself may do a great deal to foster and which enhance his own capacity.

As for the qualities that influence the technicians' productivity, we should add to the preceding list such items as technical knowledge, aptitude for applying it with humility and imagination, supervisory abilities including the quality of decisiveness, and loyalty to fellow workers and to the foreman, a loyalty that the foreman may do much to cultivate.

But for that matter most of a worker's productive qualities can be altered by an employer. And they can usually be improved in the interest of both parties. On-the-job training in skills, safety training, measures for personal security, and the like may all be thought of as programs for altering the production function for the benefit of both employer and employee.

Personal qualities are not stable over time, either for the supervised or for the supervisor. There are trends with age and experience, and shorter-term fluctuations with the state of a man's health, the changing circumstances of his life, and the day-to-day ups and downs of his spirit. Not least among the variable influences that rule the woods-going forester's spirit are black flies, mosquitoes, and other such varmints. When one sets up a production function for planning purposes, he necessarily averages out these varying influences.

The capacity and efficiency of the worker may, like those of the foreman, be expressed in terms of some other agent with which he is associated. One may measure a technician's capacity by the number of men assigned to work with him at the best combination, or a laborer's capacity by the number or size of machines or tools that he can tend or use. Efficiency, then, is the performance of the man, or of the machine or tool. In woods work, capacity may often be best expressed in terms of acreage or numbers of trees that a man is able to treat per unit of time, and efficiency as the result per acre or per tree. Or capacity and efficiency may be stated simply on a time basis in cases where the time of application is variable. You yourself have a certain capacity for study in terms of the time you can spend upon it within the limits of your best combination. Your capacity in this sense, together with your output per hour, or efficiency, determines your productivity as a student.

## PRODUCTION CONTEXT

Finally, the production function is shaped by the *production context* —the web of circumstances surrounding the agents of production in their work. Let us distinguish three ingredients of the production context: institutions, the working medium, and technology.

First, institutions: One aspect of our national life is the liberty afforded us as individuals for work, striving, and self betterment, and for receiving the rewards (or penalties) of our labor and our venturings. It was pointed up in Chapter 3 how our economic progress has been favored by the freedoms under custom and law cultivated by us out of our Western heritage. A sharp feature of this progress has been rising productivity within the firm, especially the gross productivity of labor.

Within the general setting of our national economic institutions, other institutional arrangements modify the production function. These vary all the way from our conventions respecting hours of work, vacations, health and safety of workers, social security, and other insurance, to the many particular circumstances within the individual firm, such as working conditions, the rate of pay, unionization of workers, labor turnover, and the provision of special facilities such as transportation to and from the working site. The direct effect of these institutions is upon the human agent of production, but through him there is an indirect effect upon the productivity of land and capital as well.

Second, the working medium: By working medium is meant the site where the work is done. Sites vary immensely, and this variation affects the production function. Offices and factories differ in the environment they provide for production. Some, by their location and layout, are more favorable than others to productive work. The forest as a working medium is equally variable—in location, topography, soil, drainage, condition of undergrowth, density of roads and trails, and the like. So far as work with timber is concerned, most of us have experienced how much easier it is to accomplish most jobs in a uniform, relatively open stand in level country than where the stand is varied, the undergrowth dense, and the topography rough. Other things equal, we can expect the production functions to be a good deal different in the two cases.

Production that goes forward in the out-of-doors may be keenly affected by weather, and so may show wide seasonal and irregular variations with temperature, precipitation, and wind. In such a case one may and downs of the environment over the period of the job. One may, however, construct separate production functions for major conditions and determine a best combination for each.

Third and last, technology: The methods and tools of production are a vital aspect of the production context, and surely the one that is most rapidly developing and changing in our economy today. The substitution of machine power for human and animal power, which has been a distinguishing feature of the Industrial Revolution, has worked immense changes in production functions. The rise of automation, which may well distinguish the revolution in future, promises continuing changes.

The output that the firm can win from a given input in the forest economy is influenced by all the many facets of technology, including the source and transmission of power, the design and materials of tools and machines, organization and layout of the process, and the economy of laborers' time and motion. In the woods, crew organization and the routing of travel are often of special moment.

And let us not overlook those aspects of technology that center in the minds of the key members of a working force, compounded of their education, training, experience, and innate vision. Technical sense, or "know-how," on the part of these individuals is required to put the breath of life into the whole means of production. Your own professional training, even including what you are learning at this moment, is directed toward these aspects of technology.

To summarize: We have looked into some of the determinants of the firm's best combination of agents in the short run. The influences we have mentioned may be outlined as follows:

   I. Basic production function
      A. Quality of fixed inputs
         1. Productivity
         2. Capacity
         3. Efficiency
      B. Quality of variable inputs
         1. Productivity
         2. Capacity
         3. Efficiency
      C. Production context
         1. Institutions
         2. Working medium
         3. Technology
  II. Unit value of variable inputs
 III. Unit value of outputs

## DERIVING PRODUCTION FUNCTIONS

Now it is obvious that the production function is the most significant single expression of the production process and that some knowledge of it is the first essential in production planning—that is, in management. And yet it begins to look as though the production function is so sensitive to all the influences of a varied and changing economy that to attempt to predict it may be folly, particularly where human beings, or other living things such as trees, are involved in it. Even granting that Hawkins's stand-improvement function is a valid forecast, would it be of much use to anyone else, considering how different the other person's circumstances might be? One is strongly confronted with the element of art, the unquantified element, in production. And yet we must recognize that our professional goals in an economic world are identified predominantly with science rather than art. For instance, it is in the interest of society that the ordinary forester should be able to measure certain things about a forest stand and from them predict its growth, and not have to call in an elder statesman to give his general but seasoned judgment in the matter. Science is for the young; art may become a monopoly of old-timers.

Our interest therefore lies in discovering and stating production functions.

[Take an example: Suppose you want to throw light on the subject of pruning Douglas-fir, so that other people may make more intelligent decisions about pruning their own trees. You concentrate upon one part of the problem: the cost of pruning. You carry out pruning operations in Douglas-fir under a wide variety of conditions and record these conditions and the results. Now how would you publish your findings to make them most useful? What production functions would you give, and how would you define them—i.e., what part of the circumstances under which your results were obtained would you consider it necessary to describe, and how would you describe them?]


## SUMMARY

Where the producing firm is combining two interrelated variable inputs with fixed inputs, the basic production function is three-dimensional. From this production function one may construct an iso-output (-revenue) map, the lines curving away from the origin because of diminishing returns. The least-cost combination on each line is the point of tangency with an iso-cost curve, which is a straight line for the firm with constant cost rates. The locus of all such least-cost points is an expansion path. The best combination is located on it, at the output where marginal unit revenue equals marginal unit cost. The relations among marginal revenues, costs, and rates of substitution at the best combination may be summarized in six propositions.

The basic production function is determined by three things: quality of the fixed agents, quality of the variable agents, and the production context. These three elements are heavily interdependent. For example, the quality of a foreman depends not only upon the man but also upon his laborers and upon the circumstances under which they work. The quality of an agent may be expressed in terms of its productivity, which is the product of its capacity and efficiency. The production context is made up, first, of the institutional arrangements surrounding the work; second, of the physical environment in which the work is done; and third, of the technology employed.

# Chapter 8

# CAPITAL
# AND INTEREST

So FAR, in talking about the agents of production in the forest economy, we have spoken mainly about labor and used illustrations of labor inputs. Now let us turn for a while to the subject of capital. Whereas the problems of labor use by the forestry firm are not essentially different from those faced by any other firm, the problems associated with capital are, some of them, rather distinctive. In fact, as we noted in Chapter 1 (p. 4), the distinctive characteristics of capital in the forest economy have been cited in partial justification of forestry economics as a special field of study. Be that as it may, an understanding of the economics of capital in forestry is, of all things that you may get from this book, possibly the most essential and useful to you as a forester.

## WHAT CAPITAL IS

By *capital* is meant man-made agents of production. Capital is the cultural resources of the firm, as distinguished from its human resources (labor) and natural resources ("land").

In forest management, capital includes growing stock—wildlife as well as timber, and other productive living things that man may cultivate. It also includes the various improvements, facilities, and equipment of forest production: roads, trails, bridges, and rolling stock; installations for forest protection and recreation and watershed management; buildings and other structures; and machines, tools, and supplies.

In logging, capital includes such things as trees and logs (goods in process of production), machinery and equipment, roads, and landings.

**101**

And in transportation, in manufacturing, and in marketing, the goods in process and the man-made facilities, equipment, and materials used in furthering the production of these goods all come under the heading of capital.

Finally, *working capital,* the money tied up because of production— such as that kept on hand to meet payrolls, raw-material purchases, acquisition of supplies, and the like—must be included as an important form of capital. Such money is additional to that represented in the capital goods themselves. A stock of it on hand is just as essential to the production process as any machine or road or building. In one sense, it is true, money is merely a symbol of the "real" goods and services for which it is exchanged; but in another, money has an identity of its own and an economic role somewhat analogous to that of other goods.

Now, to return to earlier remarks, you may tilt your eyebrow when capital is referred to as man-made and trees are mentioned as an example. Without trying to analyze the proposition that only God can make a tree, let us recognize that in an economic sense, making, or production, is essentially an act of human will or decision. In all genetic production, based on the growth of living tissue, man is merely the cultivator, not the creator. In fact, this is equally true of any kind of production whatsoever. The gasoline engine is a thing facilitated by man, but basically it is made of materials that he had no hand in. And so if you will accept at all the idea of production as man's doing, logically you must accept the notion of man-made trees, the product of man's will and decision. The implication is simply that if he had willed and decided otherwise, the tree in question, in this form and in this context, would not exist.

Now have we escaped the frying pan only to fall in the fire? What about forests, such as virgin forests in a new country, that clearly have not been subjected to man's will or decision? Let us class them as land, not capital. And then, on the other hand, what about the many aspects of natural resources, and of labor also, that are surely man-made if one adopts such a liberal interpretation of production? These may quite logically be classed as capital. In fact, it can be argued that there is no logical distinction between land and capital when they become resources— that all is capital. Nevertheless, let us hold, if arbitrarily, to the concepts of labor, capital, and land as separate concepts, because they can be convenient and helpful to us in subdividing our subject.

## CHARACTERISTICS OF TIMBER CAPITAL

Let us consider some of the characteristics of capital in the forest economy. Let us dwell mainly on forest capital, since this is of central interest to us as foresters. Let us speak primarily of timber, though what we shall say applies in some degree to other forms of forest capital too, such as wildlife.

Suppose that you are spending the day in Brockton, Massachusetts, and decide for the fun of it to visit one of the shoe factories. You go armed with proper introductions—and, oddly, with a hack saw and gunny sack tucked under your coat tails—and soon find yourself walking about the plant, admiring the machines that are turning out shoes. At noon, when everyone scurries away to lunch, you are suddenly seized with an ungovernable impulse. Whipping out your saw, you advance on one of the big machines, cut off a chunk of it, and drop this chunk into your gunny sack.

Returning home unapprehended, you prepare to examine your booty. You set the sack down. You open it and peer inside. You reach in your hand, grasp the contents uncertainly. When you bring out your hand, you discover that you are holding—not a chunk of steel—but part of a shoe!

Are you surprised? As a forester, you really shouldn't be. For if you were to visit a wood factory—i.e., a forest—and set your eye on one of the wood-making machines—i.e., a tree—and cut off a chunk of it, you would surely find that you had got only some of the product that was being made—wood. In timber production, generally speaking, one cannot tell the product from the machine. Again, growing stock may also be stumpage, and when the time comes for cutting, they are usually indistinguishable, for one can rarely turn out the product without also cashing in the machine, wrecking it, liquidating it.

*One characteristic,* then, of forest capital is that the timber product is also the timber-growing machine, and ultimately the machine is the product. This is more than just an interesting academic point. It is a basic feature of forestry, the consequences of which pervade forest management.

A *second characteristic* of forest capital is the long **period of production** in which it is involved: the long period between the decision to produce and the emergence of the product. As a forester, one becomes accustomed to talking about 50-year, 100-year, even 150-year and longer rotations. When one stops to think of it, what relatively immense periods these are! How vastly markets can change, and timber supplies, and forest ownership, and forestry costs, and technology, . . . while such rotations are in progress! Planning—that is, management—over such periods can be hazardous indeed in a dynamic world. The **risk**—the chances of loss—can be high. Who can look clearly so far into the future? Or what is more to the point, who will take the risks of looking at all?[1]

---

[1] What we shall call *risks* some writers divide into *risks* and *uncertainties,* the former statistically predictable, the latter not. For forestry illustrations see Worrell, Albert C.: *Economics of American Forestry,* John Wiley & Sons, Inc., New York, 1959, pp. 191–196.

To be sure, forestry is by no means the only industry that requires a long time to pay out its investments. Yet one sometimes hears the remark in industrial circles—by way of oversimplification, surely—that twenty years is about the reasonable limit of investment planning, and if one cannot see a pay-off by then, the proposition is generally too indefinite to consider. But in twenty years, the forester may just be getting well started.

[You may counter that for forests under sustained yield, the period of production actually is short. Is this true? The question deserves some thought.]

A *third* characteristic of forest capital, one that follows in part from its long period of production, is its modest rate of return. Although the rate of return is presumably the central issue respecting commercial forestry, we have as yet little data from the United States on this vital question. What we do have, gleaned here and there from permanent experimental management units and other managed areas, confirms that some of the highest rates are produced in southern pine and in West Coast Douglas-fir and redwood, that northern pine forests can also produce at a relatively high rate, and that hardwoods generally yield lower rates. A few indicative results from moderately stocked eastern study areas managed for saw timber show the following net annual percentage rates of return on the value of growing stock, before income taxes:[2]

| | |
|---|---|
| Southern pines | 7.5 |
| Red and white pines | 3.6 |
| Northern hardwoods | 2.4 |

In general, the rates of return are comparable with those on the more conservative bond issues. Of course, as we shall see later, forest investments may be more attractive than such data would suggest, because of income-tax advantages, opportunities for the firm to benefit by combining timber processing with forest management, and other circumstances. On the other hand, there is many a poor-site forest where returns would fall much below those listed.

A *fourth* characteristic of forest capital is that it dominates the costs of timber growing—notably the variable costs over which the manager may exercise control during the period of production.

Take the extreme case of the untended forest left to grow as it will until harvest. Suppose that the firm makes no special effort toward forest protection and that property taxes show little relation to stocking. Here the cost of holding the forest capital, or timber-growing stock, may represent close to 100 per cent of all variable costs.

[2] Resources for the Future, Inc., Committee: *Forest Credit in the United States: A Survey of Needs and Facilities*, Resources for the Future, Inc., Washington, 1958, table 2, p. 11.

At the opposite extreme, where the firm has an active silvicultural program, the cost of the timber capital still may overshadow that of other capital and of labor. Let us think, conservatively, of the managed forest where growing stocks may average between 5,000 and 15,000 board feet per acre, with a value somewhere between $10 and $50 per thousand. Let us take the illustrative case of a $225 total timber value which, at a conservative 4 per cent annual charge, involves a $9 holding cost per acre per year. Now if property taxes vary with growing stock and if forest planting, road maintenance, stand care, timber marking, supervision, and other such jobs are given the full time of one forester per 15,000 acres and one laborer per 6,000 acres, the variable costs other than growing stock may amount to as much as $3 per acre per year. In this case the cost of timber capital represents three-fourths of the total $12 variable cost of timber growing.[3] Where a greater value of stock is maintained, or the interest rate is higher, or there is less cash outlay for management, the timber-capital cost is relatively higher. Only rarely in most regions of the United States will it be lower.

Timber growing is virtually unique among the industries in the great proportion of its costs going into capital plant. In agriculture—in manufacturing, even the most highly automated—such proportions as we have discussed are seldom approached. In these industries, as in the other branches of the forest economy itself, such costs as labor, raw materials, and power occupy the central place. Refer again to Table 1 (p. 46) for an illustration of this fact.

A *fifth characteristic*, finally, of forest capital is its versatility. Some kinds of capital are highly versatile in the sense that they can be shifted readily into any of a variety of uses. Money is the extreme example. Raw materials such as iron and petroleum are other examples. Some kinds of machines too are versatile: electric motors, for instance. Versatile capital may represent an advantageous investment, because if the prospective rate of return declines in the capital's current use, the capital may be shifted to other uses where prospects may be brighter. What are the alternatives? If they are many and varied, values are likely to be relatively high and stable in a changing world.

On the other hand, some forms of capital have little versatility. A peavey is useful mainly for rolling logs. A sawmill is not much good for anything but making lumber. If capital cannot readily be shifted, its value may fall heavily if prospective demand for its product declines. Of course, if prospects brighten and other capital cannot readily be shifted *into* this line of production, the value of the capital already there may for a while rise immensely, and its owners reap corresponding rewards. [Why? Is the value of the capital under these circumstances re-

[3] These illustrative data are based upon an informal analysis by Prof. John Fedkiw of the Syracuse, N.Y., College of Forestry.

lated to the intensity of its use? And if so, how—as the cause, or the effect?]

Forest capital ranks fairly high in the scale of versatility. By and large, it is usable for a good many purposes. And often being alternatively machine and product, it is more readily convertible into money than most machines. Furthermore, it has rather high "time versatility"—i.e., it is durable and hence can be shifted either now or later on.

## WHAT INTEREST IS

From the standpoint of the capital owner, *interest* is the return to capital. Or from the standpoint of the user, it is the cost of using capital. Interest in the case of capital is analogous to wages in the case of labor and may be represented as a certain aggregate payment over a period of time. Or just as one may express a wage *rate* per man per hour or day, so one may express an interest rate, commonly per cent per year.

It is helpful to distinguish between interest and other kinds of return that are sometimes lumped with it and expressed as per cent of capital value per year. One lumber company operating in Alabama sold, in 1956, $986,000 worth of lumber. After deducting all out-of-pocket expenses, including its own taxes, the corporation had $351,000 left. This net sum represented nearly 49 per cent of the $720,000 capital investment of the corporation—that is, of the stockholders, all of whom were members of one family and officers of the company. However, there was much besides interest represented in this sum. Of the $351,000, the corporation first set aside $201,000, to be used in part as a depreciation reserve and in part as a contingency reserve, something to keep for a rainy day. The former reserve represented a cost; it was not part of the net return. The latter reserve probably fell under the heading of profit; 1956 was an exceptionally good year for this company. The remaining $150,000, representing 21 per cent of the capital investment, was distributed by the corporation to the stockholders. But not all, even of this, was interest. Since the stockholder-officers took their salaries in the form of dividends, part of it was payment for labor. Part of it, again, was implicitly a return to the land used by these people in their business. And another part was distributed profit. When all these items were accounted for, the share identifiable strictly speaking as interest apparently amounted to no more than about 8 per cent of the capital investment. Possibly 2½ or 3 per cent was the "pure" or "risk-free" rate of interest. The rest of the interest was apparently a margin for risk.

Even the "interest" that this firm paid on a loan negotiated with the local bank was not all interest in our sense. At least a fraction of it was the bank's cost of administration: wages, materials, and the like.

[Surely a number of questions arise in your mind as you review this example of a lumber company in Alabama. Some of these questions we cannot pursue to the very end in this book, nor do we as ordinary forest-ers need to do so. But at least we can get a little insight into them as we go along. Here are four questions to think about:

[1. How could one reasonably break down a firm's total net return into the components of wages, interest, rent, and profit? In Chapter 6 (pp. 78–80) a method was used for dividing the gross return into two parts. Is such a method applicable to the net return?

[2. Is it not especially difficult to distinguish between interest and profit? If profit arises from investment, how different is it from interest, which presumably also arises from investment? What is profit anyhow? What accounts for its existence?

[3. What determines the rate of interest?

[4. What is this business about a risk-free interest rate and an allow-ance for risk? How can there possibly be any such thing as freedom from risk in a dynamic economy? Is there not risk everywhere—except in Heaven? And again, what determines the amount of the risk allow-ance? Can one actually measure risk in economic life?]


*TIME DIMENSION OF VALUE*

If money will earn money, which apparently it is capable of doing, then the rate of earning—i.e., the rate of interest—at once steps into a strategic role as a regulator and index of value relationships over time. Here is the way it works:

Suppose $100 of capital will earn $5 of interest per year. The annual rate of interest, then, is 5 per cent. And $100 invested today becomes $105 a year hence. This is another way of saying that $100 today and $105 a year from today are equal values, since so long as the interest rate is 5 per cent and people are lending and borrowing money at this rate, one can always exchange $100 for the promise of $105 a year hence, and vice versa.

If you borrow $100 for a year at 5 per cent interest, what happens is that you sell your promise to pay $105 in a year, and the price at which it is bought is $100 today. It is this sort of selling-buying transaction, carried out each day in money markets throughout the economy, that determines rates of interest. And the statement that $100 now and $105 in a year are equal values rests on the premise that we are working with market value and that equality of value is demonstrated when two things are exchanged even-up in the market.

Such promises of future payment are necessarily qualified in terms of the degree of certainty of the payment—or, if you like, the degree of risk that the payment will not be made, at least in full. The greater the risk attached to a promise of future payment, the less the market will pay for the promise. My promise to pay $105 in a year may be judged as worth only $90 today, because of my circumstances and the use to which I will put the funds. The interest rate in this case is $105\!/\!90 - 1$, or about 17 per cent. Thus it is in the judgments of the buyers and sellers of funds that risk allowance is determined as part of the interest rate.

The rate of interest in each particular case depends upon many things, and we shall have an opportunity in Chapter 10 to discuss some of them. The rate depends, for example, upon the firm and its alternatives. It depends upon the period of years in question. In a sense, these factors all simmer down to one: the degree of risk.

## COMPOUNDING AND DISCOUNTING

Now if capital will earn 5 per cent annual interest, and $100 is left invested for 2 years along with its earnings, which are compounded annually, the end value will be

| | |
|---|---|
| The beginning value | $100.00 |
| Plus 5 per cent of $100 | 5.00 |
| Plus 5 per cent of $105 | 5.25 |
| Total | $110.25 |

That is, the end value will be $100(1.05)(1.05)$, or $100(1.05)^2$, which is $110.25. Or after any period of years, $n$, the end value $V_n$, of a single investment, $V_0$, which earns $i$ per cent annual interest (expressed in decimals) is found in the expression

$$V_n = V_0(1 + i)^n \qquad (1a)$$

What this formula says is that the initial value $V_0$, if compounded annually for $n$ years at $100i$ per cent interest, becomes the end value $V_n$. The formula is shown as number $1a$ in Table 9. Some values of $(1 + i)^n$ are given in Table 10.

Compounding, then, is the process of carrying an initial value forward in time at compound interest—that is, at a rate applied each year (or other interval) to the sum of the initial value plus all previous amounts of interest.

While the process of exchange is determining end value from initial value, it is at the same time determining the general relationship between the two in light of the interest rate. Any of these three elements may be inferred from the other two. Thus the initial investment required to become $110.25 in 2 years at 5 per cent is $110.25/(1.05)^2$, or $100. That is to say, where the rate of interest is 5 per cent, the present worth of the prospect of $110.25 in 2 years is $100. And in general the initial, or discounted, value of any end value is given by the rearrangement of formula 1a:

$$V_0 = \frac{V_n}{(1 + i)^n} \tag{1b}$$

The formula is listed as number 1b in Table 9. And we perceive that *discounting* is the process of carrying an end value backward in time at compound interest.

Where initial and end values are known, the implied interest rate may be determined from the ratio $V_n/V_0$. Thus \$110.25/\$100 is 1.1025, which may be thought of as the end value of a dollar compounded for 2 years. The corresponding rate of interest may be found by taking the second root and subtracting 1—or more simply from Table 10, by locating the ratio 1.102 in the line $n = 2$ and observing what $i$ is (in this case 0.050, or 5 per cent).

## CAPITALIZING ANNUAL SERIES

If \$100 is left invested indefinitely at 5 per cent interest, and the interest is paid out each year (not left invested), the annual payment will be \$5. That is to say, the annual income, $r$, of capital worth \$100 is \$5 where the interest rate is 5 per cent. Or, in general,

$$r = iV_0$$

This means that the promise of a perpetual annual payment, $r$, and the sum $V_0$ have equal value, or that the value $V_0$ can be found by dividing the income by the interest rate expressed in decimals:

$$V_0 = \frac{r}{i} \tag{2a}$$

The process of finding the total value of a series of payments discounted to one point of time is termed *capitalizing* the payments. Thus, any resource that promises a net annual return, $r$, for the indefinite future has a capitalized value of $r/i$. It can be shown that $r/i$ is equal to the sum of the indefinite series of discounted terms:

$$\frac{r}{1 + i} + \frac{r}{(1 + i)^2} + \frac{r}{(1 + i)^3} + \frac{r}{(1 + i)^4} + \cdots$$

Where the rate of interest is 5 per cent, it could easily be a matter of indifference to you whether you owned \$100 or a piece of forest land promising a net return of \$5 yearly. And if it were a matter of indifference, you should be willing to exchange the one for the other even-up— that is, the land is worth \$100. This assumes that the risk in the forest investment and the risk in the alternative investment of $100 which will yield 5 per cent interest are judged essentially equal.

The process of capitalization may be used not only with revenues but also with costs—or indeed with any recurring value. If you have a small parcel of woods on which the ad valorem property tax is $5 per year, this tax may be capitalized at an appropriate rate of interest. Again suppose the rate is 5 per cent. Then the capitalized tax is $100, the present worth of all the anticipated tax payments, discounted at 5 per cent interest. This $100 may be interpreted as the total subtraction from the present worth of your property on account of the property tax. Or it may be

*Table 9. Some formulas for changing the time of reference of values by means of the interest rate*

| Type of time change | Formula* |
|---|---|
| 1. Compounding and discounting single values | |
|    *a.* End value: initial value compounded | $V_n = V_0(1 + i)^n$ |
|    *b.* Initial value: end value discounted | $V_0 = V_n/(1 + i)^n$ |
| 2. Capitalizing annual series of values | |
|    *a.* Initial value of perpetual annual series beginning in one year | $V_0 = r/i$ |
|    *b.* Initial value of perpetual increasing annual series beginning in one year | $V_0 = (r/i) + (c/i^2)$ |
|    *c.* Initial value of terminable annual series beginning in one year | $V_0 = \dfrac{r[(1 + i)^n - 1]}{i(1 + i)^n}$ |
| 3. Capitalizing periodic series of values | |
|    *a.* Initial value of perpetual periodic series beginning in one period | $V_0 = r/[(1 + i)^t - 1]$ |
|    *b.* Initial value of terminable periodic series beginning in one period | $V_0 = \dfrac{r[(1 + i)^n - 1]}{[(1 + i)^t - 1](1 + i)^n}$ |
| 4. Accumulated end value of a series | |
|    *a.* End value of annual series | $V_n = r[(1 + i)^n - 1]/i$ |
|    *b.* End value of periodic series | $V_n = \dfrac{r[(1 + i)^n - 1]}{(1 + i)^t - 1}$ |

\* Meaning of symbols:

$c$ = annual change in $r$

$i$ = annual rate of interest expressed in decimals

$n$ = number of years of compounding or discounting, or in a terminable series

$r$ = value (return or cost) recurring annually or periodically (interval longer than a year)

$t$ = number of years between periodic recurrences of $r$

$V_0$ = initial value—i.e., now, or at the beginning—value as of year zero

$V_n$ = end value—value as of year $n$

[Symbols other than $c$ are those of the *Forestry Handbook* (Forbes, R. D., ed., The Ronald Press Company, New York, 1955, pp. 15.1, 15.15), except that $n$ means in every case the number of *years*.]

Table 10. Some values of $(1+i)^n$

| $n$ | $i$ | | | | | | | | | | |
|---|---|---|---|---|---|---|---|---|---|---|---|
| | 0.005 | 0.010 | 0.015 | 0.020 | 0.030 | 0.040 | 0.050 | 0.060 | 0.080 | 0.100 | 0.150 |
| 1 | 1.005 | 1.010 | 1.015 | 1.020 | 1.030 | 1.040 | 1.050 | 1.060 | 1.080 | 1.100 | 1.150 |
| 2 | 1.010 | 1.020 | 1.030 | 1.040 | 1.061 | 1.082 | 1.102 | 1.124 | 1.166 | 1.210 | 1.322 |
| 3 | 1.015 | 1.030 | 1.046 | 1.061 | 1.093 | 1.125 | 1.158 | 1.191 | 1.260 | 1.331 | 1.521 |
| 4 | 1.020 | 1.041 | 1.061 | 1.082 | 1.126 | 1.170 | 1.216 | 1.262 | 1.360 | 1.464 | 1.749 |
| 5 | 1.025 | 1.051 | 1.077 | 1.104 | 1.159 | 1.217 | 1.276 | 1.338 | 1.469 | 1.611 | 2.011 |
| 6 | 1.030 | 1.062 | 1.093 | 1.126 | 1.194 | 1.265 | 1.340 | 1.419 | 1.587 | 1.772 | 2.313 |
| 7 | 1.036 | 1.072 | 1.110 | 1.149 | 1.230 | 1.316 | 1.407 | 1.504 | 1.714 | 1.949 | 2.660 |
| 8 | 1.041 | 1.083 | 1.126 | 1.172 | 1.267 | 1.369 | 1.477 | 1.594 | 1.851 | 2.144 | 3.059 |
| 9 | 1.046 | 1.094 | 1.143 | 1.195 | 1.305 | 1.423 | 1.551 | 1.689 | 1.999 | 2.358 | 3.518 |
| 10 | 1.051 | 1.105 | 1.161 | 1.219 | 1.344 | 1.480 | 1.629 | 1.791 | 2.159 | 2.594 | 4.046 |
| 11 | 1.056 | 1.116 | 1.178 | 1.243 | 1.384 | 1.539 | 1.710 | 1.898 | 2.332 | 2.853 | 4.652 |
| 12 | 1.062 | 1.127 | 1.196 | 1.268 | 1.426 | 1.601 | 1.796 | 2.012 | 2.518 | 3.138 | 5.350 |
| 13 | 1.067 | 1.138 | 1.214 | 1.294 | 1.469 | 1.665 | 1.886 | 2.133 | 2.720 | 3.452 | 6.153 |
| 14 | 1.072 | 1.149 | 1.232 | 1.319 | 1.513 | 1.732 | 1.980 | 2.261 | 2.937 | 3.798 | 7.076 |
| 15 | 1.078 | 1.161 | 1.250 | 1.346 | 1.558 | 1.801 | 2.079 | 2.397 | 3.172 | 4.177 | 8.137 |
| 16 | 1.083 | 1.173 | 1.269 | 1.373 | 1.605 | 1.873 | 2.183 | 2.540 | 3.426 | 4.595 | 9.358 |
| 17 | 1.088 | 1.184 | 1.288 | 1.400 | 1.653 | 1.948 | 2.292 | 2.693 | 3.700 | 5.054 | 10.76 |
| 18 | 1.094 | 1.196 | 1.307 | 1.428 | 1.702 | 2.026 | 2.407 | 2.854 | 3.996 | 5.560 | 12.38 |
| 19 | 1.099 | 1.208 | 1.327 | 1.457 | 1.754 | 2.107 | 2.527 | 3.026 | 4.316 | 6.116 | 14.23 |
| 20 | 1.105 | 1.220 | 1.347 | 1.486 | 1.806 | 2.191 | 2.653 | 3.207 | 4.661 | 6.728 | 16.37 |
| 21 | 1.110 | 1.232 | 1.367 | 1.516 | 1.860 | 2.279 | 2.786 | 3.400 | 5.034 | 7.400 | 18.82 |
| 22 | 1.116 | 1.245 | 1.388 | 1.546 | 1.916 | 2.370 | 2.925 | 3.604 | 5.437 | 8.140 | 21.64 |
| 23 | 1.122 | 1.257 | 1.408 | 1.577 | 1.974 | 2.465 | 3.072 | 3.820 | 5.871 | 8.954 | 24.89 |
| 24 | 1.127 | 1.270 | 1.429 | 1.608 | 2.033 | 2.563 | 3.225 | 4.049 | 6.341 | 9.850 | 28.63 |
| 25 | 1.133 | 1.282 | 1.451 | 1.641 | 2.094 | 2.666 | 3.386 | 4.292 | 6.848 | 10.83 | 32.92 |
| 30 | 1.161 | 1.348 | 1.563 | 1.811 | 2.427 | 3.243 | 4.322 | 5.744 | 10.06 | 17.45 | 66.21 |
| 35 | 1.191 | 1.417 | 1.684 | 2.000 | 2.814 | 3.946 | 5.516 | 7.686 | 14.79 | 28.10 | 133.2 |
| 40 | 1.221 | 1.489 | 1.814 | 2.208 | 3.262 | 4.801 | 7.040 | 10.29 | 21.72 | 45.26 | 267.9 |
| 45 | 1.252 | 1.565 | 1.954 | 2.438 | 3.782 | 5.841 | 8.985 | 13.76 | 31.92 | 72.89 | 538.8 |
| 50 | 1.283 | 1.645 | 2.105 | 2.692 | 4.384 | 7.107 | 11.47 | 18.42 | 46.90 | 117.4 | — |
| 55 | 1.316 | 1.729 | 2.268 | 2.972 | 5.082 | 8.646 | 14.64 | 24.65 | 68.91 | 189.1 | — |
| 60 | 1.349 | 1.817 | 2.443 | 3.281 | 5.892 | 10.52 | 18.68 | 32.99 | 101.3 | 304.5 | — |
| 65 | 1.383 | 1.909 | 2.632 | 3.623 | 6.830 | 12.80 | 23.84 | 44.14 | 148.8 | 490.4 | — |
| 70 | 1.418 | 2.007 | 2.835 | 4.000 | 7.918 | 15.57 | 30.43 | 59.08 | 218.6 | 789.7 | — |
| 75 | 1.454 | 2.109 | 3.055 | 4.416 | 9.179 | 18.95 | 38.83 | 79.06 | 321.2 | — | — |
| 80 | 1.490 | 2.217 | 3.291 | 4.875 | 10.64 | 23.05 | 49.56 | 105.8 | 472.0 | — | — |
| 85 | 1.528 | 2.330 | 3.545 | 5.383 | 12.34 | 28.04 | 63.25 | 141.6 | 693.5 | — | — |
| 90 | 1.567 | 2.449 | 3.819 | 5.943 | 14.30 | 34.12 | 80.73 | 189.5 | — | — | — |
| 95 | 1.606 | 2.574 | 4.114 | 6.562 | 16.58 | 41.51 | 103.0 | 253.5 | — | — | — |
| 100 | 1.647 | 2.705 | 4.432 | 7.245 | 19.22 | 50.50 | 131.5 | 339.3 | — | — | — |

thought of as the fund which, invested at 5 per cent interest, would serve to pay the tax bill each year indefinitely.

The annual values in the series possibly may not be expected to stay the same. The series may be a declining one. Taxes, on the other hand, almost always go up. Suppose you anticipate that on the average the tax will increase about a nickel a year. What is its capitalized value now? It can be shown that such an annual change can be capitalized by dividing it by the square of the interest rate (in decimals). Hence, where $c$ is the annual change in $r$, we have the relationship

$$V_0 = \frac{r}{i} + \frac{c}{i^2} \tag{2b}$$

and the capitalized value of the tax is \$100 + \$20, the \$20 being attributable to the forecasted yearly growth of the tax bill.

Again, suppose the annual series is not of indefinite duration. Suppose, for example, that your woods will come under the provisions of special tax legislation after a waiting period of 6 years, and you wish to figure the capitalized value of the \$5 tax during just those 6 remaining years. You could add the discounted values

$$\frac{5}{1.05} + \frac{5}{1.05^2} + \frac{5}{1.05^3} + \frac{5}{1.05^4} + \frac{5}{1.05^5} + \frac{5}{1.05^6}$$

but this boils down into the general form

$$V_0 = \frac{r[(1 + i)^n - 1]}{i(1 + i)^n} \tag{2c}$$

where $n$ is the number of years, in this case 6, that the terminable series will run. It will be seen that this formula is formula $2a$ multiplied by a correction factor, $[(1 + i)^n - 1]/(1 + i)^n$. In your example, from Table 10, the correction factor is 0.34/1.34, or about a fourth. The capitalized series is therefore about \$25.

The annual series that we have been considering all start at the end of a year. To capitalize a series starting at any other time is a simple matter, beginning with the value from formula $2a$, $b$, or $c$. If the series starts now, add $r$, or compound for a year with formula $1a$. If the series starts after more than a year, discount for the further period of delay using formula $1b$.

## CAPITALIZING PERIODIC SERIES

Table 9 lists two other formulas for capitalizing series. These are for series of values that occur not annually but at longer regular intervals. They are included because many forestry revenues and costs are of this sort, that they come periodically. For example, harvest revenues may occur once every cutting cycle, thinning revenues and costs every 5 years or 10, planting outlays every rotation.

What is the capitalized value of a forest property if it will yield $34 net per acre every 6 years commencing 6 years hence? The general relationship is

$$V_0 = \frac{r}{(1 + i)^t - 1} \tag{3a}$$

where $r$ is the amount of the periodic value and $t$ is the number of years in the period. In our example, if the appropriate interest rate is 5 per cent, $V_0 = 34/(1.34 - 1)$, which gives the forest property a per acre capitalized value of $100.

It will be observed that at 5 per cent interest $34 every 6 years has the same value as $5 every year. The extra $4, i.e., $34 - (5 \times 6)$, is the interest imputed to the five $5 annual revenues that occur in each period while the periodic revenue is still postponed—that is, reading down the column in Table 10, $5(0.050 + 0.102 + 0.158 + 0.216 + 0.276)$. Allowing for the rounding of fractions, this equals $5 \times 0.8$, or 4.

Now if we wish to capitalize a periodic series that is terminable rather than perpetual, we can amend formula 3a with the same factor, $[(1 + i)^n - 1]/(1 + i)^n$, that we used on formula 2a. Thus

$$V_0 = \frac{r[(1 + i)^n - 1]}{[(1 + i)^t - 1](1 + i)^n} \tag{3b}$$

And so if the series terminates in 6 years ($n = 6$)—that is, if the periodic income of $34 is expected to occur only once—the correction factor is the same as we used in the earlier example: 0.34/1.34, or about a fourth, and the capitalized value of the "series" is roughly $25. We have here the special case where capitalized value is simply the anticipated single income discounted for 6 years by formula 1b. That is to say, $34/1.34 = 25$, approximately.

### END VALUE OF A SERIES

Now in the case of all series that we have considered so far, we discounted the recurring values back to a point of time corresponding to the "present," before the beginning of the series. Sometimes, however, it is useful to compound such recurring values forward, so as to express them as of a time at the end of the series. We may wish to do this for purposes of comparison—for example, to discover which of two management programs represents the higher value: (1) one that will yield $5 annually for 6 years or (2) one that will produce $35 in the sixth year. If the rate of interest is 5 per cent, we already know the answer.

We can determine the answer anew in either of two ways: First, we can discount the values involved in both programs back to the present, using formulas 2c and 1b. Second, we can take the possibly simpler route of making a direct comparison between $35 and the accumulated value represented in the first alternative as of the time when the $35 revenue will occur. The formula for the accumulated end value of an annual series is

$$V_n = \frac{r[(1 + i)^n - 1]}{i} \tag{4a}$$

In our illustration, $V_n = 5(1.34 - 1)/0.05 = \$34$, which means that the second alternative represents the higher value.

Observe that formula 4a is simply the formula for the initial value of a terminable annual series $(2c)$ compounded for $n$ years by formula 1a —i.e., multiplied by $(1 + i)^n$. One may similarly derive from formula 3b the expression for the end value of a periodic series:

$$V_n = \frac{r[(1 + i)^n - 1]}{(1 + i)^t - 1} \tag{4b}$$

### REVIEW OF FORMULAS

These nine formulas for changing the time of reference of values by means of the interest rate are all that we shall consider here. They are summarized in Table 9. Many more are to be found in books on finance, but these nine will handle virtually all the time-adjustment problems that we will tackle in this book, or that you are likely to meet as a practicing forester. Remember that the formulas, like our models, are tools, and the important thing will be to learn to understand what they mean, what they do, and how to use them—and not necessarily to memorize them. In this modern day, there are always books to be had, with plenty of formulas accurately printed in them. You can help justify the social cost of making and preserving such books by putting them to use. A really scarce commodity in life is not books but thought, and this each one of us himself can and must provide.

However, if you have a flair for memory work, here are some aids to orderly pigeonholing of these compounding and discounting relationships:

First, the basic ingredient in all the relationships is $(1 + i)^n$, which we have illustrated in Table 10. This is the value of 1 compounded for $n$ years at $100i$ per cent interest. In other words, it is the ratio of an end value (year $n$) to an initial value (year zero): the ratio of $V_n$ to $V_0$. This establishes formulas 1a and b, for compounding and discounting single values.

Second, there is the process of capitalization, which is the process of adding the discounted (initial) values of a *series* of $V_n$—that is, adding a series of $V_0$, each one equal to $V_n/(1+i)^n$. Where this is a perpetual series of annually recurring items, its total $V_0$ is $r/i$ (formula 2a), easily remembered from the obvious relationship $r = iV_0$.

Third and last, there are suffixes to be tacked on for special purposes in capitalization. To capitalize a perpetually and annually changing $r$, add $c/i^2$ (formula 2b). Where $r$ occurs at intervals longer than a year, capitalize by substituting $(1+i)^t - 1$ for $i$ in the denominator (formula 3a). Where the series is terminable, use the multiplier $[(1+i)^n - 1]/(1+i)^n$ (formulas 2c and 3b). And where capitalized value is desired as of some time of reference later than year zero, multiply by the basic ratio $(1+i)^n$ (formulas 4a and b).

## CHARACTERISTICS OF COMPOUND INTEREST

While we have Table 10 and some illustrations of its use fresh in mind, let us look at some of the peculiarities of compound interest and especially the value $(1+i)^n$.

The items in each column of Table 10 form a geometric series increasing year by year at a ratio of $1+i$. Thus a value compounded at any positive interest rate will get bigger with time; but what is more, the amount of its annual growth will also get bigger. Conversely, a value discounted over successively longer periods is ever smaller: As we peer ahead into the more and more remote future, we see its discounted values dim and fade—by diminishing amounts, it is true—but still fast enough at first for us to be able to say, "Beyond such and such a point, they don't matter a great deal."

For example, we saw that at an interest rate of 5 per cent, if we add up the present values of all the members of a series of $5 incomes that will occur every year until eternity, the sum is $r/i$, or $100. Now it doesn't take many $5 bills to total $100, and the fact that this infinitely long series adds to only $100 certainly suggests that virtually all its items have been reduced to insignificance by discounting. Only a few, at the beginning of the series, can amount to much. Indeed Table 11 shows that more than $70 of the $100 total is accounted for by the first 25 items in the infinite series and that more than half is in the first 15 items.

Comparison of Table 11 with the 5 per cent column of Table 10 shows that half of the total capitalized value is reached at the point where $(1+i)^n = 2$, and that two-thirds is reached where $(1+i)^n = 3$. In general, for any rate of interest, the fraction of total capitalized value remaining to be accounted for at any point in a series of $r/(1+i)^n$ is $1/(1+i)^n$.

Now the depth of perspective in time that is determined in the process of discounting is vastly affected by the rate of interest. Note that the items in the first line of Table 10 form an arithmetic series increasing with interest rate, while as one moves down the table into more remote future time, the items for each value of $n$ approach geometric series with continually higher ratios. It is this quality of the values of $(1 + i)^n$ which, as we shall see, makes the rate of interest critical in evaluating alternatives that have a time dimension.

Table 11. Cumulative totals of the series $5/(1 + i)^n$ for annual values of $n$ from 1 to 25 years, where $i = 0.05$

| $n$ | $5/(1 + i)^n$ | | $n$ | $5/(1 + i)^n$ | | $n$ | $5/(1 + i)^n$ | |
|---|---|---|---|---|---|---|---|---|
| | Current | Total | | Current | Total | | Current | Total |
| | | | 9 | 3.22 | 35.53 | | | |
| 1 | 4.76 | 4.76 | 10 | 3.07 | 38.60 | 18 | 2.08 | 58.44 |
| 2 | 4.54 | 9.30 | 11 | 2.92 | 41.52 | 19 | 1.98 | 60.42 |
| 3 | 4.32 | 13.62 | 12 | 2.78 | 44.30 | 20 | 1.88 | 62.30 |
| 4 | 4.11 | 17.73 | 13 | 2.65 | 46.95 | 21 | 1.79 | 64.09 |
| 5 | 3.92 | 21.65 | 14 | 2.53 | 49.48 | 22 | 1.71 | 65.80 |
| 6 | 3.73 | 25.38 | 15 | 2.41 | 51.89 | 23 | 1.63 | 67.43 |
| 7 | 3.55 | 28.93 | 16 | 2.29 | 54.18 | 24 | 1.55 | 68.98 |
| 8 | 3.38 | 32.31 | 17 | 2.18 | 56.36 | 25 | 1.48 | 70.46 |

For the present it is helpful to note in Table 10 how the values of $(1 + i)^n$ march upward with the interest rate. Note, for example, that at $\frac{1}{2}$ per cent interest, 1 compounds to $1\frac{1}{2}$ in about 80 years, while at 1 per cent interest the same half-again increase takes place in roughly 40 years. With the rate of interest at 2 per cent, the same change occurs in some 20 years; at 4 per cent, in 10 years; at 8 per cent, in 5; and at 15 per cent, in less than 3.

Note, also, the values of $n$ at which $(1 + i)^n$ reaches 10 at the various rates of interest, indicating that 90 per cent of any capitalized annual income is accounted for in the discountings up to that time. At 15 per cent interest, this happens in the seventeenth year, and all years thereafter add but another meager 10 per cent to the total. At $\frac{1}{2}$ per cent interest, on the other hand, we would find, if Table 10 were carried far enough, that $(1 + i)^n$ does not reach 10 until the four-hundred-sixty-second year! Low rates of interest are like telescopic lenses that bring distant objects up close and make them hard to distinguish from nearby objects.

Since, relative to high rates of interest, low rates magnify the future, they magnify any sort of discounted value or capitalized value. Our $100 value of $r/i$ where $i$ equaled 5 per cent becomes $1,000 where $i$ is $\frac{1}{2}$ per cent. This huge capitalized value comes about because the effects of discounting are comparatively slight at such a low interest rate.

Low interest rates tend to favor alternatives that involve postponement of revenue. High rates favor those that promise quicker returns. We saw that at an interest rate of 5 per cent, $35 in the sixth year is a better bet than $5 annually for 6 years. At 6 per cent interest, the two alternatives are about equally good. At higher rates the annual return, involving less postponement, gains the upper hand.

The foregoing characteristics we can summarize in a *principle of time comparisons:* The higher the interest rate used in time comparisons, the greater the present worth of near-future values relative to those of the far future, the lower the discounted or capitalized value of a given item or series, the higher its compounded end value, and the larger the comparative advantage of alternatives that yield a quick return.

## COMPOUNDING AND CONFOUNDING

These propositions are mathematical truths. But are they relevant to the working of the human mind in its judgment of past and future values? If not, we have been wasting our time juggling figures—scheming out neat formulas for solving nothing. The concepts and relationships of this chapter are, like any tools, valid and useful if handled with skill and discretion. It is a fact that the rate of interest can be used as an index of the efficiency of investments. It can be used, too—constructively and helpfully—as an index of the depth of human foresight. The processes of compounding, discounting, and capitalization are valid representations—within limits—of what happens both in money markets and in human psychology.

On the other hand, it is easily possible for the unwary user to run wild in Tables 9 and 10, with ridiculous consequences. By assuming a very high interest rate, it is easy to show that any investment of resources will eat up deferred returns before they ever materialize. By assuming a very low rate of interest, recurring future values can be shown to be so huge that no cost to win them is too great a sacrifice. Dealing with forever, or perpetuity, one can amass immense fortunes by compounding and create great, unmanageable gulfs between was, is, and will be. It is easy, too, to let the formulas obscure the distinction between will be and may be. We shall devote some thought a little later to such key issues as the choice of interest rate and the appropriateness of perpetuity calculations.

## WHY NOT SIMPLE INTEREST?

A fundamental question that has occasionally been raised by foresters and by others who work with long periods of production is whether it is "right" or "fair" to use compound interest. Why not use *simple interest*— that is, a rate applied each year (or other interval) to initial value alone, and not to any previous accumulations of interest? If a deferred-return investment is carried at simple interest during the period of waiting for revenues, the enterprise is thereby placed on equal footing (so it is claimed) with more "normal" enterprises that yield revenues every year. For example, if Firm B considers undertaking a $40-per-acre planting program which promises to yield its first substantial pay-off after 30 years, interest charges by that time, at 5 per cent per year compounded, will amount to about $133. The prospective revenues must be enough to cover this and the other costs, or Firm B will not go into the planting program. But wait! If the firm charges only simple interest against its investment, such interest will total 5 per cent of $40 (i.e., $2) per year, or only $60 altogether for the 30 years. Thus the investment is made more attractive —the practice of forestry is given a boost—and what not. And needless to say, the longer the waiting period and the higher the interest rate, the bigger the boost from simple interest as against compound.

The answer to this tempting argument is to look and see where the 5 per cent rate of interest came from in the first place, and what sort of interest it is. What are Firm B's alternatives that have led to its decision to do planting only if the prospective return is 5 per cent? If there are other uses of its resources that promise an equal chance of returning 5 per cent per year and if the firm has the opportunity either to reinvest the earnings of its capital or to receive them as income, then the compound interest is inescapable, just as the 5 per cent rate is inescapable.

In a sense, the crux of the issue between simple and compound interest rests in this matter of reinvesting earnings or receiving them as income. So long as the institutions of our economy provide reinvestment opportunities and annual returns—growing businesses and new businesses, many types of securities, savings banks, and so on—those particular investments that promise only a periodic return will have to pay interest on the interest they earn if they are to be made. The rate of interest may be low if the investment is comparatively safe. If not, it will be high, but still compounded. Thus to put deferred-yield forest investments on an equal footing with the "normal" ones that show a return each year, it is necessary to use not simple interest but the compound interest which is the essential feature of these annual-yield enterprises and indeed is forced upon the economy by them.

*What are the alternatives?* Pursuing this question has helped us understand the issue between simple and compound interest. Earlier, we used it in defining Hawkins's problem of the best crew size. And when Hawkins came to set a value on his own time, he surveyed his alternatives and equated his time to the best of them: $40 per day. To ask what are the alternatives provides a helpful lead, first, in setting the scope of management problems and, second, in determining the values that are basic to management. We shall be asking the question repeatedly as we move among the economic problems of forestry. The question will be perhaps our most useful analytical tool.

## SUMMARY

Capital consists of the agents of roundabout production that are made by man: the product of his will or decision. Interest is the return to capital or the cost of it. Five characteristics of timber capital are (1) the fact that the product is also the machine, (2) its long period of production, (3) its modest rate of return, (4) its predominance among timber-growing costs, and (5) its versatility.

The rate of interest is an index of the efficiency of investments over time, and of men's depth of time perspective. The rate of interest may be used for changing the time of reference of values: compounding or discounting single values for ease of comparison with other values, capitalizing time series of values to find their current worth, reexpressing the capitalized value of a series as of some different point of time. The basic ingredient in the formulas for making these changes is the quantity $(1 + i)^n$.

In making time adjustments of value, it is essential to use compound interest. Such interest is characterized by the fact that the values of $(1 + i)^n$ form in relation to $n$ a geometric series with a ratio of $1 + i$ and in relation to $i$ approach a geometric series with a very high ratio.

One of the most useful analytical tools in the economics of forestry is the question "What are the alternatives?"

Chapter 9

BEST

COMBINATION

OF FOREST

CAPITAL

N ow that we have in mind what capital is and how the rate of interest works, we are ready to get down to the main issue: how the firm may find the best combination of capital with other agents of production. We shall confine our attention here to timber growing stock. It is a good form of capital for us to study, not only because it is of major concern to us as foresters, but also because it is complicated by the special characteristics that we noted on pages 102 to 106. If we can understand the firm's use of timber capital, we have gone a long way toward grasping the problems of capital in general.

This chapter, then, is the counterpart of Chapters 5 and 6, with forest growing stock at issue instead of forest labor. You should keep in mind the reasoning of those earlier chapters and draw all the parallels you can with our current reasoning.

In the chapters on the use of labor, we took the wage rate pretty much as given, with passing reference to the principle that it tends to equal the alternative rate of return in other, comparable activity. So in this chapter we shall accept the interest rate as given, taking it also to be an *alternative rate of return:* a rate of interest determined by the firm's best alternative uses for its funds. What these alternative uses are, and how they work to set an interest rate for the firm, we shall explore in Chapter 10.

*SELECTION FORESTS*

Where the firm seeks its best combination of timber growing stock, the stock is a variable input, land is a fixed input, and the growth of timber

120

ready for harvest (which is, at the same time, stock) is the output. Perhaps the easiest case is that of a forest being managed under a selection system of cutting with a view to annual yields; and so let us begin with it.

Take as an example an average acre of selection forest of the loblolly and shortleaf pine type on good site in southeastern Arkansas.[1] The forest is owned by Firm C, a lumber company, which wants to manage it for saw-timber production so as to maximize net revenue per year. What is the firm's best combination of growing stock with land? That is, how much stock shall it carry per acre? Assume that the cost of capital—the interest rate, based on Firm C's alternative rate of return—is 4 per cent per year. And assume that the value per thousand board feet of the saw timber produced extends between $40 and $55, depending upon quality.

The production functions and derivation of the best combination are given in Table 12. Column 1 sets up the series of alternatives to be tested: variable inputs of growing stock ranging from 5,000 to 11,000 board feet per acre by 1,000-foot steps. The statement of the basic production function is completed in column 2, which gives the total timber output in board feet per acre—that is, the prospective current annual growth on each level of stock—estimated on the basis of growth studies. In order to simplify the problem, we shall suppose that this is the highest-value output procurable from each level of growing stock. We recognize that quantity of stock is only one of several management questions that arise together in the selection forest. Other questions include the best species and qualities and the maximum size of trees to grow, the best diameter distribution to maintain, and the best utilization of the harvest. Here we assume that these other questions have been settled, so that we can concentrate on the stocking problem. Compare the approach taken in Chapter 7, as summarized in point 3 on page 90. Both these cases, and indeed virtually all management questions one can think of, entail two or more sets of margins simultaneously and are well attacked by partial analysis.

We might have added to Table 12 a first column comparable to the one used in Table 5 (p. 60), showing the fixed input: 1 acre of land of good site quality. However, we know now that the fixed input is irrelevant to the best combination, and so neither the amount nor the value of it is considered in Table 12.

## CONVERSION SURPLUS

Column 3 is the value of the total growing stock of column 1. If you divide these dollar figures by the quantities of stock, you will observe

---

[1] This forest is described by Duerr, William A., and W. E. Bond: "Optimum Stocking of a Selection Forest," *Journal of Forestry*, January, 1952, pp. 12–16. The data are adapted from this source.

that value per thousand board feet rises with stocking. This is mainly because natural pruning is more efficient in the denser stands and produces a larger proportion of clear wood, which has a relatively high unit value.

Column-3 values are in terms of what has been called *conversion sur-*

Table 12. *Best stocking of a loblolly and shortleaf pine selection forest on good site in southeastern Arkansas—calculation based on annual per-acre data for Firm C*

| Total variable input (growing stock) | Total output (growth) | Total value of growing stock | Total variable cost (interest) | Total gross revenue (current annual growth) | | Total revenue net of variable cost |
|---|---|---|---|---|---|---|
| (1) | (2) | (3) | (4) | (5) | (6) | (7) |
| *Board feet* | *Board feet* | *Dollars* | *Dollars* | *Dollars* | *Per cent* | *Dollars* |
| 5,000 | 468 | 210.00 | 8.40 | 21.46 | 10.2 | 13.06 |
| 6,000 | 534 | 257.30 | 10.29 | 25.00 | 9.7 | 14.71 |
| 7,000 | 592 | 306.50 | 12.26 | 28.20 | 9.2 | 15.94 |
| 8,000 | 638 | 357.40 | 14.30 | 31.06 | 8.7 | 16.76 |
| 9,000 | 676 | 410.10 | 16.40 | 33.54 | 8.2 | 17.14 |
| 10,000 | 704 | 464.70 | 18.59 | 35.62 | 7.7 | 17.03 |
| 11,000 | 722 | 521.00 | 20.84 | 37.26 | 7.1 | 16.42 |

| Total variable input (growing stock) | In absolute terms | | Marginal value of growing stock | In percentage terms | |
|---|---|---|---|---|---|
| | Marginal unit cost (interest) | Marginal unit revenue (growth) | | Marginal unit cost (interest rate) | Marginal unit revenue (growth rate) |
| (1) | (8) | (9) | (10) | (11) | (12) |
| *Board feet* | *Dollars* | *Dollars* | *Dollars* | *Per cent* | *Per cent* |
| 5,000 | | | | | |
| | 1.89 | 3.54 | 47.30 | 4.0 | 7.5 |
| 6,000 | | | | | |
| | 1.97 | 3.20 | 49.20 | 4.0 | 6.5 |
| 7,000 | | | | | |
| | 2.04 | 2.86 | 50.90 | 4.0 | 5.6 |
| 8,000 | | | | | |
| | 2.10 | 2.48 | 52.70 | 4.0 | 4.7 |
| 9,000 | | | | | |
| | 2.19 | 2.08 | 54.60 | 4.0 | 3.8 |
| 10,000 | | | | | |
| | 2.25 | 1.64 | 56.30 | 4.0 | 2.9 |
| 11,000 | | | | | |

SOURCE: Adapted from Duerr, William A., and W. E. Bond: "Optimum Stocking of a Selection Forest," *Journal of Forestry*, January, 1952, pp. 12–16.

*plus:* the difference between the sales value of that amount and quality of the firm's end product that can be made from the trees and all the *variable* costs of converting the trees into this product.[2] In this case the end product is lumber, and the variable costs deducted from its sales value are those of timber marking, logging, transportation, milling, and selling: primarily the costs of labor and supplies in these operations. Conversion surplus is the firm's fund for paying its fixed costs of conversion and a net revenue therefrom—the fund that we identified on page 64 as being of key importance, since it is what the firm wishes to maximize. It is, in effect, the cumulative total difference between all marginal revenues and marginal costs of conversion. By ascribing it to the trees in question and using it to derive the best combination in the woods, we are putting the woods decisions in their correct relation to the firm's goal: to earn the highest net revenue per unit of time from *all* its enterprises (p. 54). The goal can be reached when the firm's timber-growing enterprise is so organized that the excess of timber *conversion* surplus harvested, over and above the variable costs of timber *growing*, is as great as possible. This is the organization—the best combination—that we are now trying to derive. Remember that finding the best combination does not assure the firm a net revenue; it may simply minimize losses. What happens depends on how high the fixed costs are.

Conversion surplus in our example is based on the sales value of lumber because lumber is Firm C's end product. If the firm sold its timber in the form of logs, their sales value would be the base, from which the variable costs of making and selling logs would be deducted to get conversion surplus. If the firm sold stumpage, its sales value minus the variable costs of such jobs as timber marking and selling would be the conversion surplus.

## BEST STOCKING

Returning to Table 12, we come next to the production function in value terms: input in column 4, output in columns 5 and 6. Column 4 expresses the variable cost, per acre per year, of holding each of the alternative levels of growing stock. The cost is 4 per cent (the alternative rate of return) on the value in column 3. (To simplify, we assume for now that interest is the only source of variable cost.) Column 5 is the value of the growth shown in column 2. [Notice that the value per thousand feet of growth is higher than of the growing stock on which the growth occurs. Why?] In column 6, growth is expressed as a percentage of growing stock. This is the stand's current annual value growth per

[2] Guttenberg, Sam, and William A. Duerr: *A Guide to Profitable Tree Utilization,* Southern Forest Experiment Station Occasional Paper 114, New Orleans, 1949.

cent. It declines as stock increases—on account of diminishing returns, as we shall see in a moment.

Column 7 in Table 12 is the total annual revenue per acre, net of the costs that are relevant to the best combination: the variable costs of timber growing and conversion. Computed as the difference between columns 5 and 4, it shows that the best input of growing stock is about 9,000 board feet per acre at the beginning of the cutting cycle, immediately after the annual cut. The stock relates to the *beginning* of the cycle because its *prospective* revenue from growth and its *prospective* cost have been used in the analysis. Best ending stock is 9,676 board feet, the sum from columns 1 and 2.

To summarize our conclusion so far: The best stocking of a selection forest is that which maximizes the excess of current value growth over the cost of holding the growing stock, value being figured in terms of conversion surplus.

Let us turn now from the totals used to this point in Table 12 and take the marginal approach as an alternative route to the best combination. The marginal approach has advantages of simplicity, particularly in pinpointing the best stock by means of graphic methods. Columns 8 and 9 in Table 12 are marginal cost and revenue in dollar terms; columns 11 and 12, in percentage of value.

In column 8, marginal unit cost (per unit, 1,000 board feet, of input) is computed by successive subtractions in column 4. Marginal cost goes up with stocking because the unit value of the stock does so. Column 9, marginal revenue, also per unit of input, is taken in the same way from column 5. Within the range of stocking that we are studying, more stock means more growth (cols. 2, 5), though the rate of increase in growth is declining. The decline signifies diminishing (marginal) returns, which arise from the existence of the fixed input, the site, that becomes more crowded or thinly spread the greater the stand density. The best combination occurs where marginal revenue falls to meet cost, or at about 9,000 board feet per acre.

In columns 11 and 12 of Table 12, the same conclusion is reached by use of percentages. Column 11 is the marginal per cent cost per unit of input. It is the extra cost of holding each extra amount of stock, expressed in per cent of the additional value of the stock. By the terms of our problem, it is 4 per cent, or 4 cents per dollar. Column 12, the marginal per cent revenue per unit of input, is the extra revenue, in cents, derived in the form of additional value growth from each extra dollar's worth of growing stock. It answers this question: If Firm C raises its growing stock 1,000 board feet, and accordingly raises the value of the stock (see col. 10, derived by successive subtractions in col. 3), how many extra cents' worth of growth will it get (col. 9) per dollar's worth of the extra growing stock? Clearly, if the firm's alternative rate of return is 4 per cent, the firm would not rationally add to its investment in growing stock beyond the point where the forest paid as little as 4 cents on the additional dollar of investment. Beyond this point, which again is found to be about 9,000 board feet per acre, the firm had better take advantage of its alternative uses for funds.

To summarize this line of reasoning: The best stocking of a selection forest is that which equates the marginal value growth per cent of timber with the firm's alternative rate of return. This is so because (1) at any lower stocking, extra investments in stock will pay more than alternatives, and so the firm had better build up its stock, whereas (2) at any higher stocking, the alternatives pay more than some of the stock is paying, and the firm had better liquidate this surplus stock.

Note that the marginal growth is something different from the current growth, or the mean growth, or indeed any other calculation of growth that you will find in your book on forest mensuration. The marginal growth is the additional current growth resulting from an addition to growing stock—or the loss in current growth resulting from a subtraction. Common sense might suggest that Firm C, with its 4 per cent alternative rate of return, would be foolish not to increase its growing stock beyond 9,000 board feet per acre, since the stand is still growing at an 8 per cent rate (Table 12, col. 6). Even at 11,000 board feet per acre, the forest investment is returning more than 7 per cent. Isn't this a desirable return for the firm? The answer is that although the growing stock *as a whole* is yielding more than 4 per cent at this high stocking, the last additions to the growing stock are not (col. 12), and it is with respect to these additions, and not to the stock as a whole, that the decision whether to leave or to cut is to be made for this selection forest.

## DETERMINANTS OF BEST STOCKING

Now we need to investigate whether the *best* level of stocking of the selection forest is influenced by the *current* level. If, in our example, the firm already is carrying 9,000 board feet per acre, it will surely decide to hold there and harvest just the growth. But what if the firm has only 5,000 board feet per acre at present? Should it plan to increase the growing stock and if so, how far and how fast? To build up the stock to 9,000 feet will take about seven years (4,000 board feet divided by the average annual growth) even if no cutting is done meantime, and interest charges on the stock will be accumulating all the while. Can the firm afford such a program?

The best schedule for raising the growing stock may well vary with the firm's commitments to its processing enterprise, its alternative sources of raw material, its supplies of cash, the silvicultural condition of the forest, and the like. But in any case its rational goal is 9,000 board feet of growing stock per acre. For, as column 12 of Table 12 shows, every accumulation of growth will itself be capable of putting on growth at a rate greater than 4 per cent and thus of giving the firm a higher return than if the growth had been cut and turned into money. True, the revenue in the form of accumulated growth will not be paid in cash, but neither will the corresponding cost of interest. These will be *implicit revenues and costs,* occurring by virtue of the firm's alternatives and implied in its internal adjustments, but not entering into its transactions with other firms. They are to be distinguished from *explicit revenues and costs,* which do arise in transactions.

At the other end of the stocking scale, if the firm is carrying more than 9,000 board feet per acre, a reduction in growing stock as rapid as conditions warrant will be to its benefit. If, for example, the firm is now carrying 11,000 board feet per acre and earning $37.26 annually (Table 12, col. 5), it can better itself by reducing its stock to 9,000 feet with an earning of $33.54 and investing at its alternative 4 per cent the $110.90 thus released ($521 minus $410.10, col. 3), for an additional revenue of $4.44, or altogether $37.98 per year. By similar figuring you will find that it would not pay Firm C to stop the reduction short of 9,000 feet, nor to carry it beyond 9,000 feet.

Now we can summarize the factors that affect the best stocking of a selection forest. In general, there are two: First, there is the alternative rate of return (marginal cost), with its various determinants that we shall talk about in Chapter 10. Second, there is the marginal value growth per cent of the stand (marginal revenue). The latter, in turn, is set by (a) the relation of physical growth to growing stock (basic production function), (b) the unit value of the growth in relation to stocking, and (c) any timber-growing costs (other than interest) that are variable with stocking. You should compare this list of factors with the list on page 67.

[How will best stocking be affected if the firm's alternative rate of return rises, other things remaining the same? How will it be affected if conversion surplus goes up 10 per cent for all timber? If site quality is improved by fertilization? If new markets are opened up for wood of lower quality, resulting in a relatively higher price for such wood?]

## GRAPHIC SOLUTION

When the idea of best stocking was first advanced in the form here described, it was presented as a problem for graphic solution by forest managers. The outlines of this solution are given in Figure 9. The upper curve in graph *a* is the basic production function in value terms, taken from Table 12. Slope is measured at intervals along the curve in order to find the marginal value growth per cent. The per cents are plotted in graph *b*, over the corresponding volumes per acre. They form a descending line. Where the line intersects the 4 per cent abscissa representing

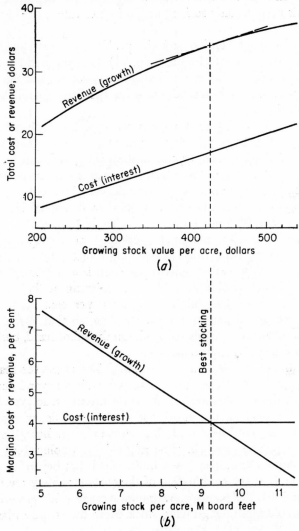

Fig. 9. Best stocking of a selection forest. (*Source: Table 12, p. 122.*)

the alternative rate of return, best stocking is determined: 9,200 board feet per acre at the beginning of the cutting cycle. The extra 200 board feet above the Table 12 approximation comes from the graph's recognition of small intervals. The same 9,200 feet is found in graph *a* at the point where the total revenue curve has the same slope (4 per cent) as the total variable cost curve and the two are therefore furthest apart.

Figure 9b shows, by the down-sloping curve, the rate of interest paid by the forest savings bank upon successive deposits into the account. And by the horizontal curve it shows the rate available to the depositor somewhere other than at this bank. And it says that the depositor will keep adding to his account only so long as the former rate is the higher of the two.

[It will help you to understand the problem of best stocking if you will compare Figure 9 with Figure 6 (p. 74). Can you find the analogous curves in Figure 6? It will be useful also to try working out the best combination of growing stock on a per-unit-of-output basis, paralleling Figure 6d and Table 5 (p. 60).]

Our study of Firm C's program has assumed implicitly that the firm follows a 1-year cutting cycle, logging each acre every year. Where the cutting cycle is longer than a year, best stocking is found by the same general method. The value growth in this case is the prospective usable growth on each quantity of stock for the period of the cutting cycle, and the periodic growth percentage is converted to an annual basis with the help of a compound-interest table such as Table 10 (p. 111). Thus if the period is 5 years and the marginal (periodic) value growth per cent is $27\frac{1}{2}$, this percentage is regarded as equaling $100(1 + i)^5 - 100$, so that $i$, the marginal (annual) value growth per cent, is about 5.0 (i.e., in decimals, 0.050). In terms of Figure 9b, a lengthening of the cutting cycle ordinarily causes the marginal value growth per cent curve to fall in consequence of diminishing returns over time, so that best stocking at the start of the cutting cycle is reduced. On the other hand, best stocking at the end of the cycle is increased.

What are the economic limits of stocking? Let us use the reasoning of Chapter 6 (pp. 77–80). The upper limit, which lies beyond our data for Firm C, is at the culmination of the total current value growth (Table 12, col. 5), the peak of the upper curve in Figure 9a, where marginal value growth per cent hits zero. If best stocking were here, the return to the variable input, timber, would be nil, and the whole return would go to the fixed input, land. The lower limit, which lies beyond our data on the other side, is at the culmination of the current value growth *per cent* (Table 12, col. 6), the point of maximum average value growth per unit value of variable input, or growing stock. Here the return to land would be nil.

## EVEN-AGED FORESTS

Now let us turn from the best combination of timber growing stock in selection management to that in even-aged timber management. Let us take the problem of Firm D, which owns a large tract of young-growth

Douglas-fir on good site in western Oregon. The firm's alternative rate of return is 3 per cent. Its management objective is to earn the maximum net revenue per year from annual sales of saw-timber stumpage. What is its best combination of growing stock with land?

We shall begin by studying the question of Firm D's best rotation: the best age at which to make the harvest cut of timber and establish a new forest generation.

The normal yield tables[3] give us data on the volumes of Douglas-fir saw timber in "fully stocked" stands on good site (index 170) at 10-year age intervals (Table 13, cols. 1, 2). On the traditional assumption that the yields represent points on the forest's developmental trend, we can figure the current growth for each decade (col. 3), and express this growth as an annual percentage of growing stock (col. 4), using the method described on page 128. We can also compute the mean annual growth (col. 5) by dividing each yield by stand age.

*BEST ROTATION*

Of the fourteen alternative lengths of rotation represented in Table 13, which one is best for Firm D? Let us assume that the normal yields are representative of what can be produced on the firm's property, and that there is no delay between the cutting that ends a rotation and the establishment of reproduction that begins the next. Then we are faced with one answer sometimes given to our question: that the best rotation is 100 years, where mean annual growth culminates and where the firm's return in the form of timber produced per acre per year therefore averages the highest. This answer we must of course reject, on the grounds that it neglects (1) the unit value of the timber, which may vary with rotation length and (2) the variable costs of timber growing, which we know to be significantly large. We would shun, on at least the same grounds, any answer taken from column 3 or 4.

Let us discover what may happen to the shape of things in columns 3 to 5 of Table 13 when we introduce consideration (1), the timber value. In column 6 is Firm D's estimate of the values represented in the yields of column 2. These values, which rise from $5 per thousand board feet at 30 years to $50 at 160 years with increasing tree size and quality and timber stocking, are in terms of conversion surplus. They are prospective stumpage sales values less the small prospective variable costs of sale preparation.

Columns 7 to 9 in Table 13, which are figured in value terms, are the

[3] McArdle, Richard E., Walter H. Meyer, and Donald Bruce: *The Yield of Douglas Fir in the Pacific Northwest,* U.S. Department of Agriculture Technical Bulletin 201, rev., 1949, table 4, p. 27.

counterpart of columns 3 to 5. The effect of introducing value is to increase the current growth per cent and to postpone the culmination of the absolute growth. Mean annual growth now peaks at 140 years. But the mean growth is still suspect as an indicator of the best rotation, be-

Table 13. Normal yields, growth, and soil rent per acre of good-site Douglas-fir in western Oregon—property of Firm D

| Stand age | Saw-timber yield | Current 10-year growth | | Mean annual growth | Value of the yield | Current 10-year value growth | | Mean annual value growth |
|---|---|---|---|---|---|---|---|---|
| (1) | (2) | (3) | (4) | (5) | (6) | (7) | (8) | (9) |
| Years | M bd ft | M bd ft | Ann. per cent | Bd ft | Dollars | Dollars | Ann. per cent | Dollars |
| 30 | 2.6 | | | 87 | 13 | | | 0.40 |
| | | 9.3 | 16.4 | | | 69 | 20.2 | |
| 40 | 11.9 | | | 298 | 82 | | | 2.00 |
| | | *15.5 | 8.7 | | | 178 | 12.2 | |
| 50 | 27.4 | | | 548 | 260 | | | 5.20 |
| | | 15.4 | 4.6 | | | 292 | 7.8 | |
| 60 | 42.8 | | * | 713 | 552 | | | 9.20 |
| | | 14.4 | 2.9 | | | 460 | 6.2 | |
| 70 | 57.2 | | | 817 | 1,012 | | | 14.50 |
| | | 12.8 | 2.0 | | | 689 | 5.3 | |
| 80 | 70.0 | | | 875 | 1,701 | | | 21.30 |
| | | 11.0 | 1.5 | | | 794 | 3.9 | |
| 90 | 81.0 | | | 900 | 2,495 | | * | 27.70 |
| | | 9.4 | 1.1 | | | *796 | 2.8 | |
| 100 | 90.4 | | | *904 | 3,291 | | | 32.90 |
| | | 7.9 | 0.8 | | | 720 | 2.0 | |
| 110 | 98.3 | | | 894 | 4,011 | | | 36.50 |
| | | 6.8 | 0.7 | | | 624 | 1.5 | |
| 120 | 105.1 | | | 876 | 4,635 | | | 38.60 |
| | | 5.9 | 0.5 | | | 527 | 1.1 | |
| 130 | 111.0 | | | 854 | 5,162 | | | 39.70 |
| | | 5.3 | 0.5 | | | 455 | 0.8 | |
| 140 | 116.3 | | | 831 | 5,617 | | | *40.10 |
| | | 4.9 | 0.4 | | | 370 | 0.6 | |
| 150 | 121.2 | | | 808 | 5,987 | | | 39.90 |
| | | 4.5 | 0.4 | | | 298 | 0.5 | |
| 160 | 125.7 | | | 786 | 6,285 | | | 39.30 |

* Asterisks mark points of culmination or points where growth percentage equals the alternative rate of return (3 per cent).

SOURCE: Columns 1 and 2 are taken from McArdle, Richard E., Walter H. Meyer, and Donald Bruce: The Yield of Douglas Fir in the Pacific Northwest, U.S. Department of Agriculture Technical Bulletin 201, rev., 1949, table 4, p. 27.

cause it represents gross revenue rather than net. The variable costs omitted are of three sorts: (a) the cost of waiting out the rotation, (b) the cost of postponing the yields from subsequent rotations (reduced by the gain from postponing management outlays, if any, in subsequent rotations), and (c) the cost of regulating the timber growing stock in such fashion that yields can be harvested annually.

Our job now is to understand the meaning of each of these three kinds of cost, the effect of each kind, and the procedure for allowing for the cost so as to find the best rotation and growing stock. To this end, let us put a magnifying glass on that part of Table 13 centering around 90 years. As we shall discover, this is the part where the best rotation falls. Table 14 shows value yields at 1-year intervals from 87 through 95 years, and various calculations of the best rotation for Firm D.

*TYPE-a COST AND FINANCIAL MATURITY*

The cost of waiting out the rotation is analyzed in columns 1 to 3 of Table 14. Column 2 is the value of the per-acre yield expected by Firm D at each of the stand ages of column 1. Let us assume that this is the entire harvestable value of the stand and that it would all be harvested at rotation age: no intermediate cuttings would be made. Values increase with age, but are not directly comparable, because they occur at different times. To harvest the higher values, the firm must wait longer. Each successive value represents a 1-year longer wait. To make the values comparable, let us therefore discount them all back to the same point in time, using Firm D's 3 per cent interest rate. Then we can see which value is the highest. Or, what amounts to the same thing, let us figure the annual rates of value increase for the series—the current annual value growth per cent of the stand (col. 3)—and observe at what age the per cent falls to 3 or below. This age (93 years) is the rotation age of highest value yield, allowing for the cost of waiting out the rotation. Here, for simplicity's sake, we are assuming that there are no sources of variable cost other than interest.

The 93-year point as determined from column 3 in Table 14 is the point of unadjusted *financial maturity* of the stand, the point where the current value growth rate equals the alternative rate of return. It is the financial maturity unadjusted for costs of types b and c (above).

The financial-maturity concept with necessary adjustments incorporated on the basis of good sense is usable in the woods for setting rotation age of a stand. It is a useful tool also in another, and more common, timber-management job, that of deciding when to mark an individual tree for cutting—under any system of management. In the selection forest, the growth that should be harvested finds its equivalent in the volume of financially mature trees. Since a tree, unlike a stand, must usually be harvested entirely or not at all, its current growth is its marginal growth, and its financial maturity based on current growth is thus seen to be set like any best combination, by the equating of marginal revenue (value growth rate) and cost (alternative rate of return). The graphic model of financial maturity takes the shape of Figure 9b, but with diameter or some other measure of tree development substituted for stock on the horizontal axis.

Table 14. Inputs and outputs per acre and best rotation for good-site Douglas-fir owned by Firm D

| Rotation (t) | Value of the yield | Current annual value growth | Capitalized value | Value of regulated growing stock | | Regulated value growth per acre | Marginal value of growing stock | Marginal value growth | |
|---|---|---|---|---|---|---|---|---|---|
| | | | | Per t acres | Per acre | | | | |
| (1) | (2) | (3) | (4) | (5) | (6) | (7) | (8) | (9) | (10) |
| Years | Dollars | Per cent | Dollars | Dollars | Dollars | Dollars | Dollars | Dollars | Per cent |
| 87 | 2,241 | | 185.40 | 41,700 | 479.30 | 25.76 | | | |
| | | 3.8 | | | | | 20.00 | 0.67 | 3.4 |
| 88 | 2,326 | | 186.40 | 43,940 | 499.30 | 26.43 | | | |
| | | 3.7 | | | | | 20.60 | .66 | 3.2 |
| 89 | 2,411 | | 187.10 | 46,270 | 519.90 | 27.09 | | | |
| | | 3.5 | | | | | 21.00 | .63 | *3.0 |
| 90 | 2,495 | | 187.60 | 48,680 | 540.90 | 27.72 | | | |
| | | 3.3 | | | | | 21.50 | .61 | 2.8 |
| 91 | 2,578 | | *187.80 | 51,180 | 562.40 | 28.33 | | | |
| | | 3.2 | | | | | 21.80 | .58 | 2.7 |
| 92 | 2,660 | | 187.70 | 53,750 | 584.20 | 28.91 | | | |
| | | 3.1 | | | | | 22.40 | .57 | 2.5 |
| 93 | 2,742 | | 187.50 | 56,410 | 606.60 | 29.48 | | | |
| | | *3.0 | | | | | 22.80 | .55 | 2.4 |
| 94 | 2,823 | | 187.00 | 59,160 | 629.40 | 30.03 | | | |
| | | 2.8 | | | | | 23.00 | .52 | 2.3 |
| 95 | 2,902 | | 186.30 | 61,980 | 652.40 | 30.55 | | | |

* Asterisks mark the culmination of soil rent and the points where growth percentage equals the alternative rate of return (3 per cent).

source: Yield data based upon Table 13.

The advantage of the financial-maturity tool is its simplicity in application to the central problem of managing the growing stock: the problem of determining the cut. The ultimate in simplicity is reached where the tree's conversion surplus per unit of volume is not strongly related to its size. Here a measurement or estimate of the tree's volume growth per cent, together with a knowledge of the firm's alternative rate of return, provides most of the basis for judging whether the tree is financially mature.[4]

The foregoing ideas about individual trees will prove useful in our study of the economics of even-aged silviculture. First, however, let us return to our rotation-length problem for the stand as a whole, continuing our analysis of the three types of variable cost.

## TYPE-b COST AND SOIL RENT

The unadjusted financial-maturity approach to the best rotation takes into account type-a cost, the immediate delays in reaching higher yields, but not the cost of type b, the implied delays in subsequent rotations. A 90-year rotation, if adopted permanently, means not only postponing the first harvest cut, say, 10 years beyond that for an 80-year rotation, but it also means postponing the second harvest cut 20 years, the third 30, and so on. That is to say, there is an implicit cost involved in keeping land tied up in the current rotation and not freeing it to get the next ones under way.

Type-b cost in the selection forest takes the form of delaying regeneration on the patch of ground occupied by a maturing *tree*.

To allow for this cost of delaying subsequent yields under even-aged management, we need to figure the relative value, not merely of alternative net revenues in the current rotation discounted to one point in time, but of alternative net revenues in all prospective rotations discounted to one point. That is, in terms of Table 14, we need to compare the present worth of $2,241 at 87-year intervals on into the indefinite future, the worth of $2,326 at 88-year intervals, $2,411 at 89-year intervals, and so forth: We need to capitalize the periodic series and compare their capitalized values.

The periodic series can be capitalized by means of formula 3a in Table 9 (p. 110), with t standing for rotation length in years. The result, at 3 per cent, is given in column 4 of Table 14. Let us assume that there are no costs deductible from the value yields of column 2, other than those we have already taken out in computing conversion surplus. Then the figures in column 4 represent the current net capitalized worth of bare land (i.e., the site, or "soil") to be managed for timber under each length of rotation: They are the per-acre values at the start of a rotation. The most valuable alternative, sometimes called the maximum-*soil-rent* rotation, is 91 years.

[4] For more on financial maturity, see Duerr, William A., John Fedkiw, and Sam Guttenberg: *Financial Maturity: A Guide to Profitable Timber Growing*, U.S. Department of Agriculture Technical Bulletin 1146, 1956.

Thus, allowing for type-*b* cost *in this case* has shortened the indicated rotation by 2 years.

## TYPE-c COST AND BEST COMBINATION

We turn now to the cost of regulating the growing stock. The soil-rent approach gives us the best rotation under a management program that will produce a revenue once every *t* years. However, Firm D's object—which is commonly the object in even-aged management—is to get an annual revenue. For this purpose the firm will need to regulate its forest in such a way that there will be stands of rotation age coming on every year. Conceptually, the scheme will be to devote $1/t$ of the forest acreage to each year's age class, and to harvest and regenerate annually this same fraction of the acreage. In this scheme, the costs of lengthening the rotation will include more than simply waiting for current and subsequent yields. The costs will also include shrinking down the proportion of the property on which the annual yield can be realized. With an 80-year rotation, about an eightieth of the property can be given a harvest cut each year, but with a 90-year rotation, only about a ninetieth. The longer rotation in this case involves a sacrifice of $\frac{1}{80}$ minus $\frac{1}{90}$ of the annual yield per average acre.

Type-*c* cost in the selection forest takes the form of extra crowding and the maturing of additional stems when the attempt is made to grow larger timber.

The additional cost of type *c* in Firm D's even-aged forest is allowed for in columns 5 to 10 of Table 14.

Column 5 is the total value of growing stock that would be carried at the beginning of the year per *t* acres in the perfectly regulated forest. It is the cumulative total value of the per-acre yield at 0, 1, 2, . . . years up to $(t-1)$ years. Thus \$43,940 is \$41,700 plus \$2,240 (from col. 2, rounded). The totals are placed on a per-acre basis in column 6, by dividing by *t*. The value in column 6 is the average value per acre of all the growing stock on a forest perfectly regulated for annual returns on the rotation in question. Then in column 7, the average annual per-acre growth and yield on this forest is recorded, again in terms of value. The figure is equal to the yield in column 2, which is the average per *t* acres, divided by *t*. Thus column 7 is what we have elsewhere termed *mean annual growth.*

Columns 6 and 7 show the production function, in value terms, for the regulated even-aged forest. They are the counterpart of columns 3 and 5 in Table 12, for the regulated selection forest. In both cases, the acre of land is the fixed input. Although silviculturally the two pairs of columns represent quite different things, economically they represent the same thing—namely, timber capital so distributed among tree sizes and ages that a regular annual output can be obtained. The problem of finding the best combination in Table 14 can be viewed just as it was in Table 12: a problem of finding the best stocking. All the same steps in calculation can be taken as in the earlier table. [You will find it helpful to work through these steps for yourself.] In Table 14 the procedure is abbreviated: Marginal value of growing stock is found in column 8 by taking successive differences in column 6. Marginal value growth is similarly computed from column 7, recorded in column 9, and expressed as a percentage in column 10. Best stocking is found where the marginal value growth per cent of Firm D's forest equals its alternative rate of return. And the best rotation, found at the same point, is 89 years. Recognizing type-c cost has *in this case* shortened the rotation by another 2 years.

The graphic model for the best rotation is in general like that for the best stocking and financial maturity. It resembles Figure 9*b*, but with age on the horizontal axis.

Let us understand the significance of the various growth percentages in Tables 12 and 14. Column 12 in Table 12 is the counterpart of column 10 in Table 14. Column 3 in Table 14, however, has no counterpart in Table 12. Its counterpart in the selection forest would be the current annual (i.e., marginal) value growth per cent of individual trees, a basis for tracing their progress toward financial maturity and for selecting the annual crop. The grand average value growth per cent of column 6, Table 12, has not been computed in Table 14. You can calculate it in the latter table by dividing column 7 by column 6. [Why are the figures you get not a usable guide to the best rotation?]

What are the economic limits of the rotation in the regulated even-aged forest? They are the same as for stocking of a selection forest (p. 128). The upper limit, for the firm with a zero alternative rate of return, is where mean annual growth (in value) culminates, where marginal value growth per cent reaches zero. The lower limit, for the firm whose rate of return is almost so high that it could not afford to grow timber at all, is where the grand average value growth per cent culminates.

## DETERMINANTS OF BEST COMBINATION

We can also summarize the determinants of the best stocking and rotation in even-aged management. In so doing, we shall also be summarizing again the influences on best stocking of a selection forest and financial maturity of a tree, since all these instances of the best combination of timber capital follow the same principle.

There are two immediate determinants of the best combination of timber capital: the capital's marginal value growth per cent and the firm's alternative rate of return. In other words, the best combination depends not only upon the forest, but also upon the owner, a matter that we shall dig into in Chapter 10 when we study the alternative rate of return.

Marginal value growth per cent, in turn, is affected by three factors: *First* is the basic production function—the rate of usable timber growth in relation to tree size, age, or stocking—as determined by site quality, forest type, stand composition, and the like. Actually it is the prospective rate of growth that counts, the rate anticipated by whoever makes the decisions. In fact, it is true of all these determinants that they are influential only in the form of forecasts. *Second* is differences in the unit value of timber (growth) with size, age, or stocking. These differences can arise from such things as a price premium on quality (this we considered in Tables 12 to 14) or the expectation of a change in price level (which we shall study in more detail later). *Third* is any timber-growing cost (other than the alternative rate of return, already accounted for) that is variable with the size, age, or stocking of timber. In even-aged management, costs such as of regeneration that occur a given number of times per rotation are a case in point. In any form of management, taxes that vary with stand value may be another case. We shall take up tax influences pointedly in Chapters 26 and 27. Prospective changes in the level of any cost rate make for a variable cost in our sense.

It is equally important to note some of the things that do *not* influence the best combination of growing stock. Among them are the condition of the timber in the past, the value of land, taxes if levied at a flat and constant rate per acre, and any other fixed cost.

Again, the level of prices for timber products does *not* affect the best combination of growing stock. This is especially interesting in view of the fact that the question of how much growing stock to carry and when to cut is central to timber management. Price *differences* between small and large timber can be influential, and so can prospective *changes* in the general level of timber price. For example, a price premium on larger timber or the prospect of a price rise for all timber will favor postponing the cut. It will do this by raising the marginal value growth rate, just as a physical improvement in the site would do.

But whether prices currently are high or low may be irrelevant. When the value of timber has risen, we might expect the growing of it to be more attractive, other things remaining the same. In the case of timber price, however, other things cannot remain the same. In terms of our model in Figure 9b, when the value of the product (growth) rises, the value of the machine (growing stock) tends to rise equally, leaving the marginal value growth per cent unchanged.

Here we get our first clear glimpse of the fact that the governing element in forest management is apt to be not the price of the product but the price of money: the interest rate.

As we worked through Tables 13 and 14, we made some harsh assumptions to simplify the problem. You now have at hand the tools for removing these assumptions. You should go back and pick them up along the way, to see what effect each of them has had upon our conclusions. [How will the best rotation be affected (and why) if planting or other cost is required to get regeneration after the harvest cut? What if there is a delay in getting regeneration? What if there are constant yearly property taxes of $2 per acre? Or if the taxes are expected to go up 5 cents annually? What if the cost of foresters' salaries amounts to $30,000 per year? What if the firm expects all timber values to show a steady rising trend in the future, amounting to ½ per cent per year? What will be the effect if a noncommercial thinning is made once each rotation? How should Firm D decide whether to make such a thinning?

[You should also think through, for even-aged silviculture, the same question that we discussed for the selection forest on pages 125–126: the influence of current conditions upon the best combination. If Firm D were at present on a 100-year rotation, would a 90-year rotation still be best? Would it if the firm were now on an 80-year rotation? What would be the best rotation for the firm to plan on if the property had no forest growth today? Or suppose the property were all in old growth at present —what then?]


## INTERMEDIATE CUTTINGS

Finally, it behooves us to think a bit about the economics of intermediate commercial cuttings: thinnings and such. Like the rest of the stocking question, this is a complex matter to which we shall give only summary attention, stressing the economic principle.

What are the firm's alternatives? If it is able economically to enter the stand during the rotation to control the growing stock, and notably if there are commercial values that can be taken in a partial cut, then the firm has an additional best combination to consider. This is the best stocking of the stand at each age short of the rotation: the stocking that will equate marginal value growth per cent *at this age* with the alternative rate of return. In concept, the firm's objectives are (1) to cut when there is an operable (loggable and salable) volume of financially mature timber, (2) to maintain the maximum value of financially immature stock, (3) to shorten the cutting cycle to the point where the marginal revenues from operable growth equal the marginal costs of operation, and (4) to end the rotation when the growing space can no longer be commanded by financially immature trees of desired species.[5]

Under such a program, as compared with the simple scheme outlined for Firm D, growing stocks are reduced and operable growth immensely increased, so that the efficiency of the forest capital is much improved. The rotation tends to be stretched out. But the question of rotation length falls into its proper place as one of a group of interconnected questions concerning the management of the timber capital. The economic problems —stocking at a given age, stand composition as to tree species and other significant tree classes, cutting cycle, and rotation—are seen to involve, in even-aged silviculture as in many-aged, a cluster of mutually related marginal revenues and costs for simultaneous equating.[6]

At the same time, it becomes evident that the normal-yield table has little value for the economic analysis required. What is wanted for the purpose is data on the alternatives of management, data on the production functions: current growth, over various lengths of cutting cycle, for the significant tree classes, by stand age and stocking. In this view, the emphasis in management planning is shifted from the long future to the short term.

## MANAGEMENT OF EXHAUSTIBLE STOCK

So far, our study of the best combination has concerned stock that was literally growing by putting on new wood. Let us conclude by having a look at stock that is not growing and is therefore exhaustible. Now ordinarily we should not consider such an analysis applicable to forests, which, we stress, are renewable. Yet there are at least two areas of application to our field: The first is the case of virgin timber, which clearly is exhaustible, and to a degree also the case of soils and some other assets of the forest watershed. The second is the case of *any* of the forest resources, including growing timber and wildlife, which an owner *believes* is exhaustible. For remember that a person's rational behavior is based upon what he thinks, and not necessarily upon what is the fact. If I have a sack of diamonds and believe it is a sack of garbage, I will surely toss it in the bucket and set it out for the garbage collector.

Back in 1914, Dr. L. C. Gray of the University of Saskatchewan published an article in which he analyzed the economics of the rate of use

---

[5] Duerr, Fedkiw, and Guttenberg: Work cited, pp. 28–29.

[6] For a discussion of thinning with emphasis on economic principles and problems, see Worthington, Norman P., and George R. Staebler: *Commercial Thinning of Douglas-fir in the Pacific Northwest*, in process, at time of writing, as a U.S. Department of Agriculture Production Research Report.

of exhaustible resources.[7] Dr. Gray took as his illustration a coal mine. Let us sketch his line of reasoning, using his own figures with a few minor changes, and you can draw the analogies to forestry.

Suppose that you own a coal mine having the input and output characteristics shown in columns 1 and 2 of Table 15. If you extract more than 200 tons of coal per year, you will encounter diminishing returns, as indicated by the rising marginal unit cost of column 4. If this mine were inexhaustible, you would do best to extract 800 tons of coal annually, at which level of output marginal unit cost and revenue would be approximately equal (cols. 4 and 5) and total net revenue the greatest.

Table 15. *Revenues and costs of mining alternative amounts of coal per year*

| Total input (cost) | Total output of coal (revenue) | Average cost per 100 tons | Marginal cost per 100 tons | Marginal revenue per 100 tons | Total net revenue | Average net revenue per 100 tons | Marginal net revenue per 100 tons |
|---|---|---|---|---|---|---|---|
| (1) | (2) | (3) | (4) | (5) | (6) | (7) | (8) |
| *Dollars* | *Tons or dollars* | *Dollars* | *Dollars* | *Dollars* | *Dollars* | *Dollars* | *Dollars* |
| 80 | 100 | 80 | 80 | 100 | 20 | 20 | 20 |
| 110 | 200 | 55 | 30 | 100 | 90 | 45 | 70 |
| 152 | 300 | 51 | 42 | 100 | 148 | 49 | 58 |
| 200 | 400 | 50 | 48 | 100 | 200 | 50 | 52 |
| 260 | 500 | 52 | 60 | 100 | 240 | 48 | 40 |
| 330 | 600 | 55 | 70 | 100 | 270 | 45 | 30 |
| 413 | 700 | 59 | 83 | 100 | 287 | 41 | 17 |
| 512 | 800 | 64 | 99 | 100 | 288 | 36 | 1 |
| 612 | 900 | 68 | 100 | 100 | 288 | 32 | 0 |
| 730 | 1,000 | 73 | 118 | 100 | 270 | 27 | −18 |

However, since the mine is not inexhaustible but contains only a fixed and limited amount of coal, you will be obliged to take into account an extra marginal cost due to depletion and also to weigh certain margins over time.

Suppose, first, that the value of the mined coal is $1 per ton and that your guiding rate of interest is zero—i.e., a dollar in the future and a dollar now are of equal value to you. Then it is evident from column 6 that if, for instance, the mine contains 4,000 tons of coal, you will want to take 10 years, not 5, to extract it, since by so doing you can get a total

[7] Gray, Lewis Cecil: "Rent under the Assumption of Exhaustibility," *Quarterly Journal of Economics*, May, 1914, pp. 466–489.

net revenue of $2,000 ($200 annually for 10 years) rather than $1,440 ($288 annually for 5 years). Or in general, whatever the exhaustible amount of coal, you will want to mine it at the rate of 400 tons per year so as to minimize the average cost per ton (col. 3) and maximize the net revenue per ton (col. 7) and hence the total net revenue from the entire mine.

This line of reasoning is a bit clouded by the consideration of fixed costs, but let us not be concerned with this difficulty, since it does not affect our main conclusions. These have to do with the influence of (1) the rate of interest and (2) the price of the product, upon the rate of extraction.

### INTEREST AND PRICE INFLUENCES

Consider the influence of the interest rate. Suppose that your guiding rate is not zero, but 10 per cent. Then prospective future net returns are

Table 16. *Present values of the net revenues per 100 tons from extracting 400 tons of coal and each extra 100 tons per year, in successive years, with interest at 10 per cent and coal at $1 per ton*

| Annual output of coal | Present value of extra net revenue if coal is mined— | | | | | | | | |
|---|---|---|---|---|---|---|---|---|---|
| | This year | Next year | 3d year | 4th year | 5th year | 6th year | 7th year | 8th year | 9th year |
| Tons | Dollars | Dollars | Dollars | Dollars | Dollars | Dollars | Dollars | Dollars | Dollars |
| 400 | 50.00 | 45.45 | 41.32 | 37.57 | 34.15 | 31.04 | 28.22 | 25.65 | 23.32 |
| 500 | 40.00 | 36.36 | 33.06 | 30.05 | 27.32 | 24.83 | 22.57 | 20.52 | 18.66 |
| 600 | 30.00 | 27.27 | 24.79 | 22.54 | 20.49 | 18.62 | 16.93 | 15.39 | 13.99 |
| 700 | 17.00 | 15.45 | 14.05 | 12.77 | 11.61 | 10.55 | 9.59 | 8.72 | 7.93 |
| 800 | 1.00 | 0.91 | 0.83 | 0.75 | 0.68 | 0.62 | 0.56 | 0.51 | 0.47 |
| 900 | 0.00 | 0.00 | 0.00 | 0.00 | 0.00 | 0.00 | 0.00 | 0.00 | 0.00 |

no longer worth their face value but are discounted at 10 per cent (divided by $1.10^n$). And an advantage is to be gained by mining sooner rather than later any amounts of coal above 400 tons per year which, despite diminishing returns, will add more to the earlier net revenue than they could to the later revenue when it has been discounted. This proposition is illustrated in Table 16. In the second column, the average net revenue per 100 tons from extracting 400 tons is taken from column 7 of Table 15, and the net revenue from each additional 100 tons from column 8. These revenues are the prospective contributions to your net income from mining done this year. But from next year's operations the contributions will be these amounts discounted for 1 year; from the third year's operations, the same amounts discounted 2 years; and so on, as laid out in Table 16. Now your best program for mining 4,000 tons will be to time each 100 tons extracted so that it will add the most to the present value of the net revenue. This program is shown by the broken line in Table 16, which has been drawn in such a way that it encloses those 4,000 tons to which the highest present values are attached. The program calls for extracting 600 tons this year and next, 500 tons in each of the following 4 years, and 400 tons the seventh and eighth years. Under this program, the net revenue is maximized, having in no case a present value less than $24.83 per 100 tons. And no higher value has been omitted from the program. Note that raising the interest rate from 0 to 10 per cent has shortened the period of exploitation from 10 to 8 years.

*Table 17. Present values of the net revenues per 100 tons from extracting 400 tons of coal and each extra 100 tons per year, in successive years, with interest at 10 per cent and coal at $2 per ton*

| Annual output of coal | Present value of extra net revenue if coal is mined— | | | | | | |
|---|---|---|---|---|---|---|---|
| | This year | Next year | 3d year | 4th year | 5th year | 6th year | 7th year |
| *Tons* | *Dollars* | *Dollars* | *Dollars* | *Dollars* | *Dollars* | *Dollars* | *Dollars* |
| 400 | 150.00 | 136.36 | 123.96 | 111.95 | 102.46 | 93.11 | 84.65 |
| 500 | 140.00 | 127.27 | 115.70 | 104.43 | 95.63 | 86.90 | 79.00 |
| 600 | 130.00 | 118.18 | 107.43 | 96.92 | 88.80 | 80.69 | 73.36 |
| 700 | 117.00 | 106.36 | 96.69 | 87.15 | 79.92 | 72.62 | 66.02 |
| 800 | 101.00 | 91.82 | 83.47 | 75.13 | 68.99 | 62.69 | 56.99 |
| 900 | 100.00 | 90.91 | 82.64 | 74.38 | 68.31 | 62.07 | 56.43 |
| 1000 | 82.00 | 74.55 | 67.77 | 61.61 | 56.01 | 50.90 | 46.28 |

Consider, secondly, the influence of product price. If your coal is worth $2 per ton instead of $1, both the average and the marginal revenues per 100 tons will be raised $100, as shown in the second column of Table 17. This across-the-board addition to this year's net revenues constitutes an inducement for you to exploit your mine more heavily in the near future and exhaust it more quickly, as illustrated by the broken line in Table 17. Your best program for extracting 4,000 tons is now a 6-year program: the higher price has shortened the period of exploitation by 2 years.

The influence, then, of the interest rate upon management of exhaustible capital is the same as upon the management of renewable capital: The higher the rate, the more the stock will be drawn down, or the faster it will be depleted. With the level of product price, however, it is a different matter. Upon the exhaustible capital, higher price level has the same effect as does higher interest rate, whereas upon the renewable capital it has no effect.

## SUMMARY

In the management of growing stock, the best combination is found, as with other agents of production, where marginal unit revenue and cost are equal.

The best stocking of a selection forest is that which equates the marginal value growth per cent of the timber (marginal revenue) with the firm's alternative rate of return (marginal cost). Value here is in terms of the timber's conversion surplus. And marginal value growth per cent is that in prospect for the next cutting cycle, expressed on a per-year basis.

The best rotation in an even-aged forest regulated for annual yield is, again, that which equates the marginal value growth per cent of the forest with the firm's interest rate. Through the marginal approach, allowance is made for three types of variable cost: (a) that of waiting out the rotation, (b) that of postponing subsequent yields, and (c) that of regulating the growing stock.

For the individual tree, financial maturity occurs when the tree's marginal value growth per cent, adjusted for costs of types b and c, above, equals the firm's alternative rate of return. The financial-maturity idea provides a useful tool for guiding intermediate and harvest cuttings of even-aged timber stands: for managing the growing stock with emphasis on the short term. It applies equally to selection management.

Marginal value growth is influenced by the relation of (1) physical growth of timber, (2) timber value, and (3) timber-growing cost to the size, age, or stocking of timber. It is unrelated to the fixed costs of forest management or to the level of product price.

Where the forest capital is exhaustible (or believed to be so), the rate at which it will be used by the firm will depend both upon the alternative rate of return and upon product price.

Chapter 10

INTEREST

RATE AND

CONSERVATION

IN CHAPTERS 8 and 9 we made free use of interest rates but did little to explain them. At one point we referred to rate setting in the money markets. Frequently we alluded to the rate as an alternative rate of return. In this chapter let us seek out the derivation of interest rates, or alternative rates of return, for the individual firm. And then let us go on to draw some useful connections between the firm's rates and its behavior in the realm of forest conservation.

The hardest part of working with interest rates is deriving them. Anyone can solve a formula if he has what he needs to put into it. The late Prof. George Wehrwein, the land economist, was amused to remark about foresters with long rotations and durable values to weigh that their problem was easy: They needed merely to find the right rate of interest. Compare Archimedes' claim for his lever and fulcrum: "Give me but one firm spot on which to stand, and I will move the earth."

Economists have, for example, had great and never quite conclusive arguments about the rate at which the long-run benefits of public works should be discounted in order to discover if the construction costs would be justified. The job of establishing an interest rate in such difficult cases may sometimes be done by using a rate which will justify the works that are considered justifiable to begin with. This approach is not quite so circular, or its users so irresponsible, as may seem. But in general what we want is an external and objective basis for rate setting.

*ALTERNATIVE RATE OF RETURN*

To work out a scheme for setting interest rates, let us make use of the question "What are the alternatives?" From the standpoint of the pro-

143

ducing firm in forestry, interest is a cost of the use of capital. How great a cost is it? Surely this depends on what other uses the firm has for its capital: what opportunities it must forego when it puts capital into the use in question. If the capital is borrowed, the firm could at least repay the loan and thus save the explicit interest thereon. But the chances are that the firm has alternative uses for its own or borrowed capital that would pay a higher rate than this, in which case the highest of these implicit interest rates, adjusted in ways that we shall discuss, becomes the alternative rate of return. The alternative rate is thus an *opportunity cost,* set by the best of the firm's alternative opportunities—just as the cost of Hawkins's time, $40 per day, was an opportunity cost based upon his best alternatives at that season of the year.

In business circles, the alternative rate of return is sometimes called the *guiding rate of interest,* suggesting its role in guiding the firm's investments. We saw in Chapter 9 how the rate guides the investment in growing stock. However termed, the rate is an interest rate, and as such it is usable in any of the compound-interest calculations—for example, those that we studied in Chapter 8.

The alternative rate of return is peculiar to each firm, and it varies also from case to case and from time to time in accordance with the firm's appraisal of its circumstances and its prospects. And, as noted, we have a *rule for setting the alternative rate:* Where there is more than one alternative open to a firm, the one that governs is the alternative on which the rate of return is highest, after allowance for any differences in risk or other circumstances affecting the value of the return.

A firm's alternative rate may be determined either by its opportunities for investing funds or by its opportunities for spending them. Where the rate is based on investment opportunities, it may be set by the firm's prospective rate of return on new forest land, on tree planting or cultural measures, on the operation of a sawmill, or on other alternatives within the firm. The rate may even be set by the return on the very operation for which the firm seeks an interest percentage.[1] Or it may be set by external alternatives, such as the bonds of some borrower, in or out of forestry. Where the rate is based on spending opportunities, the spending in question may be the firm's spending for meeting business expenses or for personal consumption. Where business expenses are the basis, the rate may be as low as the annual percentage cost of borrowing. Where personal spending is the basis, the rate is conceived as being set by the annual percentage at which the individual subjectively discounts future values in his decisions about current versus future consumption. This rate is sometimes called the *rate of time preference.*

[1] Boulding, Kenneth E.: *Economic Analysis,* Harper & Brothers, New York, 1948, pp. 813–824.

In some cases, a firm's alternative rate of return can be determined simply and directly. The rate may be recognized as such by the firm and explicitly stated by it. Or the rate may be indicated by debt charges or clearly identifiable investment or spending alternatives.

## INFERRING THE ALTERNATIVE RATE

In other cases, however, the alternative rate of return must be determined by inference from the actions of the firm. To illustrate how this may be done, let us consider the problem faced by a forest manager employed by Firm E, a timber-processing company which owns a tract of selection forest.[2] The forest manager wishes to base his timber-marking policy on the principle of financial maturity. In the absence of an explicit alternative rate of return, he must determine an applicable rate indirectly.

Firm E's forest property, like that of some other sawmill and pulpmill operators, is held in part as a defensive, risk-reducing investment to protect the competitive position of the company in its product market and to protect the capacity of the processing plant over the long run. The benefits of the forest investment are spread over the business as a whole and extend into the distant future. This is why the firm's guiding rate of return for timber management is so difficult to find directly.

But Firm E's harvesting operations on its forest property are controlled by a carefully planned cutting budget. This budget is determined in large part by the expected timber growth, the raw-material requirements of the processing plant, and the amount and price of raw material available from other sources, including the open market. The budget is influenced also by other considerations that we shall study in Chapters 13 and 14, dealing with supply. The point now is that the budget in this case reflects the firm's judgment of the whole situation and prospect into which its timber management is dovetailed. It represents Firm E's estimate of its best alternative for satisfying both present and future raw-material requirements of its plant.

Now the cutting budget implies the alternative rate of return applicable to timber management. One way of identifying this rate is to use the forest-stand table. Since for the forest as a whole the rate of tree-value increase declines with increasing tree size, the alternative rate will approximate the average rate of increase of the largest diameter class that would be left if the cut were taken entirely from the largest trees in the stand. (Needless to say, cutting would not actually be done in this way.) Columns 1 and 2 in Table 18 show the cumulative volume per acre,

---

[2] Duerr, William A., John Fedkiw, and Sam Guttenberg: *Financial Maturity: A Guide to Profitable Timber Growing*, U.S. Department of Agriculture Technical Bulletin 1146, 1956, pp. 5–6.

by diameter class, in Firm E's forest property. The company has decided on a cutting budget of 150 board feet per acre annually. The budget requires reaching into the 18-inch class of trees for the harvest. This 18-inch class, as column 3 states, is increasing in value at the rate of 4.1 per cent annually. The indicated alternative rate of return is therefore about 4 per cent.

If the alternative rate were given to the forest manager directly, he would wish to go through the same route in reverse order to determine his allowable cut. He would identify the diameter class where the average rate of value increase was equal to the specified alternative rate of return and estimate the cut from the volume of trees larger than this class.

*Table 18. Saw-timber volume per acre and rate of tree-value increase by tree-diameter class in Firm E's forest property—as a basis for inferring the alternative rate of return from the cutting budget*

| Tree diameter breast high | Cumulative total volume per acre | Rate of tree-value increase |
|:---:|:---:|:---:|
| (1) | (2) | (3) |
| *Inches* | *Board feet* | *Per cent* |
| 22+ | 42 | 3.4 |
| 20 | 109 | 3.7 |
| 18 | 437 | 4.1 |
| 16 | 836 | 4.6 |
| 14 | 1,529 | 5.2 |
| 12 | 2,467 | 6.0 |
| 10 | 3,365 | 7.1 |

An alternative rate of return may be inferred from the forest-management practice or the timber-cutting budget of any forest owner. The owner who keeps his entire forest property cut back, perhaps leaving only the smallest or poorest trees, apparently has a high alternative rate of return. If his observed actions are rational, any management planning done by him or for him must, in effect at least, be guided by this same high rate of interest if it is to result in securing his best combination— maximizing his net revenues over the (relatively short) time spans that are pertinent to his case. On the other hand, for the rational forest owner who maintains a stand of heavily stocked and slow-growing trees, a low alternative rate of return may be inferred.

Inferring the alternative rate of return from a firm's behavior in the manner just described is another form of the apparently circular approach to interest-rate setting that we first illustrated on page 143.

Whether the approach is in fact circular depends on how the observed behavior was itself determined. In the vast majority of cases we are justified in assuming that the behavior was determined by the firm as a part of its more or less carefully reasoned efforts to gain its goals. In this case the inference about the alternative rate is not circular. It simply represents our independent contribution to the analysis or guidance of the firm's decisions. We have introduced an index—the rate of interest, represented by the alternative rate of return—which reduces to one measurement all the effects of the firm's aims and policies and manifold guides to action, upon its use of resources over time. Since all its agents of production are resources and since their timing is the principal event in the firm's life, we have in the alternative rate of return a cardinal index of management. Under it may be subsumed an extraordinarily wide array of influences upon production policy. And it follows that the alternative rate may serve as either a test for or a guide to *consistency* from decision to decision on the part of the firm.

Although many firms make conscious use of the alternative rate of return—under one name or another—many do not. For example, few small woodland owners would at first know what you were talking about if you should question them on the subject. Most of them think of their actions in quite different terms. Needless to say, this doesn't deny the existence and validity of the alternative rate of return—any more than the existence of prose was denied by the fact that Molière's bourgeois gentleman spoke it for more than forty years without knowing.

## ALLOWING FOR RISK AND OTHER COSTS

Every firm has its risks. Risk, here, refers to noninsurable losses of income which may occur in the future and which the producer must bear by himself (forest insurance for reducing the firm's risks is taken up in Chapter 28). In general, losses may arise from physical damage, from increases in cost rates, or from decreases in product price. In forest management, for example, risks include noninsurable losses attributable to wildfires, trespass, and the natural and biological agencies such as wind, insects, and disease; losses associated with forest operations such as uncertainty of obtaining adequate labor and equipment when needed; and losses arising from changing market conditions. In managed, operating forests of large acreage with organized protection, stable labor forces, and skilled sales organizations these risks are low. The big forest-owning corporations that have grown by expanding and combining so as to include a wide range of manufacturing and marketing activities have been most successful in minimizing the risks of economic life. On the other hand, most owners of small forest businesses will often have to bear higher risks because of their generally lesser ability to take measures against threatened losses from natural agencies or economic forces.

Where the alternative use of funds involves a different degree of risk from that in the investment being analyzed, the alternative rate of return must be adjusted to terms of equal risk. Thus, if a forest owner's best alternative rate of return is 3 per cent obtainable from short-term government savings bonds that he judges to carry negligible risk, the alternative rate of return applicable to his forest is more than 3 per cent if his forest investment will be subject to noninsurable losses of income. On the other hand, if the risk in the alternative investment is greater than that in the forest business, the alternative rate of return should be reduced accordingly.

Wherever the alternative rate of return is to be used in making short-term decisions and, especially, if the rate is low, allowance may be made for risk by adding or subtracting an appropriate percentage as an insurance premium.[3] However, with a higher rate or longer period, caution must be exercised in such addition or subtraction, because of the way the factor $(1 + i)^n$ behaves. Refer back to Table 10 (p. 111). Suppose that you add a one-fourth allowance for risk to a 4 per cent rate, making it 5 per cent. In doing this, you change $(1 + i)^n$ at, for example, fifty years from 7.107 to 11.47. The risk allowance on the interest accumulated at this time—namely 10.47 minus 6.107, or 4.36—is no longer one-fourth. It is 4.36 divided by 6.107, or more than seven-tenths. Or, taking an example of an initially high rate and looking at the matter a little differently, suppose that you add a 5 per cent risk allowance to a 10 per cent rate, making it 15 per cent. The values of $(1 + i)^n - 1$ in the first year add nicely: $0.10 + 0.05 = 0.15$. But even as soon as the fifth year they are behaving very badly: $0.611 + 0.276 \neq 1.011$. In effect, as of the fifth year, you have added 7 per cent, not 5 per cent, in upping the rate percentage from 5 to 10. That is to say, 1.011 minus 0.611 equals 0.4, which equals $1.07^5 - 1$. Knowing of these booby traps, one can avoid them by the use of judgment, making one's risk allowance relevant to the rate and time involved in the problem at hand. Or one can allow for risk by scaling prospective returns down or costs up, rather than by changing their rate of discount.[4]

[3] Guttenberg, Sam: "The Rate of Interest in Forest Management," *Journal of Forestry*, January, 1950, pp. 4–6. Mr. Guttenberg cites Irving Fisher's method of adjusting the "pure" (risk-free) rate of interest for risk: Interest rate including risk equals pure rate divided by the difference, 1 minus the chance of loss. Thus, taking the pure rate of interest as 2½ per cent, if the chance of loss is one-sixth, the rate including risk is 3 per cent. Mr. Guttenberg's article is a general discussion of the interest-rate problem in forestry, with helpful references to the literature.

[4] See, for example, Vaux, Henry J.: *Economics of the Young-growth Sugar Pine Resource*, California Agricultural Experiment Station Bulletin 738, Berkeley, 1954, p. 26.

Where the alternative rate is based upon the net return from alternative investments, two special considerations are involved: transfer costs and income taxes. First, allowance must be made for the costs of transferring funds into the alternative investments. The existence of such costs means that the alternative return is gross and must be reduced to a net basis before the rate can be figured and used as a guiding rate. Second, and for the same reason, the rate must be estimated after income taxes upon the return from the alternative investments. The income tax in question is the marginal tax—i.e., the extra tax that would be payable in consequence of income from the alternative investments.

## EXAMPLES OF ALTERNATIVE RATE

Alternative rates of return tend to be relatively high for forest-owning individuals and families. Their rate is apt to be set by the premium they place upon current consumption, in which case it is equivalent to the rate of time preference. This rate varies with income level. For low-income firms, the requirements for current income and family working capital may be so high as to result in an alternative rate of 20 or 30 per cent or more. Rates appropriate to such firms vary considerably from year to year. They are especially high when there are medical expenses or other urgent obligations to be met. You have seen woodlands that were cut by the owner at such a time of stress. Because of the long period of production in forestry, the forest policy of the firm may well be set by the highest alternative rate that obtains during a cutting cycle or rotation. Here we have a fact of life—a perplexing problem, if you will, in forest conservation—to which we shall return repeatedly for further analysis and in search of solutions.

Rates are apt to be moderately high, also, for other forest firms, particularly small firms, that have no manufacturing operations and thus are not concerned with assuring themselves a supply of raw material. Here, alternative investment and spending opportunities outside the forest business usually have a great influence. Such opportunities are unlikely to represent less than a 5 or 6 per cent yield, and, considering the risks of managing a small forest property, the alternative rate may be substantially higher.

Among private forest owners, the lowest alternative rates of return are generally those of the big owners, especially the large corporations which manufacture timber into a variety of forest products. For such firms, the risks of managing forest land are relatively low, sources of funds relatively ample, and length of view relatively great. But perhaps most influential is the fact that the forest property is a source of raw material and thus a means for staying in business. Even if there are currently plentiful sources of supply on the outside, the firm's own supply is its guarantee of security for the long term and of bargaining power in the timber market. Hence in order to insure high net revenues from the business as a whole, the firm may rationally accept a lower rate of return on the forest part of its business than on the processing part: It may carry its forest investments comparatively far, increasing its prospective timber output and hence its security, and taking its rewards in the mill. It may require at most that forest investments return the bare cost of borrowing. Under these circumstances it is not unusual to find the alternative rate of return for forestry ranging from 3 to 5 per cent.

For public forestry firms, it is common practice to estimate an alternative rate of return from the fiscal policy of the government. For example, the current carrying charge of about 2½ or 3 per cent annually on the national debt is often used to determine the alternative rate in the management of federally owned forests. If the risks of forest management are considered, a somewhat higher guiding rate is arrived at for these timber-growing enterprises. Or if the risks are written off against other benefits of federal forests, the rate of 2½ or 3 per cent is used as it stands. Similarly, alternative rates for forests operated by other units of government are commonly estimated from the carrying charges on their indebtedness. However, the true alternative rate of return for public firms, based upon the most productive social investment and spending opportunities, may well be higher than this. One study has suggested a rate of between 5 and 6 per cent for the federal government.[5] We still have a great deal to learn about the derivation of rates for public firms. In some cases, units of government may most suitably derive guiding rates from their cutting-budget policy, as described for the case of Firm E. This policy may, of course, be influenced by recreation, game, and water requirements, in which case the derived alternative rate will reflect the whole scheme of the firm's forest management.

## FOREST CONSERVATION

From what we have said about the alternative rate of return for different firms and from what we know from Chapter 9 concerning the bearing of this rate upon forest practice, it is evident that we have at hand an interesting and useful index of human behavior respecting forests. Let us turn, therefore, to the economic problem of forest conservation and see just how we may use the idea of the alternative rate to understand more about the problem.[6]

[5] Krutilla, John V., and Otto Eckstein: *Multiple Purpose River Development, Studies in Applied Economic Analysis,* Johns Hopkins Press, Baltimore, 1958, pp. 78–127.

[6] For brief supplementary reading in the economics of conservation, see Ciriacy-Wantrup, S. V.: *Dollars and Sense in Conservation,* California Agricultural Experiment Station Circular 402, Berkeley, 1951.

According to Dean Samuel T. Dana, someone at the University of Michigan who searched the writings on conservation found fifty to sixty different definitions of the term, varying widely. That was some time ago. Probably there are several more definitions by now. Any term that has grown up as a catchall is bound to be overdefined, since everyone who uses it has to be ready to defend himself. Defining begets defining.

The idea here to be attached to the word *conservation* is as follows: saving. This definition has the apparent virtue of brevity, though it will take some explaining. A discussion of conservation in the sense of saving is pat at this point, for conservation in this sense stands at the shoulder of the whole subject of forest capital, and is a function of the rate of interest.

It has been estimated that forest properties in the United States represented, just after World War II, a $15 billion investment. In terms of today's dollars, the investment is much more than that. And the lion's share of it is the value of standing timber. Evidently people have made the decisions to hold quite a large chunk of capital in the form of timber. Why?

You have probably heard the expression "Timber in the woods is like money in the bank." This little slogan is sometimes used by extension people to persuade farmers to go easy on their woodlands. There is a lot of sense in it. We have seen how trees and forest stands grow in value, accumulating a return from year to year that is like interest on a bank account. Individuals and other firms put their savings into their business or into banks or corporate securities or public bonds or other productive outlets in order to help secure their own future or that of their families. They make the decision to forgo some current consumption in favor of future enjoyment. They often do this in return for the promise of a reward: growth in the value of their capital. May it not be reasonable to suppose that firms are swayed by similar motives in their decision to hold forest growing stock?

The theme of these pages is that the management of a forest growing stock is an act of saving and, synonymously, an act of conservation. And incidentally, though saving in general may be unrelated to investment— a fact that underlies our gravest economic problems—saving in our present sense is at the same time investment. It carries investment with it. Let us talk about why different owners manage their forest lands so differently in respect to timber-cutting practices and stocking.

## STATUS OF FOREST MANAGEMENT

In 1945 the United States Forest Service made a nationwide survey of the management status of forest lands. The Service made another survey in 1954, but its general findings are not recognizably different from the earlier results and are harder to interpret. So we will talk about the 1945 study. As a part of that job, a very large sample of timber holdings where cutting had recently been done was rated according to the character of the cutting. Five classes of cutting practice were recognized, which may be combined into three. These three classes, with their names changed to fit our terminology, were briefly as follows:

*Conservative*—cutting that leaves desirable species in condition for immediate vigorous growth, or which will help build up or maintain high quality and quantity yields.

Intermediate—cutting that will maintain any reasonable stock of growing timber in marketable species.

*Exploitive*—cutting that depletes the growing stock in quality and quantity, in extreme cases leaving the land without timber values or means for natural reproduction.

The survey showed clear and dramatic differences among the major classes of forest owners (Fig. 10). Cutting on the public forests, that made up a fourth of the acreage of recently cut holdings, was the most conservative. Among private owners, those with the largest holdings, mainly manufacturers of wood products, were doing the most conservative cutting. The most exploitive cutting was found on the smallest private holdings, mainly the property of farmers and other individuals— more than four million of them, averaging some 60 acres apiece, and accounting in the aggregate for well over half of all the recently cut forest lands in the country. On the little holdings, 4 per cent of the cutting was in the conservative class; 71 per cent was exploitive. Thus the little owners were—and are today—the crux of the problem of exploitive timber management in the United States.

### INTENSIVE AND EXTENSIVE MANAGEMENT

Incidentally, all of us apparently have a tendency to refer to the heavy stocking that accompanies conservative management as "good" stocking, and to its opposite as "poor." We are inclined to think of the exploitive forestry of Figure 10 as "poor forestry." The other extreme we are tempted to term "good forestry." Why so? Good for whom, in what respect? Good for us, in that we recognize pleasurably an old friend from out of the silviculture textbook, or from European forestry lore? Hardly. Good for the forest itself? But the forest *itself* is neutral on the issue: It takes man to bring in the notion of good. Good, then, for society, in the sense that society's interest is served when forest owners stock up heavily for the future? Possibly, but then is it "poor" forestry to carry a low growing stock? Such forestry may in many cases be "good," both for the owner and for society, in the highly meaningful sense that it represents an allocation of resources that will maximize human satisfaction.

Terms like "good" and "poor" and "best" and "worst" are terms that have meaning only in reference to some standard. There are different kinds of standards, but every one of them has to be created, or at least interpreted, by human beings before it can come into existence as a guide

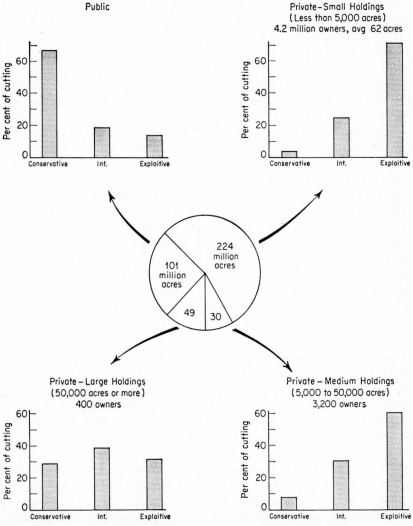

Fig. 10. Character of timber cutting by four major classes of forest-land owners in the United States, 1945. (*Source: U.S. Department of Agriculture, Forest Service: The Management Status of Forest Lands in the United States, Report 3 from a Reappraisal of the Forest Situation, Washington, 1946.*)

to human action, and the interpretation must be directly or indirectly in relation to human judgment of events or human responses to events. Thus we can apply the term "best" within the framework of a religious standard, or an ethical standard, or an aesthetic or an economic standard (as we do when we say "best combination"). And if the standard is stated or clearly implied, the word has meaning and can be understood in terms of the bearing of an event upon a human being.

You should hesitate before either making or accepting value judgments such as are implied in terms like "good" and "bad." Satisfy yourself, first, that the standard of value is clear, and second, that it is apparent from what human viewpoint the standard is being applied. Ask yourself: *What is the standard of value? From whose viewpoint is it applied?*

Often what one intends to mean by "good" and "poor" in reference to the handling of resources is what we shall prefer to call "intensive" and "extensive" management.

*Intensive management* is that which combines a large quantity of variable inputs with the fixed input. In *extensive management,* on the other hand, the ratio of variable to fixed inputs is low. These are relative terms. If Hawkins uses but five men on his crew, his operation may be called *labor-extensive.* If he uses ten men, the operation, by comparison, is *labor-intensive.* Timber growing stock is a form of capital, and management which involves heavy growing stocks per acre we can call *capital-intensive;* light growing stocks, *capital-extensive*—what in this chapter we are terming conservative and exploitive, respectively. Where the production function is steep or the variable input relatively cheap or product value relatively high, the input tends to be used intensively. In opposite cases, it tends to be used extensively. This follows from our principle of economizing productive agents (p. 89).

The forest owner who cuts timber heavily and frequently gives little attention to cultural measures or fire control, and generally makes but slight investments in his property is practicing extensive management. But he is not necessarily practicing "poor" management in any meaningful sense. His management may actually be "best" in the sense that he is maximizing his net return. We shall observe repeatedly that what is intensive is not necessarily good and what is extensive is not necessarily poor.

If you will adopt the concepts intensive management and extensive management, then you will find yourself forced into the sound position of taking the term *management* in an altogether neutral context. We sometimes hear it said that Mr. Soandso is managing his forest property, but that Mr. Whatshisname is not. On the contrary, any decision respecting resources, including the decision to do absolutely nothing with them, is a management decision, and management is then being practiced.

How intensive the management is, is a question. And how good, another and a different question.

## PROBLEM OF SMALL HOLDINGS

The Forest Service findings regarding exploitive, or capital-extensive, practices on small forest holdings verify common observation. In the eastern United States, which includes more than nine-tenths of the acreage of such holdings, the typical cross-country hike or drive by auto takes one past many a dog-eared and depleted woodland, where timber growing stock is sparse, cull trees and those of the less desired species abound, soil conditions are deteriorating, and watershed and other values of the woods are low. This situation is not peculiar to the United States, but is found in many nations of the world. Even in some of the Western European countries where forestry generally is highly intensive, management of farm woods and other small private holdings is on the exploitive side.

A great many different explanations have been offered for the character of small woodland management. Some persons believe it stems mainly from owners' ignorance of forest potentialities and cultural practices. Others stress the many diseconomies associated with small-scale forest ownership; instability of tenure; limitations upon the regulating of growing stock; high costs of managerial supervision, notably on the absentee-owned tracts; lack of opportunity to integrate the woods enterprise with processing or to mechanize forest operations (modern mechanization apparently requires a minimum of several thousand acres, even under the most favorable timber-stand conditions); handicaps to diversified utilization and to marketing; and difficulties of financing.[7] Other students of the problem call attention to the fact that most small woodland owners are not primarily or even appreciably interested in their timber: They hold forest land because they acquired it as part of a farm, or because they inherited the land, or because they value the woods for recreational use or for sentimental or other reasons.[8]

Surely the foregoing explanations are part of the story. Here, however,

---

[7] For a discussion of such problems, see Resources for the Future, Inc., Committee: *Forest Credit in the United States: A Survey of Needs and Facilities*, Resources for the Future, Inc., Washington, 1958, pp. 13–29—and the references there cited.

[8] See, for example, Christensen, Wallace W.: "A Methodology for Investigating Forest Owners' Management Objectives," doctoral dissertation, State University of New York, College of Forestry, Syracuse, 1957. Also Barraclough, Solon L.: "Forest Land Ownership in New England with Special Reference to Forest Holdings of Less than Five Thousand Acres," doctoral dissertation, Harvard University, Cambridge, Mass., 1949.

we shall emphasize that exploitive management results from owners' high alternative rates of return and low incomes—that it is a feature of a meager propensity to save. Or to look at the problem constructively, conservative management is promoted by low rates of interest, high income, and a strong propensity to save.

Let us first take up the influence of the alternative rate of return and after that go to income and the propensity to save.

### EFFECT OF ALTERNATIVE RATE

We have seen how the circumstances of risk, cost of borrowing, production policy, and time preference that may sway a firm's alternative rate of return can determine a low guiding rate of interest for public forest firms, a high rate for individuals, and intermediate rates for forest businesses, with the big, integrated corporations toward the lower end of the scale. This line of reasoning gives us a range of interest rates well correlated with the levels of growing stock represented in Figure 10. To establish the connection between condition of growing stock and the alternative rate of return, we can use our models from Chapter 9, remembering that capital costs are predominant in forestry (pp. 104–105).

If an owner's rate is low, as it generally is if he has achieved much economic security, he can afford to build up his savings in the forest bank —to forgo present consumption in favor of the future—to practice forest conservation—because to do so is his best alternative. But if an owner's alternative rate of return is high, as it generally is among owners of small woodlands, the alternative use for his resources therein represented is apt to attract his assets away from the forest savings bank, which at best pays limited returns (p. 104) and necessarily diminishing returns. He cannot afford to practice conservation. His practice is exploitive because of his high alternative rate of return. The foregoing ideas we may caption as a *first principle of conservation.*

We are illustrating now the "witness" role of forestry economics. It could lead us directly, however, into active policy issues: If high interest rates thwart conservation, what can be done to lower them and thus narrow the gap between the individual and social interest in small forest holdings? How might such action compare in effectiveness with programs of education, technical assistance, and the like? What would they cost, and would they be worth it? But we must postpone these questions.

### INCOME AND PROPENSITY TO SAVE

If it is true that the practice of forest saving, or forest conservation, runs counter to the alternative rate of return, we should find that the saving of individuals and families runs with their income, since the alternative rate of such firms is greatly controlled by, and inversely related to, their income. The direct relationship between personal income and the propensity to save is, indeed, a basic economic principle, which for our purposes may be termed a *second principle of conservation.* Let us look into this principle for the added light it may shed on forest conservation among the individual and family owners of little forest tracts, who control the biggest share of our forest lands and whose actions are the crux of the problem of exploitive forest management.

Some persons are heavy savers, either absolutely or in proportion to their income or both, while others are light savers. Some cannot and will

*Table 19. Saving by American urban families, 1944*

| Family income | Family saving |
| --- | --- |
| Dollars | Dollars |
| 1,000 | −180 |
| 2,000 | 0 |
| 3,000 | 300 |
| 4,000 | 600 |
| 5,000 | 1,000 |
| 6,000 | 1,500 |
| 7,000 | 2,000 |

not do any saving voluntarily. They spend the contents of the pay envelope at once, spurn saving in the form of insurance, run up time-payment obligations, and generally provide little for the morrow. [Would you expect such persons, if they owned forest land, to practice conservative or exploitive management?] Now theirs is not necessarily an unhappy way of life, but it is certainly in contrast to those others who put away at least a little of everything they receive and are passionately provident in their attitudes. [What sort of forest management would you expect these others to practice?]

One large factor in people's behavior with respect to saving is their income. Consider Table 19, based upon a 1944 survey of American urban families by the U.S. Department of Labor. The figures are taken from Prof. Paul Samuelson,[9] who has smoothed them and rounded them off. Note that families with higher incomes tend to save more money. Note also those with higher incomes tend to save a larger *proportion* of their income. Finally, note that the *marginal* propensity to save rises with income. As we go from the $2,000 to the $3,000 income level in the table, we find that the extra $1,000 income is accompanied by an extra $300 of saving. But at higher income levels the marginal saving is $400, and then

[9] Samuelson, Paul A.: *Economics: An Introductory Analysis,* McGraw-Hill Book Company, Inc., New York, 1955, p. 170.

$500, per $1,000 of extra income. [How conservative a job of forest management would you expect from the forest owner whose income is $2,000 per year?][10]

Now clearly, although Table 19 is suggestive, it does not complete the connection between owners' incomes and the condition of their woodlands. On the one hand, saving is a *flow*, an annual contribution to the total that is laid by. On the other hand, the condition of woodlands is represented by a *stock*, such as the value of growing stock per acre; it *is* the total that is laid by, and *not* the flow of additions to this total. To connect income with forest conservation, we must bring in the interest rate, as we did in the models for best stocking. A line of reasoning that would tie income, saving, and the alternative rate of return might run as follows:

What are the alternatives? The higher one's income, the more money one has for spending. The more one spends, the less essential or important or useful are some of the things that one buys. The less essential one's purchases for current consumption, the less the opportunity cost of postponement—i.e., the lower the alternative rate of return. And the more attractive, comparatively, the alternative to spending—i.e., saving. Suppose, then, that there is a point in a family's spending program where saving becomes absolutely more attractive than further spending. Comparing the higher-income family with the lower-income family, the former, when this point is reached, has the lower alternative rate and more income left over for saving.

## EXAMPLE OF INCOME-STOCKING RELATIONSHIP

We can expect, on the basis of these principles and on the basis of ordinary observation, that, when hard times strike a woods-owning family, the family will consider timber liquidation. Or that, when a community is depressed, it will tend to draw down its timber growing stocks more than when it is prosperous. Or that a higher-income farm will have more timber per acre of woodland than a lower-income farm. Such propositions, though logically acceptable, are hard to test statistically, because income data are scarce and there are so many other variables that can influence the forest situation.

However, the following figures[11] taken from a survey of Broome County, New York, are indicative. The total acreage of woodlands, of which about half is farm-owned, was divided into four classes that were,

[10] For some thoughts about this question as an American forestry problem, see Duerr, William A.: "The Small, Low-income Landholding: A Problem in Forest Conservation," *Iowa State College Journal of Science*, July, 1948, pp. 449–460.

[11] Davis, James E., Miles J. Ferree, and Neil J. Stout: *Broome County Forest Data*, State University of New York, College of Forestry, Syracuse, 1953, p. 19.

in effect, owner-income classes. For the woodlands in each class, the survey determined what percentage, by area, bore 2,000 or more board feet of timber per acre. These more heavily stocked stands were termed sawtimber stands:

| Owner-income class | Per cent saw timber |
|---|---|
| IV (high) | 57.2 |
| III | 36.3 |
| II | 29.3 |
| I (low) | 22.6 |

Here is a noticeable positive correlation between income and stocking.

Perhaps one could argue that the correlation just shown is not typical —that where woodlands are depleted, it is because cutting is heavy, and the heavier the cutting, the higher the income as a result. But this is not the way things work. The woodland is generally but a small part of the farm business, a slight determinant of income. The woodland economy, as is so generally true of forest economies, has predominantly an effect, not a cause, relationship to outside events. Furthermore, depleted woodlands represent low forest income, not high. Once, perhaps, when depletion first took place, there was high income—but not now. The forces of exploitation tend to be self-generating, just as do those of conservation.

We are speaking here—and this deserves to be stressed—of the relation between the *firm's* income and its practice of conservation. From the standpoint of society, the relation may well be different. High social income stems from resource use that may involve heavy physical depletion, at least of resources that are exhaustible or believed to be so. Thus the social will to conserve could conceivably require the practice of exploitation. A dilemma indeed! [What is the answer?]

[Now before we leave these models, let us review some of the kinds of questions that may be analyzed with their help. Imagine farm-woodland communities that tend to be alike in every respect except the one in question. In what way would you expect forest-management practices to differ in the one community which has suffered a farm-crop failure? In the one that has relatively high land values? In the one that has a low rate of property taxation? In the one that enjoys higher stumpage prices? In the one that has to pay a higher rate of income taxation? In the one where log buyers pay a relatively high premium for quality? In the one where forest sites are relatively poor?]

## SUMMARY

The alternative rate of return, or guiding rate of interest, is a principal index of management. It offers a means of determining the interest rate applicable to a specific use of capital by a firm. It follows the principle that the interest rate chargeable in the specific case is the opportunity cost represented by the highest rate of return obtainable from other uses of the funds, with allowance for the relative risks.

The firm's most efficient alternative use of funds may be for investment, as in other enterprises of the firm or in securities, or it may be for spending, for either business or personal use. In typical cases, if investment is the alternative, the rate is the prospective rate of return reduced to allow for transfer costs and income taxes; if business spending is the alternative, the rate tends toward that on borrowing; if the alternative is personal spending, the rate is the rate of time preference. The rate may sometimes best be determined by inference, as from the firm's timber-cutting budget.

Conservation is the act of reducing current consumption in favor of saving. It is an act associated with a low alternative rate of return or a high marginal value growth of the resource. It is consequently very much the same kind of thing as capital-intensive management. Both are furthered (through effects upon the alternative rate) by high income or a strong propensity to save on the part of the managing firm. Here the terms *high* and *low*, and *conservation* itself, are entirely relative.

Precision demands that value judgments, such as whether conservative management is "good," recognize a standard of value and a human viewpoint from which it is to be applied.

# Chapter 11

# LAND USE

L ET US turn now to the third category of productive agents: land. By *land* is meant natural resources, as opposed to human and cultural resources. Land includes, generally speaking, the surface and substance of the earth. The particular aspect of it that we shall emphasize is *place*, or space, or whatever one wishes to call the site of production. Like labor and capital, land has a quality aspect. The quality of a given unit of land is related to such things as latitude and longitude, altitude, topography, composition of the surface and subsurface, climate, geographic situation relative to other units of resources and to economic activities, and temporal situation within the flow of history. These things are attributes of land and a part of the concept of land.

Land traditionally has been viewed as unique in being fixed and finite. Our concept of resources, as developed in Chapter 3, will help us to avoid this view. The quantity, quality, value, and even, in a sense, the location of land are variable beyond the short run, subject to the quality of other agents used with the land, and to the production context. Surely, so far as forest land is concerned, nothing could be more consistent with the precepts of a forester than that the economic contribution and meaningfulness of this land are subject in part to his determination.

In this chapter we shall take up *land use:* the kind of economic activity to which land is devoted. Since our interest centers on production, we will concentrate upon the productive use of land—the product or combination of products to which land is assigned, and the circumstances of production. Thus we shall give pointed attention to some of the links in the chain of ends and means that lie beyond the ones we examined in Chapter 5, pages 53 and 54. It will become evident that the study of land use is, in a sense, merely another way of looking at the location of economic activity, and therefore at the competition among areas for the use of resources, and therefore at the problems of transportation and trade. Our study of land use consequently will serve as an introduction to all these matters, some of which we shall consider pointedly here, but others postpone. We shall postpone, too, some other parts of land economics closely related to land use—such as ownership and taxation, both of which are dealt with in Part Four of this book.

The discussion of transportation and the location of manufacturing follows the lines laid out by Prof. Edgar M. Hoover.[1]

## TRANSPORTATION AND LAND USE

Literally speaking, land cannot be moved. If one wants to work with land—and to work without it is impossible—one must go there oneself and also see to it that all the other productive agents required are assembled there. Thus land use involves transportation of other agents of production.

And then when production has resulted in an output and there is a product ready, something again must be moved. Either the product is brought out for use, or consumers are brought in to enjoy the product on the spot. In either case, land use involves transportation of goods or consumers.

It is easy to see that location is necessarily a prime factor in the quality, and therefore in the use, of land and that the significance of location is in respect to transportation. Not necessarily distance but transportation cost determines accessibility. That piece of land is high quality in a locational sense which enjoys low transportation costs for other agents of production and for product. For example, the soils of Long Island are of mediocre physical productivity for agriculture, and yet the farm land is of high quality and has a high monetary value, because transportation costs to the metropolitan markets are so low. Again, forest sites in New Jersey are by no means high, and yet forest-land quality must be rated high for reasons of location.

The *principle of transportation and land use* may be stated briefly as follows: The agents of production that work with land are variously distributed, and some stand transportation more readily and for greater distances than others. The users of products, too, are variously distributed, and products, like agents, differ in their capacity for transportation. Transportation cost, therefore, tends to sort out the uses of land into localities, a tendency that is reinforced or modified by the land's inherent

[1] Hoover, Edgar M.: *The Location of Economic Activity*, McGraw-Hill Book Company, Inc., New York, 1948.

productivity and by institutional influences. This sorting process results in establishing priorities for the use of any given tract of land. Now we shall see how the principle works.

## TRANSFER COSTS AND RATES

Let us adopt the term *transfer,* by which we shall mean both transportation, as of goods, and the movement of services—for example, by telephone or radio. The more inclusive term will be helpful later.

*Table 20. Hypothetical costs per 100 pounds incurred by a carrier in moving goods various distances by truck*

| Distance | Terminal cost | Line-haul cost | Total cost |
|----------|---------------|----------------|------------|
| *Miles* | *Cents* | *Cents* | *Cents* |
| 100 | 5 | 5 | 10 |
| 200 | 5 | 10 | 15 |
| 300 | 5 | 15 | 20 |
| 400 | 5 | 20 | 25 |
| 500 | 5 | 25 | 30 |

If a certain shipment is moved over a uniform route by any given carrier, the carrier's total cost of transfer tends to be perfectly correlated with distance. His total cost is not, however, directly proportional to distance, because some of the cost is incurred in about the same amount whether the haul is short or long. This part of the cost, which includes loading and unloading, the maintenance of terminal facilities, and various other overhead outlays by the transfer firm, is called *terminal cost.* It is the carrier's fixed cost of transfer. The other part of the cost, which takes in the running expenses of the carrier and other expenses that depend directly upon the distance the load is moved, is called *line-haul cost.* This part is the carrier's variable cost of transfer. Thus the costs of transfer by truck, in 10-ton loads, might run somewhat as in Table 20. Line-haul cost is determined largely by the type of carrier and the quality of the route over which the goods are hauled, whereas terminal cost is to a greater extent peculiar to the carrying firm, being determined by the total overhead and the total volume of business.

If the total costs of Table 20 are graphed over distance, the result is a straight line, $y = a + bx$, where $a$, the height of the curve's intersection with the ordinate, equals terminal cost and $b$, the slope of the curve, is the line-haul cost per unit distance (Fig. 11a).

Now, it happens that the major different modes of transfer have distinctive and characteristic levels of terminal and line-haul cost. Let us

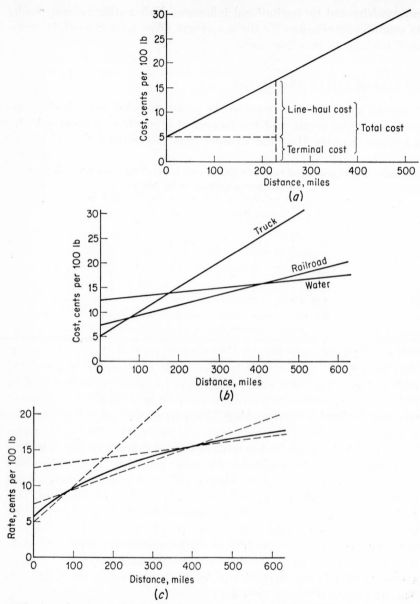

Fig. 11. Hypothetical costs and transfer rates per unit load in relation to distance.
(*a*) Carrier's trucking costs. (*b*) Carrier's truck, rail, and water costs compared.
(*c*) Competitive transfer rates paid by shipper to any type of carrier. (*For an example of basic data, see Table 20.*)

compare truck, railroad, and water transfer, for example. Truck transfer has characteristically a low terminal cost and a high line-haul cost. Water transfer, on the other hand, typically has a high terminal cost, but a low line-haul cost so long as the carrier strikes the relatively slow pace at which he is efficient. The railroad often stands in the intermediate position with respect to these costs. Then truck transfer tends to be cheapest for short distances, water transfer for long distances, and the railroad for intermediate distances (Fig. 11*b*). The three points of intersection of curves in Figure 11*b* are the so-called *break-even points.* Each such point marks the distance at which two of the modes of transfer are equally economical, the one being more economical for shorter distances, the other for longer. The break-even points between truck and rail on the one hand, and between rail and water on the other, are the significant ones, since they demarcate the major zones of cheapest transfer.

Let us understand clearly that the data used here are merely by way of example. The distances at which break-even points actually occur depend upon the many circumstances of the firm and the route, and will therefore vary widely. The important thing is the *principle of carriers' relative costs:* that different modes of transfer differ in respect to terminal and line-haul costs; that zones tend to appear, within each of which a given mode is cheapest; and that the modes which are cheapest at the longer distances are those with the lower line-haul costs.

So far we have considered only the cost incurred by the carrier. Our interest, however, centers on *transfer cost* in the sense of cost incurred by the *shipper*—that is, the *transfer rate* charged by the carrier. The carrier's cost and the rate he charges the shipper may or may not be the same on any shipment.

We may suppose that transfer rates are determined in the first instance by the various carriers who are competing on the basis of their costs. For the shortest distances, in our model, the effective competition is among the various truck and rail carriers. The rates determined for these distances would not be below carriers' truck cost if there is an enduring trucking industry, nor would they be above carriers' rail cost if there is effective competition among individual firms. The rates will therefore tend to be intermediate between these costs, and in general, for any distance, they will tend to be intermediate between the costs of the two most economical modes of transfer, as shown in Figure 11*c*. The broken curves are the cost curves developed in 11*b*, and the solid curve represents the competitive transfer rates that might result. Observe that this rate curve is necessarily convex from above. That is to say, the shipper's marginal transfer cost per unit distance tends to fall with increasing distance. We will call this rate curve, which represents the cost incurred by the shipper, a *transfer-cost gradient.*

## SPECIAL TRANSFER RATES

The simple transfer-cost gradient just derived is the type that we shall use in analyzing land use and the economics of location. This gradient is accurate in principle and generally true to fact. But in the interest of realism let us recognize that there are many influences which modify transfer-cost gradients in actual cases. Let us keep these influences in mind as we use the simple downward-bending gradient to guide our understanding of the forest economy.

Transfer rates are often established not as a schedule continuous with distance but in steps or zones. Thus all shipments to destinations between 80 and 100 miles from origin, or between two stations lying at about such distances from the station of origin, may be charged exactly the same rate per 100 pounds. Beyond the further station, then, the rate will take a jump, and thereafter again be uniform for a certain distance, until the next jump. Such a cost gradient, if graphed, will appear like the profile of a staircase, though it will still be a staircase that will sag downward as it rises.

Many carriers find themselves hauling the preponderance of their freight in one direction, with the consequence that their trucks or cars or boats make the return trip empty or only partly full. This *back-haul* of unfilled cars is a source of concern, since it costs the carrier nearly as much as if the cars were loaded. Any extra freight that could be taken on for the return trip would represent almost entirely a net gain. Therefore it is not uncommon for carriers to set special, low back-haul rates. For instance, mine props, which can be cut from almost any trees at hand, usually are taken from right around the mine. But the coal mines near Bluefield, West Virginia, have in years past obtained many of their props from central and eastern Virginia, up to three hundred miles and more away. The Norfolk and Western Railroad, which served the area, had as its chief business the hauling of coal eastward to the port of Norfolk. Empty back-hauling into the rural interior led to establishment of very low freight rates westward. It was these rates, coupled with high labor costs in the vicinity of the mines, that pushed the mine-timber supply area so far out to the east.

Carriers are usually very active in promoting industrial and other economic activity along their lines, in order to increase their business and reduce, particularly, their terminal costs. For instance, some railroads in the South have departments charged with promoting forestry and forest industry. Often, special rates are worked out in order to encourage manufacturing firms to locate at points served by the railroad. Many a wood-using plant owes its specific location partly to the arrangements worked out between the firm and some carrier, concerning transfer services and rates.

Among the various sorts of rate arrangements designed to foster industrial activity and enlarge a carrier's business is the so-called *milling-in-transit* privilege. Under this scheme, which is a little like the stopover privilege on a passenger ticket, carriers establish special rates for raw material and finished product that is hauled from origin to destination with a stop along the way for manufacture. The stop must be made at the in-transit point designated in connection with the rate, and the points or regions of origin and destination may also be specified in the rate agreement. The in-transit privilege is widely used within the forest economy. For example, much hardwood factory lumber destined for furniture and other reprocessed products for northern and northeastern markets moves by railroad from the lower South through Memphis as a milling-in-transit point, and from the southern Appalachians through Cincinnati.

Transfer rates are subject not only to the manifold forces of competition among carriers but also to the influences of trial-and-error, historical precedent, political pressure, and goodness knows what else, and all this is complicated by the fact that rates set by carriers are usually subject to review by state authorities or the Interstate Commerce Commission, whose policies therefore have a powerful bearing upon transfer-cost gradients.

## RELATIVE TRANSPORTABILITY

Before we leave the subject of transportation, let us recognize a principle that we shall have occasion to use from time to time. This is the *principle of relative transportability*. For the moment, we can state it as

*Table 21. Illustrative specific values and maximum hauling distances for three forest products*

| Product | Specific value | Maximum railroad haul |
|---------|----------------|------------------------|
|         | *Dollars per ton* | *Miles* |
| Walnut veneer logs | 150 | 400 |
| Pine pulpwood | 20 | 100 |
| Oak mine props | 5 | 25 |

follows: The transfer cost that a product can economically bear tends to vary directly with the *specific value* of the product—that is, its value per unit of weight or bulk. For example, mine props, a low-value product, normally move only short distances. On the other hand, veneer logs, though only a product in the round, may be valuable enough to ship great distances (Table 21). [Can you explain why this principle operates?] We shall come back to the principle and analyze it more critically in Chapter 22.

The principle of relative transportability is of importance in land use, playing a part in the sorting of uses by localities. The production of lower grades of a product tends to be concentrated nearer to principal consuming centers than that of the higher grades, and this tendency is reinforced when transfer rates rise. Again, those forms of forest and park recreation to which the majority of people attach a low specific value—

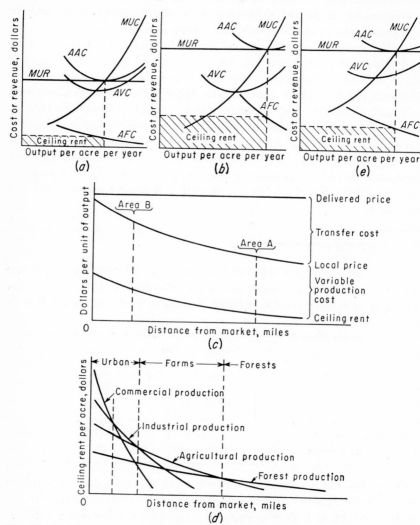

Fig. 12. Simplified models of ceiling rent and ceiling-rent gradients. (*a*) Rent in Area A, where local price is low. (*b*) Rent in Area B, where local price is high. (*c*) Rent per unit of output in relation to distance from market, one line of production. (*d*) Rent per acre in relation to distance from market, four lines of production. (*e*) Rent in Area B, assuming high variable cost of production.

i.e., value per visit to the forest or park—must be provided close to, or within, urban centers if many people are to engage in them outside the travel season. But people will generally be willing to incur much expense and inconvenience in going to the site of recreational activities to which they assign a high specific value.

Now, carrying these thoughts about transportation in the back of our minds, let us turn to our main subject. This we will develop, as usual, by the method of partial analysis, considering the various influences separately and putting them together little by little.

## LAND RENT AND VALUE

The return to land as a productive agent let us call *rent*. This rent, from the viewpoint of the land user, is the cost of the land—an explicit cost if he leases the land from someone else, an implicit cost if he owns it himself.

Take the case of a tract of land in Area A. Suppose that this tract is used to produce some annual crop or other product. Let us visualize a range of production alternatives in the short run, in which the land is fixed and the other inputs are variable with output. Average variable cost per unit of output is as shown by the curve $AVC$ (Fig. 12a), and marginal cost per unit of output is $MUC$. If the price of the product, or marginal revenue per unit of output, is at the level $MUR$, then the best combination, or best output per acre per year, comes at the intersection of this curve with $MUC$, the intersection marked by the vertical broken line. You may wish to turn back to Figure 6d, page 74, to review the derivation and meaning of these curves. Now, the highest rent per acre per year that anyone could afford to pay for the use of this land is the difference between total revenue and total variable cost at the point of best combination. Expressed per unit of output, this highest rent, or *ceiling rent,* is the difference between $MUR$ and $AVC$ measured along the vertical broken line. If such rent is actually paid or imputed, which it will be if there is sufficient competition for the use of the land, then the latter difference is the average fixed cost, and the curve $AFC$ is determined. The sum of average fixed and variable costs is the average aggregate cost, and the curve $AAC$ is necessarily tangent to $MUR$ at the latter's intersection with $MUC$. Total ceiling rent per acre per year is the area of the rectangle one corner of which is at the origin, with the diagonally opposite corner at the intersection of $AFC$ with the vertical line that marks best output.

We have seen that the value, $V_0$, of a productive instrument that promises to yield a continuing annual net return, $r$, is found in the expression $V_0 = r/i$. Where land promises to yield a continuing annual net return, a value may be determined for it from the same formula, by capitalizing the rent. This is formula 2a in Table 9 (p. 110). Formula 2b is for figuring capitalized value of land where the rent is expected to increase or decrease annually. Formula 3a is used where the return comes at intervals longer than a year. In general, capitalized land value equals the present (discounted) worth of all anticipated revenues minus the present worth of all anticipated costs other than rent.

The highest price per acre that anyone could afford to give for the tract of land in Area A is the capitalized ceiling rent. This price is the *ceiling price*. Observe that its ratio to ceiling rent is fixed by the rate of capitalization. Although we shall use the concept of ceiling rent as we continue our analysis of land use, we could as well use ceiling price, and the relationships that we shall notice would be the same.

## PRODUCT PRICE AND CEILING RENT

Consider next a tract of land in Area B. Let us suppose that Area B has exactly the same physical quality of land as Area A, the same production context and quality of other agents and therefore the same basic production function, and the same unit costs of labor and capital. Furthermore, the same kind of product is being produced. The only difference between the two areas is in the price of the product, which is higher in Area B. The curves AVC and MUC for Area B (Fig. 12b) are the same as those for Area A. However, with price higher, the gap between AVC and MUR or AAC is wider, AFC is higher, and total ceiling rent per acre per year is higher, not only because rent per unit of output is greater, but also because the output itself is larger, since with a higher price it pays to manage the land more intensively.

Evidently we are not speaking now primarily of land used for timber growing. In the case of such land, variable and marginal costs will tend to shift along with product price, so that the increase in rent and in the intensity of management will be relatively slight. However, even on timber-growing land, higher price level will mean higher ceiling rent to the extent that costs other than those of timber capital are incurred. The propositions here developed are therefore representative of forest land in kind even though not in degree, and we shall see later what influence the difference in degree has upon our conclusions.

## MARKET LOCATION AND CEILING RENT

We have now two areas, A and B, which are alike in all respects except that product price is higher in Area B. What accounts for the difference in product price? Let us suppose that the two areas are located at different distances from the point where the product is delivered and sold. This concentration point for the product—ordinarily a center of population and of marketing activities—we shall term the *market center* or, for abbreviation, the market. We may suppose that a single price obtains for the product at this market center: a single *delivered price*. The price received in Area A by the producer located there—the *local price* —is equal to the delivered price minus the transfer cost, per unit, from Area A to the market center. Now we can explain the higher local price in Area B as arising from the fact that this area is nearer market, and hence is subject to a lower transfer-cost deduction, than is Area A.

Let us plot dollar values per unit of output over distance from market, as in Figure 12c. The topmost curve is delivered price, and the one below it is local price, which varies with distance. The lower curve is placed below the upper one at spacings equal to the shipper's transfer cost. In other words, the local-price curve and the delivered-price curve are simply the transfer-cost gradient and its abscissa turned upside down. It follows that the local-price curve is concave from above. The third curve in 12c is the ceiling rent in relation to distance from market. This curve is the *ceiling-rent gradient*. It is derived from the local-price gradient by deducting the variable costs of production. The locations of Area A and Area B are shown on the graph. For each area, the heights of the local-price and ceiling-rent gradients are the same, respectively, as the heights of $MUR$, $MUC$, and $AAC$ on the one hand and of $AFC$ on the other, at the point of best combination in 12a or 12b.

At this stage we conclude that with all other conditions equal, the ceiling rent of land varies inversely with its distance from market. From here on, let us continue with this partial analysis of land use, dropping one by one the restricting assumptions that the other conditions are equal.

## MARKET LOCATION AND LAND USE

Let us retain a little longer the assumption of uniform agents and cost rates and the assumption that there is a single market center but consider now some major alternative uses of land. Let us consider (1) commercial production, including such things as retail merchandising and the furnishing of banking and other financial services; (2) industrial production, primarily manufacturing; (3) farming; and (4) forestry. We shall try to construct gradients of ceiling rent per acre for each of these four land uses, as representative of land uses in general. Note that ceiling rent will be considered per acre, not per unit of output. In other words, we will treat of the area, not the height, of such rectangles as were cross-hatched in Figure 12a and b. Land is laid out area-wise, and one's interest in land use centers on the use of acreage.

Each potential use of land has a characteristic ceiling-rent gradient, showing the most that anyone could be expected to pay for such land at various locations, if the land were to be devoted to the use in question. Rent gradients differ, first, in their height at the market and, second, in the steepness of slope away from the market.

The height of a rent gradient is a function of the intensity of use that can be made of the land when product price is at the market-center level. In commercial production, extremely intensive land use is practicable, with immense numbers of workers and quantities of goods, machines, and equipment stacked into each acre of space, customarily layer on layer within the stories of buildings. Generally industrial production lends itself to less intensive management, farming to still less, and forestry to the least. [Why is this?]

The slope of a rent gradient is a function of the transfer cost of the product per unit of area. The reciprocal of this cost we will call *transportability per acre.* Commercial production runs into great difficulties—high costs—if its product is made available only at a distance from consumers. The product per acre is immense, it is hard to move per unit, and the alternative of moving consumers is also very costly. Transportability per acre is therefore low. At the other extreme is forest production. The product, it is true, has low relative transportability. But there is so little of it per acre, and it is so durable and so unaffected by being moved that its transportability per acre is exceedingly high. Add to this the fact that intensity of management is so little influenced by product price, and the result is a very flat ceiling-rent gradient. [You should give further thought to these differences in an effort to analyze why they exist.]

Illustrative ceiling-rent gradients for our four lines of production are shown in Figure 12d. As may happen with curves differing in height and slope, break-even points appear, and between them zones where each line of production, successively, stands as the one line able to pay the highest rent. If we may suppose that the land will go to that user who can pay the most for it, then our zones become land-use zones, lying in concentric belts about the market, with commercial production closest, followed by industrial production, farming, and forestry, in that order. Here we have our first illustration of the *economic principle of land use:* Each parcel tends to be devoted to that line of production in which the ceiling rent is highest. That is to say, each parcel tends to come into the hands of the producer who can make the most out of it and thus pay the most for it.

[Where would you expect to find those lines of production whose rent gradients are both low and steep? Can you think of examples?]

Note that we are still assuming uniform agents and cost rates and a single market center.

## EFFECT OF AGENTS' QUALITY AND
## COST AND OF MARKET GEOGRAPHY

Now, however, suppose that in Area B the variable cost of producing the product in question were higher than assumed in Figure 12*b*. This would result in a higher marginal cost, a lower output and intensity of management, and a lower ceiling rent, both per unit of output and per acre (Fig. 12*e*). The condition now assumed, and depicted in Figure 12*e*, can result either from lower quality of agents—less productive soil or labor, for example—or from higher unit costs, such as wage rates or interest rates. We can observe on every hand how one area differs from another in such respects. For example, the northeastern United States has long had high wage rates but low interest rates in comparison with the South. These differences have been at least partly offset by countervailing differences in labor and capital efficiency. More locally, we know how the soils of one area can be outstandingly productive for certain crops. We can observe communities such as Grand Rapids, Michigan, High Point, North Carolina, and Jamestown, New York, where generations of furniture makers have handed down their special skills within the labor force. In other communities, such as in parts of the southern Appalachians, the woods-labor skills that abounded when the logging industry was at its height have nearly disappeared with the heavy timber, so that to revive wood production is particularly costly. Our assumption now concerning Area B is that its productive agents have suffered a loss of physical efficiency—or a gain in rates of pay relative to other areas, perhaps as a result of heightened demands for their services.

Conditions of the sort assumed for Area B will produce a downward dip in the ceiling-rent gradient. And since the different lines of production use the various agents in different proportions, their rent gradients will be affected unequally, and the result may be a change in the pattern of land use. Opposite changes may come about because of locally high quality or low unit cost of agents. Thus ceiling-rent gradients are not smooth curves as in Figure 12*d*, but contain numerous peaks and valleys as they meander outward and downward from a market center. And they may cross and recross in the course of their peaking and dipping.

Let us now remove the last of our restrictive assumptions, and consider the effect upon ceiling rents and land use of the geographic distribution of market centers. Markets are of various sizes and variously distributed. Moreover, they differ in their relative demands for the various products. As a result, they exert a complex influence upon rent gradients, raising them to differing heights in accordance with the magnitude of the market and producing various peaks around the smaller markets, in the midst of the long gradients extending from larger markets. The resulting influences upon land use are of the same order as those originating from variations in the quality or unit cost of agents. They are simply traceable to product price rather than cost.

And so we find the commerical and industrial zones of the city, perhaps broken, however, by wooded recreational areas where forest rent gradients peak. We find the adjacent farm land, the pastured valley, the truck gardens of the lowland, the hillside vineyards, the wooded swamps and dry hilltops, and the remote extensive forest. We find these and other uses of land in patterns which, though highly complex, are nevertheless attributable in large part to the conformation of ceiling-rent gradients. The latter, in turn, arise from the geography of markets and local prices, of agents' quality, and of agents' unit cost.

## EFFECT OF RAW MATERIALS: THE CASE OF MANUFACTURING

The concept of land-use patterns that we have evolved so far permits us to explain rather wide variations in the location of major production lines in relation to markets. Land very close to market can conceivably be used for forestry or farming where the product has a high, steep rent gradient. We can even conceive of commercial production being carried out away from the market center, though if you will search your experience for illustrations, you will probably conclude that they are rare. And when it comes to manufacturing production, we can easily picture and illustrate a wide variety of locational situations. For manufacturing involves *assembling raw materials* as well as converting them and distributing the product, and the location and the transfer rates of raw materials represent important variable costs that can be hugely modified by plant location. In a sense, the location of manufacturing is more flexible than of other lines of production. And since manufacturing makes up a big part of the forest economy, it will pay us to work on its land-use problems a little further in detail.

To simplify the study, let us consider the location of a particular manufacturing plant and begin by making some unrealistic assumptions. These can be canceled out after we have a model to guide our reasoning. The assumptions are: (1) The weight of product shipped from the plant equals the weight of raw material shipped in. (2) Transfer rates per unit of weight and distance are the same for raw material and product. (3) All the raw material comes from one source, and all the product goes to one market center. (4) One transfer medium connects the raw-material source and the market and serves all points between them. (5) Unit costs of manufacture—i.e., production functions for the plant's product and unit costs of agents—are the same everywhere.

Now where will the plant be located? What land will be used by the firm for manufacturing this product?

What are the alternatives? Under our simplifying assumptions, they simmer down to two: First, locate close to market, so as to save transfer cost on the product, or *distribution cost.* Second, locate close to raw material, so as to save on its transfer cost, which we shall term *procurement cost.* No other considerations enter. All costs and revenues other than these two categories of cost are unaffected by plant location. Consequently the firm's location problem resolves itself into determining the place where its total transfer cost, the sum of the procurement and distribution costs, is the least. This will be the place where its ceiling rent is the greatest.

If transfer rates per ton-mile were the same for any distance, all points on the connecting line between raw material and market would be equally good plant locations, as illustrated in Figure 13a. Here the abscissa is scaled in miles and represents the route of transportation, with raw-material and market locations as shown.

But transfer rates per ton-mile are not, as we have seen, the same for any distance. That is to say, transfer-rate gradients are not straight lines. They are curves convex from above, as in Figure 11c. This being the case, the plant's best location is more determinate. It is at the source of raw material or at the market, but nowhere else, either between or beyond (Fig. 13b).

### ORIENTATION ARISING FROM TRANSFER WEIGHTS AND RATES

Now let us remove in turn each of our five restricting assumptions, leaving the other assumptions in effect as we thus examine the influence of each variable. In this manner we will pave the way for you yourself to visualize the effects of all variables operating at once. Remember that our present analysis of manufacturing location is simply an extension of the earlier land-use analysis in terms of ceiling rents. We are now, in effect, taking from the earlier analysis the item of variable production cost and scrutinizing that part of it—namely, raw-material procurement cost—which varies systematically with location.

*First,* suppose there is weight loss in the manufacturing process. Suppose, for example, it takes 2 tons of raw material to make 1 ton of product. Then the plant is *raw-material oriented:* it tends to be located at, or near, the source of its raw material. As illustrated in Figure 13c, this raw-material orientation comes about because procurement cost per ton of product is now double the distribution cost per ton of product. Note that both costs are expressed per ton of product. They could both be stated per unit of raw material. But in any case both must be stated the same way for the graphic analysis to be valid.

Graphs aside, the raw-material orientation is the firm's means of avoiding the extra cost of carting around a lot of raw material that is destined

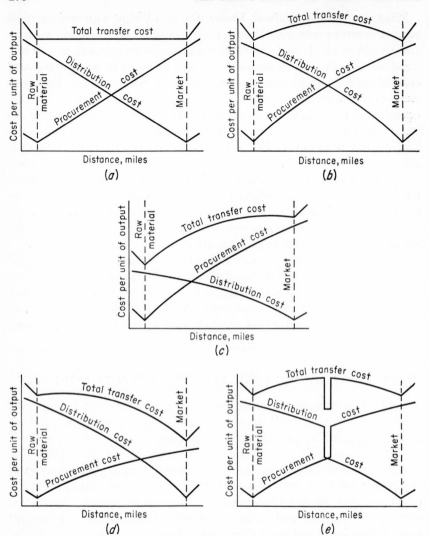

Fig. 13. Transfer-cost gradients and the orientation of a manufacturing plant. (*a*) Gradients where ton-mile rates are constant. (*b*) Gradients where ton-mile rates decline with distance. (*c*) Raw-material orientation. (*d*) Market orientation. (*e*) Orientation to a transshipment point. (*Adapted from Hoover, Edgar M.: The Location of Economic Activity, McGraw-Hill Book Company, Inc., New York, 1948.*)

to be lost or pushed aside in manufacturing. And so we find sawmills generally located near the forest rather than the market center, so that they may take water, sawdust, slabs, edgings, and trimmings away from the lumber and leave them behind before its costly journey to market begins. Pulp mills, too, with their immense water loss and other moderate weight losses, are material-oriented. [Can you think of other examples?

[One can take the simple principle of weight loss and use it to analyze many interesting problems of wood-using plants and industry. For example, if markets are developed for the parts of raw material that would otherwise go unused, where are these markets likely to be found? What influence will closer utilization of logs by sawmills have upon their location and their size?]

*Second*, suppose that transfer rates per unit of weight and distance are higher for the product than for the raw material. They usually are, at least because the product has the greater relative transportability. Fragile products such as wooden toys and many types of furniture additionally bear what amount to higher rates, in the fact that either they must be shipped in costly and heavy packaging or allowance must be made for losses in transit. Wherever distribution cost rates exceed procurement rates, the manufacturing establishment tends to be drawn toward the market, to be *market oriented*, as illustrated in Figure 13d.

In general, secondary wood-manufacturing (reprocessing) plants are market-oriented, the effect of high distribution cost outweighing that of weight loss. Perhaps our clearest and most outstanding example of market orientation is the construction industry. [Would you consider prefabrication an exception? What transfer costs will affect the growth of prefabrication, and how decisive are they likely to be?]

To summarize the analysis of orientation so far: Weight loss in manufacture makes for raw-material orientation of the plant. On the other hand, higher transfer rates for distribution than for procurement work in favor of market orientation.

## OTHER FORCES AFFECTING ORIENTATION

*Third*, suppose that the plant's raw material comes from more than one point, or that its product goes to more than one market, or both. In such cases the forces determining orientation are complex, there is no single solution, and simple graphic analysis fails us. But in general, the plant tends to be attracted to that center of gravity of market places or raw-material sources where the complex sum of procurement and distribution costs can be minimized.

If transfer routes connecting the various raw materials and markets form an important junction, this junction acts as a powerful magnet. Thus many of our great rail junctions of the central United States—for example, Chicago, St. Louis, Memphis, New Orleans—though neither raw-material sources nor the principal markets, provide good sites for wood manufacture, especially where wood is combined with other materials. They further offer advantageous sites for wholesaling many products and thus for the processing incidental to wholesaling.

In general, if raw material is strongly localized and markets widely scattered, manufacture is material-oriented. Or if the market is concentrated but raw materials are scattered, there is market orientation. For years there was a sawmill operating within the city limits of Columbus, Ohio—seemingly an odd spot for a sawmill. But the mill depended on quality logs from widely dispersed farm woods—a few logs here and a few there. So far as procurement cost went, one location was no better than another. Distribution cost then stepped in as the deciding factor: Columbus was the market for the lumber.

*Fourth,* suppose that there is a transshipment point between raw material and market. A ***transshipment point*** is a point where the transfer medium changes—from truck to rail, from rail to water, or between any carriers who do not provide through service—so that goods must be unloaded and reloaded. If unloading and reloading costs are sufficiently great, the transshipment point becomes the least-cost location for manufacturing, as Figure 13e shows. By putting his plant at the transshipment point, the manufacturer saves one unloading and one reloading operation, with a combined cost equal to the height of the vertical jogs in transfer gradient (13e), as compared with any other plant location. In other words, once the raw material is unloaded for transshipment, it had best be processed before reloading, thus killing two chickens with one hatchet. And so we find pulp and paper manufacture located at barge and sea ports, and sawmills at rail heads or other points of junction with truck roads from the woods. Milling-in-transit points, mentioned on page 167, have an effect upon location similar to that of transshipment points.

*Fifth* and last, let us suppose that production functions for the plant's product and unit costs of agents vary from place to place. Inevitably they do, as we recognized on page 173. If, as a result, any location promises unit costs of manufacture enough lower than elsewhere to offset such transfer-cost disadvantages as it may have, that location becomes a favorable one. Or if material-oriented or market-oriented manufacturers find that their accustomed spots entail too great a processing cost, we can expect to see some shift in industrial location as time goes on. Grand Rapids, with its know-how and labor skills, continues to attract furniture makers only so long as wage rates and other cost elements are low enough to offset the effects of timber-resource depletion. Low cost rates for productive agents in the South impel the pulp and paper industry to break the resistances to using the resinous southern pine as raw material. The sawmill moves out of Columbus when land rents and taxes climb too high; it moves when other land users' ceiling rents become much greater than its own.

To summarize the three points made in this section: Where a manufacturing plant's raw-material sources or markets are far-flung, it tends to be oriented to important junctions of transfer routes, or toward the raw material if this is strongly localized but markets are widely scattered, or toward the markets if these are clustered and raw materials come from many places. Plants tend to be drawn to transshipment points. And they tend to find locations where unit costs of manufacture are low.

## INSTITUTIONAL INFLUENCES UPON LAND USE

We have analyzed the use of land in terms of the revenues and costs of production that determine ceiling rents. This is not, of course, the whole story, and for some instances of land use it is not even the major part. There are other factors in land use, some economic, others sociological perhaps, still others political—though beyond a point it may not pay to attempt a fine classification of them. Let us group some of them here under the heading of institutional influences.

A place, a piece of land, is not only the site of production; it is also where people live. The use of it is more largely an act of consumption than is true of most productive agents and is therefore influenced more by the imponderables of consumer behavior. Though people today move more frequently and are less deeply rooted in their native ground than was true even a generation ago, still there are many for whom some farm or wood or village lot or other spot on the face of the earth represents a special place, with childhood or family associations. There seems to be a tendency in all of us to want such places to stay unchanged over the years. Perhaps this wish arises from our personal desire for permanency. At any rate it strongly influences the use of land. Land use is for other reasons, too, slow to change, responsive in part to the past rather than the future.

The ownership and use of land are surrounded by many conventions, laws, and regulations. (Some of these we shall explore more fully in Chapter 25.) Our customs and legal arrangements respecting land inheritance are influential in land use in some areas, as where the children of an owner divide a tract after his death and either manage it more intensively in separate parcels or exploit it in order to get the funds for reconsolidation. The passage of land from private into public ownership is often attended by changes in use. State and Federal purchase of land has in many cases hastened the change from farm to forest use. Some states have zoning laws that permit the public to restrict private land use. Some communities have strong sentiments about manufacturing—either that they want it and will make concessions to get it, or that they don't want it, because it is noisy and smoky and attracts outsiders and changes the way of life. Government subsidies to landowners in the form of education may alter their practices, while those in the form of conservation payments may sometimes alter and sometimes serve to freeze and perpetuate past uses. In general the tendency is for the land patterns of the past to be continued well after the determining conditions have changed and the new conditions call for new patterns. Custom and habit here play an important part. On the other hand, we have all seen how landowners will sometimes follow the management innovations of a community leader, making changes that would otherwise have come slowly if at all.

There is a tendency toward local clustering of land uses or combinations of uses. In dairying communities, land can be found devoted to pasture or winter feed crops which physically is not well suited to such use. The existence of highly developed local institutions centered upon dairying favor such land-use practices. And of course much farm-owned woodland in dairy sections is used for pasture, a practice which under the circumstances is often wise from the farmer's viewpoint. In the middle western states, woods can be found growing on farm lands which are no different in quality from those that have been cleared. In some such cases, the forest patch is there because originally it was left over after enough land was cleared to keep the farm family busy with crops, and subsequently tradition and the benefits from the woods have staved off further clearing. In other cases, the forest originated as a plantation, put in by some early settler who brought with him from Western Europe the custom of working with trees. In the South and parts of the Far West, one can find large, continuous blocks of industrial forest land, containing tracts which, were the ownership pattern different, would undoubtedly be farmed. In fact, some of these tracts were farmed up to the time of industrial acquisition. The present owner, however, is in the forest business. He wants "blockage," and he wants freedom from the administrative problems that a varied land-use pattern would entail. The clustering of certain lines of manufacturing land use in the city, a phenomenon that we have interpreted in revenue-cost terms, has also its institutional aspects.

This is a mere sketch of the institutional influences upon land use, but perhaps it says enough to hint at the nature of these influences and the complexity of them.

[Take some community, preferably a rural area, that you know. Picture to yourself the uses of the land, and see if you can explain why the land is used as it is and what changes are likeliest to occur in future.]

### SUMMARY

Land use is defined for our purposes as the kind of production to which land is devoted, and the circumstances of production. We have considered the following factors in land use:

1. The basic production function, governed by—
    *a.* Quality of the land
    *b.* Quality of other agents
    *c.* The production context
2. Local price of the product, governed by—
    *a.* Delivered price
    *b.* Distribution cost
3. Unit values of the other agents
    *a.* Unit cost of labor
    *b.* Unit cost of capital, including initial and procurement cost of raw material
4. The result of these: ceiling rent in each alternative use
5. Plus institutional influences
6. All leading to the land user's response

The first three numbered items in this list are the same that we have recognized before as the determinants of the best combination—that is, management intensity. This part of the list is identical even to the omission of fixed cost as a causal factor. (Fixed cost in this case—rent or its counterpart, land value—is the *result*, not the cause, of land use and management intensity. It is *ceiling* rent that plays the causal role.) In fact, the entire list becomes a general list of factors determining management intensity if one merely alters the words "ceiling rent in each alternative use" to read "the best combination of agents." And since ceiling rent is simply one aspect of the best combination, this is no great alteration. Surely it is obvious that land use and the intensity of management in the chosen use are in a sense determined simultaneously. Only the latter is somewhat more easily variable than the former and somewhat more sensitive to the anticipation of change.

# Chapter 12

# MULTIPLE-
# PRODUCT
# MANAGEMENT

WE HAVE looked at many instances of production where the firm's task was to weigh alternative outputs of a single product, or their associated alternative inputs. It is time to give at least passing attention to the firm's more complex weighings where more than one product is involved. Multiple-product management is by far the commonest sort in the forest economy as in the economy at large. It has become more common, and the product array more complex, as resource values have risen and our economic institutions grown more elaborate.

That part of a firm's business concerned with a particular product or group of similar products is called an *enterprise.* Thus a single forestry firm may have a sawmill, or lumber, enterprise; a timber (-growing) enterprise; a wildlife enterprise; and other enterprises. Just as all the values in an economy are at least remotely related because they are created in common out of the same general pool of resources, so the values of a firm's products and therefore the workings of its enterprises are closely interrelated because they depend upon some of the same agents of production.

When enterprises are combined for multiple-product management, the combining is termed *integration.* A firm may integrate in at least two ways: First, it may combine enterprises that represent successive links in the economic chain: successive stages of production, one ordinarily furnishing raw material for another. We shall call this *vertical integration.* If the firm grows timber and does the logging, it is vertically integrated. If it also manufactures and markets the product, it is more highly integrated vertically. Second, the firm may combine enterprises at the

**182**

same stage of production, perhaps enterprises that use some of the same raw material. We shall call this *horizontal integration.* Illustrations are the city that grows timber on its watershed forest and the lumber company that also operates a pulp mill. Obviously a single firm can be integrated both vertically and horizontally at the same time. [Can you think of examples?]

This chapter takes up the firm's best short-run combination for multiple products—first, briefly, those that are vertically related; second, at more length, those that are linked horizontally. The chapter is the counterpart of Chapter 7; it deals with outputs in generally the same terms as were there applied to inputs. The study of closely allied problems of product price and supply and of the firm's demand for agents are largely postponed to later chapters which have to do with these problems.

## VERTICALLY RELATED PRODUCTS

Our central example of the vertical relationship is the one already given: that between timber grown by the firm and its products of wood conversion. Other cases are water for the mill, produced from a pulp company's own lands; the pulp and paper made by an integrated concern; and the lumber, blanks, or other stock produced by a sawmilling and remanufacturing firm.

The products of a firm that stand in vertical relationship are distinguished, first, by the tendency for their outputs, when changing, to change in the same direction and proportion and, second, by the fact that this marching together is not invariable and can be altered at will by the firm.

Where there are two vertically related products, the best output of the one that is raw material may be analyzed with the help of the model we have already developed for equating the firm's marginal cost with its marginal revenue. Revenue is expressed in terms of conversion surplus. Our first problem in the best combination of growing stock (pp. 120–125) is a case in point. If the firm's capacity for producing raw material exceeds that for processing it and excess raw-material output is sold, the conversion surplus of this part of the output will probably be lower than that of the rest. If it is, the firm will have an incentive to curtail its raw-material flow below what would otherwise be the best level and to increase its output of the end product.

In any case, the best output of the end product too may be analyzed with our simple cost-revenue model. That part of the marginal cost which is represented by raw material is at first the extra cost actually incurred by the firm in producing the extra amount of raw material. Since the fixed cost of this production is not counted, the firm is in a favorable raw-material position.

However, if the firm's end-product capacity is much greater than its capacity for producing raw material, a reckoning of some sort is inevitable. Either the firm will run itself out of business, as many a lumber company has done; or it will replan its enterprises in order to keep going on its own resources; or it will start buying raw material from other firms. The course of action will depend upon the supply of raw material to the firm and upon the firm's demand for it, based on the prospective demands for its end product and the prospective costs of agents other than raw material. Considerations well beyond the short run may be involved. We will come back to the problem later, when we have more of the analytical tools that we shall need.

## HORIZONTALLY RELATED PRODUCTS

Of the various types of horizontally related products, we shall take up two that are illustrative of the forest economy: joint products and rival products. *Joint products* are those which come from the same raw material or production process in rather constant proportions—for instance, doubling the lumber tends to double the sawdust. *Rival products,* on the other hand, come from some of the same inputs, but in inverse proportions at any given level of cost outlay—for example, growing more timber generally means growing less forage on the same acre.

For any particular total expenditure, then, the firm finds the outputs of joint products essentially fixed in the short run. But the outputs of rival products are variable, one against the other. Still other kinds of products, or production situations, are sometimes recognized, in which, for a given expenditure, the firm can increase one output while also increasing the other or holding it constant.[1] But such situations, like other cases of increasing returns, lie outside the economic limits of production, and so we shall not dwell on them. However, we should note that, although we speak of "rival *products*," the condition of being rivals may not be inherent in the products themselves but may result only from the level of output. Products which at one level are rivals at another level may not be.

[In Chapter 7, where our subject was what we might call horizontally related inputs, our whole attention was given to rival agents of production. Nothing was said about joint agents. Is there such a thing? Can you cite examples? What method can you propose for finding the best combination for such agents? Compare Chapter 5, noting particularly page 61.]

---

[1] See, for example, Heady, Earl O.: *Economics of Agricultural Production and Resource Use,* Prentice-Hall, Inc., New York, 1952, chap. 7, pp. 201–237.

## JOINT PRODUCTS

The prime feature of joint products is that if the output of one is increased, that of the others is increased also by the very nature of the production process; or if the output of one is reduced, that of the others, too, is curtailed. To grow logs generally requires growing also roots, upper stem, limbs, leaves, bark, and other things. Furthermore, growing one log commonly entails producing at least a second one, so that growing one log involves growing another that has a smaller diameter, and very possibly a lower grade. If the log is further used as raw material to make lumber, then inevitably (as technology now stands) sawdust, slabs, edgings, water vapor, and what not are made too. And in the course of making lumber of particular specifications, some lumber of other specifications will be sawed as well, so long as trees are round and the quality of wood toward the center is different from that on the outside. The production of farm land by clearing carries with it the creation of logs or bolts in some form. The growing of timber necessarily means producing a certain amount of wildlife, scenery, watershed regulation, and forage, or at least browse. And the railroad that hauls people or commodities in one direction cannot escape creating capacity for the return trip.

Since joint products are produced in somewhat fixed proportions, the question of best output can be analyzed for the group as though it were one product. That is to say, it can be analyzed thus for the group that is actually joint, in the form in which the products are jointly produced. How much slabs and edgings to saw can be treated as part of the question, how much lumber to saw. But whether pulp chips will be made from the slabs and edgings is another question, depending upon the extra costs of debarking and of making and shipping the chips, in relation to their delivered value. Producing lumber necessitates producing slabs and edgings, but not chips.

Let us suppose that a firm produces two joint products, $E$ and $F$. For every two units of $E$ turned out, one of $F$ is made. The basic production function is shown in Figure 14a, which differs from those to which we are accustomed only in having two output scales. The two scales are made possible by the fact that the ratio of outputs of the two products is fixed. Figure 14b shows in another form the range of production alternatives of $E$ and $F$. The firm can produce two units of $E$ and one of $F$, or four units of $E$ and two of $F$, and so on. No other combinations of $E$ and $F$ except those lying on the curve will, or can, be considered by the firm. The curve is called an expansion path (compare Chap. 7, p. 88). In Figure 14c are shown the total cost and total revenue associated with the production alternatives. Total cost is the basic production function with physical inputs converted to value units and fixed cost added. Total

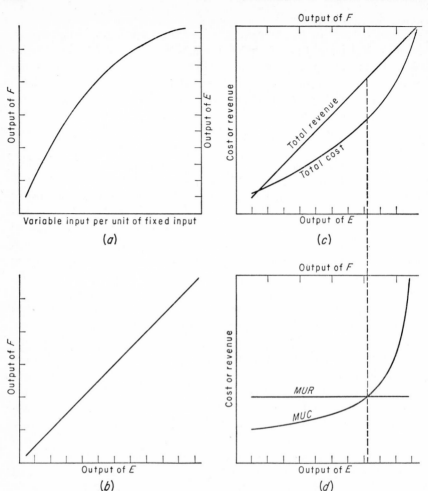

Fig. 14. Best output of joint products. (*a*) Basic production function. (*b*) Expansion path. (*c*) Total cost and revenue. (*d*) Marginal cost and revenue, and the best combination. (*Hypothetical production function. The familiar S shape—as in Fig. 5, p. 71—is simplified to an inverted J, representing continuously diminishing returns.*)

revenue is, in effect, the physical outputs of $E$ and $F$ read from the expansion path, converted to value units, and added for the two products. From the slopes of the total cost and revenue curves the marginal unit cost and revenue (per unit of output) are derived, and their intersection marks the best output (Fig. 14*d*). This is the output at which the slopes of the total revenue and cost curves are equal, and where therefore the total revenue most greatly exceeds the total cost.

Actually, the output ratio of two joint products is never quite fixed. It appears to be so when the products have constant relative value. But the more their relative values change, the more thought is apt to be given by the firm to varying the proportion of each in the output. As slabs and edgings—the *by-products,* or joint products of secondary value—grow in value relative to lumber, the proportion of them in the output can be increased. If hemlock bark should promise again to become valuable relative to the wood, resources could be allocated to selection of thick-barked or high-tannin strains.

## JOINT COSTS

The costs of making joint products—*joint costs*—cannot be allocated, except arbitrarily, to the individual products. For example, the cost of felling a tree cannot be allocated among the logs in the tree in any way that will be meaningful to the production decision. Furthermore, joint costs need not be allocated for purposes of economic analysis. This is because they are fixed costs, for these, as we have seen, are irrelevant to the production decision with respect to which they are fixed.

Take, for example, the case of Firm F, which has bought a tract of eastern white pine for a lump sum and is logging and milling the timber. There are some 10-inch trees containing two grade-3 logs, and the question arises whether such a tree is worth felling and converting. The prospective sales value of the lumber in the tree is $3.30. Prospective variable costs of logging, hauling, and milling the tree are $2.70. Fixed costs, consisting of stumpage and overhead, if allocated to the tree on the basis of its volume, amount to 70 cents and 20 cents, respectively. With these allocated fixed costs included, the tree is apparently not worth converting:

| | | |
|---|---|---|
| Lumber sales value | | $3.30 |
| Costs of production: | | |
|    Variable | $2.70 | |
|    Fixed: | | |
|       Stumpage | 0.70 | |
|       Overhead | 0.20 | |
|       Total cost | | 3.60 |
| Apparent net value | | minus $0.30 |

And yet we know that in fact, since no extra stumpage or overhead costs at all will be incurred by taking this tree, the tree can contribute $3.30 minus $2.70, or 60 cents (its conversion surplus), toward the payment of fixed costs and a net return, and is therefore worth converting. [How would this conclusion be affected if stumpage had not been paid in a lump sum but was to be paid at the 70-cent rate, on the scaled volume of trees actually felled?]

Now let us carry the case of Firm F's 10-inch tree a little further so as to show an analogy in the allocation of joint cost. The variable cost of marking and felling the tree is $1. This is a joint cost of producing the two logs in the tree. The logs thus have a total conversion surplus of $1.60 —i.e., $3.30 − ($2.70 − $1.00)—of which $1.30 is derived from the butt log and 30 cents from the second log. If the joint cost is prorated to the logs either by number of logs (50 cents apiece) or by volume (55 cents to butt, 45 cents to top log), the top log apparently has a negative conversion surplus and is a cull. Yet in fact we know that this is incorrect. The joint cost is chargeable to the tree as a whole, and the resulting 60-cent conversion surplus shows that the tree is worth felling. But the joint cost is not chargeable or allocable to the logs, because with respect to them this cost is fixed and therefore irrelevant to any decision about them. If the top log were culled, the conversion surplus of the tree would be reduced to 30 cents, which is still another way of saying that the log is worth taking.[2] [How would this conclusion be affected if stumpage had not been paid in a lump sum but was to be paid—38 cents for the butt, 32 cents for the top log—on the scale of logs actually removed?]

It follows from what has been said that there are great advantages to be gained by the firm that can find new uses for its by-products—or, in timber parlance, practice closer utilization. In this fact the economy offers a strong incentive toward intensive resource management—and, incidentally, toward the elaboration and integration of enterprises and the growth of large firms.

### RIVAL PRODUCTS

Finally, let's have a look at some of the problems connected with rival products. We can think of many examples, but there are two which are typical and of great interest. One is the various products made by much the same labor and machinery in a manufacturing plant, such as the different thicknesses and grades of plywood that can be turned out on the same cutting, plugging, and gluing equipment, driers, and sanding machines. The other includes many cases of the so-called "multiple-use" products of forest land: water, wildlife, recreation, forage, and timber. Usually within the economic range of production, where fixed resources are being crowded and diminishing returns are in effect, such products are rivals for the use of the resources: an increase in the output of one will cause a reduction in the other unless cost outlays are raised.

Take the case of a plywood-manufacturing firm that is studying the problem of the best outputs of two products, G and H. These products

[2] Compare Guttenberg, Sam, and William A. Duerr: *A Guide to Profitable Tree Utilization,* Southern Forest Experiment Station Occasional Paper 114, New Orleans, 1949, p. 4.

are for the most part rivals. The firm has a wide range of alternative outputs of the two products. It can produce little of one and much of the
other, or vice versa, or little of both, or, within strict limits in the short
run, more of both. From these innumerable alternatives it must choose
one—the one, preferably, that will maximize the net return from both
enterprises—from its whole business—per unit of time. The following
analysis may be compared with that illustrated in Figure 8, page 86.

## BEST COMBINATION FOR RIVAL PRODUCTS

Let us begin with the basic production function, which is three-dimensional. One way of depicting it is shown in Figure 15a. Here we have
the output of $H$ related to the total inputs required for both products,
at successive levels of output of $G$. The curve labeled $G_0$ is the ordinary
one-product function. It describes the output of $H$ as related to input
when no $G$ at all is produced. When 1 unit of $G$ is manufactured, it takes
more total input to make any given quantity of $H$, since some of the input
is now going toward $G$. Consequently production function $G_1$ lies below
$G_0$. The remaining curves similarly show the outputs of $H$ when the
output of $G$ is, successively, 2, 3, 4, 5, and 6 units. As more of $G$ is produced within the unit of time, $H$ is ever harder to come by, and harder
in increasing degree, as shown by the wider spacing of the curves.

Figure 15a describes how, for any given expenditure of input $I_1$ to $I_7$,
more of $H$ can be made at the sacrifice of $G$, or more of $G$ at the sacrifice
of $H$. Observe the $Y$-axis readings on the curves along each of the ordinates, $I_1$ to $I_7$. Let us now translate these readings into another graphic
form, $b$ of Figure 15. Here the alternative outputs of $G$ ($X$ axis) and $H$
($Y$ axis) are shown for each level of input from $I_1$ to $I_7$ by the solid
curves so labeled. This constitutes an iso-input (iso-cost) diagram.

Staying with Figure 15b, our next step is to see whether, for any given
level of input, there is some one combination of $G$ and $H$ (some one point
on each iso-cost curve) that is most desirable in the sense that the excess
of revenue over cost is greatest at this point. We already have cost in the
picture. Now we need to put revenue into it.

Suppose that the sales price per unit of $H$ is $1\frac{1}{2}$ times that of product
$G$. In other words, two units of output of product $H$ (point $R_H$) represents the same revenue to the firm as three units of product $G$ (point $R_G$).
Furthermore, any combination of $G$ and $H$ described along the straight
line $R_G R_H$ represents the same total revenue. [Why is this? Can you develop a proof of it?]

Not only is $R_G R_H$ an iso-revenue curve, but any straight line drawn
parallel to it in graph $b$ is an iso-revenue curve. The further the curve
from the origin, the higher the revenue. Therefore the point on each iso-

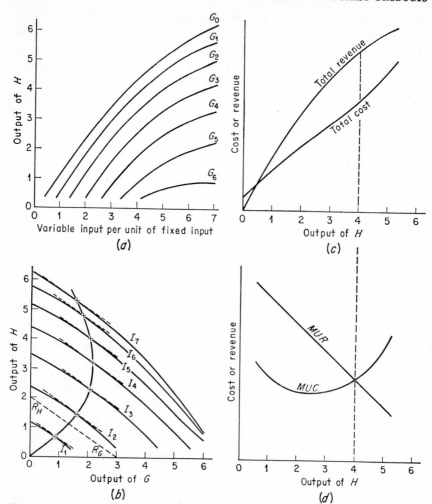

Fig. 15. Best output of supplementary products G and H. (a) Basic production functions for H with output of G fixed at levels from 0 to 6. (b) Iso-cost and -revenue curves and expansion path. (c) Total cost and revenue on the expansion path. (d) Marginal cost and revenue, and the best combination. (*Hypothetical production function. See explanation of Fig. 14, p. 186.*)

cost curve which represents the most favorable relation of revenue to cost is the point which lies on the iso-revenue curve that is furthest from the origin—that is to say, the point where the iso-cost curve is tangent to an iso-revenue curve. The points of tangency are shown in 15*b*. The curve drawn through them is the expansion path, describing the best output of G to accompany any output of H.

Now that we have narrowed the alternatives to this extent, there remains one step: to determine which of the *G*-and-*H* combinations *along the expansion path* is the best. This step is taken in graphs *c* and *d* in Figure 15. In graph *c*, total cost has been determined by adding to the fixed cost the value of the variable inputs represented in either graph *a* or graph *b*, for each level of output of *H* and the attendant output of *G* shown by the expansion path. (Evidently we might just as well have dealt from the outset with value units of cost, and in most cases it would be easier to do so, especially where there is more than one kind of variable input.) Total revenue is computed from the amounts of *H* and *G* along the expansion path, and their values per unit. Marginal cost and revenue in graph *d* are taken from the slopes of the total curves. Best output is four units of *H* and (from the expansion path) two units of *G*, per unit of time.

To summarize how we found the best combination for rival products: (1) We worked out the highest-revenue mix of products at each level of cost. (2) We then determined which of the highest-revenue combinations was the best of all in terms of total net revenue per unit of time. And we may add (3) that the firm can similarly explore various combinations involving still other products and find the best of all the best combinations. Compare the summary of steps for analyzing multiple inputs, page 90.

## USES AND LIMITATIONS OF THE MODEL

You can use the foregoing model to reason out the effects of various conditions and changes upon a firm's output of two rival products or groups of products. [What will be the effect upon the best combination if *H* is relatively harder to produce, compared with *G*, than Figure 15*a* shows—that is, if the curves are lower and flatter: the marginal rate of substitution of *H* for *G* lower? What will be the effect if the value of product *H* rises relative to the value of *G*—that is, if the iso-revenue curves of Figure 15*b* are flattened as a result of a lower rate of substitution of *H* for *G* in terms of price? What if the cost of raw material goes up?]

We can perceive a *principle of economizing outputs:* that the firm tends to expand those products that become less costly in relation to their value and to contract those that become more so. And we can see how, as a result of shifts in technology or values, multiproduct management may be replaced by management for a single product, or vice versa. Compare the principle of economizing productive agents, page 89.

Considering firms in general, with their opportunities for changing the variety and quantity of both inputs and outputs, we can interpret their decisions as a continuing search for cost-revenue equality on all the many margins of production.

If three or more products are involved, the analysis of the best combination becomes progressively more complex. Such cases are beyond the scope of this book, though the principles are much the same as those we are studying. One technique for determining the best combination where there are many products is called linear programming. This is a technique which is used by some business concerns. It is a form of marginal analysis in which the simplifying assumption is made that net revenues bear a linear relationship to the variable inputs. The equating point among the multiple margins is found with the help of mathematical formulas. Use of the technique requires, as does any method of finding the best combination, good data or expert judgment on the production functions.

The model that we have used to study rival plywood enterprises has been employed in essentially the same form by Prof. G. R. Gregory of the University of Michigan to probe the economics of "multiple use"— i.e., multiproduct forest management.[3] He points out an interesting use of the model for resolving the apparent differences between two schools of thought respecting multiple use: one, that it means producing the various goods and services together on each acre; the other, that it means producing them individually in different parts of a tract or area. He concludes that either concept of multiple use may fulfill the conditions for the best combination, depending on circumstances: The first concept is appropriate if the expansion path takes some such form as in Figure 15b. But the second concept is appropriate if the iso-cost curves are either so low and flat (relative to iso-revenue) that the expansion path lies along the X axis, or relatively so high and steep that it coincides with the Y axis.

[The statement is often made that in the hardwood forests of the northeastern and central United States, timber growing and grazing are incompatible, that woodland pasture represents poor resource use, and that the farmer would do better to put his stock on different acres from his trees. But in the southern pine forest, it is said, trees and stock go well together, at least to a degree.[4] How would you restate these propositions in terms of iso-cost and -revenue curves and an expansion path? How might you test the propositions with the use of these analytical devices?]

[3] Gregory, G. Robinson: "An Economic Approach to Multiple Use," *Forest Science,* March, 1955, pp. 6–13.

[4] See, for example (re hardwoods) DenUyl, Daniel, and R. K. Day: *Woodland Livestock Carrying Capacities and Grazing Injury Studies,* Indiana Agricultural Experiment Station Bulletin 391, rev., Lafayette, 1939; (re pine) Bond, W. E., and Robert S. Campbell: *Planted Pines and Cattle Grazing: A Profitable Use of Southwest Louisiana's Cut-over Pine Land,* Louisiana Forestry Commission Bulletin 4, Baton Rouge, 1951.

The economic analysis of multiproduct forestry may seem fairly convincing when the examples used are timber and forage, or other products to which a market attaches a dollar sign. But what about the products that do not have a market value? How, for instance, is the public firm to weigh timber and wildlife and find the best combination? When we take up the subject of valuation in Chapter 23, we will have a look at this difficult problem.

## SUMMARY

Vertical integration is the combining, by a firm, of enterprises that stand at successive stages in production, one ordinarily supplying another with raw material. The firm's best output of vertically related products hinges on the questions of selling as against using (or buying as against producing) the raw material and of making coincidental adjustments, beyond the short run, in raw-material (or end-product) capacity.

Horizontal integration by a firm is the combining of enterprises at the same stage in production. Two kinds of horizontally related products are joint and rival products.

Joint products are those that come from the same raw material or are produced together in the same process, in relatively fixed amounts at any given level of input. Their best output for the short run is that which equates marginal joint costs with marginal revenues. Joint costs should not be allocated among joint products for purposes of economic analysis.

Rival products are those whose amounts are variable (inversely) at any given level of input. The best short-run output of two such products is found at that point on the firm's expansion path where marginal unit revenue and cost are equal. The location of the path, and thus the comparative amounts of the products that might be produced economically, depend upon the relative slope of iso-cost and -revenue curves, which is in turn a function of marginal rates of substitution.

# Chapter 13

# SUPPLY OF

# PROCESSED

# PRODUCTS

As you know, the economic decisions of the producing firm depend on three factors: (1) the basic production function, or physical relation of output to input, (2) the unit values of the inputs, and (3) the unit values of the outputs. We have been studying the bearing of each factor, successively, upon economic decisions. We had a look at the production function. We considered the cost and use of labor, and then of capital and of land. These are the general categories of input. Let us turn now to the unit value of the output—i.e., product price—as a production determinant. At the same time, let us start bringing together our whole study of the firm's supply by analyzing the influence of price in relation to input costs and in light of the production function. We shall consider in this chapter the supply of processed products—such as logs, bolts, and things made therefrom—and in Chapter 14 the supply of raw products: standing timber, or stumpage.

## DEFINITIONS

We shall take the *supply* of a product to mean the amounts of the product, per unit of time, that would be offered to the market at various prices—the production function, unit costs of agents, and all other conditions remaining the same or being otherwise accounted for. Or sometimes we shall look upon supply, obversely, as the relation of product offerings to cost, while price and other conditions are given. One may speak of a firm's supply, the relation of that firm's offerings to, let us say, the market price. Or one may speak of an industry's supply, the offerings of a group of firms, equal to the sums of individual offerings at each price.

194

Take the case of Lumber Company G. Let us suppose that this firm's supply of lumber is as represented in Table 22. The supply of this firm is the relation of output offered for the market to price in the market—that is, the whole series of offerings in relation to the whole series of prices—say, column 2 in relation to column 1. A list of quantities and the prices with which they are associated in supply is called a *supply schedule*. Two different schedules are given in Table 22.

*Table 22. Lumber supply of Lumber Company G*

| If price of lumber per M bd ft, f.o.b. mill, is— | Then the company will offer, per unit of time, this quantity— (Schedule A) | But with a change in the company's cost setup, quantity offered may be— (Schedule B) |
|:---:|:---:|:---:|
| (1) | (2) | (3) |
| Dollars | Thousand board feet | Thousand board feet |
| 50 | 400 | 490 |
| 55 | 460 | 550 |
| 60 | 500 | 600 |
| 65 | 530 | 640 |
| 70 | 550 | 670 |

Supply in this sense is an abstraction. It is not a pile of lumber, or a pondful of logs to be sawed, or anything else that one can point at in the mill or put his hand on. Supply exists only in the minds and judgments of producers. It might be determined by asking, "How much would you want to sell if the price were so-and-so?" or it might be determined by observing how the firm actually responds to price change, though in either case one would need to make sure that other things were equal or explicitly accounted for.

If offerings are plotted and curved with price, the result is called a *supply curve* (Fig. 16). In drawing a supply curve, it is customary to put the price or other independent variable on the Y axis and quantity, the dependent variable, on the X axis. This scheme, though it breaks with general tradition, has the advantage of putting values and quantities into the same relation as in graphs of the best combination. Refer, for example, to graph d in Figure 6, page 74. The advantage hinges on the fact that certain cost curves derived in such a graph are at the same time supply curves, a point that we shall go into very soon.

If there is a change in the relation of output to price, as from Schedule A to Schedule B of Company G, this is spoken of as a *change in supply*. Any shift in the supply curve represents a change in supply. A shift to the right (higher quantity at a given price) is an increase in supply; a shift to the left (lower quantity), a decrease.

The quantity at a particular price level—e.g., 550 M board feet at $70 under Schedule A—is not the supply; it is the *amount supplied* at this price. If quantity changes solely in response to price, as from 550 M board feet to 500 under Schedule A, this is not a change in supply. It is merely a change in the amount supplied.

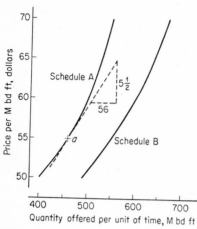

Fig. 16. Lumber supply of Lumber Company G.

Any change in the amount supplied, whether or not accompanied by a change in supply, we shall term a *supply response*. Thus, the shift from 550 M board feet to 500 under Schedule A is a *negative supply response* to price. A change from 550 M board feet on Schedule A to 670 on Schedule B, price remaining at $70, is a *positive supply response* to cost change.

[Suppose the price drops from $70 to $55, and at the same time a change in cost occurs, from Schedule A to Schedule B. Offerings remain at 550 M board feet. Has there been a supply response?]

## ELASTICITY OF SUPPLY

Comparing Schedule A with Schedule B in either Table 22 or Figure 16, or comparing the different parts of each schedule, it is clear that the degree of responsiveness of quantity to a given change in price varies a good deal. Thus a 10 per cent price increase, from $50 to $55, results in a 15 per cent rise in quantity on Schedule A ($^{46}\!\%_{00} = 1.15$), but only about a 12 per cent rise on Schedule B, even though the absolute amount of the rise is the same, 60 M board feet. The responsiveness of quantity to price in a supply schedule or curve is termed *elasticity of supply* and is measured as the ratio of percentage change in quantity to percentage change in price. From $50 to $55, supply has an elasticity of +1.5 on Schedule A (+15/+10); the elasticity on Schedule B is +1.2. These instances of *positive elasticity* signify that the curve slopes up to the right: A higher price calls forth a larger offering of product.

Supply with an elasticity greater than 1.0 is termed *elastic;* less than 1.0, *inelastic.* You will find that on Schedule B, supply has **unitary elas-**

*ticity* between $55 and $60 and that it is elastic at lower prices, inelastic at higher.

You will also find that, except for unitary elasticity, the measurement between two points differs according to whether one is moving up the curve or down. This discrepancy arises from considering chunks of curve and can be eliminated by taking the measurement at a point—that is, taking the ratio of any quantity interval on the tangent, to the corresponding price interval, each interval expressed in percentage of the reading at the point. For example, at point *a* on Schedule A ($q = 460$; $p = 55$), the tangent cuts a quantity interval of 562 minus 506, or 56, in a price interval of 65 minus 59½, or 5½ (see Fig. 16). Thus the $q/p$ ratio is 56/5½, or, in percentage of the point readings, about $1\frac{2}{10}$, and *point elasticity* is +1.2.

It isn't easy to judge by eye the elasticity of a supply curve on arithmetic scale. Any vertical line has an elasticity of zero (quantity totally unresponsive to price), and any line approaching the horizontal is approaching infinite elasticity (maximum response to the slightest price change). But between these extremes, the meaning of a given slope depends on where the curve is located. It is helpful to remember a *rule for the elasticity of supply:* Any straight line or small segment of a curve that points directly at the origin has unitary elasticity, regardless of its slope. Consequently lines or segments that point at the $Y$ axis are elastic, and those that point at the $X$ axis are inelastic. (Note that in Fig. 16, the origin is situated about 2 inches to the left of the vertical scale and about 4 inches down from the horizontal scale.) The rule applies to curves having a positive slope.

## CONDITIONS OF SUPPLY

When a firm's supply is highly inelastic in relation to price, it must mean that special conditions are operating to limit the firm's range of offerings, conditions such as steeply diminishing returns. If other conditions prevailed, the firm's supply might be quite different. Let us take an example to illustrate how one firm's responses may vary with the *conditions of supply:*

Suppose that the lumber industry is entering a period of strengthening markets, of higher demand for its product. Lumber Company G, which has been operating at an output of about 500 M board feet per unit of time, finds an opportunity to sell seasoned lumber at a new and higher price, provided shipment can be made in the current week. To take advantage of this opportunity, the company would have to draw upon such stocks of seasoned lumber as were already on hand or emerging from the kiln. There would be no other way for the company to supply the lumber within the required time. And so the response that the company could make to the higher-price prospect under this condition would be sharply limited: Its supply is relatively inelastic.

That supply which is determined by the disposition of stocks (whether drawn down or withheld), and not primarily by the rate at which they are replaced through new production, we shall term the *stock supply.* Evidently the stock supply is the supply that exists in the minds and judgments of processors when they are looking only a relatively short way into the future. The view is such that all the agents of production (other than stocks) appear fixed.

However, returning to Lumber Company G, if the managers think that their market will stay strong for some little time, then they may well envisage other adjustments beyond those in stocks alone that would lead to a different and perhaps larger positive supply response. For, given enough time, they could arrange to get more logs, put on more men in the mill, maybe adding an extra shift, and make fuller use of the kiln, even to speeding up the drying schedule. It is in such ways, let us say, that the responses in Table 22 would be made possible. The extent of such responses would be limited only by diminishing returns in lumber sawing and drying—that is, by the sawing and drying plant's being fixed. The responses would actually be set in motion by the firm only in the belief that demand would still be favorable when the new output started flowing from the kiln and would so remain long enough to justify the necessary changes in variable inputs.

That supply which is based upon the rate of output that goes into stock, this rate being controlled by varying some of the inputs but holding a substantial part of them fixed, we shall call the *short-run supply.* The short-run supply is that which exists in producers' minds and judgments when the producers are looking far enough ahead to consider alternative inputs of some of the agents of production (other than stocks). Generally, however, much of the input appears fixed, and technology also. Compare our definition of the short run on page 58.

But perhaps Company G looks even further into the future. Suppose it foresees a continuing strong market for its product. Then still other alternatives for increasing output become relevant: to enlarge its capacity through new mill and kiln investments, with matching adjustments in log intake, labor employment, and other inputs. By thus changing the greater part of all its inputs, including some that would be fixed in the short run, the firm would be able to make good a more substantial supply response than any we have yet examined, a response limited only by the firm's judgment of its managerial capacity, of the supply of other inputs, and of the size of the market. An actual decision in favor of such a response would depend upon the firm's belief that its prices, relative to costs, would stay up until output started to flow from new facilities, and would continue high long enough thereafter for the new investments to pay off.

Supply based upon changing the rate of output by means of changing most of the inputs let us call the *long-run supply.* Long-run supply is that which exists in the minds and judgments of producers who are looking so far ahead that most of the agents of production appear variable. (And the *long run,* therefore, is the condition of there being few, if any, fixed elements in production.)

To summarize: Stock supply describes the responses that could be made without changing the rate of output that goes into stock. Short-run supply and long-run supply describe the responses that would be based upon changing the output rate, the former with more, the latter with less, of the inputs remaining fixed.

The three conditions of supply are all conditions foreseen for the future. In general, the stock, short-run, and long-run supply conditions are those of a successively further future. But production firms are always making plans and decisions, making supply choices, setting responses in motion that relate variously to all the kinds of supply. The decisions for all can be made "now." In this sense all the kinds of supply exist "now." Firm G is making stock, labor-force (short-run), and investment (long-run) decisions "now," all the while. The three differ only in the time when they may bear fruit—in their period of gestation—and thus in the length of the forecasts made in support of them.

Let us take special note of the fact that our choice of three supply conditions is largely arbitrary. We might as well have selected six or a dozen. Actually there is a large number of conditions, ranging from that in which all agents are fixed to that where they are all variable. We have divided the range into three parts. Furthermore, we have defined the parts in such a way that their positions within the range are relative, not absolute.

Our study of supply conditions should serve to throw more light on the meaning of the terms *fixed* and *variable*, that we have used throughout Part Two of this book (see p. 61). Now it is evident that the terms are relative: What is fixed and what variable depends on the time period in view.

[Our illustrations of supply response in this section have all used the case of a price rise. Select some process of production (other than timber growing) with which you are familiar, and try analyzing the stock, short-run, and long-run supply responses to a price drop. How do the three differ? How would a firm's current short-run supply differ from its short-run supply as of the time when a long-run supply response had been completed? What about its stock supply in the two cases? How would you expect stock supply to be affected by short-run supply responses?]

## STOCK SUPPLY: NATURE OF STOCKS

Consider the nature of the stocks upon which stock supply rests. Bear in mind the importance of such stocks, the vast quantity of them on hand in the forest economy. The quantity of stocks normally amounts to a substantial fraction of annual output, and for some types of products in

Table 23. *Estimated annual production and year-end stocks of softwood and hardwood lumber in the United States, 1934–1955*

| Year | Softwood lumber | | | | Hardwood lumber | | | |
|---|---|---|---|---|---|---|---|---|
| | Produc-tion | Stocks | | | Produc-tion | Stocks | | |
| | | Mill | Whole-sale and retail | Total | | Mill | Whole-sale and retail | Total |
| | *Billion bd ft* | *Billion bd ft* | *Billion bd ft* | *Billion bd ft* | *Billion bd ft* | *Billion bd ft* | *Billion bd ft* | *Billion bd ft* |
| 1934 | 14.6 | — | — | 13.5 | 4.2 | — | — | 3.6 |
| 1935 | 18.2 | 6.0 | 6.5 | 12.5 | 4.7 | 2.0 | 1.3 | 3.3 |
| 1936 | 22.0 | 6.4 | 7.1 | 13.5 | 5.6 | 2.1 | 1.4 | 3.5 |
| 1937 | 23.1 | 7.6 | 7.7 | 15.3 | 5.8 | 2.5 | 1.6 | 4.1 |
| 1938 | 20.0 | 8.0 | 7.9 | 15.9 | 4.9 | 2.6 | 1.7 | 4.3 |
| 1939 | 23.3 | 7.3 | 8.7 | 16.0 | 5.5 | 2.4 | 1.7 | 4.1 |
| 1940 | 25.7 | 5.2 | 8.3 | 13.5 | 5.5 | 1.8 | 1.5 | 3.3 |
| 1941 | 29.9 | 5.7 | 8.6 | 14.3 | 6.6 | 1.9 | 1.6 | 3.5 |
| 1942 | 29.5 | 3.7 | 5.3 | 9.0 | 6.8 | 1.3 | 1.0 | 2.3 |
| 1943 | 26.9 | 2.6 | 3.4 | 6.0 | 7.4 | 0.8 | 0.7 | 1.5 |
| 1944 | 25.2 | 2.2 | 3.0 | 5.2 | 7.8 | 0.7 | 0.6 | 1.3 |
| 1945 | 21.2 | 1.9 | 1.8 | 3.7 | 7.0 | 0.6 | 0.4 | 1.0 |
| 1946 | 25.9 | 2.2 | 2.5 | 4.7 | 8.3 | 0.7 | 0.4 | 1.1 |
| 1947 | 28.0 | 2.7 | 3.6 | 6.3 | 7.4 | 0.9 | 0.6 | 1.5 |
| 1948 | 29.6 | 3.9 | 4.0 | 7.9 | 7.4 | 1.1 | 0.7 | 1.8 |
| 1949 | 26.5 | 3.9 | 4.0 | 7.9 | 5.7 | 1.1 | 0.7 | 1.8 |
| 1950 | 30.7 | 3.5 | 4.3 | 7.8 | 7.4 | 1.2 | 0.7 | 1.9 |
| 1951 | 30.4 | 3.8 | 4.6 | 8.4 | 8.0 | 1.4 | 0.8 | 2.2 |
| 1952 | 31.4 | — | — | 8.2 | 8.0 | — | — | 2.2 |
| 1953 | 31.0 | — | — | 8.5 | 8.0 | — | — | 2.3 |
| 1954 | 29.7 | — | — | 8.1 | 7.8 | — | — | 2.1 |
| 1955 | 32.0 | — | — | 8.6 | 8.0 | — | — | 2.3 |

SOURCE: U.S. Department of Agriculture, Forest Service and Commodity Stabilization Service: *The Demand and Price Situation for Forest Products 1956*, Washington, 1955, pp. 9, 11. Supplemented by author's estimates.

some years—for example, lumber in time of depression—may nearly equal annual output (Table 23). These stocks are capital, an agent of production. That is, they are a means for bringing the manufactured product to consumers. And note that they are simultaneously the source of the product—like a machine—and the product itself (compare p. 103). If the value of the product changes, the value of the stock changes also, in the same direction and degree. This is the case of standing timber all over again (p. 136), though we are talking not about

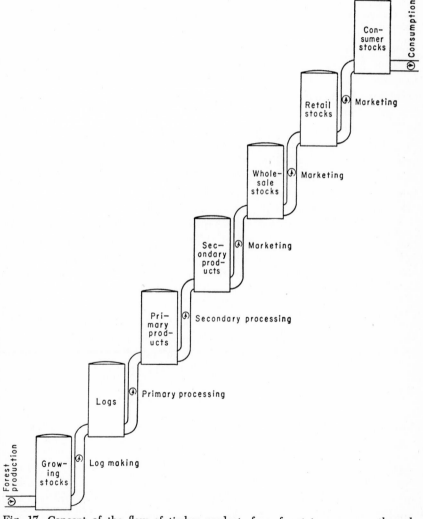

Fig. 17. Concept of the flow of timber products from forest to consumer, through the pumps of production and the tanks of stocks.

standing timber, but about processed products! Bear these thoughts in mind as we go along.

We may think of the production of forest products as a flow, through pipes and tanks, from the forest to the consumer (Fig. 17). The tanks hold stocks in successive stages of production. In the connecting pipes are pumps, representing processing, marketing, and other production facilities. The material in each tank is the product of the productive process that comes before it, and the raw material for the process that follows. Here we have vertical integration (p. 182) in a social sense. As the pumps operate, they draw down the stocks in the tanks behind them and build up the stocks in the tanks ahead of them. And the whole movement of stocks through the economy is punctuated by selling, buying, processing, transportation, and storage.

From day to day and from year to year, the level of stocks in the tanks moves up and down and the rate of flow through the connecting pipes accelerates and slackens—partly in a regular, somewhat periodic, manner and partly in an apparently random fashion. For example, stocks rise and fall with long-term economic trends, with the building cycle, and with the business cycle. You have perhaps met with the term *inventory recession*, referring to the time when stocks have been built up and owners' efforts to move them are accompanied by declining prices and perhaps falling production and rising unemployment. Stocks rise and fall seasonally, and in shorter periods in response to changes in the market.

Any of the tanks or pumps may send signals back through the economy calling for materials to be pushed along at a faster or slower rate. Price is such a signal. Often it takes a while for the economy to respond to the signals. The delay occurs while the rate of output that goes into stock is being changed. The study of such response is the study of short-run and long-run supply.

Stocks in any of the tanks may be held up or drawn down on very short notice, without waiting for a change in the rate at which they are replenished. Stocks are manipulated thus in response to hurry-up signals from stations further along the pipe line. The study of this sort of response is the study of stock supply.

### ECONOMICS OF STOCK HOLDING

What determines the stock of product held by any firm at a particular time? For an example, let us take the case of Firm H, a retail lumber yard, whose stocks consist of quantities of the various species, dimensions, grades, and workings of lumber. The principles for this type of firm will apply to any holder of stocks.

The quantity of stock held in the yard can be thought of as roughly

the result of the firm's effort to weigh the advantages (revenues) against
the disadvantages (costs) of stock holding. The firm aiming to maximize
its net revenue per unit of time will seek, directly or indirectly, that level
of stocks to which the last additions represent an added advantage just
equal to the added disadvantage.

The advantages to Firm H of holding stocks are mainly of two sorts:
First is the opportunity to meet customers' requirements, varying in kind
and quantity, on short notice and in a steady flow. Readiness to provide
what is wanted when wanted is the main feature of the retailer's service,
and through it he satisfies and holds his regular customers and gets new
ones. From this follows the tendency of stocks to be proportional to a
firm's volume of business. The second kind of advantage of stock holding
is the opportunity to gain if the value of the product rises either because
of an increase in customers' demand or because of a decrease in wholesalers' supply.

The disadvantages to Firm H of holding stocks may likewise be
grouped into two: First is the attendant cost outlay—interest on the investment in stocks and in storage
space and facilities, handling the
stock, deterioration, and insurance
against fire and other hazards. Second is the risk of loss from a decline in product value resulting
either from a fall in customers'
demand or from a rise in wholesalers' supply.

As stocks are increased, the additional advantage of holding more
stocks declines. This is because the
bulk of Firm H's potential business becomes more and more fully
provided for, and the chances for
further gain are limited to less and
less important transactions, or important ones that are less and less

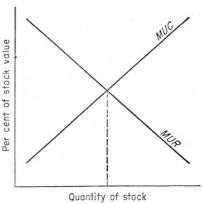

Fig. 18. Best level of stock for Firm H.
Where advantage of any small change
just equals the disadvantage, there is
nothing to be gained by a change.

likely to materialize. At the same time, the additional disadvantage of
holding more stocks certainly becomes no less as stocks increase and may
become greater if space, capital, or labor is limited or the rate of risk
associated with declining product value rises. Figure 18 shows the additional advantage (marginal revenue) as diminishing with stock, and the
additional disadvantage (marginal cost) as increasing with stock. Both
are expressed in per cent of the value of the stock, just as in Figure 9*b*
(p. 127) we expressed the marginal growth per cent of a timber stand

and the alternative rate of return in per cent of stand value. The inter-section of the two curves marks the best level of stock—or, to complete the analogy, the best stocking.

Here, then, is a model for analyzing stock holders' responses to changes in the determinants of stocks. Let's see how the model works.

## STOCK-SUPPLY RESPONSES

Suppose that the price of the product rises as a result of an increase in demand. The firm's stock-supply response then will depend on what further change in price the firm anticipates within the relevant period.

Case 1. If the firm thinks that the price will quickly fall again, it is anticipating a downward shift in marginal revenue in relation to marginal cost. A new equilibrium is set, at a lower stock level than before, and this equilibrium is attained by drawing down stocks—that is, by exhibiting a positive supply response.

Case 2. If the firm anticipates a continued price rise, this anticipation represents a shift in both marginal revenue and cost. A rising price trend, or growth in the value of the stock, means an upward shift in revenue, just as an increase in timber growth rate raises the marginal value growth per cent. At the same time, the expectation of rising price implies a reduced allowance for the risk of decline in stock value, which is a cost factor; and marginal cost shifts down. These changes cooperate to set a higher point of best stocking, and so the immediate supply response of the firm, in its effort to build up its stock, tends to be negative.

The firm's ability to carry through a negative supply response under the circumstances just described will depend on several factors: First, any negative response that is exhibited may tend to raise price and thus to materialize the anticipated upward trend in stock value. This, in turn, will fortify the tendency toward a negative supply response. Meanwhile, however, if the firm's actions do have an effect upon the market, the firm may be under pressure to release stocks in order to satisfy the increased demands of its customers and retain its share of business. And if the firm anticipates that the cost of replenishing stocks will not rise in proportion to product price—i.e., if it believes that competing firms will make good their negative responses—then its own compulsion toward a negative response will be that much less. The upshot will be to moderate, or even reverse, the initial tendency toward a negative supply response.

Case 3. If the firm thinks that price, once risen, will remain unchanged thereafter, it sees no change in either its marginal cost or its marginal revenue from stock holding. Consequently the best level of stock is unchanged, and there is no supply response one way or the other. Since people very commonly assume that today's prices are the best estimate of what prices will be in the near future, the nil stock-supply response to price change is fairly frequently encountered.

[Now that we have discussed supply responses following a price rise, you should take the opposite case, where the price has fallen, and use the model in Figure 18 to analyze responses assuming various price expectations on the part of the firm. Do you come to the conclusion that the initial price change is irrelevant—that only the firm's judgment of the future affects its supply response? Or do the direction and size of the initial change bear upon the response? Suppose that there has been no price change at all, but the firm comes to anticipate one. Will there be a supply response, and if so, to what is it a response?]

Notice that what matters—what produces a supply response—is not simply a change in price, but a change in the relation of price (revenue) to cost. Now a consummated change in product price necessarily means a proportional change in stock value and thus in the cost of holding stock, so that the price shift, under stock-supply conditions, is just canceled out. *Anticipations* of price change, on the other hand, can affect revenue without affecting cost, or vice versa, and hence can have a net influence upon the firm's combination of the agents of production in stock supply.

Notice, again, that we have not attempted to draw the firm's stock-supply curve. Our analytical model for the stock-supply problem is a model for the best level of stock. Conclusions about supply response come from this model only by inference: An increase in the best stock infers a negative supply response, because in order to build up the stock the firm must for a while reduce its stock withdrawals below the rate at which new stock is produced—that is, it must curtail its offerings to the market. By the same token, a decrease in the best stock infers a positive stock-supply response.

We have spoken only of the firm's stock supply. The industry's stock supply is the sum of the supplies of the firms—existing firms, with their existing stocks.

### TIME RIVALRY

Now before we leave the subject of stock supply, let us introduce an interesting and useful idea about stocks, which we may term the **time rivalry** of supply from stocks. Within the period when the rate of replenishing stocks is fixed, the firm must always choose between alternative points of time for the releasing of stock. For instance, it can release less now and more later, or more now and less later. The amount released at any one time will affect the amounts that can be released at all other times, and the relationship is necessarily inverse because the stock as a whole is essentially fixed. There are, in effect, a great number of different products that can be taken from any stock: product at time A, product at time B, and so on. These products are rivals for the use of the stock, the machine that produces them. The more of product-at-time-A made from the stock, the less of product-at-time-B that can be made. Compare our earlier definition of rival products, page 184. The supply of such products we may term *rival supply,* which is in contrast to the *joint supply* of joint products.

It is the time rivalry of supply from stocks that sets the pattern of stock-supply responses. The firm departs from a constant rate of stock release to the extent that it can benefit from anticipated changes in price or profitability of sales without later suffering a countervailing loss of business. Because of the durability of most stocks in the forest economy, time rivalry wields an effect upon supply over considerable periods. Stock levels at widely spaced points of time are obviously interrelated to some extent. Note, for example, in Table 23 how the high lumber stocks of the economically depressed 1930s bolstered the nation's reserves during the heavy-consumption years of World War II in the face of dwindling mill output, and how slowly the country recovered from stock depletion at war's end.

## SHORT-RUN SUPPLY

As we have seen, short-run supply is the relation, to price, of the quantity that would be determined by varying some of the inputs, while a large part of them remained fixed. In processing, the manufacturing plant typically is fixed in the short run. The rate of output is changed by changing such inputs as raw material, labor, power, and supplies. We have given so much thought already to the short run and the firm's adjustments in this period that our present discussion can be brief and mainly a review.

For the firm whose level of output does not affect its markets—the firm that can sell any amount of product at the same price—the short-run supply curve follows the curve of short-run marginal cost per unit of output. Or rather, the supply curve follows the cost curve above the lower end of the economic range of production. All that is needed in order to read this cost curve as a supply curve is to change the cost axis to read "price," leaving the quantity axis as it stands.

Let us see if we can understand why the supply curve thus coincides with the marginal cost curve. Return to our definition of supply (p. 194) and of the supply curve (p. 195). Does not the latter define the marginal cost curve as well? To take a case in point: Study the marginal cost curve in Figure 6d, page 74, and see if it does not also depict what the (rational) firm's offerings (output) would be at given prices, just as do the curves in Figure 16 (p. 196).

Below the lower end of the economic range of production—below the point where average variable cost per unit of output is a minimum—supply departs from marginal cost. So long as price is high enough to cover at least the variable costs and even if it does not cover the fixed costs as well, the firm will do best to continue operating in the short run, since under this condition the fixed costs cannot be escaped in any case. But if price falls below average variable cost and promises to stay down, a better alternative appears. This is to cease production, since the variable costs can be escaped in the short run. This is another way of looking at the lower economic limit of production, though it amounts to the same proposition as developed on page 78—namely, that the lower limit is the point where the return to the fixed agents is nil.

Then it follows that the firm's complete supply curve in the short run comes in two sections as shown by the solid lines in Figure 19a.

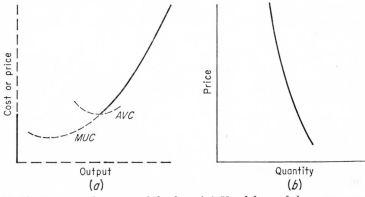

Fig. 19. Short-run supply curves of the firm. (a) Usual form of the curve, as related to marginal and average variable costs. (b) An unusual case, negative elasticity.

The amount of product that the firm will supply in the short run at any price is therefore the same question as the effect of price upon the best combination of agents or intensity of management. In general, if price rises and is expected to stay up long enough for output to be increased, a positive supply response results. Or, similarly, a fall in price elicits a negative response. [Compare the role of price under short-run conditions with that under stock-supply conditions. Would you say that in the short run it is the current price or the anticipated future price that determines supply response?]

As in the case of stock supply, it is of course the relation of price to cost that really matters. If a price rise is accompanied by a cost rise which raises marginal cost the same amount as price, the net effect upon the best combination will be nil, and the short-run supply response will be nil. (Compare the question posed on page 196.)

## SOME SUPPLY ODDITIES

Returning to Figure 19*a*, the point where the supply curve breaks off holds special interest. If price ordinarily stands somewhere near minimum average aggregrate cost, then the extent of the price decline (or cost increase) that the firm can tolerate without closing down depends upon its ratio of fixed to variable costs. The higher the ratio, the more drastic the price cut or cost rise the firm can stand in the short run. The ability of old softwood pulp mills to keep going in such disadvantaged areas as New York and the Lake States rests mainly on their high fixed inputs. At the other extreme, the small, family-operated sawmill keeps going in depressed times principally by virtue of its low variable costs. When the family has no employment alternatives and is willing to work for whatever the lumber may bring, and when it has its own woodland and logs, its own raw material, its only variable cost may be for fuel and minor supplies.

The supply of lumber from the family sawmill under the circumstances just described tends to be very inelastic. In fact, it may have zero or even *negative elasticity*, the curve sloping up to the left. If the family derives a substantial share of its cash income from lumber, and the price falls, the family may counteract the effect upon income by making more lumber. The resulting supply curve of negative (but low) elasticity is illustrated in graph *b* of Figure 19.

During World War II, there was a greatly increased demand for ginseng root, which was gathered in the northern forests and used for medicinal purposes. Buyers sought some way to increase the output of the pickers, and decided that this might be accomplished by raising the price per pound offered to the pickers. Accordingly the buyers raised the price, but the result was the opposite of what they expected. The pickers gathered less ginseng than before. The price having been raised, they could now satisfy their desire for income by four days' work instead of five. Apparently if the buyers wanted more ginseng, they should have lowered the price!

Here is a seemingly odd case, where the price signals sent back through the pipeline get output flowing nicely all the way along, until suddenly a point back in the line is reached where the signals are no longer interpreted in the customary fashion, and that part of the economy simply refuses to act in the manner expected of it. Society under these circumstances is baffled, because it wants something, sees the opportunity to get it, but doesn't know how to ask for it.

Price-signal troubles of various sorts are common in forestry. In fact, they are a major aspect of our timber-management problem in the United States, as we shall see in Chapter 14.

## LONG-RUN SUPPLY

Long-run supply, as we said, is the supply when most or all costs are seen as variable. In the long run, plant and other such relatively permanent facilities can be depreciated or enlarged, and perhaps the enterpriser himself can seek alternative uses of his labor.

The length of view implied in the long-run supply—the gestation period for long-run supply decisions—varies immensely with the type of productive operation. For the positive long-run supply responses of expanding operations to be made good may take only a matter of days, or it may take years, as where new fixed facilities require long planning and construction or where the product takes much time to emerge in finished form. The pulp industry offers examples of long spans for planning, site location, and mill construction. Some branches of the hardwood lumber industry traditionally have had very long periods of production because of the seasoning process.

The negative long-run supply responses of contracting operations may take even more time to materialize if fixed facilities are durable and not versatile and fixed inputs are large in comparison to variable inputs. Again the pulp and paper industry provides examples.

The price relevant to long-run supply is, as for the other supply conditions, a prospective price. Or rather, it is the whole price prospect for the future period when the changes now contemplated would have been made and become fixed. It includes also those price prospects for the nearer future which affect the long-run outlook. The costs, also, relevant to long-run supply and supply responses are those of the same future periods.

## FIRM'S LONG-RUN SUPPLY

If the firm foresees a price high enough to cover its average variable cost in the long run, it may plan to operate, but it cannot be expected to do so otherwise. In this respect, the long run is no different from any other supply condition. But of course when we are speaking of the long run rather than other conditions, we are including much more under the heading of variable cost. In the ultimate long run, when all costs are variable, to cover the variable costs is to cover all costs, which surely is the minimum standard that anyone would use in assessing a prospective new business.

From time to time we have emphasized that the best short-run combination is not necessarily profitable. For example, in Chapter 5, on page 67, we have shown that, if Hawkins's alternatives were good enough, the timber-stand-improvement enterprise might not attract him.

Clearly, Hawkins had two questions to answer before going ahead. The one that we studied at length was this: Assuming that he decided on timber-stand improvement and thus "fixed" the cost of his own time, how should he best organize? This was the short-run question. But there was a second, comparatively long-run (or longer short-run), question: Should he do timber-stand improvement at all? This is the kind of problem that we are talking about now, and the cost of Hawkins's time, being variable in this connection, is relevant to the solution. We are also talking about even longer-run questions (presumably answered before our study in Chapter 5 began) such as whether Hawkins's firm should get into the forestry game in the first place, considering the cost of timber land and all the costs of operating it. Faced with a question of this order, the enterpriser might foresee no costs at all but those that appeared variable and thus were subject to decision. And what we are now saying about the long run is that the enterpriser, to be attracted, would have to foresee a price at least high enough to cover the minimum average variable cost (i.e., cost subject to the current decision) at which he could operate.

The minimum cost in question here is not necessarily the least cost at which facilities of a given scale could be operated. Rather, it is the least cost at which a given output could be produced with facilities of any scale. For, again, we are considering the long run, and thus the scale of productive plant is an open question, a variable element.

The firm's long-run supply curve may have positive slope, as in the short run, or it may be horizontal, negative, or U-shaped, according to whether average costs are expected to rise, remain constant, or fall with increasing scale—and according to the output range covered by the curve. The trend of cost with scale in the long run depends upon the net result of the firm's economies and diseconomies of scale, both those internal within the firm and those external to it.

Rising costs in the long run—that is, diminishing returns—come about somewhat as they do in the short run, by a crowding of one or more of the agents of production. Although not fixed in the long run, agents may nevertheless become crowded because of their lack of interchangeability. The condition here represented is one of internal diseconomies of scale. Thus the manager of the firm may be a limiting factor in operations such as handicrafts or furniture making which may require a great deal of personal attention, and even in such lines of production as cooperage manufacture and in some branches of the hardwood veneer industry. Modern forms of corporate organization and management, which are designed to overcome human limitations in supervision, are not generally applicable in such lines of manufacture as those mentioned, because the economies of scale are not sufficient to warrant the necessary cost outlay. Diseconomies of scale arise also from limited raw material. To get more hardwood veneer logs for a bigger plant requires reaching out longer distances at higher cost—either that or building more plants, which may entail rising cost through the management factor.

Constant cost in the long run is the case that comes closest to fitting most firms in the mechanical wood-conversion industries throughout a wide range of production. In part, constant cost here represents a balancing off of economies and diseconomies of scale, but to a great extent this cost-output relationship arises directly from the character of the raw material and the manufacturing process. Take sawmilling for example. If the firm wants to increase its scale, it must do so primarily by installing, not bigger saws or faster saws, but more saws. Thus, plants are enlarged mainly by adding more production lines just like those already operating. The firm may grow, alternatively, by adding more plants just like those already operating. There is little saving in unit cost represented here. The limitation stems from the character of the raw material. Logs come in a certain size and quality range, and are handled one at a time, in succession. To put more wood through a mill requires more logs—seldom bigger logs, and often smaller and lower-quality logs. You may say that the fundamental limitation is really technological and point out that there is no need for technology to be fixed in the long run. This is true, and yet the fact remains that the mechanical wood-conversion industry is as described.

Falling cost in the long run is exemplified by the chemical wood-conversion firm, notably the pulp and paper firm. Here falling cost results from both internal and external net economies of scale: bigger digestors; larger pipes and pumps (much of the material that is used *flows*, which offers a huge advantage technologically); bigger and faster machines; bulk purchases of raw material, power, and water; and bulk sales. Except for the problem of wood procurement and in some cases of water, economies of plant scale continue over a wide range of output. And beyond that, the firm can keep on gaining many economies through building additional plants.

Falling cost is, in a sense, an anomaly in economic life. Its logical outcome is the domination of the industry by one or a few firms, and eventually monopoly. [Can you explain why this is? Do you think it will happen in the pulp and paper industry?]

*INDUSTRY'S LONG-RUN SUPPLY*

An industry's long-run supply schedule is the sum of the schedules of the individual firms. But not, of course, only of existing plants or even of existing firms. New plants and firms may appear in the long run, or existing ones drop out.

Whereas for the individual firm the supplies of the agents of production are commonly elastic, this is not so for the industry, at least beyond a point. Notably, wood-using industry faces in the end an inelastic supply of raw material. Even the pulp and paper industry, which enjoys virtually the last call upon timber resources, ultimately is confronted by diminishing elasticity of pulpwood supply. Thus even this industry's long-run supply curve may be expected at some point to turn upward into a rising-cost phase.

## MARGINS OF AVAILABILITY OF RAW MATERIAL

In Chapter 14, we shall begin to study the role of price as a signal for the production of stumpage as raw material for the timber economy. But here, while we are considering the raw-material problems of the long run and the supply responses in processing, we should say something about the price relations of the logging industry, which is the first processing industry in the timber pipeline, and the first station in the pipeline to react to price signals in a way that is considered "normal."

Let us bear in mind the manner in which a price change can discourage output or call forth increased output. It does so by impinging upon the countless margins to which an industry has carried its combinations of productive agents. The price change alters marginal adjustments among firms and within firms. It alters marginal adjustments in the use of labor, machines, raw material, and all other details of the operations of firms. Price thus serves as one social device for allocating and reallocating resources, and the device is in constant use, shifting effort throughout the economy in somewhat the desired directions.

Where logging is concerned, the alteration of marginal adjustments through price change alters what we may call the *margins of availability* of the raw material of all wood-using industry, logs and bolts. When the price of this raw material rises relative to cost—or promises to rise—it makes possible (or promises to do so) the logging of smaller and lower-quality logs and bolts. That is, the marginal log or bolt becomes smaller and of lower quality. Again, the marginal tree changes in size, quality, and species. The marginal stand is a lighter or otherwise less valuable stand. The marginal logging chance moves further back from market, or into less accessible ground. The marginal supply regions of the nation and the world shift outward toward higher-cost situations. The marginal firm is a different, less efficient firm. And new margins are set for all the agents and instruments of production that the firm uses. Such shifts, even in the long run, tend to be in the direction of rising cost.

But meanwhile society works upon the production context. Technology is changed in directions conducive to falling cost.

And so arises the contest of which we had a glimpse in Chapter 3—between the forces of falling and of rising cost, between man, equipped with ingenuity, and his refractory environment, between technology and natural-resource depletion.

## SUMMARY

Supply is the whole relation between price (or, in some of our work, cost) of a good or service and the quantity that would be offered in the market. A change in supply is a change in the relation of quantity to price. A supply response is any change in quantity. The elasticity at any interval or point on a supply schedule or curve is the ratio of percentage change in quantity to percentage change in price. Price is significant to the firm's supply behavior primarily in its relation to variable costs of production.

Stock supply is determined by the management of stocks on hand. The best combination respecting stock is that which equates the marginal costs and revenues of stock holding. To reduce stock is to make a positive supply response; to accumulate stock, a negative response. A given stock can be offered in the market either now or later, but not both: There is a time rivalry of supply from stocks.

Short-run supply is determined by the combination of variable with fixed inputs. The firm's short-run supply curve coincides with its curve of marginal cost per unit of output within the economic range of production.

Long-run supply is determined by the combination of largely variable inputs. In the long run, the firm or industry can change output by changing the scale of productive plant. Higher output may entail rising cost per unit of output, as is typical in the short run, or it may be achieved at constant or falling cost, depending upon internal and external economies and diseconomies of scale.

# Chapter 14

# SUPPLY OF STANDING TIMBER

L ET US turn now from the supply of processed timber products to that of standing timber, or stumpage. The principles will be the same. But many of the conclusions we draw will be interestingly different. Mainly we shall talk about the firm's supply and cover the industry's supply by implication.

In the case of processed products, we found that our three supply conditions sorted themselves out rather neatly. The variable and fixed agents that determined the supply condition were clearly distinguishable. And the stock, short-run, and long-run supply represented a fairly continuous, lengthening series of price-cost forecasts and of gestated quantity responses. However, in the case of stumpage, there is no such neat sorting, and responses of the stock-supply variety tend to overshadow the others. Behind this situation lie the characteristics of timber capital that we studied in Chapter 8 (pp. 102–106). You should review these characteristics as an aid to grasping the arguments of the present chapter.

The stock supply of stumpage is that which rests on the disposition of growing stocks (whether they are drawn down or withheld), and not primarily on the rate at which they are replenished or created. The latter is the basis for the short-run and long-run supply. In the short run, more of the agents for producing new growing stock appear fixed; in the long run, less or none.

Note that when we consider growing stock, which is not a single commodity but a variable sheaf of commodities, we must have in mind not so much the whole quantity of it as the amount by categories of quality, or value.

214

## STOCK SUPPLY OF STUMPAGE

When the firm designates timber for cutting and makes preparations for a cut, or when it refrains from doing so, it is generating a stock-supply response. Timber marking for cut and leave relates to stock supply. When we reflect how central to the whole practice of timber management is the decision regarding cut and leave—how even under the most intensive practice this decision is the firm's chief means for carrying out its policy —and how the preponderance of silvicultural effort culminates in marking—we can at once grasp the peculiar importance of stock supply in the economics of woods forestry. Stock supply relates to the management of what we characterized in Chapter 8 as the principal cost element in timber production.

Furthermore, stock-supply responses, determining as they do the quantity of remaining growing stock, determine the scale of the productive plant. For the remaining stock *is* the productive plant. In timber growing, therefore, the subject of stock supply invades what we have heretofore regarded as the special province of the long run. And in view of the modest rate of return to timber capital—the slow rate of growth— and the long period of production, stock-supply responses carry direct implications for the distant future. That is to say, the economic prospect relevant to stock-supply decisions is a very long one. A large positive or negative stock-supply response today may set the pattern for the firm's timber output for the rest of the rotation and thus dominate the whole range of time within which both short-run and long-run supply decisions might be bearing fruit.

We have characterized short-run and long-run supply as that based on the rate of output that goes into stock. In timber growing, this is still an essential characterization. But note that, of all the means usable in forestry for controlling the rate of output going into stock, controlling the stock itself is most influential. That is to say, the character and amount of growing stock is the chief determinant of growth on any piece of forest land. And so again stock supply invades the domain of the other supply conditions.

Now that we have a glimpse of the overriding importance of stock supply in timber production, let us study the workings of supply under this condition.

## GROWING-STOCK SUPPLY RESPONSES

We have already constructed a model for analysis of the firm's stumpage stock-supply responses. It is the best-stocking model of Chapter 9 (pp. 123–128, 134–137), in which stock is related to the marginal value growth per cent of the stand and the firm's alternative rate of return. Any change, or prospect of change, in price which affects either of these two determinants can be expected to alter the best stocking and thus produce a supply response. Supply responses to cost change can similarly be predicted by means of this model.

The model of best timber stocking is essentially the same as that for the best stock of processed goods, and its use leads to similar conclusions: The prospect of a price rise tends to bring a negative supply response through the firm's effort to build up growing stocks. The prospect of a price decline tends to elicit a positive response. And if the firm believes that the future price will be about what it is today or if unanticipated changes in price occur, no response is to be expected, except in the case, also studied in Chapter 9, where the timber is exhaustible or believed so.

Let us look beyond these rather mechanical propositions and get at least a glimpse of what they mean in real life. Take the case of the forest owner who sells stumpage on the open market. The typical such owner is the small owner. This man commonly sits back and waits for offers from stumpage buyers. The offers come in periodically, and they vary a good deal. They vary with the state of the general market, and they vary individually according to the buyer's judgment of his alternatives and to the psychology of the moment. When the prospective seller receives an offer which in his view represents about as high a price or as favorable a deal as is likely to come his way for some time, he is then in the position of forecasting a price decline and is apt to exhibit a positive supply response, allowing his growing stock to be drawn down. On the other hand, if an offer looks low to him, his response is likely to be negative, and he will let his growing stock accumulate. The buyer's aim, of course, is to draw out a positive response with a low price. This, to be sure, is difficult, but there may be ways of accomplishing it. For example, a buyer, alone or in league with others, may simulate a price decline by making successively lower offers for a timber tract, until the owner is led to expect still further cuts in price and hastens to sell before they material-ize. These are instances of stumpage supply response to price. [Perhaps you can draw others from your own experience or reading and analyze them by means of our model.]

What we have so far is a first step toward understanding the stock supply of stumpage. We need now to bring in some other considerations, notably two: stock-holding costs and integration with timber processing.

## STOCK-HOLDING COSTS

One cannot stress too often that, so far as supply response is concerned, it is not price alone that counts, but price in relation to cost. Or, what is the same thing, cost in relation to price. The anticipation of a price decline may be viewed alternatively as a rise in the opportunity cost of holding timber. But in no case does the anticipation result in a supply response unless the two blades of the shears, price and cost, move in reference to each other.

Now unanticipated changes in price often bring out no stumpage-supply response from the firm, because their effect is canceled by the accompanying change in the value of the stumpage as growing stock. But actual changes in cost commonly do lead to a response from the firm, for they may be unattended by countervailing shifts in revenue. The influence of both price and cost upon best stocking (and hence upon the stock supply) of stumpage was examined in Chapter 9, pages 125–126 and 135–137. Clearly, if one is looking for a factor to which the stock

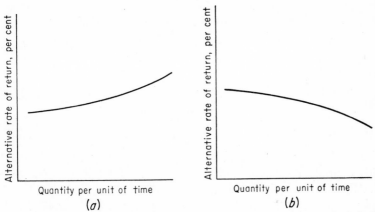

Fig. 20. Stumpage supply in relation to the alternative rate of return: (*a*) Stock supply. (*b*) Short-run or long-run supply.

supply of stumpage is sensitive, a factor upon which the supply is elastic, he will not find it in price. He will, however, find it in cost, and notably in the alternative rate of return.

A stock-supply curve which relates quantity to the alternative rate of return is illustrated in graph *a* of Figure 20. The quantities represented on the curve are alternative current offerings from a stock of given size.

Since the alternative rate of return applicable to a timber stand may change rapidly but marginal value growth per cent is slow to change, one can expect to find many stands where they are not equated. Two such cases deserve special thought:

First, there is the firm with a low alternative rate of return, which is building up its growing stock, but whose marginal value growth per cent is still relatively high. The stumpage offerings of such a firm tend to continue low. Consider how strong the contrary influences must be in order to draw a positive response from the firm.

Second, there is the firm with a very high alternative rate of return—
a rate so high, indeed, that the stand is not physically capable of matching it with value growth, no matter how heavily the growing stock is
reduced. Yet the firm owns the timber stand (let us suppose the firm
cannot readily get rid of it or turn the land to other use), and all it can
do is cut or sell timber as heavily and frequently as logging requirements
will allow. Here is a case very common among the small private holdings.
Now if price (strictly speaking, the price of logs or bolts or more highly
processed wood) rises, a positive supply response may be expected
through a change in the margins of availability of raw material. Timber
not formerly merchantable is now merchantable, and this timber is
offered by the firm for cutting.

### GROWING-STOCK SUPPLY OF INTEGRATED FIRMS

We need to touch again upon the case of the forest-land-owning firm
which also owns and operates a processing plant, the situation first
brought up in Chapter 12 (pp. 183–184). This firm uses its own timber as
raw material, and its sales are in the form of processed products. What
are the *stumpage*-supply responses of such a firm?

Suppose that the prices of the firm's end products rise and promise
to stay up long enough to warrant both short-run and long-run increases
in the firm's processed output. Soon the firm will begin to make good its
positive supply responses, and these will call for the use of more raw
material. Meantime, however, the price rise has probably produced no
supply response in the firm's woods enterprise. So far as stock supply is
concerned, it will not do so, and when it comes to short-run or long-run
supply—that is, responses in terms of growth—if there are to be any such
responses, they are probably still in the future.

And so the firm finds itself in conflict with itself, one part of it wanting
to do one thing and another part wanting to do something different and
incompatible. What happens?

If there is an open market from which the firm may draw wood, this
may make it possible for the firm to make good both a nil or small
positive response in its woods and a large positive response in its mill.
The open market is ordinarily receptive to price increases and exhibits
a positive response, both because of the high alternative rates of return
of sellers in this market and because price increases spur the efforts of
timber buyers and loggers. We can see how the social quest for wood
tends to fasten upon those wood-owning members of society whose
alternative rates are high. They constitute the element which is pliable—
responsive to price.

Or the firm may seek to buy more timber land that is ready for harvesting, a response that we shall look into a little further in a later section. But if neighboring firms are meeting with the same experience as this one, the land-buying alternative may not be promising.

If the firm finds that it cannot afford to buy enough open-market wood or operable timber land to make up the difference between the ordinary supply responses of its woods and processing enterprises, then the firm must strike some sort of compromise internally. The compromise will be complex, but we may think of it for the time being as an average supply response, weighted by the product values involved in the two enterprises. The processing enterprise tends to carry the heavier weight, and it may easily dominate the woods enterprise, even to the point of running it out of business.

### SHORT-RUN STUMPAGE SUPPLY

Now let us turn from the stock supply of stumpage to a brief consideration of short-run, and then of long-run supply: Supply that depends upon the rate of output, or timber growth. We have already remarked on the relation of stock supply to growth rate. We cannot escape the fact that in timber production, only growing *stock* grows: Only stocks yield a product. Thus there is no getting around the fact that the variables governing stock supply, primarily the alternative rate of return, pass upon all efforts, of whatever sort, to produce timber for use, and determine what these efforts shall come to. Here, however, let us bypass this issue and look for kinds of growth response that stem, at least to start with, from decisions about the input of land, of labor, or of capital other than timber itself. These may be either short- or long-run supply responses.

The subject of short-run timber supply takes in such activities as forest roading and other development, forest protection, and cultural measures including pruning, weeding, fertilizing, and planting. The fixed inputs often include land or timber, and the variable inputs typically are labor, equipment, and supplies. The cost of the variable inputs determines supply; and within the supply thus determined, the amount supplied is related primarily to product price. The models are those of Chapters 5 and 6.

It is worth noting that the short-run supply of stumpage is that which exists in producers' minds and judgments when the producers are looking possibly a very great way into the future. When it comes to woods forestry, there is not necessarily anything short about the short run. (Why use the term then? Because it has currency. Using it to describe a mixture of fixed and variable inputs is logical for most lines of production, as we saw in Chapter 13.) True, the firm making a decision about fighting a forest fire has highly immediate values in view. But on the other hand, there are more distant values also in view in most short-run woods decisions, and in many the product values are all distant, perhaps up to a forest rotation away. Think back to the case of Hawkins and his timber-stand improvement. His best combination was set by the price of his product, released trees, and this price was estimated by forecasting the values at the end of the rotation and discounting them back to the present. For discounting purposes a rate of interest, the firm's alternative rate of return, was used.

These observations lead us to the thought that even in short-run timber supply, which we may relate to price, the alternative rate of return still plays a role behind scenes—and, it may be, a decisive role. If Hawkins's firm had a very high alternative rate, no foreseeable price would be sufficient to prompt any timber-stand improvement, even disregarding the longer-run consideration of the value of Hawkins's own time.

## LONG-RUN STUMPAGE SUPPLY

As for the firm's long-run stumpage supply, it clearly includes at least those major decisions of the firm regarding the scope of its business, and most notably the ultimate decision whether to invest in timber land. Here all the inputs that the firm sees are variable; it has choices respecting them all.

Our analysis of the long-run supply in processing (pp. 209–211) applies generally to timber growing. The long-run supply, like the other conditions of supply, is a cost function, and this function may take various shapes. In timber production, perhaps the most representative for the firm is the cost curve that descends with increasing scale but approaches constant cost. Cost decreases rapidly in the early stages of the firm's growth because of the opportunity to escape the handicaps of small-scale forest ownership, such as we reviewed in Chapter 10 (pp. 155–156). Still further expansion by the firm may bring within reach additional economies: opportunities to integrate on a large scale, tax advantages, numerous gains of specialization, savings through the volume of purchases and sales, and, most especially, a lower alternative rate of return. However, with advancing size, such economies diminish and come to be increasingly opposed by the penalties of bigness and ultimately by the price of land itself. [Is this reasoning about the supply curve consistent with our earlier remarks (e.g., p. 218) concerning the ready supply of timber from smaller holdings? What other shapes may the cost function assume? How might you explain these other shapes?]

We should take note of some respects in which the long-run supply of timber may differ from that of processed products. For one thing, a firm's new investments in timber land may not be long-term investments. They may represent purchases of stock for liquidation, and thus their use may follow the principles of stock supply. For another, if the investment is for a long term, the return from it may be subject to far greater delays than are common in processing and thus be more subject to the influences of the interest rate.

In connection with processing, we had the proposition that output will flow in the long run only if the prospective price is sufficient to cover all prospective costs. For timber growing, this proposition is not clearly valid unless one interprets the idea of cost rather specially. The mere conclusion by a landowning firm that timber price will not be high enough to cover growing cost is not sufficient to stop production. Timber of some sort may grow whether the firm wants it to or not, unless someone goes to the trouble to put the land into other use. And it may continue to grow despite the calls made upon it from time to time by the determinants of stock supply. This is not, of course, to say that there will be enough of the various kinds to satisfy everybody's concept of what is desirable. The amounts of the timber will depend upon landowners' individual judgments of the moment regarding best stocking.

[In what sense, then, is it true that price must in the long run cover timber-growing costs? Must it cover the cost to the individual firm? To society? Must today's price cover past costs? Is there a tendency for it to do so? How fully is any such tendency realized?]

## COST, PRICE, AND SUPPLY

Before we leave the topic of standing-timber supply, let us review briefly some of our ideas about supply determinants. It is the operation of the supply mechanism that controls society's success in providing itself with forest products. Society's concern for the forest future, and the forester's concern, center upon the problems of supply.

We have seen what a large part stock-supply responses have to play in the timber economy. We have become acquainted with one of the consequences of the stock-supply condition: the time rivalry of supply from stocks. Positive supply responses in the near future, because they draw down growing stocks, foreshadow a lower supply in the further future. It is the great dilemma of forestry, as it is to some extent of all conservation, that society must choose between higher output now and higher output later. To have both is usually out of the question.

We have become acquainted also with another consequence of the dominant stock-supply condition (as well as of the long period of production in forestry): the large influence of the interest rate upon timber supply. The rate in question is the alternative rate of return of the landowning firm. We have seen, in this chapter and in Chapters 8 to 10, something of the rate's effects. Depending upon its magnitude, the rate may cancel most other forces that might bear upon the supply, notably the force of price.

We have discussed the role of price in stumpage supply. Let us review the main features of this role. If a firm foresees a relatively high price for stumpage, how will its behavior differ from that of a firm which forsees a relatively low price, other things being equal? Let us suppose that the firm's alternative rate of return is such as to open the way for price influences.

First, the firm with the high-price prospect may intensify its timber-land management by increasing inputs of labor and of capital other than growing stock. Thus it may shorten the cutting cycle, expand the road network, do more protecting, thinning, pruning, planting, and so on. The extra outlays may, however, be sharply limited by diminishing returns and by interest charges.

Second, the firm may expand its whole timber-production enterprise by acquiring more land or by withholding some of its land from abandonment. Where land acquisition enters the picture, it may be accompanied by a shift in land use in favor of forestry as a result of the higher ceiling rent in forestry. But in general, land acquired by one firm will need to be taken from another, and where the use of this land was previously forest, the supply response as seen by society will depend mainly on the difference in the alternative rates of return of the two firms.

Third, the firm may plan to bring into production those forest areas or categories of timber that will become newly merchantable as the margins of availability shift. This may well be the principal supply response to price on the part of the firm with a high alternative rate of return. Note, however, that the response can materialize only if the anticipated price increase comes to pass. The anticipation itself puts no wheels in motion. And if the anticipation is based upon a past price increase and the assumption that the higher price will hold in future, the supply response then is likely to be negative as a result of growing stocks having been drawn down earlier.

Fourth, the firm may intensify its timber-land management by increasing inputs of growing stock, provided it anticipates an indefinitely rising trend in the price of stumpage as compared with other things and provided the trend materializes currently. Under these conditions, marginal value growth per cent of timber will be increased: The rising price trend acts as a sort of financial fertilizer, with effects comparable to those of a chemical fertilizer. If the firm's alternative rate of return is low, immediate supply responses will be negative while growing stocks are accumulated, and the resulting subsequent positive supply response will be augmented by shifts in the margins of land and timber availability. This may well be the surest way for a rising price to induce a positive stumpage-supply response in the long pull. The resulting higher supply will be maintained only so long as prices continue to rise. For a small gain to society, this seems like a heavy payment! Nevertheless, it is a payment that society has in fact been making. We shall be studying its causes and some more of its effects in Chapter 19.

Stumpage-supply responses to price, then, while generally positive, are feeble: The price elasticity of supply is low. Evidently society can bid lavishly for the wood products it wants, without the basic producers paying much attention. This is the price-signal trouble referred to in Chapter 13, page 208.

The trouble lies with the signals used in the bidding. While the supply of stumpage is inelastic in relation to price, it is comparatively elastic in relation to the alternative rate of return. [Can you explain the derivation of the supply curve shown as graph *b* in Figure 20? Why does this curve differ from the one to the left, graph *a*?

[Here are some questions to think about, concerning the supply of timber: What sort of price scheme favors forest conservation? Is conservation favored by general inflation throughout the economy: a general decline in the purchasing power of the dollar? How can society lower the alternative rate of return of forest-land owners? Or how can it increase the forest value growth per cent—other than through the price trend? Is the forest economy necessarily an economy of scarcity? Do nations tend to postpone the practice of intensive forestry until too late? How does a nation go about reversing a forest-depletion trend?]

## SUMMARY

In timber production, the three supply conditions overlap in some respects. Because the stock of standing timber is at the same time the timber-producing machine, stock-supply responses tend to dominate those of the short- and long-run. And because of this in turn, and because of forestry's long period of production, the alternative rate of return is the key determinant of supply, tending to overshadow product price.

The stock supply of stumpage is that which depends upon the disposition of growing stock. It is sensitive primarily to the alternative rate of return, secondarily to anticipations of price change. It may also be influenced by price level through the effect of the latter on margins of timber availability.

Both short-run and long-run stumpage supply depend upon the rate of timber growth. They may be sensitive to price level as well as to the alternative rate of return. The short-run and long-run supply curves tend to have positive price elasticity. Both are negatively elastic with the alternative rate.

# Chapter 15

## MANAGEMENT PLANNING FOR THE FIRM

Forestry economics, as was remarked in Chapter 1, offers useful tools for two purposes: for understanding what goes on and for participating in events. In Part Two of this book up to the present point, we have taken now the one and now the other view of our subject. Let us conclude this study of the producing firm by giving pointed attention to the second view, which is that of the planner.

Our interest here centers on the firm's decision making—but not on the process itself: rather, on the basis for it. Just as, in general, economics is a basis for policy, so, specifically, economic planning is a basis for decision making. The two functions, planning and decision making, may be performed for the firm by two different persons or groups. Or they may be performed by one person, but, if so, he is playing two roles.

The management planning of the forestry firm is an immense subject. In cutting the subject down to fundamentals, we will restrict ourselves in this chapter to questions about the general nature and procedures and purposes of planning; and in Chapter 16 to a discussion of three methods of planning, with scattered illustrations, and of the implications of planning, especially regarding the need for data, or knowledge.

### NATURE OF PLANNING

The essence of *planning* is weighing alternatives so that decision and action may be taken. The purpose of *planning for the firm* is to help fulfill the firm's objectives as nearly as possible. To the degree that meet-

224

ing the objectives requires resource allocation, especially that based upon
market values or their equivalent, we have *economic planning.* Such
planning—or any planning, of course—is looking ahead. It means forecasting. If there is no looking ahead and forecasting, then what we have
is not planning but history, and we are back in the other part of our field,
the part for witnesses.

Planning is not necessarily highfalutin, nor necessarily socialistic. It is
something that everybody does, all the time, mainly about small affairs,
and often as a matter of course. You plan your hour of rising in the
morning (as we said, the plan is one thing, its execution another); you
plan your lunch, or someone plans it for you. In general, you plan your
day, and so manage to get to class, attend ball practice, and do other
things you like. You plan, to a degree, your week, your year, your life.
Some persons, and some firms, plan more elaborately than others, and
some plan further ahead, but the so-called "planless existence," taking
the term literally, is inconceivable.

We said that some firms plan more elaborately than others. All managers make at least their trivial plans in their heads and carry them there.
Some handle all their planning in this way. The little sawmill operator
may do his planning on the back of an envelope, jotting down his orders
as a guide to his output and making notes on his timber-buying program.
He may save his old bills for such jottings. In contrast, when the United
States Forest Service wrote *A National Plan for American Forestry*
(1933), the document came to 1,670-odd printed pages. Some private
corporations within the forest economy have even lengthier and more
detailed planning statements.

We also said that some firms plan further ahead than others. For some,
the contours of the future dip sharply away, and the *planning horizon,*
beyond which they peer not, is close at hand. For others, the vistas are
flat and far-spreading, and the horizon is formed only by the distant, inevitable mists of uncertainly. Such differences are the product of the
persons whose attitudes and vision represent the firm, and of the firm's
line and facilities of production, particularly its period of production and
the durability of its capital. They are also the product of the social circumstances that surround resource use, especially those determining risks.
We have seen in Chapter 8 how the rate of interest, reflecting risk, may
function to set a planning horizon. The professional forest manager, by
virtue of such influences, is typically a long-range planner as human
ranges go. He may well, also, be a detailed planner, substituting in part
the intelligent use of principles for experience as a means of meeting new
problems successfully.

Regardless of detail or horizon, all planning in the last analysis comprises certain steps. Let us group these steps for convenience into seven.

## STEPS IN PLANNING

*The first step* in planning is to identify the firm's objectives. What does the firm want to accomplish that may be furthered by this plan? Let us suppose that the firm is a state Park Board, and that its objective is to maximize net biennial returns on the basis of its appropriations. That is to say, at a given cost, the board aims to manage its affairs in such a way that revenues in the form of people's free enjoyment of the state parks will be, in its judgment, the greatest. Such a broad objective stems from the firm's policy on the most general plane, its top-level policy. Thus planning is bracketed by policy, taking its guides from policy at a more general level and in turn guiding policy at a more specific level.

*The second step* is to identify the question or questions to be considered. Here a start is made toward setting the plan's scope. We will assume for an example that the question concerns the type and location of facilities and roads that would be built on a certain 4,000-acre forest tract if the tract were acquired as a park. The plan, then, is to be one unit in the master plan for state-park development.

*The third step* is to identify the alternatives worth spelling out—that is, those that cannot reasonably be eliminated at the outset on the basis of general judgment. This is an interesting step, because the planning may end here if all but one of the alternatives are thrown out. In such a case, it is most likely to end if the firm is small and tightly held, if there is comparatively little at stake in the plan, and if planning and decision making are seated in the same persons. If there is a predominant element of judgment or art in the planning and the function of decision making is separate, the firm may keep its alternatives alive by commissioning more than one person to do a plan. However, in our park example, the planner retains three alternatives. In all three, he centers the principal development around a small lake at the east end of the tract. Here the service area of the park is to be located. The three plans differ in the road layout. One calls for a short road from the east direct to the lake, leaving the central and western areas untapped, except by the more adventurous hikers. In the second, the road enters from the west, following a scenic ridge. The third alternative also brings in a long road from the west, but on a less scenic and less expensive lowland route—which, however, gives ready access to short trails into the scenic upland.

*The fourth step* in planning is to get data on the inputs and outputs of each alternative: the basic production function. *The fifth* is to assemble information on values of inputs and outputs: the rates of cost and revenue. These two steps are well mentioned in the same breath, since they are so closely allied and may in fact be combined. Yet in principle they are separate, the fourth step lying in the realm of biology or engineering and the fifth step being an accounting function. Our park planner at this point works up forecasts of construction and maintenance costs and brings together what measures he can, from experience and judgment, of the benefits to be expected from using the central and western areas of the park in the alternative ways. Where a measure of benefits is, as in this case, not provided by any market, the planner must stay in especially close touch with the decision makers in order to reach agreement on measures that are valid and meaningful.

In *the sixth step*, the plan is put together and comparisons drawn among the alternatives. Here we see the essential role of economic analysis as a guide to policy: forecasting the consequences of different courses of action in terms that may be used by the policy makers to reach a choice in light of their objectives. Of course, the more cut and dried the objectives are and the more measurable the alternatives, the further the plan may go toward tagging the best alternative and foreshadowing the ultimate decision. At any rate, with this step the plan is ready for policy review. It may seem that the planning process is complete. But there is one more step.

*The seventh step* is replanning. This step is essential where plans remain in effect long enough for circumstances or prospects to change materially. Parts of our park plan may become obsolete because of unforeseen changes in population, in income, in leisure time and the manner of using it, in tastes, in highway systems, in adjacent property ownership and use, in construction costs, and many other things. And so the plan must be brought up to date, the alternatives reidentified and reassessed.

Sometimes replanning is not done very often. In Western Europe one can find forests being managed under plans made a century ago. Here is evidence of original foresight, subsequent luck and bullheadedness, and, above all, slowness of economic change. In general, we must expect many of the essentials of a timber-management plan to stay in force for a long time—compartment layout, forest type, silvicultural system, and the like. Here frequent revision may cause chaos. But usually the firm must count on frequently revising many features of its plans. A good formal plan contains a section on replanning, recommending review of the various parts at various intervals. Many a young forester finds himself assigned for a while to timber-management replanning.

Economic planning, as was said, is designed to guide decisions. Let us recognize, somewhat arbitrarily, three types of decisions for which plans may be made—that is, three subjects for planning: first, enterprise planning; second, organization planning; third, operation planning. As you will see, the three types of planning merge and overlap to some extent. But they are worth considering separately, because they typically differ in scope, in the administrative level at which they are considered, in length of view, and in method of attack.

## ENTERPRISE PLANNING

*Enterprise planning* is broad planning for investment in new business or in a new enterprise or product line. Such planning pertains primarily to the long-run supply.

Enterprise planning considers such questions as these: Shall we enter this business? Where shall we locate? On what scale shall we begin? It includes questions of vertical integration: Shall we invest in timber land to supply our plant? Shall we do our own logging? Set up our own sales organization? It includes also questions of horizontal integration: Shall we expand our business to include hardwood dimension as well as softwood lumber? Shall we attempt multipurpose forest management?

The essence of enterprise planning is that it considers ventures that are new for the firm—enterprises in which the firm may have no substantial experience. Out of such planning may come some of the firm's largest decisions in point of investment and some of its riskiest decisions. Of course all ventures, or changes of any sort made by the firm, are in a sense new and risky. But those in which enterprise planning is involved are new to the firm in point of technology and economics, and not merely in point of time. And they bear risks not only because of their newness but also because of the length of view in which they are caught up.

The risky thing about the long view is, obviously, the likelihood of unforeseeable change in the circumstances surrounding the firm. Probably prices will change. To eliminate long-term risk, the firm would need to know the long-term price trend. One can make intelligent forecasts but can never be sure they are accurate. It is even impossible to know the range of the probable errors in such a forecast. Planning helps to reduce risk and to measure it but cannot get rid of it. Wage rates and other cost rates, too, will be likely to show some sort of trend over the long term. To the degree the firm is uncertain about the trend, it faces risks. The only factors that matter in the firm's economic life are those that are variable with its alternatives. In planning for the long term, everything may appear variable.

## PLANNING ENTERPRISE INTEGRATION

Since the weighing of vertical or horizontal integration is perhaps the most characteristic task in enterprise planning, let us mention some of the considerations in this weighing, so as to illustrate what enterprise plans deal with.

The planner for the landowning firm must consider that vertical integration to include processing will give the firm access to markets that reflect quality. We discussed in Chapter 9 (p. 136) how such markets encourage intensive timber management. Integration with processing will also admit the firm to markets that are better organized, more competitive, and more stable over the business cycle. It may bring the firm within easier reach of loan capital, credit being more readily obtainable on plant than on forest security. It may permit more efficient use of the varied skills in the labor force and steadier use of labor over the seasons, thus reducing labor costs. Or looking at woods-mill integration from the standpoint of the manufacturing enterprise, the planner will recognize that it may lend strength to the firm's bargaining position in the open market for raw material and in general give the firm greater assurance of raw-material supply. He must weigh numerous tax considerations and possible advantages, such as we shall talk about in Chapter 27.

Of course the planner must take account also of the dark side of woods-mill integration. He must have in mind the disadvantages that may come with diffusing the firm's effort and interest—the problems, for example, of the landowning pulp manufacturer who finds himself inadvertently producing saw logs, or forage for the neighbors' hogs, or recreation and hunting grounds for the general public, or oil, or other oddments. (Admittedly, striking oil is the least of these problems.) And the planner must give thought to the necessity for balance among enterprises, so as to help avoid the overbuilding of one in relation to others (compare pp. 184, 218–219).

The small forest owner has fewer opportunities than the large for planning a vertical lengthening of lines. Yet even his plans may well explore the possibility of the firm's joining a cooperative milling or marketing association, enlisting the services of public or private consultants, or leasing land to a wood-using concern.

In weighing horizontal integration of manufacturing enterprises, the planner will again have benefits and drawbacks to consider. Integration may reduce risks by means of diversification. It may help the firm escape for a while the diseconomies of scale. It may permit use of leftover raw material, which, as we saw in Chapter 12 (pp. 187–188), need not be intrinsically profitable to be attractive. It may allow fuller use of market contacts and sales organization already established, fuller use of the firm's research and development department and production experience and special skills—in general, more efficient use of overhead. But of course, if carried beyond a point, it may overuse the overhead, and it may come against the old principle "Shoemaker, stick to your last."

In the woods, horizontal integration (multipurpose management) provides a way for the private firm to diversify and for the public firm to broaden its services.

These are some of the considerations with which the enterprise planner must work where horizontal integration may be involved. And of course he must also, as with vertical integration, consider the tax effects and look for possible advantages.

### ORGANIZATION PLANNING

*Organization planning* is planning for the organization or arrangement of the going lines of production within the business, or of a particular existing enterprise. It includes planning for enterprise expansion or curtailment, and in general deals primarily with durable investments and with overhead. Thus, like enterprise planning, it pertains mainly to the long-run supply, but it has to do with areas in which the risks are somewhat less. Should the plant be enlarged? Another plant built? What lines of output should be emphasized for the long run? What investments are needed to keep abreast of technological improvements? How should the firm's woods department be organized? How should its forest holdings be compartmented? What sort and size of forest-protection organization should the firm have? Are wood-procurement facilities and procedures adequate for the long pull?

One of the commonest questions in organization planning is that of the firm's scale. We remarked in Chapter 13 (p. 210) that the best scale is a function of internal and external net economies, and we touched upon the subject again in Chapter 14 (p. 220). The analysis of these economies is a major part of organization planning, especially analysis of capital and labor markets and raw-material supplies in relation to the firm's potential expansion, and analysis of product markets. Since the technology of production may be the main element involved in a firm's failure to enjoy falling costs in the long run, studies of technology provide a major basis for organization planning. This is so both in the mechanical wood-using industries, where technological change comes hard and is in a sense doubly essential to the firm's growth, and in the chemical wood-using industry, where growth is invited by a dynamic technology.

### OPERATION PLANNING

*Operation planning* is planning for the use of fixed facilities, and is therefore primarily short-run and stock-supply planning. For the woods enterprise, it covers a multitude of questions such as the amount and timing of work upon the various management jobs, timber and otherwise;

rotation and cutting-cycle length; choice, timing, and method of cultural operations; scheduling of cutting or sales; logging and short-term protection plans; road maintenance; and inventories. For processing and marketing enterprises, it encompasses parallel questions.

Of the three types of planning, operation planning is apt to require the greatest sum of effort from the firm. It goes on continuously. Much of it is reviewed at the lower levels of administrative responsibility. And the day-to-day success of the firm depends upon it in large measure.

We have noted how enterprise planning must give sharp attention to the long-term movements, or trends, in price and in cost rates. And the same is true of organization planning. For operation planning, which concerns the shorter period, the vital movements are the cycles and more frequent ups and downs of business variables that characterize our economy. The most successful forest business is the one that is geared to respond on short notice to changes in price and cost—to exhibit the short-run and stock-supply responses that we considered in the last two chapters—while maintaining reasonable integrity of its long-range plans. The most feasible silvicultural system is that which, for example, permits the timing of harvests at price peaks and of improvements at times of slackened general demand for labor. A dynamic economy requires a flexible, alterable program of genetic and mechanical production.

However, this is not to say that planning bends passively to fluctuating economic winds. In fact, an essential feature of all constructive planning, private as well as social, is counter-cyclical and counter-dynamic. There is still a touch of Adam Smith's invisible hand in the firm's response which counteracts the change that prompted it: the sales response to price, the hiring response to unemployment; and the prompter these responses, the more they subdue the change. Beyond such immediate self-interested responses of the firm are those, and perhaps the greatest number, in which the constructiveness of the firm's planning must depend in part upon the firm's social consciousness and farsightedness. Every intelligent private planner comes to recognize that continuity, stability, reasonable freedom from up-and-down values and employment are best for society as well as the firm. In the forest economy, where such ups and downs may seriously conflict with the long-range program, the constructive short-range planner does what he can, in a small way, to dampen them.

Although it is a convenience for us as students to recognize enterprise, organization, and operation planning as three different types, it would be a great mistake to think of them as organically separate, for they are certainly not. Each type implies the other two and, ideally, depends upon them. For example, suppose that a potential investor is sizing up the opportunities in the Christmas-tree business. He is thinking of buying land and planting it up. He is forecasting the returns on his investment and estimating the risks. This is enterprise planning. But obviously he cannot finish the plan without considering the sales arrangements that he will make, which is organization planning, or his planting methods and costs, which is operation planning. And operation planning depends on organization and enterprise planning. [Can you explain the nature of this dependency and give an example?]

## SUMMARY

Planning, which means looking ahead in order to guide decisions and thus come nearer one's objectives, is a common activity in the ordinary business of life. It is an important activity in the life of every firm, though firms differ greatly in the elaborateness and length of view of their plans.

The process of planning for the firm may be analyzed as seven steps: (1) Identifying the firm's objectives, (2) identifying the subject of the plan, (3) identifying the alternatives to be weighed, (4) getting input-output data, (5) getting value data, (6) putting the plan together so as to compare alternatives in light of objectives, and (7) replanning.

Three types of planning for the firm may be arbitrarily recognized. First is enterprise planning: long-run planning of a new business or enterprise. Here a major question may concern the vertical or horizontal integration of enterprises by the firm. Second is organization planning, which includes all other long-run planning. It differs from enterprise planning mainly in that it concerns more familiar, less risky ventures. Third is operation planning, which treats of the use of fixed facilities in short-run or stock supply. All three types of planning are necessarily engrossed in the problems of change, limitations in human foresight, and resultant risk.

Chapter 16

METHODS OF
ECONOMIC
PLANNING

L ET US now have a look at three methods that the firm may use to carry out its management planning. These are primarily alternative methods of taking step six in the planning process (Chap. 15, p. 227): putting the plan together so as to trace the consequences of the different courses of action that are open to the firm. Thus they are methods for making the central calculations of the plan. The three methods are (1) the budget method, (2) the marginal method, and (3) the break-even method.

## COMPARING ALTERNATIVES

The three planning methods are all devices for comparing specific alternatives that the firm wants to weigh in light of its objectives. We shall be assuming that the firm's chief objective is to make the most net revenue per unit of time. We shall therefore present the methods as ways for calculating the comparative net revenues of the alternatives. The procedure, fundamentally, will be always the same: (1) Estimate for each alternative the total revenue per unit of time, including at least the revenue items that differ from one alternative to another. (2) Estimate for each the total cost in the same unit of time, again including at least the costs that vary with the alternatives. (3) For each alternative, subtract cost from revenue to arrive at net revenue. (4) Compare the net revenues to discover which is largest.

On the foregoing fundamental procedure, we shall work out variations adapted, first, to the planning method we are using and, second, to the nature of the planning problem and data. These variations will be represented, generally speaking, in the following range:

First, if the revenues from the alternatives are the same in amount and timing, make a direct comparison of the costs. If the costs differ in timing, convert them beforehand to the same point of time by compounding or discounting at the guiding rate of interest. The least-cost alternative is best.

Second, if the costs of the alternatives are the same in amount and timing, make a direct comparison of revenues, again with time adjustments as necessary. The highest-revenue alternative is best.

Third, if both revenues and costs differ among alternatives in amount but not in timing—for example, if both are constant annual quantities—make a direct comparison of net revenues. The highest-net-revenue alternative is best.

Fourth, if both revenues and costs differ among alternatives in both amount and timing, convert them all to the same point of time by compounding or discounting at the guiding rate of interest, and calculate the net revenue for each alternative as of this time. The highest-net-revenue alternative is best. The common procedure is to discount all prospective revenues and costs to the starting date, or "now"—i.e., capitalize them—in which case the end result for each alternative is the current worth of the estimated net revenue.

Where a firm is weighing alternatives in the management of a prospective investment, such as a tract of land, current net worth may be figured exclusive of the cost of the land, in which case the highest net worth not only designates the best management alternative but also becomes a guide to the amount the firm might afford to pay for the land. And if the firm is weighing the purchase of alternative tracts of land, that tract is best whose highest net worth most greatly exceeds the price at which it can be bought.

In some cases the firm may wish to compute not the current net worth of a prospective investment but its net income expressed as a percentage rate of return on the amount of the investment. Such a computation is not, as we have seen (pp. 54–55) a sufficient basis for choosing among alternative investments, but it may serve the following purposes: (1) If there are alternative ways for managing *an* investment, the alternative that will return the highest net percentage on the investment is indicated as best, since it is necessarily the one that will earn the greatest net revenue per unit of time (i.e., have the highest current worth of estimated net revenue). (2) A comparison of this highest percentage with the guiding rate of interest will show whether the investment is worth making. (3) If a firm puts a given amount of capital into those investments which, risk considered, promise the highest percentage rates of return, it will be following a rational course. Note that it is in the process of such exploring as we have described here that the firm's guiding rate of interest (alternative rate of return) may be found.

## BUDGET METHOD—EXAMPLE OF FARM A

The *budget method* is the least technical of the three planning methods, and the most widely useful. The essence of it is a tabulation, or "budgeting," of anticipated revenues and costs of each of the firm's alternatives and then a direct comparison of the results—the sort of thing that one might do simply on the back of an envelope, or more elaborately in account books. The method is applicable where the alternatives to be weighed are few, or can be reduced to a few—typically two to four. The method is effective in any type of planning but is especially well adapted to enterprise and organization planning. Although it can be used on the simplest problems, its merits show up most strikingly in complex problems, such as where interrelated enterprises and products are represented in the alternatives. For an example, take the rather complicated weighing of alternative woodland, crop, and livestock programs on "Farm A," as analyzed by Drs. Barraclough and Gould.[1] This is organization planning.

The owner of this farm is a young man dealing in an unusual way with a difficult situation commonly found in the more remote areas of New England. He is a skillful and energetic farm operator with a varied background of vocational training and work in agriculture and logging. A flexible imagination is a great help to him in planning the development of what was once a typical "run-down" farm.

The owner has worked successfully in better developed areas, but a few years ago decided to return to this small town. The family likes the location and they have worked together to remodel the house into a comfortable home despite the lack of a telephone and electricity and the probability that such conveniences will not be available in the near future.

The farm has a good deal of value to the family as a residence, and they get considerable pleasure from merely owning the land. But it is also necessary to develop the income-producing capacity of the operating unit so that they can continue living here.

Until recently the operator has spent at least half of his time working off the farm, but now he wants to look ahead and see what the farm opportunities are and how he can best develop them. He has long been convinced that forest production has a promising future, and he has added to his woodland holdings whenever purchases could be made cheaply. To date the operating unit that he has assembled and the improvements he has made in it have been aimed

[1] Barraclough, Solon L., and Ernest M. Gould, Jr.: *Economic Analysis of Farm Forest Operating Units*, Harvard Forest Bulletin 26, Petersham, Mass., 1955, pp. 13–35.

at building up crop, livestock, and forest enterprises that will support his family and in the long run have value for his children.

Here we have the background for the plan—the firm's circumstances and objectives and the subject of the plan—the first and second steps as we identified them in Chapter 15 (p. 226).

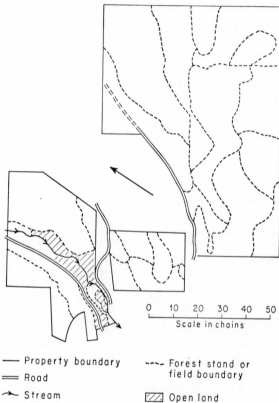

Fig. 21. Forest stands and fields on Farm A. (*Adapted from Barraclough, Solon L., and Ernest M. Gould, Jr.: Economic Analysis of Farm Forest Operating Units, Harvard Forest Bulletin 26, Petersham, Mass., 1955, p. 15.*)

Continuing with the second step and laying the basis for the third, Drs. Barraclough and Gould describe the farm and the conditions surrounding its operation. There are 42 acres of open land and 869 acres of woodland, in three closely adjacent parcels (Fig. 21). The planners explain soil conditions in each field and forest conditions in each stand. The timber is predominantly northern hardwood second growth, varying in age up to sixty years. Quality is reasonably high, and opportunities for sustained yield appear favorable. The authors consider the availability of labor, credit, and technical assistance; the present and prospective markets for farm products, primarily dairy and wood products; and the taxes and tax outlook. They then describe the buildings, facilities, and equipment on the farm and the practices being followed.

The herd of Jersey cows has been built up to five, and some promising heifer calves have been purchased. Considerable reseeding and moderate fertilization have already greatly improved roughage production. The operator has fed little grain, since only a small amount of milk can be sold locally. Each year he makes about five hundred pounds of butter and sells half of it in the neighborhood; the balance of the milk is used by the family or given to the calves or pigs. . . . Two pigs and a beef animal are kept for home use.

The operator has also carried on some woods work, cutting the equivalent of about ninety-six cords of pulpwood each year in addition to fuelwood. Most of these operations have been patch cuttings in small stands of older trees and reproduction has become established promptly. The owner has been able to hire most of his work done and to pay part of the wages in the form of cottage rent and milk.

## ALTERNATIVES FOR FARM A

The planners now proceed into the formal portion of the third step, in which they identify the alternatives to be weighed—the alternatives which they have discussed with the owner and singled out as the most promising. In doing this, they hold in the background three possible programs of timber management: A low-intensity program in which stands would be clear-cut or high-graded whenever they contain enough value to attract a buyer, a high-intensity program calling for cultural treatments at five- to ten-year intervals in all stands and harvest cuttings made to promote prompt and valuable reproduction and timed with the trees' most profitable development, and an intermediate, medium-intensity program. They then lay out three alternatives for the whole farm business, as follows:

Alternative I is to continue operating the farm pretty much as at present. Emphasis is upon off-farm work by the owner, part-time operation of the livestock enterprise geared to home needs and the local milk and butter markets, and medium-intensive timber management.

Alternative II is built upon a heifer program and intensive forest production. The present herd of five milk cows is retained, and about six fresh heifers raised each year for sale. These enterprises take the full time of the owner. He gives up outside work. Adjustments are required in the use and treatment of farm fields and buildings, and an item or two of new equipment is needed.

Alternative III features the wholesaling of milk from an eleven-cow herd, intensive forest production, and again the giving up of outside employment. This alternative calls for investments in milk-cooling equipment, a milking machine, perhaps a new stable, and various other items.

In what we have identified as the fourth and fifth steps, getting input-output and value data (p. 226), Drs. Barraclough and Gould next gather together what information and forecasts they can that will be needed to assess the three alternatives. They outline the labor, capital, and land requirements of each alternative. They consider, for the livestock enterprise, the feed and forage needs in relation to output. For the woods enterprise they consider growth and yields in relation to cultural and harvesting practices. Here they attempt to look ahead ninety years and to forecast average annual outputs in each decade. They also have a try at estimating probable prices and wage rates and other costs in the first decade ahead. Their assumptions and results are spelled out in some detail.

## BUDGETING FARM-A ALTERNATIVES

The planners now turn to our sixth step, the last step that they undertake. In this step they do the actual budgeting of the alternatives and arrive at a comparison in net-income terms. Their figures are reproduced in Table 24. The budgets relate, in general, to the first coming decade—for the woods enterprise, to an average year in the decade, and for the other enterprises, to a typical year following the completion of necessary farm adjustments. Alternatives II and III look distinctly better, from the standpoint of net income, than alternative I. As between II and III, the latter has the edge. In the plan, the advantages and disadvantages of each alternative are fully discussed, including such considerations as owner's time away from home and the necessity to hire labor and borrow money.

Let us now briefly review the characteristics of this budget method as revealed in the planning for Farm A. One is struck by the fact that the method lends itself to highly methodical, detailed planning. It is well suited to a firm-wide view of interdependent enterprises: It recognizes the principle of unity of the firm (p. 54). It appears to lend itself well to analysis of general judgment factors such as must supplement revenue-cost figures as a basis for decision. One can see that the method would provide a logical device for enterprise planning, in which *absolute* net income or rates of return on new investments may need to be spelled out on the basis of *all* revenues and costs (since all may vary with alternatives). One can also see that the method would fit in well with the planing of organization and operation alternatives, where it suffices to compute *relative* net advantage or net income on the basis of *part* of the revenues and costs (those that vary with alternatives). In the case of Farm A, the plan was originally drawn up in 1946, using decade prices and costs that then appeared most probable. These are the figures shown in Table 24. Subsequent inflation radically raised price and cost levels. But it had negligible effect on the *relative* merits of the three alternatives. And it is, of course, their relative showing that matters in guiding the owner's choice. Finally, it is now obvious that in order for the budget

*Table 24. Financial summary of three alternative programs for Farm A: annual receipts and expenses in the first decade*

| Item | Alternative I | | Alternative II | | Alternative III | |
|---|---|---|---|---|---|---|
| | *Dollars* | | *Dollars* | | *Dollars* | |
| Receipts: | | | | | | |
| Milk | | 279 | | 279 | | 2,185 |
| Cows | | 100 | | 50 | | 100 |
| Calves | | 4 | | 16 | | 24 |
| Heifers | | — | | 810 | | — |
| Butter | (250 lb) | 125 | (250 lb) | 125 | | — |
| ACP refund | | 28 | | 28 | | 28 |
| Pulpwood | (90 cd) | 810 | (171 cd) | 1,539 | (171 cd) | 1,539 |
| Saw logs | (3 M bd ft) | 54 | (27 M bd ft) | 486 | (27 M bd ft) | 486 |
| Rent of cottages | | 250 | | 250 | | 250 |
| Off-farm work | | 1,050 | | — | | — |
| Total receipts | | 2,700 | | 3,583 | | 4,612 |
| Expenses: | | | | | | |
| Grain | | 207 | | 531 | | 906 |
| Labor | (6 months) | 780 | (5 months) | 650 | (7 months) | 910 |
| Seed | | 35 | | 45 | | 45 |
| Calves | | — | | 30 | | — |
| Other stock | | 10 | | 10 | | 10 |
| Miscellaneous dairy | | 50 | | 50 | | 110 |
| Fertilizer and lime | | 88 | | 257 | | 211 |
| Gas, oil, grease | | 100 | | 150 | | 250 |
| Other truck and tractor | | 25 | | 25 | | 25 |
| Building upkeep | | 100 | | 100 | | 100 |
| Equipment upkeep | | 80 | | 90 | | 180 |
| Taxes | | 217 | | 230 | | 230 |
| Insurance | | 21 | | 21 | | 26 |
| Interest | | — | | 54 | | 142 |
| Depreciation—horses | | 15 | | 25 | | 25 |
| Depreciation—machinery | | 100 | | 125 | | 125 |
| Total expenses | | 1,828 | | 2,393 | | 3,295 |
| Net farm income | | 872 | | 1,190 | | 1,317 |

SOURCE: Barraclough, Solon L., and Ernest M. Gould, Jr.: *Economic Analysis of Farm Forest Operating Units*, Harvard Forest Bulletin 26, Petersham, Mass., 1955, table 8.

method to be workable, the number of alternatives for detailed analysis must be pared down as far as possible. Otherwise the planning will be very cumbersome.

A footnote to the plan for Farm A is provided for us by Drs. Barra-clough and Gould, in their comments upon the owner's decision:

In light of the broad alternatives spelled out in this analysis, and with the owner's special knowledge of the local situation, he has devised a program for operating the farm that will lead him toward [alternative] III. He has gotten a better paying off-farm job, but he has also worked out a scheme with a neighbor for delivering milk to the wholesale pick-up route. In addition, he is moving as far toward a high intensity of forest management as he is able to do with hired labor working under his supervision. Thus he hopes finally to give up off-farm work, sell wholesale milk, and use intensive forest manage-ment. The present arrangements will carry him at least part way through the growing period necessary to build up the size of his forest enterprise.

### BUDGET METHOD WITH TIME ADJUSTMENTS

In budgeting alternative programs for Farm A, a fairly close planning horizon was recognized. This was done because it was considered ap-propriate to the firm and the data and because prospective income and cost differences between the first and later decades were believed to be insufficient to change the conclusions about the relative merits of the alternatives. Consequently it was possible to draw up budgets of revenue and cost for a single, illustrative year.

By way of contrast, there are many problems in forest-enterprise plan-ning which, at least on their face, appear to require a longer view because many revenues and costs are postponed and their timing varies among the alternatives. Consequently the planner finds himself forecasting time series of revenues and costs and reducing these to terms of value at one point of time through compounding or discounting. We may regard such a process as a variant of the budget method.

For an example, take the classical forestry problem of the best rotation length. This is a problem that we studied from another viewpoint in Chapter 9 (pp. 128–135). In this section and the next we shall go at the problem through the soil-rent approach, which, as we explained, may give only an approximate solution. Then in the following two sections we shall work our way back toward the unadjusted financial-maturity ap-proach, which is also an approximation. In the course of the presenta-tion, we shall try out additional short cuts. Our purpose will be three-fold: first, to illustrate the mechanics of planning methods; second, to illustrate the sort of simplification and roughing-out (which of course represents departure from rigidly precise analysis) that the planner may use to good effect so long as he is aware of the errors and sure that they are well within his tolerances; third, to reemphasize that it is not necessary, in planning permanent forestry, to take account of all eternity.

Let us confine ourselves to the sixth step in the planning (p. 227), assuming that aims, alternatives, and data have been determined and we are ready to do the budgeting. We shall be referring to Tables 9 and 10 in Chapter 8 (pp. 110,–111).

A tract of bare land is being considered for planting and perpetual management under an even-aged system. In outline, the management program would consist of planting, periodic thinnings, a harvest cut, replanting, and so on, at intervals indefinitely. Conceptually, the process is unlimited in time. Should the firm invest in the bare land and launch the program? (This is enterprise planning.) And if so, how long a rotation should be followed? (This is operation planning.) The alternative rotations to be studied have been reduced to four. These, with the anticipated yields and net revenues per acre from the harvest cut, are as follows:

| Rotation length Years | Harvest yield Thousand board feet | Net revenue Dollars |
|---|---|---|
| 50 | 10½ | 210 |
| 60 | 16 | 320 |
| 70 | 23 | 460 |
| 80 | 29 | 580 |

We are given the following additional estimates of revenue and cost per acre:

Net revenue from thinning: $10 every 10 years beginning at age 30
Planting cost: $10
Annual cost of administration, protection, and taxes: 50 cents
Alternative rate of return: 4 per cent

Let us approach this problem by estimating the current net worth of each alternative. Take first the 50-year rotation as an example.

### CURRENT WORTH OF ALTERNATIVE ROTATIONS

*One.* Compute the periodically recurring net revenue as of rotation age 50. For this purpose, add (1) net revenue from harvest cut, $210; (2) net revenue from first thinning, which comes at rotation age $(t)$ minus 20 years and must therefore be compounded for that period: $10 × 2.191 (see Table 10) = $21.91; (3) net revenue from second (last) thinning, which comes at $t - 10$ years; $10 × 1.480 = $14.80; and (4) the (negative) value of the planting cost, which must be compounded for 50 years: −$10 × 7.107 = −$71.07. The sum of these four items is $175.64.

*Two.* Set down the annually recurring net revenue. In this case only cost is involved. It is given as (negative) $0.50.

*Three.* Capitalize the net revenues by means of formulas 3*a* and 2*a* (Table 9) to determine $V_0$, the current net worth of the management program:

$$V_0 = \frac{175.64}{7.107 - 1} - \frac{0.50}{0.04} = 28.76 - 12.50 = \$16.26.$$

These same steps are followed in Table 25, where the current net worth of each of the four alternatives is budgeted out. The alternative that uses a 60-year rotation is seen to have the advantage over the others, with a current net worth of $17.33 per acre. This $17.33 is what is referred to

Table 25. *Budgets of estimated revenue and cost in perpetuity and calculation of current net worth* ($V_0$) *per acre under four alternative lengths of rotation*

| Revenue or cost item | Rotation length ($t$)—years | | | |
| --- | --- | --- | --- | --- |
|  | 50 | 60 | 70 | 80 |
|  | *Dollars* | *Dollars* | *Dollars* | *Dollars* |
| Periodic net revenue: |  |  |  |  |
|   Harvest cut | 210.00 | 320.00 | 460.00 | 580.00 |
|   Thinning at $t$ − 50 years | — | — | — | 71.07 |
|   Thinning at $t$ − 40 years | — | — | 48.01 | 48.01 |
|   Thinning at $t$ − 30 years | — | 32.43 | 32.43 | 32.43 |
|   Thinning at $t$ − 20 years | 21.91 | 21.91 | 21.91 | 21.91 |
|   Thinning at $t$ − 10 years | 14.80 | 14.80 | 14.80 | 14.80 |
|   Planting | −71.07 | −105.20 | −155.70 | −230.50 |
|   Total | 175.64 | 283.94 | 421.45 | 537.72 |
| Net revenue capitalized: |  |  |  |  |
|   Periodic | 28.76 | 29.83 | 28.93 | 24.39 |
|   Annual | −12.50 | −12.50 | −12.50 | −12.50 |
|   Total ($V_0$) | 16.26 | 17.33 | 16.43 | 11.89 |

in the older forestry literature as "soil expectation value." In our terms, it is an approximation of the ceiling price of this bare land for the forest use described: If a firm were to buy the land for no more than $17.33 per acre and follow the program envisaged and if all the assumptions and forecasts about the program proved accurate, the firm would make no less than a 4 per cent return on its investment, before income taxes. The latter "if" is a gigantic one—in fact, taken literally, the supposition is preposterous—but presumably the immense risks inherent in this perpetuity calculation have been allowed for in the price and cost estimates. [What conclusions should the firm draw if all the figures in the last line of Table 25 were minus quantities?]

However, let us see what happens when we shorten the view somewhat. Compare Table 25 with Table 26, where the current net worth of the four alternatives is calculated from the same revenue and cost data but considering only the first rotation. Since the major revenue comes from the harvest cut at the end of the rotation, one rotation is surely the shortest time view that can be taken in appraising these alternatives. The loss in current net worth incurred by dropping all but the first rotation is

Table 26. *Budgets of estimated revenue and cost during one rotation and calculation of current net worth* ($V_0$) *per acre under four alternative lengths of rotation*

| Item | Rotation length—years | | | |
|---|---|---|---|---|
| | 50 | 60 | 70 | 80 |
| | *Dollars* | *Dollars* | *Dollars* | *Dollars* |
| Discounted value* of: | | | | |
| Harvest cut | 29.55 | 30.42 | 29.54 | 25.16 |
| First thinning | 3.08 | 3.08 | 3.08 | 3.08 |
| Second thinning | 2.08 | 2.08 | 2.08 | 2.08 |
| Third thinning | — | 1.41 | 1.41 | 1.41 |
| Fourth thinning | — | — | 0.95 | 0.95 |
| Fifth thinning | — | — | — | 0.64 |
| Planting cost | −10.00 | −10.00 | −10.00 | −10.00 |
| All items | 24.71 | 26.99 | 27.06 | 23.32 |
| Capitalized value† of annual net revenue | −10.59 | −11.31 | −11.70 | −11.96 |
| Current net worth ($V_0$) | 14.12 | 15.68 | 15.36 | 11.36 |

* From formula 1b, Table 9.
† From formula 2c, Table 9.

not, perhaps, so great as might be supposed. For the 60-year alternative, still the best even when the shorter view is taken, the loss is $17.33 minus $15.68, or $1.65, amounting to less than 10 per cent of the perpetuity figure. At interest rates above 4 per cent, the loss would, of course, be less. All things considered, the more conservative estimate of ceiling price may be the more usable.

## OPERATION BUDGETING OF ROTATION LENGTH

We have been talking about enterprise planning, where the question was whether to invest in land for forest planting. In such planning, one must take account of all the prospective revenues and all the prospective costs, since all are variable with the major alternatives in view (to invest or not to invest). However, once the land has been bought and planted, the attendant costs become fixed, and the major alternatives, in our example, are the different lengths of rotation. Thus the problem changes to one of operation planning. Let us consider our example now as one of operation planning, in order to bring out a final point about the budget method.

The budget method as applied to operation planning offers good opportunities to cut corners and simplify the work without appreciable sacrifice of validity. Such streamlining is effected by throwing out fixed items, abbreviating the estimates of variables that have a minor influence on the result, and concentrating on those variables that carry weight. This

*Table 27. Net revenues per acre from harvest cuts under four alternative lengths of rotation, discounted to the beginning of the rotation at three different rates of interest*

| Rate of interest | Length of rotation—years | | | |
|---|---|---|---|---|
| | 50 | 60 | 70 | 80 |
| *Per cent* | *Dollars* | *Dollars* | *Dollars* | *Dollars* |
| 3 | 47.90 | 54.40 | 58.10 | 54.50 |
| 4 | 29.60 | 30.40 | 29.50 | 25.20 |
| 5 | 18.30 | 17.10 | 15.10 | 11.90 |

calls for good judgment on the part of the planner. There are no set rules to help him with the particulars. Each case will be a little different from others. As an example, let us see how we can streamline this particular rotation-length problem.

Refer again to Table 26, the one-rotation case, which is appropriate to operation planning. Let us try to identify the variables that count most in determining the *relative* values of the four alternatives. Only the relative values concern us now. Immediately we are struck by the fact that besides the cost of planting, the returns from the first two thinnings also are quite irrelevant. If you experiment by trying different yield, price, and cost figures in the table, you will find that the following are very influential: the alternative rate of return, the relative quantity and quality of yields at different ages, and the prospect of price or cost changes. [Why is this?] On the other hand, you will discover that the absolute level of prices and costs, other than interest rate, is comparatively insignificant. For example, the 60-year rotation is still best if the assumed revenues from the harvest cuts are doubled or quadrupled. [Again, why?]

A streamlined budget is illustrated in Table 27. This budget considers only the discounted net revenue from the harvest cut at the end of the first rotation. No account is taken of price or cost trends, but three different rates of interest are tested. The budget shows that if the rate is 3 per cent, the 70-year rotation is best; if 4 per cent, the 60-year rotation;

and if 5 per cent, the 50-year rotation. These are the same findings that you would get from complete, perpetuity budgets of the type of Table 25.

Note that both in Table 26 and in Table 27, comparisons are drawn among values that, precisely speaking, are not comparable: The revenues and costs are, variously, per 50 years, 60, 70, and 80. However, the effect of these discrepancies is made small because the periods themselves are all so long.

## MARGINAL METHOD

Let us turn now to the second of the three planning methods, the *marginal method.* Wherever there is a wide range, especially a continuous series, of alternatives to be weighed, and it is possible to identify the marginal revenues and costs associated with the series, the marginal method is applicable. The method finds its greatest usefulness in operation planning, in cases where the operation's revenues and costs can be singled out and logically kept separate from those of other operations by the firm. The alternative which equates marginal revenue and cost (within the range of diminishing returns) is that which represents the greatest excess of revenue over cost.

We have dealt so fully with the marginal approach in foregoing chapters that a brief illustration will suffice here. For the purpose, let us continue to use the operation-planning question of the best rotation length, taking the same data as in our example of the budget method. By so doing, we can compare the budget and marginal approaches. We can also show how the marginal method lends itself to telescoping the complexities of the budget that involves scheduling alternatives, provided planning can be focused on a discrete operation and a short-term view is acceptable.

Suppose that the planted stand is already well established, and in fact is approaching an age when the harvest cut should perhaps be made, the rotation ended, and a new one started. For example, let us say that the stand is now 50 years old, and the planner must analyze the relative merits of cutting now and of waiting to the end of another 10-year cycle. The prospective marginal revenue from this stand during the coming cycle is equal to the extra net revenue that it will yield if allowed to grow. Expressed as a ratio $[(1 + i)^n]$, this marginal revenue approximates the prospective value of the harvest cut at age 60, divided by the harvest value now minus the value of the 50-year thinning that would be forgone if the stand were harvested now. That is to say, marginal revenue equals approximately

$$\frac{\$320}{\$210 - \$10} = 1.60$$

From Table 10, by interpolation, this 10-year value of $(1+i)^n$ represents a marginal revenue of about 4.8 per cent per year.

Similarly, if the stand is now 60 years old, the marginal revenue is

$$\frac{\$460}{\$320 - \$10} = 1.48, \text{ i.e., } 4.0 \text{ per cent per year}$$

Or if the stand is now 70 years old, the marginal revenue is

$$\frac{\$580}{\$460 - \$10} = 1.29, \text{ i.e., } 2.6 \text{ per cent per year}$$

The above annual marginal revenues are plotted and curved over age in Figure 22. The marginal cost is the alternative rate of return. (Note that we are making no allowance for type-*b* or type-*c* cost—see p. 131). If the alternative rate is 3 per cent, the best harvest age, to the nearest 10-year cycle, is 70 years. If the rate is 4 per cent, the best harvest age is 60. If the rate is 5 per cent, 50 is the best harvest age. You will note that these results agree with the budgets in Table 27. If the firm anticipates a price trend, the curve in Figure 22 can be raised or lowered accordingly. Can you see that what we have done here, in the name of the marginal method of planning, is simply to estimate the unadjusted financial maturity of the stand?

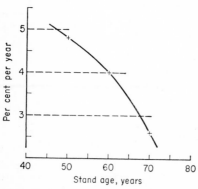

Fig. 22. Prospective marginal revenue, in per cent per year for the next 10-year cutting cycle, as related to age of a hypothetical planted forest.

[It is interesting that one reaches about the same conclusion in this case whether one considers the interminable future or only a decade. How often, and under what circumstances, would you expect to meet with cases of this sort? Surely in such cases long-range planning is a waste of time and an unnecessary hazard!]

### BREAK-EVEN METHOD

Consider, finally, the break-even method of planning. This is perhaps the most specialized, and the most limited in application, of the three methods we are studying. The break-even approach is useful in operation planning, and sometimes in broader planning, where there are two alternative methods or procedures to be weighed, especially where the two alternatives are to be weighed numerous times, for different cases. It follows that the marginal and break-even methods are almost never applicable to the same problem. If one method fits the problem, the other generally doesn't. The budget method, however, can substitute for the break-even approach just as it can for marginal analysis.

The *break-even method* consists in determining the level or size or point in the operation at which the two alternatives are equally good, one alternative having the advantage on one side of this point and the other on the opposite side. The point in question is called the break-even point, and knowledge of it provides a basis for deciding between the alternatives in any case that may come up, where the same data are applicable. For example, refer back to Figure 11*b* on page 164. This graph shows three break-even points between pairs of transfer media, occurring at distances of approximately 80, 180, and 400 miles. At distances less than each of these points, one medium of the pair has the advantage over the other, and at farther distances the advantage is reversed. If one knows the break-even distance, he knows which medium has the advantage for any length of haul, so long as the given cost rates hold good. For other cost rates, new break-even distances would have to be determined. You will perceive that the break-even method is usable on three, or even more, alternatives if they are taken in pairs.

Sometimes the term *break-even point* is used quite differently, to mean the scale of production at which a firm's total revenues just reach its total costs and above which, therefore, the firm must operate if it is to earn any net revenue. Such a point is the intersection of the two uppermost curves in Figure 6*c*, page 74. Now, however, we are referring to the point of equality, not of revenue and cost, but of the revenue *or* the cost of two alternative methods. Both methods or neither may prove profitable. Our calculations will show only which is the better.

Break-even points can be found graphically, as in Figure 11*b*, page 164. Or they may be calculated by formula, which is the approach we shall use in the illustration to follow. The approach takes three well-defined steps: (1) Set down for each of the two alternatives the formula that expresses cost, or revenue, or whatever, in relation to the independent variable (e.g., cost in relation to distance in the case of transfer). (2) Equate the two expressions of the dependent variable. (3) Solve this equation for the value of the independent variable thus determined; the result is the break-even point. Let us test the approach with some data on two methods of girdling southern upland hardwoods.[2]

In a study near Birmingham, Alabama, machine girdling of unwanted hardwoods proved twice as fast as hand girdling with an ax. The machine was a

[2] Yocom, Herbert A.: *Machine Faster than Ax for Girdling*, Southern Forest Experiment Station Southern Forestry Notes 94, New Orleans, November, 1954, pp. 1–2. Mr. Yocom's simplified formulas are substituted in the quotation.

"Little Beaver," manufactured by a Texas firm. This 2-cycle gasoline-motored machine weighs approximately 35 pounds and is carried on the operator's back. The cutting wheel is on the end of a flexible shaft.

The machine (with a 1-man crew) was used on 3,140 trees—mostly oaks but including some hickory, blackgum, and other upland hardwoods. From the data, a formula was derived which predicts the girdling time from . . . sum $D$ (the sum of d.b.h.'s of trees girdled, in inches) . . . :

$$\text{Man-hours} = 0.0025 \text{ (sum } D)$$

For the same area and type of timber a formula for notch-girdling with an ax is:

$$\text{Man-hours} = 0.005 \text{ (sum } D)$$

Provided that crews work with similar efficiency, the formulas are applicable to other upland hardwood stands where not over 25 per cent of the terrain is steep and the rest is moderately sloping to level.

### FINDING BREAK-EVEN POINT

Suppose that you have a forest and labor situation to which the foregoing two formulas are applicable. Assume that used girdling equipment has no resale value. Cost rates, let us suppose, are as follows:

|                                          | *Dollars* |
|------------------------------------------|-----------|
| Little Beaver:                           |           |
|   Initial cost:                |           |
|     Price f.o.b. Jackson, Miss. | 180.00 |
|     Shipment from Jackson | 4.00 |
|       Total initial cost | 184.00 |
|     Operating cost per hour | 0.32 |
|   Girdling ax:                 |           |
|     Initial cost     | 4.00 |
|     Operating cost per hour | 0.02 |
|   Wage rate per hour           | 1.48 |

If your trees to be girdled average 10 inches d.b.h. (in diameter at breast height), how big a girdling job must you have, to make it more economical for you to invest in a Little Beaver than to use axes? To answer this question, let us follow the three break-even steps outlined earlier.

1. Relate the total cost of girdling with Little Beaver ($B$) to number of trees girdled ($N$):

$$B = 184 + [0.32 + 1.48][0.0025(\text{sum } D)]$$

Since, in your problem, sum $D$ equals 10$N$,

$$B = 184 + 1.80(0.025N)$$
$$= 184 + 0.045N$$

Similarly, the cost of ax girdling $(A)$ is

$$A = 4 + 0.075N$$

2. Equate the two expressions of cost

$$184 + 0.045N = 4 + 0.075N$$

3. Solve for $N$

$$0.03N = 180$$
$$N = 6,000$$

Thus the break-even number of trees—the least number that you must have for girdling before it will be more economical to invest in a Little Beaver than to use axes—is 6,000. For any smaller number of trees, the ax has the advantage.

Now you can refer to the basic plan that called for the girdling job in the first place, the plan that presumably compares the probable revenues and costs of girdling. In light of the number of trees in question and of your break-even analysis, you may need to revise the cost estimate in the basic plan. You can then come to a final decision: whether to do the job and, if so, by what method. In practice, the break-even calculation may be simply a part of the basic plan.

The break-even problem can be simplified as follows: Considering initial costs, the ax starts out with an advantage over the Little Beaver, amounting to $180. But with every tree girdled, the Little Beaver, because of lower operating cost, gains an advantage of 3 cents. At 3 cents a tree, how many trees have to be girdled before the Little Beaver can overcome its initial disadvantage of $180?

[The principles involved here will become clearer if you will plot the costs over number of trees so as to find the break-even point graphically. You will find it helpful also to try solving this same problem by means of the budget method: Figure the total cost of girdling 1,000 trees, 2,000, and so on, with each of the two tools.]

It is often a great advantage to the manager or the planner to be able to think readily in break-even terms. For one thing, thinking in this way sharpens his appreciation for the influential variables in a problem: the weight they exert and the direction in which they pull. [In the girdling example, the break-even point may be affected by many things. If the point is raised, this represents an added advantage for the ax; if it is lowered, an extra advantage for the Little Beaver. Which of the two tools would gain advantage if the trees to be girdled were bigger? Which would gain if hourly wage rates were higher? If the Little Beaver were more expensive to buy? Or to operate? If labor were less skillful with an ax? If topography were less hilly, resulting in shorter travel time between trees? If there were fewer trees to be girdled per acre?]

## SOME PHILOSOPHY ABOUT PLANNING

Now before we leave the subject of planning for the firm, it will be helpful to draw together some general philosophy about the methods of planning—ideas suggested by the examples that we have covered. Needless to say, the importance of these examples is not in their content but in the principles they illustrate.

There is always a wide choice of approaches to any planning problem. The best approach is the simplest one that will do the job. Simplicity—in planning horizon, in assumptions about the future, in scope, and in calculations—lends strength to a plan in at least two ways: First, it lessens the likelihood of errors and confusion on the planner's part. Second, it renders the plan more understandable and acceptable to the decision maker, who often must be convinced, at some effort, that the plan is sound and reliable. Superficiality, of course, is not to be mistaken for simplicity.

Any plan can be budgeted out, and many plans are best handled by budgeting. But within the budget approach, opportunities may be found for short cuts via the marginal or the break-even method. And opportunities may be found for omitting irrelevant or unimportant items. Items that are unchanging over the range of alternatives being studied are irrelevant. Items that exert little influence on the choice among alternatives are unimportant. In respect to the latter items, judgment will suggest which of them may safely be omitted—and, in general, the degree of detail that the plan merits. Like the process of production, the process of planning for production is subject to diminishing returns. There comes a point when the extra benefits obtainable from further detail in planning will no longer justify the extra costs that would be entailed.

Basic to all good planning are reliable data. And for reliable data, experience and pilot testing and, above all, research are essential. The economic planner has a long way to go before he can be even as effective as are the physician and the attorney in guiding people's decisions. He needs more knowledge of prices and cost rates and their forecasting in order to do his work well. But he is even more in need of data on basic production functions—physical inputs and outputs. For example, what will be the response of the forest to various treatments? What is the efficiency of labor in various processes? We alluded to such problems at the close of Chapter 7. The forestry profession, despite much experience and the growing efforts in research, is still pathetically short of such knowledge. Even the subject of forest growth prediction, of all biological subjects perhaps the most central to forestry, has scarcely been tapped.

The forester concerned with economic, or management, planning for the firm has two relations to biological and engineering data. First, he uses them. Second, he is in position to help get them. He recognizes, for example, the superiority of input-output information in physical terms over that in value terms: Value measures to suit the case at hand may be attached when they are needed. He emphasizes the necessity for keeping separate records of the fixed and variable inputs. He sees clearly the need for accurate description of both inputs and outputs, especially concerning their quality, and the need for specifying the conditions under which the inputs and outputs were experienced, and for devising good ways of describing such conditions.

While full knowledge is essential for the ultimate planning job, judgment is the substitute that is used rather liberally meanwhile. If one is to accomplish anything, he does not always wait until all the data are in. He gives his bootstraps a tug and works things out as best he can.

### PLANNING DATA—AN EXAMPLE

Consider the problem of the forester who was commissioned by a land-owning firm to make a plan for the development and operation of its property. The firm was an oil company, engaged in producing and refining. The property in question was some 70,000 acres in southwest Louisiana, acquired in the belief that it was underlain by oil deposits. The company had already established several producing wells in one corner of the property.

The tract was originally occupied by a longleaf pine forest. Clearcut for lumber around 1920, it was burned over soon and repeatedly thereafter. At the time the company bought it, few trees remained. There was a well-established cover of grasses and herbs, which, as a long-standing custom and without charge, was used by neighboring farmers as range for their cattle and hogs.[3] The company wished to learn if the surface could be put to profitable use rather than be permitted to lie virtually idle, producing little but tax bills and free forage.

Consider, then, the knowledge and the data that this forester needed for the planning job, and visualize for yourself the procedures and problems involved in arriving at information and judgments. A partial itemization follows:

1. Objectives and plans of the company—information required to establish objectives for the forestry plan and define possible policy limitations upon the forest use of the land: How long does the Company foresee holding this property? How much use of the surface is likely to be

[3] For a description of such land and its use, and a budget type of approach to the planning problem, see Bond, W. E., and Robert S. Campbell: *Planted Pines and Cattle Grazing: A Profitable Use of Southwest Louisiana's Cut-over Pine Land,* Louisiana Forestry Commission Bulletin 4, Baton Rouge, 1951.

made by the oil enterprise? If parts or all of the property are likely to be sold before a planted forest would mature, will the market for the land reflect the forest values invested in it? Who might buy the land? Does the company have any set policies bearing on whether it might itself undertake logging or milling?

2. Local customs, attitudes, and climate of opinion—information needed for judging limitations upon production functions: How friendly is the attitude of the community toward the company? What are the prospects for passage of a closed-range or fencing law? Would people be willing to pay a grazing fee in return for improvement and management of the range by the company? How would the people feel if the company should attempt to exclude hogs from the range? What is the local sentiment toward timber production on these lands? Are there any significant attitudes bearing on the problem of fire control?

3. The production functions—information on inputs and outputs, on which to base a plan:

*a.* Timber. What species are adapted to the site? What yields of various products may be expected at various ages? What planting methods and spacings are to be considered? What cultural treatments may be used, and what will their results be?

*b.* Forage. What yields of forage and what carrying capacity for stock may be expected under forest stands of various ages? What kinds of stock may be grazed successfully?

*c.* Other enterprises. What other enterprises, such as farming, should be considered in the use of the land surface, and what are their inputs and outputs?

*d.* General. What additional administrative and protective organization and facilities will be needed for managing the various enterprises? What losses may be expected from fire and other agencies? What type of logging and milling enterprises might fit in with the prospective timber yields?

4. Rates of revenue—needed to attach values to the prospective outputs: What prices may conservatively be expected for stumpage? Logs? Processed products? What grazing fees may reasonably be charged? What prices are applicable to other products that may be produced?

5. Cost rates—needed to attach values to the prospective inputs: What is the prospective supply of labor and the prospective wage rate? What will be the cost of necessary technical and administrative assistance? Of raw materials such as planting stock? Of administrative and protective facilities and installations? How would the company finance the land-surface enterprises, and what would be the cost of financing? What minimum rate of return would the company expect on its land-surface investments? How would the company's taxes be affected by the development of these enterprises?

*SUMMARY*

Three methods of planning, with special reference to the sixth step in the process, are the budget, marginal, and break-even methods.

The budget method is widely adaptable but is especially useful for enterprise and organization planning where interrelated lines of production are involved and where there is a substantial nonquantified element of judgment in the planning. It is applicable where the alternatives to be weighed are few. Its central feature is an itemized accounting of the benefits and costs of the alternatives—either (1) for a given year or other short period or (2) for a longer period, through use of capitalization or other time-adjustment devices.

The marginal method is especially useful in operation planning, where a wide range of alternatives is to be weighed and where their marginal costs and revenues can be identified. The method consists of determining the alternative that equates these costs and revenues.

The break-even method is applicable to operation, or occasionally broader, planning where there are two alternative methods or procedures (or more, that can be analyzed in pairs) whose relative advantages depend on the size of the job or some other measurable variable in the operation. The method consists of finding the break-even point, or point of equal advantage of the alternatives, in terms of this variable, and then of inferring which alternative has the advantage in the case at hand.

Basic to all planning are reliable data. To find data and to encourage and guide research leading to fuller knowledge, especially of biological and engineering inputs and outputs, is a big part of economic planning for the forestry firm.

Part Three

# THE MARKET FOR
# FOREST PRODUCTS

**Chapter 17**

**DEMAND FOR**

**FOREST**

**PRODUCTS**

Part Two of this book explored the supply side of the forest economy. Now in Part Three we adventure into the demand side and then into the meeting places of supply and demand, the markets, where the flow of most goods and services is decided and their values determined.

In the very first chapter of the book, it was contended that the economics of forestry is oriented to the consumer—that it's the consumer who calls the shots, and that the forestry profession exists solely because of consumers. It is, in a way, indicative of the status of social science and of forestry that, notwithstanding this early protestation of faith, the consumer has been put off until the middle of the book. For the consumer is a perplexing fellow, and we don't know so much about him as we should like. A few stanch souls, mostly women home economists and consumption economists, have studied and reported upon consumers from the standpoint of the consumer. A few brash souls, mostly advertising psychologists, have had a go at consumers from the viewpoint of the salesman. A few general economists have tried explaining the consumer as an "economic man," while others have set him forth as a man doubtfully economic. While these efforts were in progress, the rest of humanity who took notice have exercised their talent for skepticism. We have, therefore, some rough ground to cover in this chapter. Let us step out with enthusiastic caution.

### CONSUMING FIRM

In the forest economy, where social and individual goals frequently diverge and where the public interest, therefore, is a common preoccupation, the consumer is more than an ordinary figure. He is, in one aspect, the public. What makes him still more special is that he is you—us. What higher claim could he have to our attention? Bear in mind as we go along who it is we are talking about.

The principal consuming unit, or *consuming firm*, in our economy is the household. In the United States, the head of this firm, who makes the bulk of decisions about consumption, commonly is the wife, or mother of the family. Incidentally, men can never learn to understand women, and perhaps this is why the subject of consumption economics is so difficult for us. The managerial role of women in consumption, which has been verified statistically, is made much of by the women's magazines. They try to point out that, since the woman is the buyer, her magazine is the place to advertise all consumer goods, including men's shirts and shaving soap. The men's periodicals retort that though the wife may do the buying, it is the husband who dictates the choice of brand, style, and so on. [What do you think? How does it go in your family? Suppose you were advertising bond writing paper; to which sex of buyers primarily would you address your appeal? What if you were advertising tropical hardwood wall paneling? Or a forest vacation resort? Would the direction of your appeal be the same in any nation of the world?]

Besides the household's acting as a consuming firm, the members of the household sometimes act as individuals in making consumption decisions. In such cases they are setting themselves up as separate firms. Again, there are unattached individuals who continuously act as consuming firms. Finally, consumer goods are bought by many kinds of groups other than households in the usual sense—for example, manufacturing firms, penal institutions, and lumber camps. These, too, then become consuming firms.

## OBJECTIVES OF SOVEREIGN CONSUMER

To understand the consuming firm, one must understand its objectives and motivations—that is, what its goals are, and why. This is a tall order. In Chapter 2 it was assumed that the members of an economy have as their goal the satisfaction of their wants. Since there are degrees of satisfaction, it is customary to suppose that the firm seeks to maximize its satisfaction. This it presumably does by obtaining the greatest possible excess of pleasure over pain, just as the producing firm may aim for the largest excess of revenue over cost. But even the producer's goals are not simple, and the consumer's are, if anything, less so. Whereas there are substantial aspects of both revenue and cost that are measurable, neither pleasure nor pain can be quantified at all. It is not always possible for even the consumer himself with conviction to rank things or events in respect to net satisfaction—that is, to express a clear preference, let alone measure it.

The basic problem of defining satisfaction is only little further complicated by the wild profusion of bases for satisfaction—of consumer motivations. Wants are said to be biologically determined and socially conditioned. If this is true, the part of biology seems clear enough: Wants arise from the basic drives of hunger, thirst, sex, bodily discomfort, fear, and the like. Thus, you want a house for shelter and protection. It is in the social conditioning that the story loses its simplicity.

What kind of house do you want: how constructed, where located, what size, and how arranged and furnished? The answer depends on a great many things. The customs of your forebears are one, determined, in turn, by their race, religion, social status, and numerous other circumstances. Also vital are the customs of your community, which depend on all sorts of things from climate to the whims of some bygone social leader who set the style. Then there is the matter of your own status in life, your occupation and position, the present and prospective size of your family and of your possessions. You will be influenced in the desire for a home by the experience and advice of friends and associates, and perhaps also by the wish to outdo them, or to conform with them, or not to compete with them, as the case may be. And needless to say, the friendly suggestions of your real estate agent will have a bearing on your preferences. Indeed, it appears that nothing substantial in your life or the lives of other members of your consuming firm is without effect upon your want for a home, or anything else. The psychologists who indulge in motivation research, which is known affectionately as "M.R." in the advertising trade, would no doubt list as one factor, whether you had been a breast-fed or bottle-fed baby.

Given your wants for a house, then whether you will get one, and what kind, will depend upon your wealth and income and upon what may be had at various prices. The price in question, or cost to the consuming firm, is most often a matter of the terms of financing obtainable and the prospects for resale of the place if you are obliged to resell.

When your firm makes its choice, who can question the preferences that led to it? People may take exception to your taste, but the most they could prove would be that it is different from theirs. They may call you old-fashioned because you like a frame house with clapboards and a paneled interior. Or perhaps they will call you old-fashioned if your tastes run instead to brick and plaster. They may think you foolish for spending such a high proportion of your income on housing, or such a low proportion. And they may frown at you for painting your place purple with red trim. But unless the public interest becomes involved, what you do is your business. Certainly there is nothing in the principles of economics that would permit one to determine whether your preference is good or bad. The ultimate voice of the consumer in his affairs and thus in the whole economy is referred to as *consumer sovereignty.*

It is, however, possible to criticize the sovereign consumer on more than purely subjective grounds. For one thing, he may not have command of the facts. He may, for example, buy a house built of green lumber without knowing that the lumber is green or perhaps without knowing the consequences of green lumber. For another thing, he may misjudge his own interest as between the short and the long term. He may, for instance, saddle himself with a house that looks flashy but soon begins to deteriorate, and he may live long to regret it. Such deficiencies in the consumer's performance trace fundamentally to the problem of forecasting.

## FORECASTING BY CONSUMERS

You will recall that in early chapters we pointed out the great amount of forecasting that a producer must do. He forecasts a production function and judges the uncertainties attached to it, and he predicts prices and cost rates and their probable errors. Every decision he makes is based in the first instance upon a forecast. The consumer is no better off. He seeks satisfaction in the goods and services he acquires, but he can never know if he has got it, until too late. At best, therefore, what guides the consumer is not the satisfaction from a good or service, but the *wantedness* of the good or service, its predicted power to give him satisfaction.

Around the concrete problem of forecasting has appropriately been centered much of the effort of the so-called *consumer movement:* the collective attempt by consumers to know the market and the product, to describe the latter factually and to measure its performance, to realize for consumers a high return in satisfaction per dollar of outlay, and to match the size, strength, and objectivity of producers. In the United States, the consumer movement has never grown big as it has in some European nations—Sweden, for instance. Nevertheless, it has had a part in raising the status of consumers by increasing their knowledge, which is the basis for accurate forecasting and intelligent decisions.

The sellers of goods to consumers are also concerned with consumers' knowledge. Each seller is primarily concerned lest this knowledge be deficient with respect to the merits of his product. Advertising is considered the best remedy for such deficiency. By many sellers, the *brand* is offered to consumers as a device for reducing the uncertainty in consumers' forecasts. In general, the seller's interest in the buyer's factual knowledge of the product tends to run to a somewhat different depth where the buyer is a consumer than where the buyer is a producer. In the latter case, where the product is a *producer good,* such as a factory machine, it is likely to be described by the seller in the cold, impersonal language of specifications. The seller's interest is that the buyer should know as much as possible about the machine so that he can get the best service and revenue out of it. If, on the other hand, the product is a *consumer good,* such as a piece of furniture, the seller may feel that it is neither necessary nor desirable, nor even possible, to convey full knowledge to the buyer. Nowadays full knowledge is for specialists, and few buyers acting as individuals can qualify.

[During World War II, wholesale and retail lumber stocks in the United States were drawn down low as a result of heavy demands. Turnover between mill and consumers was rapid, and a good deal of insufficiently seasoned lumber was put into use, as well as lumber not best adapted to the purpose in view. Where this happened consistently, lumber made a bad name for itself. After the war, some of the trade associations put on special educational campaigns, with careful descriptions and specifications, to encourage suiting the type of lumber to its proposed use and thus getting maximum satisfaction from the lumber dollar. Such campaigns applied primarily to the construction industry and were directed at contractors and architects. The ultimate aim was to recapture and strengthen lumber's position in the consumer's scale of preferences. How do you explain the use of a factual sales approach in this case?]

Just as the producer makes his forecasts of input and output in light of a choice or prediction regarding technology, so the consumer's forecasts also assume a certain technology of consumption. The *technology of consumption* is the approximate counterpart of production technology: It is the machinery and materials and methods and immediate circumstances of consumption. In the case of your house, it is the length of your occupancy during the year, whether continuous or seasonal; the number and identity of occupants; the uses they make of the various rooms and yard for working, playing, sleeping, entertaining guests, storing things, and so on; the kind of furniture and other consumption equipment employed; and other such matters. The technology of consumption is important to us for two reasons. First, along with the good or service and the consumer, it determines the satisfaction derived from consumption, just as a worker's tools help determine his productivity. The decoration of the dining space and the manner of serving the meal have a great deal to do with your enjoyment of the food. Second, consumption technology affects also the consumer's choice of goods and services, because time is required to change technology. So long as you have a built-in broiler in your patio, you are apt to be in the market for charcoal.

## DEMAND MODELS

Now let us consider some analytical models of consumer wants and demand, models to help explain consumer choice of goods and services (or, as we shall sometimes call them, *commodities*). For this purpose, let us imagine a consuming firm whose decisions are rational—that is, they are consciously directed to the end of maximizing net satisfactions per unit of time. Such a firm is an abstraction, not fully human, but yet a step higher on the evolutionary ladder than the so-called economic man.

The firm has to make decisions—choices—regarding the consumer goods and services it will buy. Choices are necessary, first, because the firm's resources are limited and, second, because its capacity for satisfaction is limited.

The firm sees arrayed in the markets a variety of goods and services in ample quantity. Actually, we may suppose that what the consumer sees is not the commodities themselves, but their *attributes:* the qualities with reference to which he exercises his tastes and preferences and makes his choices. When you look at a chair, you interpret it in terms of comfort, beauty, durability, versatility in use, and so on, and it is these attributes that you are acquiring when you buy the chair. Consumers in New Haven, Connecticut,[1] who prefer a frame house to a masonry house see the following desirable attributes in the former (the numbers are percentages of all the answers given by consumers interviewed):

| | | |
|---|---:|---|
| More pleasing appearance | 42 | ⎫ |
| Permits changing outside color | 21 | ⎪ |
| Superior insulating qualities | 14 | ⎬ 100 |
| Structural advantages (over poor local brick) | 11 | ⎪ |
| Owner can do his own repairing | 7 | ⎪ |
| Easy to keep neat outside | 5 | ⎭ |

On the other hand, those New Haven consumers who prefer masonry houses take quite a different view. In their eyes, the masonry house bestows the following advantages on its owner:

| | | |
|---|---:|---|
| Greater durability | 46 | ⎫ |
| Less maintenance work | 38 | ⎬ 100 |
| Superior insulating qualities | 12 | ⎪ |
| Low fire hazard | 4 | ⎭ |

You will notice that these views are partly contradictory. They are, nonetheless, valid and relevant attributes of the houses in question. As we have seen before, what guides people's action is not necessarily the truth but what they think is the truth.

Now, to continue with our assumptions, when the firm looks at the

[1] Zaremba, Joseph: "Some Problems in Forecasting Future Wood Requirements," doctoral dissertation, Harvard University, Cambridge, Mass., 1958.

variety of market commodities and their attributes, it knows that there is a price attached to each commodity and that, whatever the price is, the firm may buy any amount of the commodity, now or later, at substantially this same price. The firm is able to forecast whether any given quantity of a commodity or group of commodities will yield the firm more satisfaction, or less, or the same amount as any other. (Notice that it is not necessary to assume that the firm has perfect knowledge of commodities or that its forecasts of satisfaction are accurate.) The firm is able to predict its income per unit of time, part of which income will be spent for consumption. Let us see what may happen in the consumer's short run —that is, when alternative rates of consumption can be considered but when durable consumer goods and consumption technology appear fixed (compare p. 198).

## DIMINISHING SATISFACTION AND BEST COMBINATION

In planning its consumption for the time period ahead, the firm, we may suppose, takes into account a sort of principle of diminishing returns (compare pp. 55–56) as applied to consumption—what we may call the *principle of diminishing satisfaction:* that the more units of a commodity it consumes in the period, the less satisfaction it will get from the marginal unit. Thus if the firm should begin its plan by considering the purchase of that commodity which has the greatest wantedness of all, it will soon realize that, before it could carry its consumption of the commodity very far, its satisfaction per dollar would have diminished to the point where it would do better to spend its next outlays on other commodities that would now have assumed the priority position. And so, in its plan for the period ahead, the firm, in its mind's eye, puts first a few units of this commodity and then some of that into its market basket, continuing to fill the basket always with those items that have the greatest (marginal) wantedness per dollar, of all the items arrayed in the markets. Using this procedure, the firm arrives at the shopping list, or budget, that uniquely promises to maximize the firm's total satisfaction during the planned period, for the amount of expenditure intended.

We may look upon the firm's budgeting process as being guided by the question "What are the alternatives?" So viewed, the cost of any commodity to the firm is the opportunity cost of forgoing the most wanted alternative commodity that could be bought with the same money. And the object of the budgeting is to arrive at a shopping list of commodities having the lowest possible opportunity cost for the given money outlay.

[In this model, what will determine the amount of expenditure, the proportion of income devoted to consumption? Can you use this same model to reason out the amount of the firm's saving and the firm's alternative rate of return?]

Now when, as we assume, the firm has completed its ideal shopping list, or budget, the contents of the list will have four characteristics that it is helpful for us to understand: *First,* as we have already observed, the total satisfaction represented in the list is the greatest that the firm can anticipate from spending the amount of money in question in the

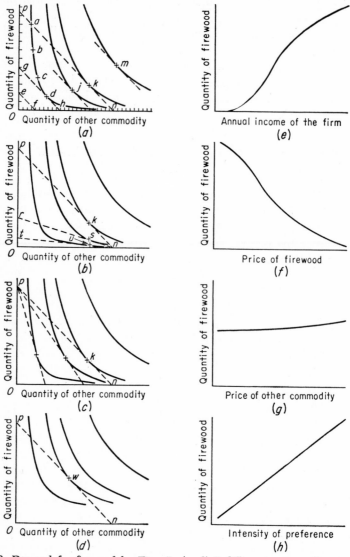

Fig. 23. Demand for firewood by Firm J: (*a–d*) Indifference curves illustrating the effect on demand of changes in income, firewood price, other prices, and preferences, respectively. (*e–h*) Demand in relation to income, firewood price, other prices, and intensity of preference, respectively.

given time. *Second,* the (marginal) satisfaction that the firm expects from a unit of any commodity in the list is about the same as that from any other commodity in the list, per dollar of price. *Third,* it must therefore follow that, if a very small quantity of any item is deleted from the list and replaced by increasing (by an equal money value) any other commodity on the list, or replaced by the money equivalent itself for purposes of saving, the substitution would be a matter of indifference to the firm. *Fourth,* it therefore follows also that not only are the forecast marginal satisfactions per dollar the same for all commodities in the budget but also these satisfactions are the same as that expected from a dollar itself used in the most satisfying way. In other words, the best combination for the consuming firm, like that for the producing firm, is the one which equates marginal cost and revenue.

It follows that the amount of any commodity that the firm budgets for consumption depends upon (1) the firm's income, (2) the price of the commodity, (3) the price of other commodities, and (4) the firm's tastes and preferences.

## INDIFFERENCE ANALYSIS

To illustrate the foregoing model, consider the demand for firewood by a rural family, Firm J, that will use the wood for cooking and heating. In order to bring out the concepts of substitution and indifference mentioned earlier, let us consider also another commodity—any other, that we can take as representing all commodities other than firewood. Our analysis of these two commodities will partly parallel our two-input analysis in Chapter 7 (especially Fig. 8, p. 86) and our analysis of two rival outputs in Chapter 12 (Fig. 15, p. 190). In Figure 23a, quantities of firewood and of the other commodity are scaled off on the axes. Let point *a* be any point on the graph, representing certain amounts of firewood and the other commodity—a package consisting, say, of ten units of firewood and three units of the other commodity. This package represents for Firm J a certain anticipated satisfaction, or wantedness. Now suppose another package is made up, containing seven units of firewood. How much of the other commodity will have to be included in order for this package to have the same wantedness as the first? Since the two commodities are rivals, there must be more of the other commodity than before, but, as it turns out, not much more, Firm J's preferences being what they are. The firm's judgment of the precise contents of the second package is shown by point *b*. Points *c* and *d* represent still other packages of equal wantedness to package *a*, and the curve drawn through them is the locus of all such points, an *iso-satisfaction curve,* or curve of equal forecast satisfactions. It is a matter of indifference to the firm which of the packages along this curve it has for consumption, and so the curve may be called an *indifference curve.*

Notice that the indifference curve is concave from above. This characteristic shape follows inevitably from the principle of diminishing satisfaction. The lower reaches of the curve, around point $d$, represent relatively small amounts of firewood. Such small amounts would need to be carefully economized—used for only the most essential purposes. Each stick would have high use value, and to give up one without loss of satisfaction would require that Firm J receive in return a comparatively large amount of the other commodity. That is to say, the marginal rate of substitution of firewood for the other commodity is low. Or to say the same thing in still another way, the slope of the indifference curve is low. However, the upper reaches of the curve, around point $a$, represent relatively large amounts of firewood. Here, giving up one stick would promise comparatively little loss of satisfaction, which could therefore be regained by the substitution of only a little of the other commodity. That is, the marginal rate of substitution of firewood for the other commodity is high: The slope of the curve is high.

The curve $abcd$ is the indifference curve relating to one particular level of wantedness. But how about other levels? Reflection suggests that there must be a large number of indifference curves. Figure 23a shows four altogether, by way of a sample. From left to right, the curves stand for increasingly larger packages of the commodities and for increasingly greater anticipated satisfaction—the latter, however, in less than direct proportion to the former, as we have seen.

Given this sheaf of indifference curves, what can we learn about Firm J's consumption of firewood? Let us begin by considering the curve $abcd$. Which one of the many packages arrayed along this curve is best: Which one would the firm want to buy? Presumably the cheapest one, since they are all equally desirable. The solution to our problem, therefore, rests with the prices of the packages. Now if goods were priced according to their value in use, all the packages would bear the same price tag, and our search for a best package would be futile. However, we know this cannot be so, at least because the firm experiences diminishing satisfaction whereas we have assumed constant prices. Our question has a determinate answer. Just as the fact of diminishing returns requires that there be a best combination for the producer, so diminishing satisfaction necessitates a best combination for the consumer.

## INCOME DEMAND

Suppose that the price of firewood is twice as much per unit as the price of the other commodity. For example, two units of firewood cost the same as four units of the other commodity. If we find these two points on the axes of graph *a* and connect them with a straight line, *ef*, we have an iso-cost curve, or *iso-price curve:* All packages represented along this line will be priced the same. Furthermore, any curve drawn parallel to *ef* will be an iso-cost curve, the curves situated higher and farther to the right representing the greater cost.

Since the indifference curve *abcd* lies altogether to the right of, and above, the iso-cost curve *ef*, we know that it would be necessary for Firm J to incur a greater cost than is represented by *ef* in order to buy any of the packages on *abcd*. Let us slide the iso-cost curve up and to the right, keeping it parallel to *ef*, and continuing until it just touches *abcd*. Now for the first time we have represented, in *gh*, a cost outlay that is sufficient to buy one of the packages: the one at *d*, the point of tangency. And this is the cheapest of all the packages along *abcd*, for all the other points lie on iso-cost curves that are higher and farther to the right than *gh*. We conclude, therefore, that Firm J's least-cost combination on *abcd* is the point of tangency with an iso-cost curve: The point where the marginal rate of substitution of firewood for the other commodity is the same as the price ratio between the other commodity and firewood.

Now if the cost outlay on *gh* should by any chance equal Firm J's income that is spendable for these commodities, then the firm has in package *d* its ultimate best combination, which possesses the four characteristics stated on pages 264–265. That is, if the firm is to lay out the amount represented on *gh*, the best point, or package to buy, is that at *d*, since every other point lies on an inferior indifference curve. But suppose the firm has more income to lay out? Then it will seek its best combination on a superior indifference curve, as at *j* or *k* or *m*. The points *d*, *j*, *k*, and *m* therefore trace an expansion path that relates the quantity of firewood demanded by the firm to the income of the firm, given the commodities' prices and the firm's preferences.

Let us now leap the gap between the "other commodity" and all commodities other than firewood and, guided by the expansion path *djkm*, construct the relation between quantity of firewood demanded (per year) by Firm J and the (annual) income of the firm. The result is the curve in Figure 23*e*. [How might you explain the position and shape that have been deduced for this curve?]

The curve in graph E is a *demand curve*. It is Firm J's income demand curve for firewood, at given prices for wood and other commodities and at a given state of the firm's preferences and consumption technology. This demand curve may be thought of as the result of plotting a *demand schedule,* or list of quantities per unit of time in relation to income. Either the curve or the schedule is, as a whole, a representation of *demand,* in this case *income demand,* an abstraction that we may regard as a sort of program that a rational and very methodical firm might plan out to remind itself how much wood it should stand ready to buy as soon as it could foretell what its income was going to be. If price expectations or preferences change, the demand curve may move, and if it does, we may refer to the shift as a *change in demand*. However, if income alone changes, the firm's resulting shift along the curve is not correctly termed a change in demand. It is merely a change in the *amount demanded*. Either this type of change or a change in demand may be referred to as a *demand response*. You should note that this reasoning and terminology is in every respect parallel to that suggested for *supply*, pages 194 to 196.

## PRICE DEMAND

When we worked on supply, we studied it in relation to price. What about demand in relation to price? In Figure 23*b*, the four indifference curves of graph *a* have been copied. The iso-cost curve through *k* has also been copied, and labeled *np*. The package *k* is the best combination at the income level and prices represented on *np*. But suppose the price of firewood were higher, so that only *Or* units, instead of *Op*, could be bought for the price of *On* units of the other commodity. In that event, spendable income would be represented on the iso-cost curve *nr*, and the best package would be at *s* on this curve: A smaller amount of firewood is bought at the higher price. Similarly, the best combination *u* is determined if the price of firewood rises still further, as represented by *nt*. Note that the iso-cost curves *np*, *nr*, and *nt* all stand for the same cost outlay. Their positions are different because they represent different firewood prices. Thus we have in the expansion path *ksu*, when it is projected on the vertical axis, the relation between the firm's demand for firewood and the price of firewood, income and other prices being constant. This relation is translated into the form of a demand curve in graph *f*.

The curve in graph *f* is a *price-demand* curve, whereas that in graph *e* is an income-demand curve. Like the income-demand curve, the price-demand curve is but one of a conceivably large series. It is the one applying to this particular level of income, other prices, and intensity of preference of the firm. And like graph *e*, graph *f* is a representation of *demand*, and analogous rules of reasoning and terminology apply to it.

## OTHER DEMAND FUNCTIONS

The remainder of Figure 23 holds only passing interest for us. It depicts the relation between demand and the other two of the four relevant factors: other prices and the intensity of preference. As before, the relation illustrated is the net relationship, other factors being constant.

In graph *c*, the successive iso-cost curves beginning with *pn* show the result of alternative, higher prices of the other commodity. In this case it is found that if the price of the other commodity were higher, the amount of firewood demanded would be somewhat greater, and this finding is translated to graph g. [Under what conditions would you expect the opposite relationship: a smaller quantity of firewood associated with a higher price of the other commodity? And what sort of correlation would you anticipate in the case that really concerns us here, between the amount of firewood demanded and the price of *all* other commodities?]

Graph d contains a new sheaf of indifference curves. These curves are higher than the others: farther from the horizontal axis. Thus they symbolize a greater preference for firewood in comparison to the other commodity. The iso-cost curve pn is identical to that in graph a and hence represents the same income and prices. It is apparent that the greater the intensity of preference for firewood, the further up toward point p the best combination will be located. Compare the location of w with that of k. The relationship between quantity of firewood demanded and intensity of preference, with income and prices constant, is sketched in graph h. The sketch is merely symbolic, for there is no way of scaling off the horizontal axis.

## HOW TRUE ARE THE MODELS?

Now that we have our consuming firm all neatly tucked away into eight graphs, let us reflect a bit on the implications, especially of income and price demand, the two concepts that we shall want to use the most. How true are these concepts?

In the first place, let us direct our criticism to the right target. Let us not be concerned with the fact that very few consumers have any explicit notion of substitution or indifference, or even demand. This fact is irrelevant. What we want to know is whether it will be helpful for *us* to use the idea of demand and its related ideas in order (1) to explain human action truthfully and (2) to guide human action successfully toward a goal.

Next, let us put in perspective the seeming difficulties of any orderly explanation of a disorderly process. How can we ever encompass within neat graphs and schedules the consuming firm's varied and tangential motivations—the fact that you buy books to read, whereas your neighbor buys them for the bindings? The answer is that we subsume these demand factors under the heading of preference, where they are no more troublesome and no less quantifiable than any of the other items we have had to toss into this ragbag. And the important thing about preference from our viewpoint is not its complicated origin but the fact that it is reasonably stable and, for large numbers, predictable.

Then how about the consumers who apparently behave in just the opposite way from what our model says? We incline, for instance, to believe that people buy less if the price is higher; but with respect to some goods, there are some consumers who seem to prefer to pay a higher price. We stress decision making by consumers, but we know very well

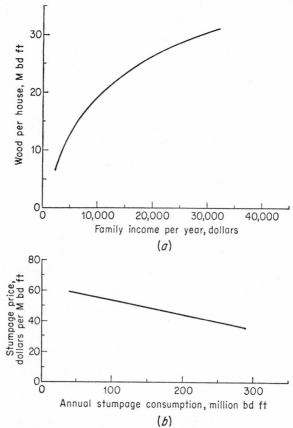

Fig. 24. Aggregate demand curves: (a) Income demand of average New Haven, Connecticut, families for wood in single-family houses, 1954. (*Source: Zaremba, Joseph: Some Problems in Forecasting Future Wood Requirements, doctoral dissertation, Harvard University, Cambridge, Mass., 1958.*) (b) Price demand for all sugar pine stumpage, a forecast into the next century. (*Source: Vaux, Henry J.: Economics of the Young-growth Sugar Pine Resource, California Agriculture Experiment Station Bulletin 738, Berkeley, 1954.*)

that there are persons to whom the making of decisions is distasteful, so that they will go to almost any ends to avoid it. We emphasize the plan, or budget, as being of central importance to the consumer's role, but listen to the words of this young woman, a cashier, who was asked by the "inquiring reporter" from the newspaper, "Do you think it helps to live on a budget?"

"No. I just spend my money until it is gone. I have tried living on a budget but it never works out because I always see something I want to buy. First I pay my bills, which is a part of budgeting, and then I just spend what I have left on clothes and whatever else I need."[2]

The best answer we have to all these perplexing questions is the concept of *aggregate demand:* the total or average demand of a group rather than the demand of a particular firm. Such demand takes on reliability from large numbers. The aggregate income demand involves, conceptually, the summing up of the quantities and corresponding incomes of firms such as that represented in Figure 23e. The aggregate price demand, similarly, comes from the summing of quantities at each price, taken from individual demands such as that of 23f. It is the aggregate demand with which we shall be working largely from now on. Both the aggregate income and price demands are useful analytical tools. They are real in the sense that they produce acceptable explanations of or guides to human action. As the economics of forestry gradually begins to mature, we find foresters using these tools to help answer vital forestry problems. For example, we find Dr. Joseph Zaremba working out the average income demand for house-construction lumber by families in New Haven, Connecticut, and Dr. Henry Vaux projecting the national demand for sugar pine lumber in relation to price (Fig. 24). Both these men intended their work to be used to steer social and individual policy, in ways that we shall study in later chapters.

You will notice that the axes of the price-demand curve in Figure 24b are reversed from their position in Figure 23f. Price, though it is the independent variable, is placed on the vertical axis. This is done in order to get the price and quantity axes in the same position for demand as for supply, with a view to plotting both on the same graph later. We shall work from now on with price always on the vertical axis.

Now let us take in turn each of the two major ways of expressing demand, in reference to income and in reference to price, and use them to make some final points about consumer demand.

## CONDITIONS OF DEMAND

The income demand curves of Figures 23 and 24 both show positive correlation between income and the quantity of the product. Occasionally, however, one runs across a case of negative correlation, where the amount of the commodity demanded falls with rising income. Such a down-sloping income-demand curve can, indeed, be found for firewood, the product used for illustration in Figure 23. Let us see how this may happen:

[2] *Syracuse* (N.Y.) *Herald-Journal,* May 9, 1955. Quoted by permission.

We have already analyzed how a rural family may increase its purchases of firewood if its income goes up. The enlargement of income represents an opportunity to gain more satisfaction through consumption. One source of greater satisfaction is to consume more firewood for cooking and heating. This, as we noted on page 263, is a short-run analysis.

However, in the long run, other, contrary forces may enter to reverse the relation between income and wood consumption. Given time for wood stoves to be used and scrapped and for the technology of consumption to be changed, families may with higher income escape the dirt and drudgery of burning wood. They may turn to substitutes that they consider superior, such as appliances that burn bottled gas. Such long-run demand responses have in fact been made good in rural America in past decades. The consumption of firewood has decreased with rising incomes.

Goods for which the long-run income demand is down-sloping are commonly known as *inferior goods.* Their story is typically like that of firewood: They tend to be supplanted by superior goods. Only the firms that cannot afford to do otherwise continue to consume the inferior good.

While long-run income-demand responses such as the foregoing are taking place, the short-run demand is changing, but the correlation between consumption and income continues to be positive. In the case of firewood in the United States, the new short-run demand is based upon fixed durable goods and consumption technology that also are new. Typically, the wood is burned in the fireplace of suburban homes—primarily for aesthetic satisfactions and only secondarily for heat. If the income of such wood-burning families rises in the short run, they will tend to burn more wood.

Even in the long run, the use of fireplace wood as distinguished from stove wood is positively correlated with income. Families that have ceased altogether to burn wood may resume its use if they can afford a home with a fireplace. Those families that rise into the higher income brackets may indulge themselves to the extent of two or more fireplaces. Thus, although firewood under the old technology is an inferior good, under the new it is not.

## ELASTICITY OF DEMAND

It is not only the position and general orientation of the demand curve that concerns us, but also its shape and tilt. The tilt *at any point or interval* on the curve is referred to as *elasticity of demand,* which is measured as the ratio of the percentage change in quantity to the associated percentage change in income or price, as the case may be. Hence the elasticity of demand is the counterpart of supply elasticity (pp. 196–197).

The income elasticity of demand expresses the sensitiveness of demand to changes in income. If a given percentage change in income would result in a less-than-proportional change in the amount demanded—that is, if elasticity is less than one—the demand is called inelastic. If elasticity is greater than one, the demand is referred to as elastic. The intermediate case is unitary elasticity. The same rules apply to the price elasticity of demand. In general, the measurement of elasticity of positive-sloping income demand follows the same principles as measuring the elasticity of supply. [Under what circumstances (of the commodity and

*Table 28. Demand for Cambridge chairs by a group of college seniors*

| If price of Cambridge chairs is— | Then the class stands ready to buy this number— | And to incur this total outlay— |
|---|---|---|
| *Dollars* | *Units* | *Dollars* |
| 2 | 159 | 318 |
| 8 | 91 | 728 |
| 14 | 59 | 826 |
| 20 | 38 | 760 |
| 26 | 26 | 676 |
| 32 | 10 | 320 |

the consumers) would you expect an elastic income demand? An inelastic income demand?]

Measuring the elasticity of negative-sloping price demand brings in some new principles. Let us take for illustration the demand for Cambridge chairs on the part of a class of senior students in forestry economics, as calculated by the students themselves. The Cambridge chair used in the experiment was a sturdy, comfortable, black-lacquered armchair of colonial design, built of hard maple and adaptable to a wide variety of uses in the home. It was appraised in light of several alternative chairs representing a range of design and price. The results are given in Table 28 and Figure 25.

If a rise in price would bring about a less than proportional reduction in consumers' purchases of a commodity, their total outlay for the commodity would increase. An increase in outlay with price therefore is evidence of an inelastic demand, as in the upper part of Table 28. Where demand has an elasticity greater than one, an increase in price would be accompanied by a reduction in total outlay, as in the lower part of Table 28. It appears, then, that the demand of the class for Cambridge chairs was inelastic at low prices, elastic at high prices, and of unitary elasticity at an intermediate price of around $14. We have illustated here the *first rule for price elasticity of demand.*

The elasticity of demand can be measured with greater precision on a graph. In Figure 25, where the price and quantity data of Table 28 have been plotted and curved, the elasticity at any point, $D$, is found by constructing the tangent at $D$, extending it to both axes, and computing the ratio of the distances $DF/DE$. In the illustration, the ratio is 0.4, signifying comparatively inelastic demand. Since the curve slopes down to the right, a negative sign is affixed: Elasticity is −0.4. Unitary elasticity

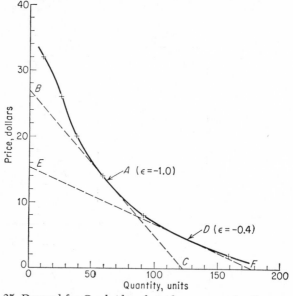

Fig. 25. Demand for Cambridge chairs by a group of college seniors.

is found by trial and error at point $A$, where $AC$ is equal to $AB$. This *second rule for price elasticity of demand* holds for any graph on arithmetic scale where the axes are the principal axes that pass through zero price and quantity. The rule implies that for any straight-line demand curve—except a vertical one, where elasticity is zero, and a horizontal one, where it is infinite—elasticity must be different at every point on the curve and must always increase with price. [How would you go about drawing a demand curve whose elasticity is uniform: say, −1.0?]

## DETERMINANTS OF ELASTICITY

The seniors who experimented with the Cambridge chairs attributed the increasing inelasticity of their demand at low prices to the fact that at such prices they would become sated. Elasticity at high prices they charged to the growing attractiveness of the relatively inexpensive alternative chairs, which would weaken their attachment to the Cambridge chairs. In general, indeed, the concept of consumers' attachment to the product is a useful one in explaining the elasticity of demand for various commodities. Thus, consumers are apt to be but weakly attached to a commodity that has close substitutes. If its price should go up, they would widely abandon it in favor of the substitutes: The elasticity of their demand for it is relatively high. Conversely, if its price should fall, they would abandon the substitutes in its favor. Advertising, which is designed to strengthen consumers' attachment to particular commodities or brands, serves to decrease demand elasticity. And the elasticity of demand tends in any case to be comparatively low for the essentials of life.

The wealth of the consumer and the place of the commodity in his expenditure stream are also useful guides to explaining the price elasticity of demand. Things that are bought mainly by high-income families tend to have a relatively low elasticity of demand, since a rise in price would matter comparatively little to this class of consumer. By the same token, commodities used principally by low-income consumers tend to have a more elastic demand. It follows that people have a relatively inelastic demand for commodities that represent only a small fraction of their yearly outlays, and a more elastic demand for the things that take a large share of spendable income.

[Considering the various forces that determine the elasticity of demand, would you expect the aggregate demand for softwood construction lumber to be elastic, or inelastic, or somewhere in between? How about the demand for railroad ties? For fireplace wood in the city? For sulfite bond stationery? For box boards? In considering these questions, distinguish carefully between short-run and long-run demand. And observe that virtually no commodity is an open-and-shut case of elastic or inelastic demand, that contradictory forces play upon nearly all demands.]

### DERIVED DEMAND

Some of the commodities included in the foregoing inquiry are not consumer goods but producer goods. Thus, for example, railroad crossties are not bought by consumers, but by railroads. The demand for them is not a direct, consumer demand, but a *derived demand:* a demand on the part of producers that is derived from consumer demands for other goods and for transportation service. Before we leave the subject of demand, let us look briefly at the workings of derived demand. An example is the demand of a sawmilling company, Firm K, for logs, derived from the demand of consumers for lumber and its products.

The labor production function of Firm K is given in Table 29, columns 1 and 2. Labor costs the firm $2 per man-hour. Other variable costs, not including logs, are $20 per thousand board feet. Lumber sells for $100 per thousand feet. What is the firm's demand for logs? We will assume that the firm aims to maximize its net revenue per day, and we will also assume that logs and lumber are measured in identical units, with no overrun.

For the seventh thousand board feet of output, the marginal labor input is 49.7 man-hours minus 42.0 man-hours, or 7.7 man-hours. The

Table 29. Derived demand of Firm K for logs

| If labor input per day is— | Lumber output will be— | And marginal cost of— | | And hence if log price per thousand is— | Firm will stand ready to buy logs, per day— |
| | | Labor will be— | All inputs will be— | | |
| (1) | (2) | (3) | (4) | (5) | (6) |
| Man-hours | M bd ft | Dollars | Dollars | Dollars | M bd ft |
| 42.0 | 6 | | | | |
| | | 15.40 | 35.40 | 64.60 | 7 |
| 49.7 | 7 | | | | |
| | | 17.40 | 37.40 | 62.60 | 8 |
| 58.4 | 8 | | | | |
| | | 20.00 | 40.00 | 60.00 | 9 |
| 68.4 | 9 | | | | |
| | | 23.20 | 43.20 | 56.80 | 10 |
| 80.0 | 10 | | | | |
| | | 27.00 | 47.00 | 53.00 | 11 |
| 93.5 | 11 | | | | |
| | | 31.40 | 51.40 | 48.60 | 12 |
| 109.2 | 12 | | | | |

marginal labor cost, then, at $2 per hour, is $15.40 per thousand board feet. This figure and the marginal labor costs at the successive higher levels of output are entered in column 3 of Table 29. The sum total of the marginal costs per thousand board feet other than for logs is the labor figure plus our assumed $20. This sum is shown in column 4. Now if the firm's price (marginal revenue) is $100 per thousand feet and the firm is to equate its marginal revenue and cost, then its marginal cost also must be $100. Thus, if the firm is found operating at the 7,000-per-day level, it must mean that logs are costing $100 minus the sum of $15.40 and $20: $64.60 per thousand board feet. That is to say, if the price of logs is $64.60 and Firm K can buy all it wants at the price, it will buy 7,000 board feet per day. This fact is recorded in columns 5 and 6, followed by the remainder of the demand schedule similarly computed.

You will observe that Firm K's demand for logs exhibits the usual negative correlation between price and quantity. However, the correlation in this short-run case arises not from diminishing satisfaction but from diminishing returns.

Compared to the consumer demands from which they stem, derived demands tend to be relatively inelastic.

## SUMMARY

The consuming firm, which consists of an individual or family, strives with more or less rationality and success to maximize its satisfactions per unit of time. Its specific goals in consumption are based on the firm's forecasts of consumption technology and of the accompanying flow of satisfaction.

Guided by its objective of greatest satisfaction, the firm may be supposed to choose among commodities (attributes) in such a way that the units of commodities on its shopping list covering any period of time represent equal marginal satisfactions per dollar of price, which in turn are the same as those expected from a dollar itself used for any purpose. This best combination for the consuming firm is attainable because of the existence of diminishing satisfaction. It is determined by the firm's income and preferences and by commodity prices.

The consuming firm's best combination may be explained by means of indifference analysis, a graphic device for representing which of many equally satisfying alternatives is the cheapest—or which of many ways of spending the same income will yield the greatest satisfaction.

Through indifference analysis one may derive a representation of the firm's demand—that is, the quantity of a commodity it stands ready to buy in a given period, ordinarily as related to its income or the price of the commodity. The firm's demand and the aggregate demand (of a group of firms) may be expressed as a schedule or as a curve. Like supply, demand relates to a particular length of run, and the responsiveness of the quantity variable to price (or income) may be expressed in terms of elasticity. Generally, the more closely attached the consumer is to a commodity or the smaller the portion of his income he spends for it, the less elastic is his demand for it.

Derived demand, the demand by producers for the agents of production, follows some of the same laws as consumer demand. The character of it, however, arises from diminishing returns rather than diminishing satisfaction.

# Chapter 18

# PRICE AND QUANTITY DETERMINATION

N ow THAT we have in mind both the idea of supply and the idea of demand, we are ready to begin putting the two together. In putting them together, we shall be learning more about the central function of the economy, to satisfy human objectives by converting resources into consumables. In this case we shall be learning about the marketing of basic and finished commodities—the circumstances under which they change hands, the quantity of them, and the price at which they are exchanged. We shall, in effect, be learning how the links are made in the economic chain that connects first producers with ultimate consumers. So far as forest products, both raw and processed products, are concerned, we shall be learning how they acquire value—how they are converted from neutral, sterile things into the prized objects of mankind's striving— and how at the same time the tangible rewards for production are generated.

The purpose of this chapter is to offer and explain some models for analyzing how the quantity and price of commodities are determined when the supply of them and the demand for them meet in the market. These will be models of the best combination, for producers and for consumers. They will include as a special case the competitive models used in Part Two of this book, and thus will help to give a fuller setting and meaning to those models. They will consider primarily the social adjustment of supply and demand. And they will concern mainly static situations; the study of change will be taken up in Chapter 19.

278

## SUPPLY AND DEMAND

A *market*, generally speaking, is the place and time and persons and circumstances involved in exchanges of a commodity. Consider how a commodity—say, fir two-by-fours—may change hands through buying and selling in a market. Suppose that the quantity that sellers stand ready to offer in this market per unit of time increases with the price they can obtain: A higher price would attract more sellers and permit them all to enlarge their offerings. The resulting supply curve is drawn in Figure 26. Also drawn is the correspond-ing demand curve for two-by-fours, which states that as price fell, more buyers would be attracted, and all would increase the amounts they stood ready to buy in this market per unit of time. Given an inter-section between the two curves, this intersection determines both the quantity that would actually change hands and the price at which the exchanges would be made, as marked by the broken lines in Figure 26. At any lower price, demand in the market would exceed supply, and buyers would bid up the price in order not to be left out. At any higher price, sup-ply would be greater than demand, and sellers would bid the price down in order to obtain an outlet for their offerings. Likewise, any greater amount than the one indi-

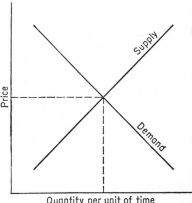

Fig. 26. How a commodity's supply and demand determine, in the market, the quantity of it exchanged per unit of time and the price at which the ex-change takes place. (*Curves are hypo-thetical. Supply curve represents supply of a group of firms such as that illus-trated on p. 196. Demand curve is given the usual form of aggregate curves, as for instance that on p. 274. For sim-plicity, both are shown as straight lines.*)

cated could not be exchanged, because sellers would not offer it except at a higher price nor buyers take it save at a lower price. And any lesser amount would fail to satisfy either buyers or sellers and so would tend to be raised. The indicated price and quantity thus are equilibrium amounts, representing a best combination in the market.

Notice some of the conditions that obtain in this particular market: One is that the commodity is describable in terms of a supply and a de-mand. This ordinarily means that it is a uniform commodity. Another condition is that there is a large number of buyers and sellers, who have full knowledge of the market: demand, supply, and price. Furthermore, the market is a unit in the sense that buyers and sellers are in full communication with one another and that they or the commodity may move economically from one part of the market to another. Any differences in supply, demand, or price within the market at any time arise only because of transfer cost. Finally, there is another condition worth emphasizing. The market model of Figure 26 is an abstraction, in which other things are equal. Other prices and costs, and people's preferences for commodities and occupations, remain unchanged during the period in question. The foregoing are conditions for a *perfect market.* We shall begin our discussion of price and quantity determination with this sort of market in mind.

### INCIDENCE OF CHANGE IN SUPPLY AND DEMAND

In studying Figure 26, one can visualize the effect of changes in supply or in demand in the market. If supply increases, as through cost reduction, one would expect equilibrium price to fall and quantity to rise. That is to say, a shift of the supply curve to the right would move the point of intersection with the demand curve down and to the right. And of course the opposite change would have opposite results. Or if demand should increase, as through growth in income, one would expect both price and quantity to go up—or to go down if demand should fall.

The general principle here is that if the demand curve moves, the effect on the best combination follows from the direction in which the supply curve is running—that is, from the elasticity of supply. And if the supply curve moves, the result depends on the elasticity of demand. A few of the many possibilities are illustrated in Figure 27. [You should test out more for yourself, particularly the cases, not illustrated, where supply changes while demand remains the same.]

The question answered in Figure 27 concerns the effect, or impact, or *incidence* of changes in demand and supply in the market. Consider changes in demand. Suppose demand decreases. Who will bear the brunt of the readjustments that have to be made, the sellers or the buyers? If the sellers are relatively inflexible as compared with the buyers, if they are less able to shift, or to dodge the calamity—that is to say, if supply is comparatively inelastic, as in Figure 27a—then the sellers must take the consequences. They must be prepared to offer virtually the same quantity of the commodity as before but at a greatly reduced price, Op instead of Op'. Consequently, pricewise, they are worse off than before. The buyers, on the other hand, have made no sacrifice: Pricewise, they are better off than they were. For example, in Community Y there are woodcutters who supply consumers in the town. These men depend upon their work for their livelihood, and they have few employment alternatives: For most of them it is woodcutting or nothing. What happens to price and quantity if the demand for wood declines? That is, what is the incidence of a decline in demand? The answer is that the woodcutters bear most of the consequences.

Of course, immobility in the woodcutting trade can work to its advantage in opposite circumstances. If demand for the product rises from

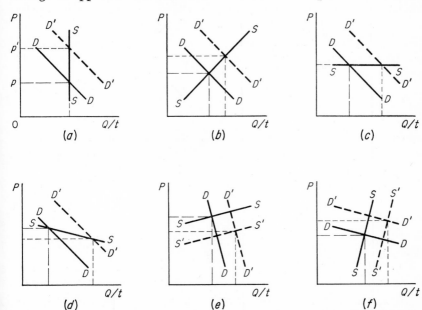

Fig. 27. Effect of changes in demand and supply upon equilibrium price and quantity in the market: (a–d) When demand alone changes, the result, qualitatively, depends on elasticity of supply. (e, f) When both supply and demand change, the result depends on the two elasticities and the amounts of change. (*Hypothetical curves. Compare Fig. 26.*)

*DD* to *D'D'* (Fig. 27a) and the change does not bring either more effort or more workers to the woodcutting game, then buyers will simply have to be content to pay a lot more for the same amount of wood they were getting previously, and their loss is the sellers' gain.

On the other hand, if we are looking at Community Z, where employment opportunities are varied and woodcutters can easily find other work (or others move into woodcutting) if there is an advantage to be gained, then the consequences of a change in demand will be quite the opposite, something like those depicted in Figure 27c.

## INCIDENCE OF COST OR BENEFIT

Out of such cases comes one of the most useful principles in economics, which we may call the *principle of incidence:* Both benefits and costs

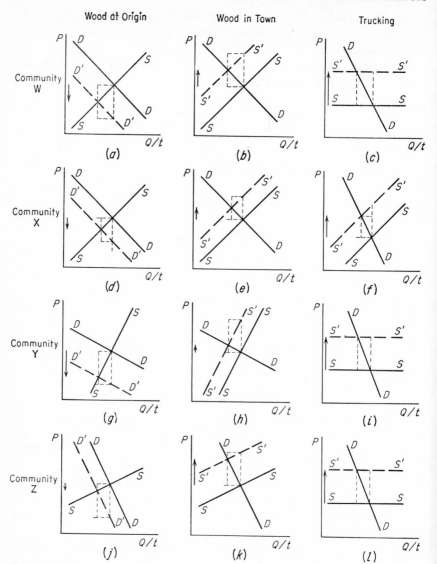

Fig. 28. Incidence of a change in the cost of trucking firewood in four different markets.

tend to be shifted by those parties that are flexible and to be borne by those that are inflexible. You will recognize here a special application of the general analytical question, What are the alternatives? The principle seems obvious even to the point of triviality. Yet we can use it to guide us through many difficult problems. What is the incidence of this tax?

Of the increase in income in that community? Of the rise in wage rates for these firms? To illustrate how an answer may be worked out, let us study the incidence of a transportation charge, using as an example the cost of trucking firewood into town from the surrounding forests.

## COMMUNITY W AS EXAMPLE

Take, first, the case of Community W, where both the supply of firewood and the demand for it are moderately, and about equally, elastic. Both the woodcutters and those who use the product have reasonably good alternatives to which they may shift as occasion demands, although they are not highly mobile. The truckers, on the other hand, are extremely flexible, so that the supply of trucking has very high elasticity. In fact, the truckers set a price for their service, and anyone who doesn't like it can go hang; there is more than enough other trucking to do. What happens in this market if the cost of trucking goes up?

Suppose, to make a good, substantial case of it, that the cost of trucking doubles, as represented in Figure 28c by the shift from SS to S'S'. The amount of the increase is shown by the altitude of the rectangle drawn with finely broken lines between the two supply curves. From the viewpoint of the woodcutters, the effect of this increased tariff is to reduce the demand for their product. We may suppose that the demand curve for wood at origin, as seen through the eyes of the cutters, falls as in Figure 28a, by an amount equal to the same rectangle altitude, from position DD to D'D'. The price of wood at origin, however—the local price —does not fall so far, because the cutters hold back on output. A new equilibrium price is reached at the intersection of SS with D'D', a price that is lower by only about half of the amount of the increase in the trucking tariff. Well, then, who pays the other half?

It appears that the wood buyers pay the other half of the increase in trucking cost. Seen through their eyes, the supply of wood in town falls in consequence of the higher tariff: The curve shifts upward as from SS to S'S' in Figure 28b. The vertical distance of the shift is again the altitude of the same rectangle, but again the price change—the change in delivered price—is less, in this case because buyers reduce their purchases.

The price changes that have taken place are summarized by the three arrows alongside the price scales in graphs a, b, and c of Figure 28. As a result of the increase in trucking cost, the price of trucking has risen equally, the amount being measured by the length of the arrow in c. The burden of the price increase is borne about equally by sellers in the form of a lower local price (the arrow in a) and by buyers in the form of a higher delivered price (the arrow in *b*). The lengths of the arrows in *a* and *b* add to that of the arrow in *c*.

Now have a look at the change that has taken place in our other variable, the quantity of firewood. Because both the demand and the supply of wood have elasticity, quantity has fallen off with the rise in the trucking charge. The amount of the decrease is equal to the horizontal distance between the two supply-demand intersections, the two points of equilibrium, in graph *a* or graph *b*. This amount is represented by the base of the two rectangles in those graphs.

If the base of the rectangle in graph *c* is now scaled off equal to those in *a* and *b* and in the same position on the quantity axis, the resulting lower-right and upper-left corners of the rectangle must be the two points of equilibrium, or supply-demand intersection, respectively before and after the change in trucking cost. The curve representing the demand for trucking service must therefore pass through these two points. Such a curve is drawn as a straight line, *DD*, in graph *c*. This is a derived demand, stemming from the consumer demand for wood. [Note that the elasticity of the demand for trucking is markedly less than that for wood. Can you figure out why? Are derived demands necessarily less elastic than the consumer demands that originate them?]

Here, then, is what has happened in Community W. Remember that in this market both the supply and the demand for wood are moderately and about equally elastic, while the supply of trucking is infinitely elastic. Following a rise in trucking cost, the price of trucking service has risen in the same amount. Thus truckers have incurred no price penalty from the higher cost. Rather, the incidence of the cost is entirely (and about equally) upon the cutters and the users of wood, the price of wood falling at origin and rising in town. At the same time, less wood is produced and consumed. Woodcutters, receiving a lower price for a smaller output, find their income and employment as a class reduced. We can imagine that there may be some tendency for cutters to leave their trade and turn to trucking. In town, the wood users, consuming less and incurring about the same total outlay, are worse off than before. And of course the truckers are hauling less wood, though apparently it matters little to their business as a whole. Society, meanwhile, is making less intensive use of its forests.

[You should give more thought to this simple case of the incidence of a cost, tracing the possible effects further through the forest economy, weighing the alternatives that are presented to the firms involved. Particularly, what may be the impacts of the various changes upon the forest resource? You have the tools for analysis from Part Two. You should similarly explore the cases of Communities X, Y, and Z, which we are about to take up.]

## COMMUNITY X AS ANOTHER CASE

In Community X, the circumstances surrounding the wood market are the same as in Community W, with but one exception: Truckers are not so mobile, because their alternatives are not so wide. Hauling wood makes up a large part of their business. Consequently they are more humble before their wood customers. That is to say, the supply of trucking has finite elasticity, represented by the sloping SS curve in Figure 28f. As a result, when the cost of trucking goes up—and let us suppose that it doubles, just as it did in Community W—the truckers do not pass the whole amount of the increase along to their customers in the form of higher rates. They absorb some of it themselves. We can determine how much, because we can draw the demand curve for trucking, DD, which is necessarily the same as in Community W. Consequently, when trucking cost rises to the position S'S', the new price of trucking is set at the new intersection with DD. The price increase is symbolized by the altitude of the rectangle and the length of the arrow in graph f. The rectangle is shorter than the one in graph c by the length of the vertical projection from its upper-right corner to S'S', and this projection therefore signifies the amount of the extra cost that the truckers themselves bear and do not pass along.

The smaller rise in tariff in Community X is again shared about equally by wood sellers and buyers. This conclusion is worked out, by the same analysis as before, in graphs d and e and is represented by the arrows there. These arrows are, of course, shorter than those in graphs a and b. The penalty upon sellers and buyers is less because the truckers are less flexible.

Furthermore, the curtailment in wood output and consumption is less severe in Community X than in W owing to truckers' lesser mobility. The magnitude of the curtailment in X is shown by the base of the rectangles and is compared with that in W by means of the short horizontal projections from their left-hand corners.

## COMMUNITIES Y AND Z

We have investigated the effect of two different situations with respect to truckers' supply. Now let us see what may be the influence of different situations in the supply and demand for wood upon the incidence of trucking costs. We find these different wood supplies and demands in Communities Y and Z. In both markets, the supply of trucking is like that in Community W. Consequently we know that any rise in trucking cost will be passed along by truckers in the form of higher charges. The question is how the extra charges will be shared as between wood sellers and buyers. The answer, as we can imagine, is that whoever is relatively inflexible or inelastic will be saddled with most of the cost.

In Community Y—as we observed earlier, when we were talking about Figure 27—the supply of wood is inelastic. The demand for it, on the other hand, is elastic. A good deal of wood is used in town for heating and cooking. Coal is also available for these purposes, and if the price of wood rises, many families will make a substitution. The upshot is that when the cost of trucking goes up, the local price of wood falls steeply, but the delivered price rises only a little. A smaller quantity of wood is produced and consumed, but not quite so much smaller as in Community W. The analysis is made in graphs *g, h,* and *i* of Figure 28.

Community Z is quite different from Y. The supply of wood, as we have seen, is elastic. The demand for it, however, is relatively inelastic, because the wood is burned mainly in fireplaces for aesthetic purposes, and the consumers are not strongly influenced by price. They, therefore, are the ones who pay most of the increase in trucking rates. The price of wood at origin falls comparatively little. Again quantity is reduced, but not by so much as in Community W—that is to say, the demand for trucking is less elastic than in Community W. The story is illustrated in graphs *j, k,* and *l* of Figure 28.

Now there is one point, particularly, in the account of these four communities that requires more attention. This is the point that truckers' supply may in some cases be highly elastic but in others, relatively inelastic. The differences were explained on the ground of truckers' alternatives, but what, precisely, does this mean? Indeed, how does it come about in general that the elasticity, not only of supply but also of demand, on the part of essentially similar groups for virtually identical products, can vary so much with circumstances? And what is the consequence of the variation? Such questions bring us to a study of competition, monopoly, and intermediate conditions of price and quantity formation.

### PERFECT COMPETITION

Consider, first, *perfect competition,* which is the kind of competition to be found in a perfect market. Let us understand how it may come about that the aggregate demand or supply of a commodity, which from the viewpoint of society is perhaps considerably inelastic, may appear to the firm almost infinitely elastic. Taking demand as a case in point, look again at the curve of Figure 24*b* (p. 270), the price-demand curve for sugar pine stumpage. This curve is reproduced in Figure 29*a*, together with its companion supply curve. At the equilibrium quantity of 155 million board feet per year, the elasticity of demand is about 3. You can verify this by making the measurements illustrated in Figure 25 (p. 274).

Now take the case of a small landowner whose forest property has a capacity to produce, say, 150,000 board feet of sugar pine annually. His contribution to the market would, at the most, be somewhat less than a thousandth of the total. If he enters the market, the total offerings will be

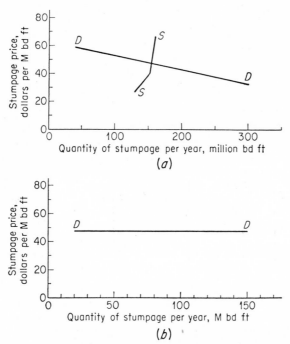

Fig. 29. How a comparatively inelastic aggregate demand (a) can appear almost infinitely elastic from the viewpoint of the competitive firm (b).

155 million board feet. If he stays out entirely, they will be little different: 154.85 million feet. If we could read the price scale of Figure 29a closely enough, we should find that the change in price accompanying a shift down the demand curve from 154.85 to 155 million feet is about 1½ cents, or somewhere in the neighborhood of ³⁄₁₀₀ of 1 per cent of the equilibrium price. Thus the operations of this small firm have a negligible effect on the market.

The demand for the small firm's product is that section of curve DD in Figure 29a which extends between 154.85 and 155 million feet on the quantity scale. In 29b this section is taken out and redrafted on a quantity scale appropriate to the firm's alternatives, ranging up to 150,000 board feet. The resulting curve represents the demand for the product of the firm. That is, it is the demand curve as seen through the eyes of the firm. Its elasticity is roughly 3,000; for all practical purposes, it is a horizontal line. It states that the operations of the firm are a negligible part of the market and have a negligible effect upon the market.

The perfectly competitive producer, then, sees a perfectly elastic demand for his product. He can sell any amount at the same price. The price

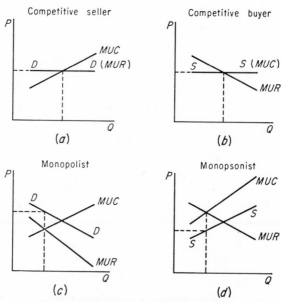

Fig. 30. Formation of price and quantity under perfect competition (*a* and *b*) and under perfect monopoly and monopsony (*c* and *d*).

in question is his average revenue, and since it is constant, it is also his marginal revenue. When, therefore, the firm equates its demand and supply, it is finding the best combination in the sense developed early in Part Two: the equation of marginal unit revenue and cost (Fig. 30*a*; compare Fig. 6*d*, p. 74). No wonder such competition is termed perfect! It not only involves a perfectly *atomized* market, but also it perfectly harmonizes the individual and the social gain through the agency of our old friend, the invisible hand.

By the same token, the perfectly competitive consumer, either the ultimate consumer or the producing firm in its role as a buyer of agents of production, sees a perfectly elastic supply of the good or service that he will purchase. He can buy any amount at the same price. The price in question is his average cost, and since it is constant, it is also his marginal cost. When, therefore, the firm equates its demand and supply, it is equating its marginal revenue and cost—not, this time, per unit of output but per unit of input (Fig. 30*b*; compare Fig. 6*f*).

## MONOPOLY AND MONOPSONY

The opposite of perfect competition is where there is no competition: The whole market is occupied by a single seller or by a single buyer, and there is no fear that competitors will enter the market. The single-seller case we may term *monopoly*. The case of the single buyer we may call *monopsony*.

The monopolist, who controls the entire supply in his market, faces the whole aggregate demand rather than a small fraction of it. The demand as he sees it is therefore relatively inelastic compared to what the competitive seller would see. Whatever the monopolist does will have an effect upon the market. Since his demand, or average revenue, is down-sloping, his marginal revenue is less, and more steeply sloping. Its intersection with the firm's marginal cost determines a relatively low quantity of sales, but the demand permits sale at a relatively high price, as compared with the competitive case (Fig. 30*c*). In other words, compared to the competitive seller, the monopolist who seeks to maximize his net revenue per unit of time tends to raise his price and curtail his output.

As for the monopsonist, who controls the entire demand in his market and therefore faces the whole supply, so long as this supply is less than perfectly elastic, his marginal cost will be greater than supply price, and his tendency will be to curtail his input and to lower its price (Fig. 30*d*). In other words, monopsony is like monopoly in its effect on quantity, but opposite in its effect on price. In contrast to the atomized power of firms under perfect competition, their power under monopoly and monopsony is *aggregated*.

Something very much like perfect competition is to be found in the forest economy of the United States, and also situations resembling its opposites are to be found. Ultimate consumers generally resemble perfect competitors. In forest production, the situation of the tree and even of the timber stand is highly atomistic, and many firms are competitive in their demand for capital and even for labor. The lumber-manufacturing industry, especially that of the East, is often referred to as essentially competitive. It was on such grounds that perfect-competition models were so freely used in Part Two of this book. At the other extreme, and thinking now of certain localities in the United States, some timber sellers such as the Federal government are monopolists (though since the government does not seek to maximize its net revenues in the sense of Figure 30*c*, this model does not apply to its actions), and some timber buyers such as pulp manufacturers approach the status of monopsonists.

## IMPERFECT COMPETITION

However, a good share of the buying and selling in the forest economy is carried out under conditions that are neither perfectly competitive nor completely monopolistic or monopsonistic, but somewhere in between. These intermediate cases, which we shall blanket under the term *imperfect competition*, are perhaps not so heavily predominant in the forest economy as they are elsewhere in the economy at large. Nevertheless, they are highly important and merit your careful study and fullest possible understanding.

As we get into the subject of imperfect competition, let us recognize three types of imperfection that are common in the forest economy and build our discussion around them. The three are imperfections in sellers' or buyers' knowledge, imperfections in their numbers, and imperfections in the commodity, or product.

Let us take only very brief note of the first of these three, imperfections in knowledge, with the intention of coming back to it in Chapter 20, where it can be discussed more appropriately in connection with marketing institutions. For it is a fundamentally different kind of imperfection from the other two, in that it leads to quite unpredictable results. A market may have large numbers of buyers and sellers, deal in a uniform product, and possess other characteristics necessary to perfect competition, but if knowledge is imperfect—if, for example, sellers and buyers cannot measure the product very well, as often happens in timber markets—then surely we cannot expect the competitive model to describe the resulting price or prices, and indeed it is hard to believe that any model could do so at all closely.

The other two types of imperfection—in numbers and in the product —lead to comparatively predictable prices and quantities. These types of imperfect competition have a trademark that clearly distinguishes them from perfect competition. Either the selling firms face sloping demand curves, or the buying firms face sloping supply curves, or both. The firm therefore has a choice of prices: It is in position to *administer prices*. Generally speaking, the imperfectly competitive seller tends to administer his prices upward at the expense of output. And the imperfectly competitive buyer tends to administer his prices downward, at the expense of input. That is, both parties are inclined to behave like their respective prototypes, the monopolist and monopsonist.

### SMALL NUMBERS: OLIGOPOLY AND OLIGOPSONY

Consider, now, the sort of imperfect competition that results from the fact that either the sellers or the buyers are few. Since they are few, each of them occupies a significant share of the total market and can exert an influence upon it. The case where sellers are few is sometimes called *oligopoly*. That where buyers are few may be called *oligopsony*. We need to think about two different situations that can lead to limiting the number of firms in the market. One is aggregation within an industry. The other is the geographic barrier.

## DECREASING COST AND SMALL NUMBERS

If you will glance back to page 211 in Chapter 13, you will recall the mention there of decreasing cost and its strong influence toward aggregation. The American manufacturing industry is mainly of this sort, that it enjoys economies of scale, so that as the market grows, firms become larger and commonly fewer, the smaller and less efficient ones dropping out or being absorbed by their more successful big brothers. In the forest economy, the chemical-conversion industry follows the American trend. And through cross-consolidations into the mechanical-conversion industry, it has drawn the latter to some extent into the stream.

The basis for economical aggregation is the discovery of power sources, machines, and processes that speed and cheapen production in such a way as to outstrip the growth of the market. [A man from Merrill, Wisconsin, has designed and developed a machine that produces 5 million toothpicks an hour. What effects might such a machine have upon competition in the toothpick industry? What are the major factors that would determine and limit these effects? What roles might be played by our patent laws, the technology of consumption, and the Antitrust Division of the U.S. Department of Justice? The inventor himself, by the way, "is not worried about running out of work with his high-speed machine. He said there was a bigger demand now for toothpicks than ever before. The traditional markets have been expanded greatly, he said, with the advent of cocktail parties."[1]]

## GEOGRAPHY AND SMALL NUMBERS

The geographic barriers that limit the number of firms in the market are of comparatively universal effect in forestry and forest industry. They apply to at least the timber-buying operations of all manufacturing industry and to many of the markets beyond manufacturing.

One sometimes hears wistful reminiscences on the good old days when American firms were small and family enterprise was common—when

[1] *The New York Times*, Oct. 15, 1957. Quoted by permission.

every little community had its tiny grist mill, sawmill, and general store, and real competition reigned. Those times may well have been good, but competition had little to do with it. Whereas big firms usually signify a departure from competition, little ones by no means confirm its existence. As a matter of fact, the little mills and stores of bygone rural America were more nearly monopolistic. They were shielded from competition by the costs of transfer, in such forms as the mud, ruts, and bumpiness of the road and the slowness of the horse and buggy. Except when the occasional itinerant peddler came through or customers ventured away to town, the local sellers had the market pretty much to themselves. They were protected by transportation tariffs just as modern American industry is protected—or wishes to be—by import tariffs. Of course they were not complete monopolists, for if local prices were to go beyond a point, goods would flow in over the tariff dam.

Similarly, in their role as buyers of local produce, the little merchants of yesteryear were strongly monopsonistic. The same wretched transportation and long distances that held customers in and goods out kept the produce in and the buyers out. Admittedly, again, their monopsony was incomplete, for if prices went too low, the produce could move out over the tariff.

As transportation has been improved, the barriers to competition have been lowered. Today, buyers, sellers, and commodities move with comparative freedom. The market for many goods of high specific value is essentially national in scope. In the forest economy, however, the example of the olden rural merchant is still highly relevant. The stumpage market is still typically local. We can cite cases, such as that of the Forest Service sale of Alaskan pulpwood stumpage, where the market is virtually worldwide in the long run. And yet, once the plants are built, even this market again becomes local. As for roundwood, its movement is generally restricted, and only in exceptional cases, such as the old Puget Sound log market, where transportation facilities are highly favorable, or in cases where the wood is very valuable, do the boundaries of the market extend beyond immediate localities. Such narrow boundaries necessarily enclose only a few buyers. Similarly, at the stage of manufacturing and beyond, many of the mechanically processed products, especially those of the lower grades, move with difficulty and thus permit the competition of only a limited number of sellers. And throughout the forest economy, the small-scale sellers and buyers can seldom afford to travel far and so are able to negotiate with but few of their opposite numbers in the market.

## PRICE ADMINISTRATION WHERE NUMBERS ARE SMALL

Where the sellers or buyers are few and so face a less than perfectly elastic demand or supply, how do they go about taking advantage of their opportunity to administer prices? The formal models that we might develop to answer this question would be numerous and complex, and scarcely appropriate to the scope of our studies. Let us look briefly and informally at the highlights of the matter.

Whatever price policy the firm adopts, it must take close account of the actions of competitors in the market. If the commodity being traded is uniform, the policy must recognize the virtual necessity for the firm's price to be the same as that of the other firms, save perhaps for a transportation allowance. If the firm's price is different, someone will suffer a disadvantage that can be remedied only by bringing prices into line. One might presume that a uniform price (*not* necessarily, you will note, a *constant* price) would be socially quite respectable, considering that it is the scheme of things under perfect competition. Not so. Uniform prices in oligopolistic industry are viewed by many with mistrust. In the 1957 hearings of the Senate Antitrust and Monopoly Subcommitee, much time was devoted to the question. One industrial executive forthrightly stated that his firm's policy is to "quote prices as near the prices of our competitors as we can learn so that we will get at least as much as they do, and we ought to be ashamed if we do not." However, another executive offered this interesting defense of uniform prices: If all prices are the same, "then the customer is free to buy from any producer he chooses. But if prices are different, then the buyer has no real freedom of choice because he must buy from the company that sells the cheapest."[2] [How do you explain this explanation?]

Accepting uniform prices as the rational policy under oligopoly or oligopsony where the product is uniform, the question then is how such prices are achieved. There are many ways. The ones of doubtful legality in the United States are for the firms to meet periodically for price conferences or to establish an association to set prices and allocate sales. A price list may be published as a guide to all the firms. In the forest economy, perhaps the commonest scheme is the one called *price leadership*, whereunder some one firm becomes the recognized leader of the group in price matters, and the others match the price changes of this firm. In the newsprint paper industry, according to Prof. John Guthrie of Washington State College, the International Paper Company, the largest firm in the industry, has served as leader for all Canadian and United States mills east of the Rockies; while Crown Zellerbach, the dominant western company, has usually taken the lead in that region.[3] News items such as the following[4] are common in the forest economy:

[2] *Time*, Nov. 18, 1957, p. 101. Quoted by permission.
[3] Guthrie, John A.: *The Economics of Pulp and Paper*, State College of Washington Press, Pullman, 1950, p. 113. Chapter VII of this book, on prices and price policy, is all relevant to our subject.
[4] *The New York Times*, Sept. 27, 1957. Quoted by permission.

Last week fir plywood producers, watching a steadily growing order backlog, were thinking about increasing prices, which have been at the lowest point in several years. This week they translated their thoughts into action. R. B. Pamplin, president of the Georgia-Pacific Corporation, confirmed yesterday that his company raised prices Tuesday on quarter-inch plywood from $68 a thousand square feet to $72. The United States Plywood Corporation said it would make a similar advance next Monday.

And other firms thereafter followed the lead. Obviously it takes a big firm to make the first move toward a price increase.

[You may be interested in finding out what prices are being charged by various lumber retailers in your local market for some standard item such as fir studs. Are the prices uniform? If so, how do you suppose they got that way?]

Finally comes the question of what price level is sought by the group of oligopolists or oligopsonists. Generally speaking, we may suppose that each firm would like to see the price at the level that will maximize its net revenues. Considering, however, that such maximization must be in relation to others' actions, the price in question many range at least from the level of monopoly or monopsony to that of perfect competition. And for the least efficient firms in this as in any group, the price may fall short of what is necessary to yield a profit. The group of sellers will be wary of setting the price too high (or the group of buyers, too low) for fear of attracting new firms into the group, developing too much excess capacity within the industry, price war (it is the oligopolists and oligopsonists who engage in such wars), antitrust action on price grounds, and competition from dealers in substitute products. At the other end of the range, the group of sellers will want to avoid setting the price too low (or the buyers, too high) so as not to cut profits needlessly and so as not to kill off the less efficient firms, reduce the number of competitors, and thus invite antitrust action.

## MONOPOLISTIC COMPETITION

So far, in our study of imperfect competition, we have taken up imperfections in knowledge and imperfections in numbers. Let us turn now to the third and last type of imperfection that we shall take note of, that in the product itself. Hitherto we have been talking about price and quantity formation for uniform products. Consider now the case of *differentiated products,* by which is meant products that are regarded by buyers as different from others in the same category because they bear a distinguishing company name, or brand, or mark of some sort that has been advertised or otherwise impressed upon the buyer's mind, or because they are sold by someone concerning whom the buyer has a

prejudice, or because they are sold under circumstances that are preju-
dicial, as in a store that is very comfortably furnished. We must also include in this category differentiated purchasers, such as of forest raw
material, toward whom sellers have a prejudiced reaction because of personal relationships.

For illustration, suppose that you manufacture and sell wooden chairs.
Your chairs, let us say, are virtually identical with those of many other
manufacturers in your market, save only that they bear your name. You
have advertised the name and described your chairs as having special,
desirable qualities. In this way you have built a reputation. You are now
engaged in what we may call *monopolistic competition:* Your product is
differentiated. What happens?

The answer is that you (and your competitors, who have meantime
been taking similar action with respect to their chairs) have given the
market a distinctive characteristic. The chairs, no matter how nearly
identical they may be in substance, can no longer be regarded as alike.
You have divided the market, attached some of the buyers to you with
special bonds, built a fence around the group of you so as to keep you
together. Your competitors' products are not full substitutes for yours
in buyers' minds, as they would be under perfect competition. You have,
in fact, a monopoly upon the chairs that bear your name and are protected by copyright laws against infringement on the part of anyone who
would share your advantage. Thus, even though there is a very large
number of firms in the industry, you will face a sloping demand curve
and can administer your prices.

However, price is quite differently determined from the pure case of
oligopoly. Since the product is not uniform in buyers' minds, you will not
feel any necessity to meet your competitors' prices, though of course you
cannot disregard them completely. Furthermore, you have advertising
and other promotional expenses that would be unnecessary if you were
an oligopolist with an undifferentiated product. You may well take advantage of the protection given to your differentiated status under the
law, to build up a research and development program. You may use some
of the gains from your monopolistic position to establish a small laboratory with the hope of discovering plant and product improvements, or
at least of impressing your customers with your sincerity. These interesting and exciting steps are beyond anything that you would need to take
if your market handled a uniform product. Indeed, you may well find
yourself "competing" hardly at all on the basis of price but rather on the
basis of advertising, promotion, salesmanship, research, and "service."
You may need to expand these activities to the point where their costs
have reduced your net return to a competitive level. If this happens,
then possibly your situation will be standoff, society will be buying your

advertising, and the agencies will be doing the extra business. Or possibly the advertising that you and your competitors have done has increased total consumption, permitted a reduction in other costs greater than the advertising expense, allowed you to lower your price, and so left everyone happier. We hope so.

## MONOPOLISTIC COMPETITION IN FOREST ECONOMY

In the American economy as a whole, monopolistic competition is the rule. In the forestry segment of our economy, however, it is more nearly the exception. Differentiation is not easy to accomplish with many non-timber products of the forest, or with timber products in the earlier stages of production. Taking account of species, grade, and manufacture, a log is a log and lumber is lumber, whether you made it or your neighbor. A few lumber manufacturers have tried branding, and advertising their brand, and with some success; but still the practice is very limited. Many kinds of paper, such as newsprint and container board, are highly standardized. And being producer goods, they are doubly hard to differentiate. Even in the retail field there are forest products to be found that are largely uniform. How often do you find a retail lumber dealer who does big advertising? One sometimes hears sales experts criticize lumber dealers for their lack of "progressiveness" and urge them to plunge more heavily. Actually, are the dealers not wise to stick with their present policy?

But this is not to say that there is no such thing as monopolistic competition in the forest economy. Among differentiated goods are most of the highly fabricated products of mechanical conversion, all those forest raw materials whose markets are dominated by personal relationships between buyers and sellers, and many products of the pulp and paper industry. It is significant that two-thirds of all the expenditures upon forest products research in company laboratories in the United States are made by pulp and paper firms.[5] Also significant is the fresh emphasis that the industry places upon sales promotion when times are dull. Following is a memento of the excess-capacity recession of 1956:[6]

TOTAL MARKETING, is the way that G. J. Ticoulat, senior vice president, Crown Zellerbach Corporation, put it. . . . Total marketing encompasses the entire distribution system. . . . And it means more than just product development, but also the stimulation of consumer demand for these products through progressive advertising and sales promotion. . . . As a matter of cold reality,

[5] Kaufert, Frank H., and William H. Cummings: *Forestry and Related Research in North America,* Society of American Foresters, Washington, 1955, table 28, p. 169.
[6] *The Rice Barton Cellu-Letter,* Worcester, Mass., March, 1957. Quoted by permission.

the emphasis within the industry will *have* to be changed from production to marketing, if we are to utilize fully the capacity that will be available to us and if the industry is to continue to grow and develop along economic and durable lines.

Now, looking back over the whole subject of competition and monopoly in the forest economy, and the various intermediate forms, it behooves us to make at least a brief appraisal of their social significance. We are perhaps inclined to feel that, in view of the price and quantity effects of monopolistic and monopsonistic market elements, perfect competition is our best norm. Surely we may incline to believe that perfect competition is most conducive to consumer well-being. And yet this is no open-and-shut case. For one thing, points of view may differ. For example, from the viewpoint of labor, a degree of monopoly that will raise wages and prevent cutthroat competition for employment may be ideal. Again, perfect competition is a system in which we have amazingly little real and actual experience. And that which we do have, in this imperfectly competitive world, is not all happy. Those American industries that have been sickest and most depressed have been the ones that came closest to the competitive model: agriculture, coal, lumber, and, before World War II, housing. [How do you explain this paradox? What goals do you think society should set regarding the competitiveness of its enterprise?]

## SUMMARY

Supply and demand for a commodity in a market determine the quantity of it exchanged per unit of time and the price at which the exchange takes place.

The incidence of a change in supply depends on demand elasticity, and that of a change in demand depends on the elasticity of supply. In general, the incidence of any cost or benefit is shifted by those parties that are mobile to those that are inflexible.

In perfect competition, the seller faces an infinitely elastic demand; the buyer, an infinitely elastic supply. For perfect competitors, equating supply and demand means equating marginal cost and revenue.

Monopolists and monopsonists face sloping demand and supply curves, respectively. To equate marginal cost and revenue, the monopolist raises his price above, and reduces his quantity below, the competitive level. The monopsonist reduces both price and quantity.

Imperfect competition includes the cases intermediate between perfect competition and complete monopoly and monopsony, with generally intermediate effects upon price and quantity. Two sorts of imperfection are of immediate interest:

Imperfection in numbers (small numbers of sellers or of buyers) arises from firms' decreasing cost or from the transportation barrier. Where the commodity is uniform, the market is characterized by some device such as price leadership for obtaining uniform prices. The price level is set by complex interfirm considerations.

Imperfection in the product (product differentiation) leads to a market characterized by advertising, product research and development, and other forms of nonprice competition. Price, which need not be uniform, may be just sufficient to cover production and selling costs and leave a competitive net return.

Chapter 19

CHANGES IN

PRICE AND

QUANTITY

LIFE GOES by ups and downs, and economic life no less than affairs of the spirit. If you could measure and plot hour by hour the moods of the most mercurial of your friends, the fuzzy caterpillar that would emerge on your graph sheet would feel at home among the best economic indices. The moodiness of our economy has long been one of its conspicuous traits. Viewed as a threat to security, it has been a trait to bend and suppress. But viewed as evidence that free competition survives, it has given lingering comfort to those who place faith in such competition. And for anyone who has planning to do—that is to say, everyone—it is a source of frustration and fear as well as of hope and excitement.

When economic activity changes, the aspect of it that matters most is the change in income and its distribution among individuals. Directly behind income are the values determined when supply and demand meet in the market: price of commodities on the one hand, and the quantity of them produced or consumed on the other. Continuing with our study of the market, we shall keep our eye on price and quantity as we trace the changes in the forest economy over time. We shall observe that some of these changes are generated within the forest economy itself, though most of them are thrust upon it from the outside. We shall be reminded repeatedly of the strong interconnections between the event at hand and other events, between the values in forestry and other values, the interconnections emphasized in Chapter 2.

There are all sorts of changes in price and quantity that differ with the time period. Standing very close to events, one sees mainly the irregular day-to-day fluctuations of the market. From a little further back, he can detect the periodic seasonal changes over the year. Given a still wider vista, he finds that these little variations are merely the ripples on the surface of longer waves, such as business cycles that cover a few years and building cycles that cover many. And a yet more distant view reveals that even these great ups and downs are but disturbances in a slower movement of economic life—a trend, the limits of which may be invisible to us from any attainable vantage point. Let us take up some of these sorts of change in the forest economy, beginning with the shortest period, and let us study primarily their causes and effects.

## IRREGULAR VARIATIONS

*Irregular variation* in price from sale to sale during a six-year period is illustrated for two rather different markets in Figure 31. Graph *a* describes the market for pine saw-timber stumpage on national forest lands in one of the southern states. Here was one seller and a large number of buyers, though only a few buyers were in the market in connection with any one sale. The seller made the decision in each case regarding the location of timber to be sold, the time, the amount of timber, and other conditions of the sale. He then advertised the sale, stating the minimum price per thousand board feet that he would consider, based on an appraisal. Potential buyers who found the advertisement attractive examined the timber. Each figured how much he would be willing to pay for it, considering the probable value of the end product, his costs of production, the proposed terms of sale, and so on. He then submitted a bid to the seller, who proceeded to consummate the sale with the highest responsible bidder. Figure 31*a* was constructed by plotting the consummated price in each sale over the date of sale and connecting the points with straight lines.

What we have in Figure 31*a* is a fuzzy caterpillar. Let us disregard the bends in the caterpillar's back, which are presumably cyclical variations associated with such influences as the Korean War, and concentrate on the fuzz. Why did price bob up and down like this? Probably these irregular variations were due partly to differences from sale to sale in the commodity itself: The commodity was not absolutely uniform, but varied in location, total amount of timber, amount per acre, proportion of pine, quality of the trees, and so on—all factors relevant to the stumpage's attractiveness to buyers. Probably also the irregular variations arose partly from differences in the competitiveness of sales, as represented by the number of bidders.[1] And surely another element in the ups and

[1] For an analysis of such influences upon stumpage price, see Guttenberg, Sam: *Influence of Timber Characteristics upon Stumpage Prices,* Southern Forest Experiment Station Occasional Paper 146, New Orleans, 1956.

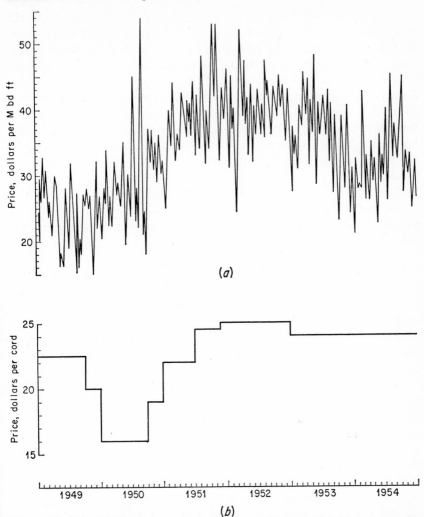

Fig. 31. Irregular variations of price in individual sales, 1949 to 1954—two contrasting cases: (*a*) Pine saw-timber stumpage on a southern national forest. (*b*) Unpeeled spruce pulpwood on railroad cars for shipment to one Lower Michigan pulp mill. (*Graph b adapted from James, Lee M.: Marketing Pulpwood in Michigan, Michigan Agricultural Experiment Station Special Bulletin 411, East Lansing, 1957, fig. 17, p. 53.*)

downs was the adjustment of the market to changes and revisions in the firms' outlook, their judgment of economic circumstances, and their forecasts of the bidding, in the process of price formation itself. Such variations might be thought of as errors and efforts to correct them. [Suppose that the commodity had been perfectly uniform and the buyers very numerous. What would Figure 31*a* look like then?]

Figure 31*b* illustrates a different sort of market during the same six-year period. It is the market for pulpwood in the Lower Peninsula of Michigan, an incompletely monopsonistic market. The buyer was a pulp mill. (The price picture would not look much different if all mills in the Lower Peninsula had been included, since prices were essentially uniform.) The sellers were timber owners and operators, a great many of them. (We will leave aside the dealers who stood between the mill and the ultimate suppliers, since they are not a necessary part of this particular story.) The wood may have varied as much from sale to sale as did the southern pine stumpage. Yet the buyer set a single price that he would be willing to pay per cord of wood, merely revising it from time to time as necessary in order to adjust the flow of wood to his requirements and keep his suppliers reasonably happy. Evidently changes in supply or in demand or both made it necessary in some cases to change the price within three months, though in one instance it was possible to hold the same price for at least two years.

You may well argue that Figure 31*b* shows virtually no irregular variations at all—that the buyer's price policy has served to erase all but the cycle (and trend) from the picture. Or perhaps there is just a little irregular variation represented in some of the more frequent price changes: The buyer might have wished to avoid such changes if he could have foretold more accurately the results of a change. That is, part of what was done was in the nature of trial and error.

[It is interesting to speculate on the significance of these two illustrative cases, one where the problem of bringing buyer and seller together is solved by bidding, the other where it is solved by setting a price. Each system does the job intended. Each has its weaknesses. Do you feel that one system is better than the other from the standpoint of the individuals involved? Or from the standpoint of society? Suppose that the two cases were reversed, that the national forest fixed a price for any and all stumpage while the pulp mill permitted sellers to bid for the delivery of specified quantities of wood. What effect would this have on the practice of forestry? Why do you suppose it isn't done this way?]

## SEASONAL VARIATIONS

Now the next longer period of change in quantity or price, beyond that of the irregular variations, is the yearly period of *seasonal variation.* Many parts of the forest economy, especially those parts that are near the woods, experience ups and downs that trace basically to weather and the calendar. Forest recreation is highly seasonal in most regions, reaching its peak with summer vacationing or with fall hunting or with winter sports. In parts of the West, winter weather keeps loggers out of the woods, with the result that log production declines then to a low point but rises to a peak each summer. Elsewhere in the North, however, winter snow may facilitate skidding and so create a winter peak in logging activity. Where stream driving is used in the Northeast, most of it comes in spring. In many bottomland forests in the South, winter rains and high water chase the loggers from the woods and thus occasion a strong yearly rhythm in both logging and lumbering.

Seasonal variations in the timber economy, it will be observed, do not result from the annual growing season for trees, as in farming they result

Fig. 32. Average seasonal variation of saw-timber prices in South Carolina, 1948 to 1955. (*Source: Anderson, Walter C.: Sawtimber Prices Are Highest in the Fall, Southeastern Forest Experiment Station Research Notes, 105, Asheville, N.C., 1957.*)

from the growing season for crops. Since trees are stored on the stump, as it were, the timber economy is independent of the tree-growing season. However, it is often greatly influenced by the farming seasons. In many parts of the East where part-time farmers do much of the timber cutting and sawmilling, these activities regularly undergo two recessions each year, during crop planting and at harvest time, with peaks of output occurring in between.

Although production, and employment too, fluctuate seasonally, seasonal variations in price are relatively unimportant in the timber economy. They occur most commonly not near the woods end but near the processor or consumer part of the marketing chain. For example, the hardwood lumber market is influenced by the annual furniture shows and related order placing. And the softwood lumber market reflects to a degree the seasonality of the construction industry. At the woods end of the economy, both sellers and buyers are able largely to ride the punches of the seasons. The fluctuations in supply that might otherwise cause price swings are met by countervailing regulation of stocks, for the goods are generally easy to store. Of course storage is a cost. Where forest products are handled mainly by small-scale operators who are handicapped both by poor storage facilities and by expensive credit, we can expect to find a noticeable seasonal price movement.

Thus a seasonal price variation has been observed in the case of saw timber in South Carolina (Fig. 32). The high occurs in October. It cannot be counted on every year but was rather faithful over a stretch of eight years. It is attributed to an increase in sawmilling, and thus in the demand for timber, after the fall harvest, and to the fact that at this time of year the lumber market is active and the weather is the driest and hence most conducive to milling. [What do you think will happen if timber sellers and buyers become generally informed of the October high?]

## CYCLICAL VARIATIONS

Now let us have a look at the longer movements in economic life. There is a surprising variety of them. Experts have uncovered at least five kinds of cycles of direct interest to us. There is a short cycle of general business activity, ranging from more than one to ten or twelve years between troughs and averaging about forty months. There is also a separately identifiable cycle of about equal length in the building industry, and a longer building cycle that has ranged mostly between fifteen and twenty years and averaged about eighteen years. Then there are two slower-moving cycles in the economy at large: a major cycle about three times the length of the short cycle, and a trend cycle equal to perhaps five to seven major cycles. Slicing through this complex at a convenient place, let us devote our attention, first, to the short cycle in general activity, terming it the *business cycle;* second, to the longer *building cycle;* and third, to whatever is left over for a still longer period, under the heading *trend.*

In the study of business and building cycles, we shall use mainly examples from the lumber industry, thus taking advantage of the work done upon lumber cycles by Prof. John Zivnuska[2] of the University of California. Lumber is perhaps the best single commodity to illustrate the two types of cycles, since both of them are generated by changes in demand, and the demand for lumber is divided between those construction uses that are linked to the building cycle and those manufacturing, shipping, and other uses that vary mainly with the cycle in general business activity.

[2] Zivnuska, John A.: "Business Cycles, Building Cycles, and the Development of Commercial Forestry in the United States," doctoral dissertation, University of Minnesota, St. Paul, 1947. A revision of this work was published by the Institute of Public Administration in 1952 under the title "Business Cycles, Building Cycles, and Commercial Forestry."

## BUSINESS CYCLES

The alternations of expansion and contraction over the business cycle are felt throughout the forest economy. They are felt in consumer demand, and thus in the derived demands, for all forest goods and services. Through the demand for forest products, and also through the supply and employment of productive agents, they strike at both price and production in the forest economy. They are the common and universal

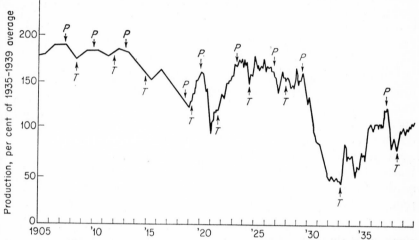

Fig. 33. Lumber production in the United States, 1905 to 1939. Arrows mark the peaks and troughs of business cycles. (*Source: Zivnuska, John A.: Business Cycles, Building Cycles, and the Development of Commercial Forestry in the United States, doctoral dissertation, University of Minnesota, St. Paul, 1947, p. 239.*)

source of risk in the short term. Their origin, after many years of study, is still not clearly understood. The theories that have been advanced—sunspots, war, monetary maladjustments, underconsumption, overconsumption, innovations, and so on—are beyond our scope.[3] The important thing for us to grasp is that business cycles originate primarily outside the forest economy, that they have numerous causes, and that the chief causes may differ from cycle to cycle. It is also important for us to emphasize that business cycles, and indeed all economic cycles, are of varying length and of varying amplitude. It is, of course, in this variation that uncertainties arise.

The movements of lumber production in the United States are graphed in Figure 33—year to year from 1905 through 1918, month to month

[3] Here you can refer to any of the good, brief explanations of business cycle theory, such as that in Newbury, Frank D.: *The American Economic System*, McGraw-Hill Book Company, Inc., New York, 1950, pp. 516–522.

thereafter through 1939, with the seasonal variation removed. Along the production line are marked the dates of the peaks and troughs in general business activity. You can see that there is considerable correspondence in most of the cycles. In many of the cycles, the change in lumber output was small. In some, however, it was immense. Notice the long contraction between 1929 and 1933, and the expansion from then until 1937. This was the Great Depression, which crippled all industries.

Because cycles hit the forest economy largely in the form of changes in demand for products, price tends to move right along with production, rising during the expansion and falling during the contraction. The relative amplitude of price and quantity movements, however, may be quite different. Those industries that have strong elements of oligopoly or monopolistic competition are apt to be found holding the price line rather firmly during the course of the cycle and meeting the changes in demand principally by varying their output of goods. Generally speaking, the pulp and paper industry behaves in this way, so that its output fluctuates by a higher percentage than does its price. The lumber industry, on the other hand, often tends to maintain its output and to adapt itself on the price side of the market. In a study of the ten business cycles that occurred between 1904 and 1940, Mr. Frank TerBush found that southern pine lumber prices fluctuated at least $3\frac{1}{2}$ times as widely as production.[4]

## BUILDING CYCLES

Unlike the business cycle, the building cycle does not affect all parts of the forest economy with full force. Since it is a cycle in the construction industry, it impinges mainly upon construction materials: softwood lumber, hardwood flooring, plywood, certain fiber products, and the like. One view of the building cycle's effects is given in Figure 34, which follows the average annual wholesale price of lumber in the United States over the course of $4\frac{1}{2}$ cycles from 1861 to 1946. These prices are *current prices:* They are derived from the dollar prices as they actually stood in each year, with no adjustment for changes in the purchasing power of the dollar. The dates of peaks and troughs as determined by one of the standard indexes of real estate activity are marked along the price line. The correspondence is distinguishable, particularly from trough to trough.[5]

[4] TerBush, Frank A.: "Southern Pine Prices and Business Cycles," master of forestry thesis, State University of New York, College of Forestry, Syracuse, 1951, pp. 43–44.

[5] For an analysis of building cycles in the American economy, see Long, Clarence D., Jr.: *Building Cycles and the Theory of Investment,* Princeton University Press, Princeton, N.J., 1940.

Fig. 34. Current wholesale lumber prices in the United States, annual averages, 1861 to 1946. (*Sources: Compton, Wilson: The Organization of the Lumber Industry, American Lumberman, Chicago, 1916, for years through 1910; U.S. Department of Labor, Bureau of Labor Statistics thereafter.*) Arrows mark the peaks and troughs of building cycles. (*Source: Roy Wenzlick & Co.: Fundamental Factors Affecting Real Estate, St. Louis, 1953.*)

## CYCLICAL EFFECTS UPON TIMBER CONVERSION

In recent years there has been a good deal of talk about the disappearance of economic cycles. The business cycle has at times seemed to be smothered in government's preventive money and credit measures and in overriding prosperity. The building cycle has appeared to give way to a continuing construction boom. Yet it is hard to believe that our economic world has changed its habits so readily. For want of conclusive evidence to the contrary, let us go on the conservative assumption that the problem of the cycle is beginning to be understood but is yet to be solved.

Meantime, in our effort to know the forest economy better, let us see how it is affected by the cycles and how it may adjust to them. Economic cycles hit forestry with great force. In the lumber industry, which cuts nearly two-thirds of all the timber other than firewood harvested in the United States, the cycles are amplified in various ways. Because of

. . . the economic pressures to produce and the ease of entry, the lumber industry is almost constantly plagued with the problem of adjusting supply to demand. Due to its tendency to overproduce its markets, lumber production has been a "feast and famine" industry, with short periods of high profits widely separated by prolonged periods of low profits or loss. Both the peaks and troughs in production tend to be more pronounced than the corresponding peaks and troughs in demand.[6]

And we have seen that the fluctuations in price in this industry are even greater than those in output. The lumber segment of the forest economy has its cyclical problems further increased because of its close relation to the building cycle, which is typically a wide-swinging cycle. Not only this, but lumber since World War I has come to depend more and more upon residential construction as a market, and residential construction is

. . . one of the most notably unstable markets of the entire American economy. . . . Studies of national income by Simon Kuznets show that for the period 1919–1935 the fluctuations in total construction were almost twice as great, in total private construction four times as great, and in residential construction (in which the value in the peak year was about 13 times that in the bottom year) nearly eight times as great as the fluctuations in consumers' outlay during the same period.[7]

When the forces of the business and building cycles work together, as they did in the trough of the Great Depression and in the peak after World War II, the result is doubly severe.

In the pulp and paper industry, which accounts for most of the remainder of our timber harvest other than firewood, the cycle strikes with different effect. Fluctuations in the price of the industry's product are relatively mild. But quantity variations are more marked. The latter are translated into changes in both quantity and price in the markets for wood.

## CYCLICAL EFFECTS ON FOREST MANAGEMENT

Now that we have seen something of the effects of the cycle upon the major timber commodities, lumber and paper products, let us have a look at the manner in which these effects are passed on back to the forest. The fact is that the ups and downs of both quantity and price of proc-

[6] Zivnuska, John A.: "Commercial Forestry in an Unstable Economy," *Journal of Forestry*, January, 1949, p. 7.
[7] Same reference, p. 9.

essed goods are magnified and exaggerated at the level of forest production and that forest income, which is the product of quantity and price, thus tends to be extremely unstable. Let us understand how this comes about.

Take the case of Firm L, a dealer in a commodity, and Firm M, the supplier. Suppose that Firm L carries stocks equal to a half year's sales. It sells 100 units of its commodity per month and stocks 600 units. To replenish its stock, it buys 100 units per month from Firm M. Now imagine that demand increases. L's sales rise 10 per cent, to 110 units per month. The firm now wishes to build up its stock to 660 units. If it is to do so, and even if it is to spread the job out over half a year, it must increase its purchases from Firm M by 20 per cent—to 120 units per month. Thus a 10 per cent increase in the demand for L's product has resulted in a 20 per cent rise in the demand for M's. Now of course we must grant that firms do not all carry such heavy stocks, and furthermore they may not succeed in keeping their stocks just proportional to sales, even though they should want to. Nevertheless, the force here illustrated, the *acceleration effect of stock,* that runs back from the ultimate consumer toward the first producer, has a strong tendency to multiply the quantity increases that occur during the expansion phase of the cycle, sending them up higher and higher in each successive step toward the basic raw material and giving the timber manager a giddy ride. And if you will take the same example of Firms L and M and suppose that there is a 10 per cent drop in demand for L's product, you will find that the acceleration effect of stock works also to exaggerate the consequences of a contraction.

Not only are quantity changes magnified as their effects approach the forest from the consumer side of the economy, but price changes also are made more severe. This is caused partly by the acceleration effect itself, quantity changes leading to price changes. And partly it results from the fact that since raw-material prices are lower than the prices of the products into which they are made, a given dollar change in both prices represents a higher percentage of the raw-material price than of the product price. Hence the income of basic producers such as forest owners tends to be more unstable than any one of its determinants.

We must take note also of another acceleration effect that operates upon forestry over the cycle: the *acceleration effect of availability.* In Chapter 13 (p. 212) we investigated the margins of availability that shift with changes in price. A timber tract that is inaccessible today may become accessible if stumpage values generally rise, and it will be out of reach again when they fall. When incomes go up, people can afford to visit the more remote places for recreation, but in hard times they must restrict themselves again to the local park. A change of a few percentage points in price or income can cause an infinite change in the rate of use of the marginal portions of the resource. As we learned in Chapter 11, forest resources tend to be the more remote and to bear the higher unit costs of transfer. Forest resources, therefore, through the acceleration effect of availability, are peculiarly subject to extreme fluctuations in rate of use.[8]

It is to be emphasized that both the timber and the nontimber uses of the forest are subject to cyclical instability.

Now one of forestry's outstanding characteristics is that it thrives best in an environment that lends it stability and continuity. The long period of production in forestry and the fact that product is machine in timber growing are what make forest practice peculiarly sensitive to change and to uncertainty. And yet here we have in the midst of the forest economy cycles of wide amplitude, the timing and severity of which are largely unpredictable. The consequences are manifold. Alternative rates of return are increased and conservation thus discouraged. Forest land changes hands more frequently than otherwise, and the continuity of management is interrupted. The lowest incomes, highest alternative rates of return, and strongest other incentives to liquidate that obtain in the course of the cycles tend to govern the whole forestry program: The small owner who has overcut his timber cannot mend the trees back again whenever he likes. The costs of forestry that are rather inflexible —the taxes, interest on indebtedness, protection expenses, and the like— must be borne in depression as well as prosperity if the firm is to produce anything at all. The forest worker suffers in the exaggerated depressions of his trade, and may not enjoy the same last-ditch advantage as his rural brother, the farmer, who at least has a full pantry.

Therefore one of the most challenging problems of forest management is adjustment to an unstable world. The concept of sustained yield, which has come to us from Europe in pure and simple form, needs drastic revising to be useful in the United States. It can be interpreted meaningfully only for the longer stretch, and even then not statically, as we can infer when we study the economic trend. The cycle requires of timber management that the cutting program be not only a changing program, but also a flexible and quickly adaptable one. If the firm can schedule its improvement cutting for prosperous times and reserve some of its choice areas for harvest during depression, its income may not be maximized but will be made more uniform, which is basic to conservation in the face of the cycle. Integration of enterprises—between timber and

[8] For an example of this acceleration effect, see James, Lee M.: *Marketing Pulpwood in Michigan*, Michigan Agricultural Experiment Station Special Bulletin 411, East Lansing, 1957, fig. 2, p. 10. Note that Wisconsin's pulpwood imports from distant sources varied much more widely than those from nearby Michigan, and the latter more widely than within-state production.

other forest uses, between lumber and other timber products, and vertically toward the consumer—offers the firm some hope of spreading the impacts of the cycle. For all such programs in an unstable world, expert planning and replanning are essential.

## TRENDS IN FOREST OUTPUT

However, changes in economic life are not all ups and downs. Some of our most dramatic changes are, so far as the historical record goes, mostly in one direction.

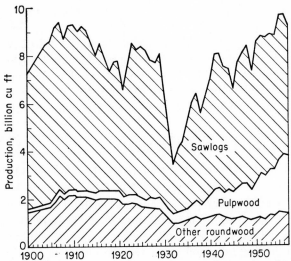

Fig. 35. Annual production of commercial roundwood (other than firewood) in the United States, 1900 to 1957. (*Source: U.S. Department of Agriculture, Forest Service and Commodity Stabilization Service: The Demand and Price Situation for Forest Products, Washington, 1957, p. 27.*)

The whole use of the United States forest resource shows but one change over the long pull, and that is upward. Most of the forest uses share in this growth trend. During the first half of the present century, while population approximately doubled and the national product more than redoubled, urbanization and industrialization and new agricultural procedures pushed up the use of artificially supplied water some five times. Forest recreation showed even steeper growth as people found more and more time for it and were given better means for traveling. For example, the number of recreational visits to the national forests increased about tenfold between the late 1920s and the late 1950s. The use of forest game and fish increased as a part of forest recreation. With the spread of stock farming in the South and the thinning of woodlands in many sections of the country, forest grazing grew more prevalent. Of all the major forest uses, the timber use alone fell off. Though if one considers only the commercial uses of timber—the uses other than fire-wood, whose decline we noted in Chapter 17—he finds that these did somewhat hold their own, after suffering a vast cyclical change, in the course of fifty years.

Indeed, in the long upward trend of the timber economy since the first settlement of the country, a peak in total output of logs and bolts was reached in the period 1906 to 1913 (Fig. 35). Then lumber logs made up three-fourths and more of the production, and the lumber industry was thriving on our lavish per-capita use of well over 500 board feet annually. There followed a quarter century of contraction in the timber economy, a sharp trough in the year 1932, and after that an equally long period of expansion. When, in 1955 and 1956, the old peak of five decades before was slightly exceeded, the products primarily responsible for shoving output over the top were not saw logs but pulpwood and veneer logs, which now comprised 25 and 6 per cent, respectively, of the total cut, as against negligible percentages in the earlier period.

## TRENDS IN LUMBER CONSUMPTION

At the time of the second output peak, the lumber industry, though it had experienced a marked revival, had failed by several billion board feet to reenact its earlier performance. Even total lumber consumption, boosted as it now was by a small amount of net imports, was scarcely greater than before; and per-capita consumption was half or less of what it had been, having fallen off at an average rate of nearly 2 per cent per year (Fig. 36). In all its uses—construction, accounting for about three-fourths of the volume, and manufacturing and shipping, each making up roughly half of the remainder—lumber has been heavily replaced by other materials. These substitutes are mainly metals, masonry, plastics, and competing wood products such as plywood and paperboard. Substitution apparently has taken place because lumber was considered in some cases to have inferior qualities and because its price in almost every case was rising relative to the prices of the other commodities.

Thus lumber has been replaced in urban construction by the more fire-resistant, stronger, and more durable metal, stone, and clay products. It has been hard pressed in such areas as sheathing and subflooring of frame houses by laborsaving plywood. It has stood its ground more successfully on the farm than elsewhere, but here today its use is confined chiefly to repair and replacement, whereas, in the early years of the century, new farms were still being founded at the rate of some fifty thousand annually.

In the field of manufacturing, lumber has virtually lost two outlets that were major earlier in the century: railroad cars and motor (and horse-drawn) vehicles. The other great outlet, furniture, has been held relatively successfully by lumber, though metals have moved into the

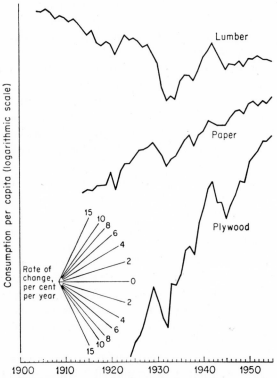

Fig. 36. Annual per-capita consumption of timber products in the United States: Lumber, 1904 to 1955; paper and paperboard, 1914 to 1955; softwood plywood, 1924 to 1955. (*Source: U.S. Department of Agriculture, Forest Service; supplemented by author's estimates.*)

field of office and institutional furniture, and per-capita use of home furniture has eased off with the diminution in per-capita floor space.

In its shipping uses—boxes, crating, and dunnage—lumber has held its own in total volume over the years, but the vast increase in the use of containers in our economy has been seized upon mainly by the pulp and paper industry. The shift in emphasis that has taken place, during the half century, away from railroad transportation and toward trucks has put a crimp in the use of lumber for crating.

Much of the change in wood use has been accompanied by fundamental shifts in consumption technology and in tastes and preferences.

Wood has lost a good deal of the warm regard that it once enjoyed from American consumers.

## OTHER CONSUMPTION TRENDS

By way of contrast with the lumber situation, let us now turn to the two wood products that have been among lumber's chief competitors in recent decades—the two products whose rising per-capita consumption is graphed in Figure 36: paper and plywood.

Since 1900, the pulp industry has been based principally on wood as raw material, and paper and paperboard have been adopted wholesale into the ordinary lives of Americans. In fifty years, the per-capita use of pulpwood increased sixfold, and that of paper even more steeply by virtue of heavy imports, chiefly newsprint from Canada. The per-capita consumption of paper and paperboard, following a rather consistent upward trend of about 3 per cent annually, had by 1955 risen well above 400 pounds per year. The technological and market developments that made possible this amazing growth were reviewed in Chapter 3, where we used them as an illustration of the dynamic concept of resources.

If the consumption trend of paper is amazing, that of plywood is no less than spectacular. Softwood plywood has enjoyed during thirty years and more an essentially unflagging trend in per-capita use, pitched at about a 12 per cent annual rate of increase. Originally, softwood plywood was used largely for drawer bottoms and door panels. Subsequent developments have led to the use of this product for many other purposes, some of vast proportions. One development was public recognition of the attributes of softwood plywood: strength with light weight, large size, durability, and workability. Another development was the successful adaptation of the industry to its special raw-material problem, the receding and shrinking Douglas-fir peeler log; the concurrent increase in productivity in the industry; and the reduction in the price of its product. As a consequence, softwood plywood has come into such varied uses as packaging, furniture, partitions, paneling, sheathing, and concrete forms. Its use in construction, accounting for more than three-fourths of its total use, has grown particularly fast.

At the same time that the pulp-paper and plywood industries were filling the space vacated by lumber, other timber products were mostly declining in use. Excelsior, once in brisk demand, is now little used. Wooden cooperage has largely been replaced by other types of containers in all but the liquor industry. Posts, poles, piling, and mine timbers have faced substitutes, or declines in their user industries, or the effects of better preservative treatment, which has slowed down the rate of replacement. The consumption of railroad ties made from wood, for which no substitute has been found, has nevertheless shrunk because of preservatives and the passing of the railroad era.

Now, while the foregoing trends were being experienced in the quantity of forest products, what was happening to their prices? We have seen how, in the course of the economic cycle, quantity and price are apt to move together. But in the trend it is a different matter. We have already observed that the declining consumption trend of lumber was partly associated with rising prices and that, in the case of softwood plywood, quantity moved up and price down. Indeed, while cyclical changes are generated mainly by shifts in demand, trends are of long enough duration to permit movements also in supply, and where such movements are dominant, quantity and price may show contrary behavior.

## PRICE TRENDS: DOUGLAS-FIR STUMPAGE

During the half century in which total roundwood output just about held its own in the United States, stumpage prices moved up substantially. This, however, was not a sustained rise. In fact, it occurred mainly

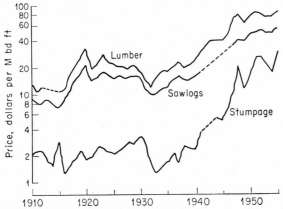

Fig. 37. Douglas-fir stumpage, saw-log, and lumber current prices, 1910 to 1955. (*Source: U.S. Department of Agriculture, Forest Service: Price Trends and Relationships for Forest Products, 1957, p. 23.*)

in the last decade or so. In Figure 37, Douglas-fir saw-timber stumpage prices are graphed as an illustrative trend, along with the coincident prices of Douglas-fir saw logs and lumber. Two distinct periods stand out:

The first period extended from the time when Douglas-fir broke into the national market until World War II. The graph shows the stumpage price holding about constant during this time, at around $2 per thousand board feet. These data need to be interpreted. They are taken from cur-

rent stumpage sales. During the period in question, the quality of stumpage was falling a good deal. For one thing, sale areas were becoming
more remote. Consequently the horizontal trend may signify merely that
stumpage lying near the margin of availability did not change much in
value during the period, a finding that should surprise no one. If we had
data on the market price of identical stumpage over the years, we would
unquestionably discover a rising trend. This trend, however, might not
be so steep as that which developed after World War II, because timber
was generally abundant during the earlier period, land was abundant,
and there was much stumpage liquidation going on from time to time as
a result of private timber owners' efforts to meet and escape high carrying charges.

In the second period, following World War II, Douglas-fir stumpage
prices rose steeply: nearly 15 per cent per year, according to the graph.
Here again, the steepness of the trend is probably understated, since the
stumpage represented in the data was of declining quality. Because the
stumpage-price rise was so much greater than the rise in lumber prices,
stumpage came to represent a rather large fraction of total lumber value,
whereas previously its proportion had been relatively negligible (particularly when overrun, not allowed for in Figure 37, is considered). The
behavior of prices in this era is attributable to both demand and supply
changes. On the demand side, there was rising national income and growing requirements for lumber and plywood. There were also the many
factors—among them prosperity, income taxation, and the prospect of
inflation—that led firms to buy forest land (at mounting prices) for future development. Between 1945 and 1953, the land holdings of wood-
using industry in the United States increased from 51.4 to 62.4 million
acres. On the supply side, private land owners were to an increasing
extent holding their stumpage for their own management and use, and
not releasing it for sale to others. Public and other purchasable stumpage
was thus becoming doubly scarce: through present reservation and
through past use.

## OTHER RAW-MATERIAL PRICE TRENDS

What happened to the price of Douglas-fir stumpage happened also,
in a degree, to stumpage price of most of the commercial timber species,
both in the West and in the East. The second-period price rise (after
World War II) was almost universally more marked in the case of plywood and lumber stumpage than for pulpwood stumpage. In the latter
case, the consuming industry was in a more commanding position com-
petitively and was able to use raw material of a size and quality not
generally in demand. Thus, between 1940 and 1955, while the price of

southern pine saw-log stumpage, for example, rose some 610 per cent, the price of southern pine pulpwood stumpage went up 350 per cent (and of southern pine pulpwood, 240 per cent). The trends in stumpage price for all the various commodities are highly relevant to our understanding of the forest economy, for about three-fourths of all timber that is cut in the United States is sold in the form of stumpage.[9]

We have had reference to the first and second periods, preceding and following World War II. These periods, and the war as their turning point, had significance in the American economy far beyond Douglas-fir stumpage prices or even stumpage in general. The war marked our transition as a nation from surplus to deficit status with respect to many basic raw materials. It saw tremendous increases in the real prices of such raw materials—that is, in the amounts of finished goods that a unit of the raw materials would buy.[10] In its postwar price rise, therefore, and in its increase in value relative to processed wood, stumpage was simply behaving like other basic materials.

And now here is a contention to think about: The new scarcity of materials was in relation to our new and different national acceptance of conservation, formed as a result of the war experience and the prospective continuing need for national preparedness. With more lighthearted attitudes and forecasts, the nation might have continued in its freer use of timber and postponed the steep price rise. Whenever it would come, however, the rise in stumpage price would be primarily the result, not the cause, of our more intensive forest conservation. (In reference to these thoughts and the analysis to follow, compare Chap. 14, pp. 221–223.)

## LUMBER AND PAPER PRICE TRENDS: CAUSES

To finish our study of the trend, let us extend our analysis of prices to the case of finished products. Let us think about the two principal timber products, lumber and paper. These two products represent the two great camps into which the forest economy is divided—the former, technologically viscous; the latter, technologically fluid (compare Chap. 13, p. 211). Lumber shows a rising price trend over a very long period. Paper shows a more nearly level price trend. We have seen some of

[9] Data in this and the preceding three paragraphs are taken from U.S. Department of Agriculture, Forest Service: *Price Trends and Relationships for Forest Products,* 1957.

[10] For essential reading on this subject, which you may temper as need be with the philosophy of Chapter 3, see, President's Materials Policy Commission: *Resources for Freedom,* U.S. Government Printing Office, Washington, 1952, vol. I, especially pp. 1–22.

the consequences of such trends. Let us now try to understand their cause and in so doing get a glimpse of one of the most exciting problems in the economics of forestry. Our thinking will follow lines traced by Prof. Joseph Zaremba[11] of the Syracuse, New York, College of Forestry.

The price trends for lumber and for paper, paperboard, and pulp are graphed in Figure 38. Lumber is taken back to 1798; data for the early

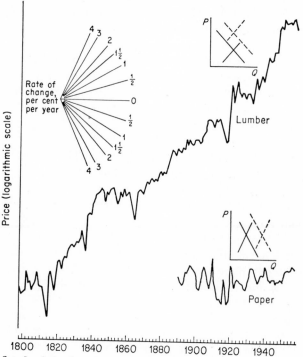

Fig. 38. Deflated wholesale prices of timber products in the United States, annual averages: Lumber, 1798 to 1957; paper, paperboard, and pulp, 1890 to 1957. (*Sources: Warren, G. F., and F. A. Pearson: Wholesale Prices for 213 Years, 1720–1932, Cornell University Agricultural Experiment Station Memoir 142, Ithaca, N.Y., 1932; U.S. Department of Labor, Bureau of Labor Statistics.*)

years are unreliable, but still of great interest. Paper is taken back about as far as one can go with it as a forest product. The prices used here are not the current prices of our earlier graphs. They are current prices divided, or *deflated,* by the current index of the wholesale prices of all commodities, as calculated and published by the U.S. Bureau of Labor Statistics. The graphs in Figure 38 thus show the trends in *deflated, or real, prices* of lumber and paper, or the prices in dollars of constant

[11] Zaremba, Joseph: "The Trend of Lumber Prices," *Journal of Forestry,* March, 1958, pp. 179–181.

wholesale-market purchasing power—or, if you like, the prices of lumber and paper in comparison with the prices of all commodities. The upper graph says that the lumber price trend was steeper than that of all commodities, to the tune of about 2 per cent per year, perhaps a little less in the earlier years, a little more in the later. The lower graph states that the paper price trend was about the same as that of all commodities. The two insets show the increase in total aggregate demand for both paper and lumber that has occurred over the years, and the changes in supply —a fall for lumber, a rise for paper—that would explain the price trends observed.

Now long-term price trends such as we are studying represent trends in the unit cost of production. Why, then, has the price of lumber been going up? The price of lumber has been rising because costs have been rising. Costs have been rising because productivity in the industry (output per man) has not kept pace with the increase in wages (cost per man) in the industry. Wages in the industry have been rising because those in the economy at large have done so. And wages in the economy at large have been rising because productivity in the economy at large has been rising. Here we must remember that over the trend, if the proportion of output allocated to investment stays about the same, wages and productivity are equivalent. That is to say, per-capita real income and per-capita productivity are the same thing.

And so we may explain the rise in lumber prices by the rise in per-capita real income in the United States, productivity in the lumber industry lagging meanwhile. And by the same token, constant paper prices evidence the success of this industry in keeping abreast of the national gains in productivity (compare Chap. 3, especially pp. 35–36).

To state the same ideas in another way, let $Q$ and $q$ equal annual rate of change in output per worker, or productivity, and in the whole economy and in an industry, respectively, and $P$ and $p$ equal annual rate of change in prices in the whole economy and in an industry, respectively. Since any industry, in order to compete successfully for labor in the long term, must pay wage rates that are comparable to those in other industries, it follows that returns per worker in an industry will move proportionately to those in the whole economy:

$$(1 + p)(1 + q) = (1 + P)(1 + Q)$$

or
$$\frac{(1 + p)}{(1 + P)} = \frac{(1 + Q)}{(1 + q)}$$

The term on the left is the slope of the trend in deflated price, such as is plotted in Figure 38. The term on the right is the ratio of changes in productivity in the economy as a whole to those in the industry. And the equation states that the deflated price trend is explainable in terms of this ratio.

## SUPPORTING EVIDENCE AND CONCLUSIONS

There are some wisps of evidence to bear out the preceding reasoning. First, we know that real income in the United States has since 1850 increased at an annual rate of about 2 per cent, a little less in the earlier years, a little more in the later. Second, we have some reason to believe that, at least between 1899 and 1939, productivity in the lumber industry was about constant while that in the pulp and paper industry rose approximately in step with the whole manufacturing economy (Table 30).

*Table 30. Increase in manufacturing output per man-year of labor, 1899 to 1939*

| Industry | Per cent increase | Industry | Per cent increase |
|---|---|---|---|
| Timber products (except paper) | 2 | Chemicals | 170 |
| Leather products | 32 | Printing | 245 |
| Foods | 52 | Transportation equipment | 285 |
| Iron and steel | 100 | Petroleum, coal | 335 |
| Beverages | 104 | Tobacco products | 488 |
| Textile products | 118 | All industries | 113 |
| Paper products | 133 | | |

SOURCE: Fabricant, Solomon: *Labor Savings in American Industry, 1899–1939,* National Bureau of Economic Research Occasional Paper 23, New York, 1945, p. 16; adjusted by the author.

Put together in the terms of the formula just above, these pieces of evidence suggest that the trend rate of increase in the real price of lumber

$$\frac{(1 + p)}{(1 + P)} = \frac{1.02}{1.00} = 1.02$$

or 2 per cent per year, and that for paper

$$\frac{(1 + p)}{(1 + P)} = \frac{1.02}{1.02} = 1.00$$

or a level trend, which is what we observe in Figure 38.

If stumpage prices continue to go up as they have in recent years, they will constitute a new and additional element of pressure upon product prices. However, throughout most of the period that we are considering, stumpage was a negligible element of cost.

Lagging productivity in the lumber industry is the net result of two opposing forces. On the one hand, there has been some technological progress over the years in logging, in transportation, and in milling. But on the other hand, this progress appears to have been counteracted by such trends as the declining size, quality, stocking, and local accessibility of timber and the increasing distances between forest and consumer. The consequence is what is termed a *sick industry:* an example of the American success story in reverse—an industry that tends to produce not more abundantly at lower cost but less at higher cost.

Not the lumber industry alone but virtually the whole forest economy outside of paper and plywood—woods, mills, and yards—is affected by the sickness of low productivity. To find a cure, to find an effective deterrent to rising prices and consequent gradual economic paralysis, is one of the difficult and urgent tasks facing foresters and wood processors. Obviously the cure does not lie in the direction of holding wage rates down. It therefore does not admit of using labor lavishly. When the classics in silviculture were written, Europe had a labor horde that was available cheap for fighting wars and practicing "forestry." Those times are gone, even in Europe. Survival of the forest economy today depends partly on finding ways of producing forest products without handling and rehandling individual pieces of things and without tracing and retracing ground, whether in the woods or in the mills. If you want to help forestry endure, then you must innovate. Invent, for instance, a mechanical hedgehog that will work its way up the bole of a tree, pruning as it goes, and stop and turn around at the proper height. Or breed a tree that will prune its own limbs. Or find a process that will utilize the tree, limbs and all. Or give over your forest to the stancher services of providing scenery and catching the rain.

### SUMMARY

Irregular variations in price of forest commodities occur in the process of price formation and help reveal the competitiveness of the market.

Seasonal variations in price and quantity are associated with weather and the calendar.

The short business cycle, averaging forty months, and the building cycle, averaging eighteen years, reach the forest economy in the form of changes in demand. The lumber industry, strongly affected by both cycles, adjusts to them primarily through price. The pulp and paper industry is influenced chiefly by the business cycle; its main adjustment is in output. Both cycles hit forest management hard and require counter measures. Their impact is heightened by the acceleration effects of stock and of availability.

Trends in output in the United States for a half century have been generally upward for nontimber products of the forest, downward for timber products. Lumber, a prime example, has undergone a 50 per cent cut in per-capita use. Paper and plywood, however, have shown increases. Stumpage prices were low and level until World War II, then pointed sharply upward. Real prices of paper show a level trend, indicating that the industry has kept abreast of the economy in productivity. However, in the lumber industry, which has failed to keep abreast, prices have long been rising. To raise productivity is a central problem in the forest economy.

Chapter 20

# MARKETING

# AND ITS

# FUNCTIONS

THROUGH the preceding chapters of Part Three we have entered the subject of forest product marketing. To our earlier idea of supply we added that of demand. We then went on to the meeting of the two, the determining of price and quantity of things exchanged, and the behavior of market price and quantity. These are all fundamental ideas. Now it is high time we progressed to larger and more familiar notions about marketing.

## WHAT MARKETING IS

*Marketing* is the performance of market services by firms. The services include, of course, exchanging commodities, but they also include a number of other, related functions that we shall touch upon in this chapter, such as market reporting, advertising, and risk taking. Marketing is a social function of wide scope.

If all markets and competition were perfect, the subject of marketing would be much simpler than it is. The subject takes on breadth and significance mainly through the market's "imperfections." It is largely these imperfections that give rise to the performance of so many sorts of marketing services by firms. The imperfections make marketing a major branch of production.

Now some persons are prone to regard basic production, such as mining and forestry, and possibly also manufacturing, as in the steel mill and sawmill, as the only "real" forms of production. The middlemen situated between these basic lines and the consumer are, as the thought runs, just hangers-on, parasites upon the economy.

Well, no doubt we have all run across instances of middlemen's effort —some examples of advertising, perhaps—that we felt might have been forgone without social loss. But then how about the miners who come up empty handed, and those sawmillers who make such shoddy lumber that it has to be redone? And as for the dependence of middlemen upon imperfections, all economic life is, in a sense, thus dependent. The transportation industry exists because of "imperfect" distribution of resources. The forestry profession owes its livelihood to "imperfections" in natural bounty or in human wisdom. Imperfections give rise to cost, and to firms prepared to bear cost in return for revenue. That is to say, they give rise to production.

Production is the act of creating wantedness in commodities: predicted power to yield satisfactions of various kinds. Most obvious are the *satisfactions of form,* such as in the substance of the steel made from ore and of the lumber made from a tree. Form, however, is only one source of satisfaction. Equally vital are *satisfactions of possession, satisfactions of place,* and *satisfactions of time:* owning the lumber, and having it where you want it, at the time when you want it. And these are satisfactions toward which marketing is directed. The lumber retailer's services can be just as noble as those of the timber grower.

At any rate, we have the performance of marketing services by firms that use for the purpose resources, or agents of production, or inputs, and bring forth outputs, in accordance with a production function that is generically like any other. These firms seek their best combinations just as others do. They may integrate enterprises—within marketing, or between marketing and manufacture—according to the principles that we studied in Chapter 12. In any case, they can use the rule of equating marginal cost and revenue in marketing, like the industrial executive who wrote, "It is my belief that when the sales of the product and the advertising are both running along on a level, a company can wisely spend an *additional* dollar on advertising even if that dollar brings in net only an additional dollar and one cent."[1]

To conclude our definition of marketing, let us reemphasize a point: We need to avoid interpreting the term as is commonly done in the business world, to mean simply finding an outlet for commodities. This is but one side of the matter, the seller's side. For the buyer, marketing is finding a source. And for both, it is producing or using manifold services that help selling and buying.

[1] Lambert, Gerard B.: "How I Sold Listerine," in *The Amazing Advertising Business,* by the editors of Fortune, Simon and Schuster, Inc., New York, 1957, p. 57. Quoted by permission.

## SIGNIFICANCE OF MARKETING

Marketing in the forest economy involves a variety of commodities. Forest land is marketed, and the other agents of production, capital and the services of labor. Then there are the outputs of these agents: forage, wildlife, watershed services, recreational services, and timber products. Many of the marketing principles that we shall study are widely applicable to these commodities. However, most of our illustrations of principles will be taken from timber and its products. The question of value of the forest products that are not ordinarily marketed at all—such as protection of life and property from floods, and the privileges of recreation in the public forests—will be touched upon in Chapter 23.

Of course, some wood that is produced is not marketed but remains in the possession of the producer. Such wood includes standing farm timber cut and used by the farm family. It includes also the timber owned and converted and perhaps carried as far as the stage of retailing by the same vertically integrated firm. Nevertheless, in the United States possibly nine-tenths of all timber consumed is marketed at some stage, and this act of marketing is of profoundest significance to everyone in the production-consumption chain, establishing their material rewards or costs, as the case may be.

For forest management, marketing is a focal point. In marketing, the products of the forest are released for consumption. The policy of the forestry firm is both shaped and tested. The work of the forest manager bears fruit. The efficiency of the market in reflecting consumers' demands determines how well forest resources serve the immediate purposes of society. Furthermore, in forestry, and especially in timber management, the physical connection between primary production and marketing is peculiarly close. Considering that three-fourths of all timber harvested is marketed first in the form of stumpage, the art of silviculture finds expression chiefly at the time of sale. Renewal of the forest, provision for growth of favored timber products, and execution of policies with respect to soil and water relations and the other values of the woods must on most forest properties be considered and accomplished largely at the time of sale. And while the silvicultural and other management considerations relate mainly to the further future, those of marketing itself relate mainly to the immediate future and for this reason carry great weight in the firm's decisions. At the same time, they keenly affect the future course of management: The longer the rotation or cutting cycle, the greater the effect. Choices made in the act of marketing are for a while irrevocable.[2]

[2] Duerr, William A.: *The Economic Problems of Forestry in the Appalachian Region*, Harvard University Press, Cambridge, Mass., 1949, pp. 162–163.

For conversion management, too, the marketing of the product is a focal point. Although the seller of manufactured goods is not marketing his capital in quite the same sense as is the seller of timber and therefore is not ordinarily involved in quite such critical decisions for the longer term, the choices he makes are obviously crucial in the life of the firm and in some cases have great long-range significance. We have seen (pp. 296–297) how firms in the pulp and paper industry have come to emphasize marketing—"total marketing"—and how such emphasis is regarded in the industry as necessary to its long commitments and plans for expansion.

## QUANTITATIVE POSITION OF MARKETING

It is true both of the American economy at large and of the forest economy that the passing years have seen a rapidly mounting emphasis upon the marketing part of production. An increasing amount, and also an increasing proportion, of total resources goes into marketing, and thus the proportion of the consumer's dollar taken by the various "middlemen" has risen. These changes have come about because of resource aggregation: departures, as we termed them, from "perfection."

Think how vastly the character of the furniture industry has changed. Once it was made up of small-scale cabinetmakers serving their communities. Now the little cabinetmaker has been edged out. The product can be made more economically with machines. Of course, if machinery is used and the best scale of operations achieved, it means quite a substantial output in a year, more than the immediate community would care to buy at prices that would satisfy the manufacturer. And so he takes measures, and incurs costs, to widen his market. He seeks buyers away from home. He sets up a sales organization. He advertises at home and away. He undertakes any additional cost of transportation, selling, and the like which will at least pay for itself in the form of economies of scale or higher price or the avoidance of a price cut. He has now ceased to be a cabinetmaker taking a small markup above his labor and other shop costs, on a low annual volume. He has become a furniture manufacturer taking a small markup above his labor, machine, and other factory costs and his selling costs, on a high annual volume.

What has happened to this firm? What changes have occurred in the industry? Conceivably, there have been only two changes: First, the number of firms has dropped and their average size has risen. Second, selling costs have been substituted for the manufacturing costs saved through mechanization and growth. [If this is the case, is the manufacturer better off than he was? Are his employees better off? How about society?]

Attending aggregation in the furniture industry may be some reduction in the price of the product, or at least some curtailment in the rate of rise in price. This is perhaps likeliest to take place for the simpler items of furniture made from ordinary raw materials and given a slap-on finish. It is much less likely to occur with quality items of complex design. The latter are most sensitive to the viscous technology in the industry. Furthermore, attempts to mass-produce them run into special costs both of raw-material procurement and of product marketing, for the necessary timber and the necessary customers are widely scattered.

In the paper industry, for another example, the same substitution of marketing for manufacturing costs has been made. However, such price reductions as have attended aggregation have occurred more nearly throughout the range of product quality, and in fact the most conspicuous change that has taken place has been a general increase in quality per dollar of real price. This change has followed from fluid technology, from the ability of the industry to use ordinary and widely available raw material, and from the growth of massive demands for the product.

Throughout the forest economy, the quantitative position of marketing has grown with the passing decades. This growth is the price paid by society for its valued gains and economies of specialization and scale in manufacturing. When we study marketing, therefore, we are studying a segment of economic activity in which productivity of agents (measured in units of the commodity) has been going down, counter to the general trend and yet facilitating the general trend. [Does this mean that it is useless to seek technological and other productivity improvements in marketing?]

## MARKETING FUNCTIONS

Now the market and the process of marketing can be viewed from any of several aspects. Let us study marketing from three points of view. Let us study it, first, from the viewpoint of its functions, the services performed as a part of marketing. The rest of this chapter will be devoted to these functions. Second, let us study marketing agencies and their practices. Third, let us take up the geography of marketing. Chapters 21 and 22 will be given to marketing agencies and geography, respectively. Remember that this division of the subject is artificial and is used simply for convenience in telling the story. Every marketing function—storage, for example—has an agency that performs it and a place where it is performed. Were it not for mechanical complications, it would be better to talk about all three aspects at once.

What are the functions of marketing? So far as forest products are concerned, the principal ones may be outlined as follows:

1. Information
   *a.* Commodity description and measurement
   *b.* Price and quantity reporting

2. Exchange
   a. Selling and buying
   b. Price and quantity determination
3. Physical supply
   a. Concentration and dispersion
   b. Transportation
   c. Storage
4. Financial service
   a. Risk-taking
   b. Credit

## COMMODITY DESCRIPTION AND MEASUREMENT

In Chapter 18 (p. 279), the perfect market was described as one in which, among other things, sellers and buyers have full knowledge of the commodity, the quantities of it being exchanged, and the prices at which the exchanges are taking place. The perfect marketing system has devices for disseminating freely such information.

The accuracy and efficiency of commodity description and measurement vary greatly among the markets of the forest economy. In general, they improve as one leaves the woods and moves toward the consumer, for it is in this direction that the commodity becomes more and more standardized. Of all the forest commodities, forest property itself is the most difficult to describe and measure. Its qualities as watershed, wildlife habitat, and source of forage are proper subjects for special study by the respective experts. Its values for recreation are even more special, being peculiar not only to the property itself, but also very commonly to the individual consumer. Even its potentialities for timber production are not readily measurable, silviculture on the one hand being an inexact science and mensuration on the other being fraught with large sources of error. The factor of location, bearing on the quality of the logging chance, is by no means the least difficult to describe.

It follows that stumpage, as a commodity quite apart from the land, is also hard to define. Indeed, no method has been devised for describing and measuring it precisely. Whatever method is used necessarily involves a forecast of many things, including the net yield of logs and bolts that can be taken from the standing timber. This, in turn, is a matter of some conjecture. External indicators of a log's soundness may be misleading. Even the measurement of its gross content is complicated by the existence of many different units of measure, some of which may be applied in numerous ways. For example, for the measurement of the board-foot content of saw logs in the Northeast, twenty-three different log rules are in use. One of these is the Doyle rule. One version of the Doyle rule states that the gross board-foot content of a log is equal to the length of the log in feet multiplied by a certain figure, obtained by subtracting 4 from the small-end, inside-bark diameter of the log in inches and squaring the difference; the gross volume of the log so calculated is reduced to net by subtracting a measured cull allowance. However, this is only one of the procedures followed in the name of the Doyle rule. There are fourteen others in common use, all leading to different results for the same logs.[3]

Whereas the measure, one board foot of logs, may have a hazy meaning, one might suppose that measures based on the cubic foot—which is presumably 12 inches on a side, no more and no less—would be indisputable. But if you have ever tried to agree with an adverse party on the volume of a pile of cordwood, you know better. You are unlikely to reach a meeting of minds even on the question of where the top of the pile is located, let alone how high the pile is, or how wide or long. The measurement of stacked wood is further cast in doubt by the existence of several different kinds of cords and other units. And then the cubic foot of wood, even when precisely scaled, is but an indifferent measure of raw material for chemical conversion.

No wonder that the pulp industry is buying more and more of its wood by weight. Or that research foresters are studying the feasibility of measuring sawlogs, too, by weight.

The confusion and uncertainties in the sphere of stumpage and roundwood measurement, great as they are, are exceeded by those in the realm of grading these commodities. With a few exceptions, reasonably well-standardized grading systems have been introduced and accepted into the timber economy only in quite recent years. It was not until after World War I that local and company rules for grading lumber began to be widely replaced by regional and national systems developed under the leadership of the U.S. Department of Commerce. Standardized systems for grading roundwood and standing timber began to be widely and vigorously developed, under United States Forest Service guidance, principally after World War II. Such systems, however, are slow to catch hold. Government efforts to standardize the rules for measuring and grading timber have met with some resistance from forest industry.[4]

Rules for grading timber and logs are seldom simple, for the problem to which they are addressed is not simple. To apply them, one usually needs special training or considerable experience. The same is true of lumber grading, which takes an expert to do it properly.

[3] Information from Fred C. Simmons, Northeastern Forest Experiment Station.

[4] See, for example, *Southern Lumberman*, Feb. 15, 1956, p. 20. How might one account for the editorial opinion here expressed, that establishment by the state of a standard legal rule for measuring saw logs is unnecessary and undesirable?

## EFFECTS OF DESCRIPTION AND MEASUREMENT PROBLEMS

The foregoing characteristics of forest commodities with respect to description and measurement contribute to the risks and costs of marketing. Among their effects are the following:

First, they may necessitate *sales and purchases by inspection* rather than *by sample* or *by description:* Often both parties to the transaction have to go to the commodity and look it over carefully before they can do business. This is expensive.

Second, even then, the seller or the buyer may feel that, because of the uncertainties of measurement and grading, he must add (or subtract) a liberal safety allowance to protect himself. When stumpage in farm woods and other small tracts is bid for by little operators, the latter make notoriously large safety allowances if they can, and may succeed in harvesting several times as much timber as they supposedly bought.

Third, the hazards of measurement and grading encourage the use of various costly systems for increasing accuracy. These systems commonly involve inspection of products piece by piece. For instance, the widely advocated solution to stumpage-sale problems of the sort mentioned in the preceding paragraph is for the seller to refuse to sell his wood in a *lump-sum transaction* but require the buyer to pay for it on the basis of log or lumber scale after cutting—that is, require a *scale transaction.* However, provided the trees to be sold are marked and their volume carefully estimated, the lump-sum transaction is much to be preferred. Subsequent laborious remeasurement is avoided; disputes over the scale are escaped; and the seller is able to side-step the troublesome problem of enforcing utilization standards.[5] Furthermore, lump-sum transactions are socially desirable in that they foster voluntary close utilization of trees.

Fourth, when measurement or grading has to be done by a specialist, the small firm is put at a disadvantage by comparison with the large firm whose volume is great enough to keep a specialist busy and thus more clearly justify employing him. In the stumpage market, when both the seller and the buyer are little fellows, both may act in genuine ignorance and the result be in the balance. Usually, however, the buyer of timber from small private tracts is the more experienced or the more able to get expert assistance, in which case the terms of trade will go consistently against the stumpage owner. The small sawmilling firm may similarly be disadvantaged in the wholesale lumber market.

Fifth, clear recognition of timber volume and grade by the market is

[5] Duerr, William A., John B. Roberts, and R. O. Gustafson: *Timber-products Marketing in Eastern Kentucky,* Kentucky Agricultural Experiment Station Bulletin 488, Lexington, 1946, p. 47.

essential to the economic motivation of the firm that grows and sells timber. Together, volume and grade are the physical basis for the firm's revenue: the value growth. The firm's best combination in timber growing has little meaning if its market cannot take account of timber volume any closer than 50 per cent one way or the other. And there is no point in the firm's working for quality growth if its market does not pay a reward for quality. Where the markets for raw timber products are insensitive to quality, the firm that would carry out a conservative timber-management program may need to integrate vertically in order to gain access to markets that can pay for products in accordance with grade. Or, to put the matter negatively, the firm that cannot gain access to such markets is forced into relatively extensive management, and the little timber owner is a case in point.

Refer back to our early models for the intensity of timber management, such as the best-stocking model (p. 125). The firm's best combination is determined by the equation of the marginal value growth per cent with the alternative rate of return. In our discussion of the model, we took value growth largely as given. The value production function was viewed as being set by the site and the silvicultural program, under the assumption that tree quality was measured and awarded its share of end-product value. The main emphasis was put upon the alternative rate as explaining variations in intensity from firm to firm. Now we are in position to place appropriate stress upon the other blade of the shears, the value growth, recognizing that this growth can vary from firm to firm because of differences in the market, even though site and silviculture are identical.

It looks as though one of the sharpest issues in timber marketing and management lies in the area of forest mensuration.

## PRICE AND QUANTITY REPORTING

Now, besides describing and measuring the commodity, the ideal market assumes also the function of reporting prices and quantities. On the stock exchange, traders know at all times the numbers of the different types of shares being bought and sold, and the prices at which the sales are taking place. The same thing happens, after a fashion, in the markets for forest products. The information is disseminated, not by wire and ticker tape, but by word of mouth and printed list.

In the markets for stumpage, when a sale is consummated, the news gets around the community. If the sale was of public timber, price and quantity are public information. If the sale was of private timber, price and quantity information may seep out in various ways. In some cases the parties make it known freely. In many markets, however, the information is treated as confidential. Where the commodity is timber from small woodlands, the buyer may keep the facts of the sale under his hat in order not to stir up competition or give other timber owners smart ideas, and the seller may regard the facts as private and personal, just as he does other items of his income. He may give out the data only to close friends. And of course we must remember that in some cases he does not have the data in very meaningful form. "Some of the timber from one tract: $8,500" may be the extent of his knowledge, and if he has sold the timber in a lump, the buyer may be under no obligation to reveal the yield.

As one moves along through the chain of forest-product markets, he finds that wherever the commodity is relatively unstandardized, difficult to describe and measure, and especially where any of the parties are small and unspecialized firms such as farm-woods owners or farm-mill operators, information on price and quantity tends not to be freely published. This situation apparently arises not only from the uncertainties of measurement but also from the belief of buyers or sellers that they benefit from the state of (others') ignorance.

On the other hand, one finds quite the opposite state of affairs in the markets for the more standardized commodities, especially the large markets and those lying toward the consumer end of the chain. Here, as in the wholesale and retail markets for lumber, plywood, pulp, paper, and the like, there is considerable formality of market organization based upon freely published price and quantity data. And the printed list largely takes the place of more personal communication. At one time the trade associations and larger firms were the chief publishers of wholesale-price data. In recent decades, however, antitrust action by the Federal government has largely closed out their public price-reporting work, which has been taken over by others, such as independent commercial journals or subscriber services for current data and the U.S. Bureau of Labor Statistics for periodic summaries and trend analysis. The trade associations still are the chief source of current quantity reporting, as in their "trade barometers," which show for the week or month the new orders, production, and stocks as indices of market activity.[6] [Why do you suppose that it is regarded as consistent with the public interest for trade associations to publish quantity reports but not price reports?]

## PUBLIC REPORTING OF THE MARKET

Sellers and buyers in the higher markets of the forest economy make heavy use of price and quantity reports to organize and stabilize their

---

[6] It will help you to gain more specific understanding of price and quantity reporting for the wholesale market if you will search out and study some examples for your region of the country. Lumber is probably the best commodity to choose, from the standpoint of the availability of reports.

markets, reduce risks, and generally prosper their affairs. Why don't traders in the lower markets do the same? Partly it is because the small firms are not in position to, and the big ones don't need to. Partly it is because of the difficulties of product description and measurement. A stumpage price does not mean much unless the stumpage is accurately described. Again, no price is fully meaningful as a guide to the market unless one knows the terms of sale, and these vary widely in the lower markets and are cumbersome to describe. One man sells his stumpage for cash when the contract is signed. Another takes a deposit, the remainder to be paid when the logs are scaled. A third waits for his payment until the mill has sawn the logs, sold the lumber, and been paid for it. If all three received $10,000 for identical stumpage, the first man, with the lowest deductions for interest and risk, got the highest net price. The third man received the lowest net price.

In recent years, many of the public agencies have moved in to fill the gap in timber-market reporting. State agricultural extension services were among the first. They have been joined by some of the state foresters' offices and forestry schools. Bulletins have been released, in some cases regular periodicals, listing stumpage or roundwood buyers and quoting prices in recent sales. Data are collected by mail canvass or directly by local officials and are sent out to everyone who wants them. Some progress has been made in research to develop methods for describing commodities accurately. The United States Forest Service has contributed to such research. The Congress has shown some interest in starting Federal price reporting for timber products, as a counterpart of the price reports for farm commodities. Of these developments, especially the Federal developments, the wood-using industries and other organized buyers of timber appear to take a dim view.[7]

## SELLING AND BUYING

Concerning the second major function of the market, the function of exchange, a good deal has already been said in preceding chapters. The

[7] Again you may wish to acquaint yourself with the reports in your state or region. For an example of research that would facilitate price reporting, an analysis of the problem of describing stumpage, see Guttenberg, Sam: *Influence of Timber Characteristics upon Stumpage Prices,* Southern Forest Experiment Station Occasional Paper 146, New Orleans, 1956. For sidelights on the controversy over public price reporting, see, for example, papers given in the Society of American Foresters Division of Forest Economics and Policy meeting in 1956 (published in the *Proceedings*) and in the Division of Private Forestry meeting in 1957. See also the interesting bulletin on available market information, which forms a part of the industry case against public price reporting—Forest Industries Council: *Marketing Information Available to Forest Owners,* New York, 1957.

subject of price and quantity determination was taken up in Chapters 18 and 19. Here let us touch upon the matter of selling and buying.

It is obvious to anyone who looks around at economic life that, except in the nearly perfect markets, there is always one group, either the sellers or the buyers, who take the major initiative in making market contacts and pushing negotiations along. As consumers, we are inclined to think of the sellers as being the aggressive ones. They ordinarily are, in that part of the economy where selling firms are bigger than buying firms and perform more largely under the influence of imperfect competition. However, on the other side of the economy, where title to commodities is often being transferred from the many to the few, from smaller firms to larger ones, and where the preponderance of imperfections tends to rest on the buyers' side of the market, it is commonly the buyers who take the initiative.

For instance, in the stumpage market in farm woodland country, the primary business of sellers is farming. They seldom deal in timber, for their operations are small and when they do make a sale, they are apt to part with several years' cut at one time. The timber buyers are sawmill operators or other manufacturers, independent loggers, log or pulpwood dealers, and the like. They are in the business more nearly full time, and it is up to them to make the first move if they wish to stay in business. By their drives for revenue, they are impelled to search out the timber and the owners who may be willing to sell, work with these potential sellers, gain their confidence, persuade them that the proposed transaction is in their interest. While the buyers are thus engaged, they are at the same time performing a service to the wood-using industry and society in undertaking the difficult and laborious and unrewarding task of assembling scattered resources for efficient use.

The fact that it is the buyers and not the sellers who take the lead in the markets that serve the little timber owner is often cited as a cause of the meager rewards that come to this owner from his sales. In evaluating such a contention, one must not overlook the social service that the buyers perform. Many a pulp and paper company owes its prosperity to the presence, out in the country, of persons who are able and willing to spend time scavenging for odds and ends of timber. Society at large would be living less abundantly were it not for this class of middlemen. The costs of their activities are paid partly by timber owners—but partly also by users, in accordance with the principle of incidence.

The manner in which initiative is shared among buyers and sellers in the forest economy is evidenced by the character of advertising done by forestry firms. We may distinguish three kinds of advertising by these firms:

First, *informational advertising:* factual classified advertising and other matter-of-fact public notices of commodities wanted or offered. The commodities in question are largely undifferentiated. Examples are the newspaper and bulletin-board advertising of public timber for sale, and buyers' and sellers' advertising of wholesale lumber in the trade journals. There is a good deal of such advertising in the forest economy.

Second, *differentiated-product advertising:* that intended to increase the demand (or supply) and reduce its elasticity in monopolistic competition. Examples are popular advertising of branded writing and tissue papers, and the attractively illustrated calendar sent at Christmas time by the wood-using firm to its raw-material suppliers. We should also include campaigns to differentiate wood in general from its substitutes, such as the national wood-promotion program ("There's nothing in the world like wood") launched in 1959 by the National Lumber Manufacturers Association.[8] But, as we saw in Chapter 18, there is little advertising of this type in the forest economy as compared with other segments of our economy.

Third, *policy advertising:* the advertising of ideas. This is a major form of popular advertising in the forest economy. It is not, however, a part of marketing in our sense. We shall postpone discussion of it until Chapter 24, which treats of the pressure groups that do this kind of advertising.

### CONCENTRATION AND DISPERSION

The third major function of marketing, physical supply, includes concentration-dispersion, transportation, and storage. Let us devote our attention to the first.

In the United States there are, as you know, well over four million basic timber producers—that is, forest owners. And at the other end of the economic chain are some fifteen times that number of ultimate consuming firms. The task of physical supply is to convey title to commodities from the former horde to the latter, meantime accomplishing the necessary processing of the commodities. In order to take advantage of the economies of specialization and scale, this vast process of conveying is accomplished first by *concentration* of the timber into relatively few hands and then *dispersion* of it toward consumers (Fig. 39).

In territory where timber was widely held in small parcels and consumers also were widely distributed, the process of concentration and dispersion might ideally be carried out as follows: First, there would be a moderately large number of local logger-dealers buying timber from owners. The number of these dealers would be great enough to permit the necessary close personal contacts between the dealer and the timber

[8] *Life*, Feb. 16, 1959, pp. 42–45.

**336**                              THE MARKET FOR FOREST PRODUCTS

owners in his community. Next, there would be a smaller number of concentrators whose function would be to receive roundwood from dealers; measure, grade, and pay for it; sort it according to use; and consign it to the appropriate processors. The processors would perhaps be the least numerous agencies in the chain and thus represent the stage of maximum concentration. The fewer (and hence larger) the processing firms, the lower (let's say) their processing costs, and the higher their procurement and distribution costs, per unit of product. Their numbers would be determined so as to minimize the sum of the costs. Beyond the processors would be diversified wholesalers each of whom would take

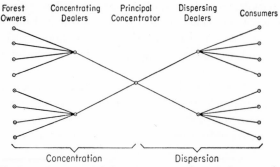

Fig. 39. Concentration and dispersion in timber products marketing.

the product of several types of processors. There might be a greater number of wholesalers than of processors for the same cause that there were more roundwood concentrators than processors: the limits placed upon scale economies by transportation cost and the necessity for close personal contacts with the agencies situated nearer the extremity of the chain. Admittedly, though, the wholesalers would have less urgent need for such contacts than the concentrators, since the wholesalers would probably be dealing in a more highly standardized commodity, easier to market by description. Beyond the wholesalers would be the retailers, numerous enough to serve the local communities, and beyond them the consumers.

[Can you visualize how the pattern of concentrating and dispersing firms tends to be set by the technology of transportation and of the firms' other operations? How would the pattern be likely to differ between a region where transportation was cheap and one where it was costly? How would it differ between a commodity the handling of which permitted great economies of scale and one that lacked this advantage?]

The ideal pattern of concentration and dispersion is always in real life disturbed and changed by many influences. Aggregations often occur at the ends of the system—big forest owners, big users such as building contractors—and these firms are in position to bypass some of the adjoining stages of marketing. The big forest firm, for example, may be vertically integrated to the point of doing its own concentrating, processing, and wholesaling, and even some of its retailing. Again, diversification, or horizontal integration, which is an essential feature of dealers in the ideal system, may be absent—because, for instance, the manager of the firm has insufficient personal capacity. Still again, the pattern of concentration and dispersion may be confused because the economies of scale take effect differently in different branches of the forest industry. For example, in the lumber industry in the East, scattered forest holdings, lax utilization of timber, and the consequent domination of the industry by small processors throw the point of maximum concentration over into the stage of wholesaling. In the West, however, maximum concentration tends to come much earlier in lumber marketing. In the pulp and paper and the plywood industries, the mill is generally the chief concentrator.

In any case we can summarize the influences that tend to determine the degree of concentration at any stage in marketing—that is, the number of firms at any stage. Working in the direction of fewer firms are the various economies of manufacturing scale, diversification, and consolidation. Working in opposition are the resistant costs of transportation and of market negotiation for buying and selling, and the advantages of close specialization.

## RISK TAKING

Consider, finally, the financial services of the market: risk taking and credit. The latter is a principal topic of Chapter 28, and so we shall mention only a point or two about it in the present chapter.

Risks in timber marketing are mostly of three sorts: risk of physical loss, as through fire, storm, insects, and decay; risk of financial loss, as through price declines or the delinquency of debtors; and risk of technical misjudgment, as in measurement and grading. The existence of such risks increases the cost of marketing. It also curtails the services of marketing. Where risks are high, marketing agencies tend to reduce their stocks, shorten their periods of production, and pull in their planning horizons. In the forest economy, such actions are, as we well know, contrary to resource conservation.

There are many ways for the firm to combat risk other than to draw in its horns. And social action, too, may be taken. Countercyclical measures may be used to lessen economic ups and downs and their attendant risks (Chap. 19). Insurance may be employed to spread risk (Chap. 28). Increase in knowledge, improvement of the informational services of the market, cuts risk. So does more effective planning. In some of the very well-organized commodity markets, the firm may attack price risk by buying or selling futures—that is, hedging. Various interesting schemes have been proposed for dealing with the problem of price and time in the timber economy. One is that in order to reduce the risks of the small-scale stumpage seller and encourage him to intensify his timber management, the firms in the wood-using industry that would stand to profit from his increased output should buy his young timber for delivery at a stated future date. The price could be such as to allow for insurance against physical loss, the risk of which would thus be assumed by the buyer. The buyer would spread this risk by entering into similar contracts with many timber owners. [What do you think of the idea?]

### CREDIT

The foregoing proposal is realistic at least in one respect: It assumes that credit in timber marketing can reasonably be expected to come to the small seller from the large buyer. In the story of forest credit in Chapter 28, it will be pointed out that ordinary credit from the specialized lending institutions flows rather readily to the large firms with attractive collateral and a good life expectancy, but is out of reach of many smaller firms. Then how do the smaller firms at the two ends of the marketing chain finance their operations, which involve in the aggregate immense costs in the form of inventories, wages, and other outlays? The answer is that the credit very commonly comes from the market agencies nearer the center of concentration, those that have readier access to general sources of capital. Thus we find wholesalers helping to finance retailers by accepting delayed payment for goods and rendering other services. These credit facilities are in the end passed on to the consumer. Back in the other direction, the little logger, timber dealer, and millman are financed by the larger concentrator to whom they sell their output. Such *merchant credit* is regarded in financial circles as highly risky. The concentrator is in the best position to offer it, since he is closely familiar with the borrower's business and able to regulate it in defense of his loan. Even so, he must charge a high rate of interest. He levies his interest against the price he receives or pays for the commodity.

One clear illustration of the working of merchant credit is found in the South in the relation between lumber *concentration yards* and their suppliers. The typical yard is a wholesaling establishment that buys pine lumber rough and green from small, scattered sawmills and dries, finishes, grades, and markets this lumber. Some of the yard's suppliers may be entirely independent financially, merely selling their lumber to the yard upon delivery. Others become attached to the yard in various ways in the process of obtaining credit. The yard may advance money to the little mill for buying stumpage or for other purposes. Or it may purchase stumpage and take the title itself, contracting with the mill operator to do the logging and sawing. The greater its financial stake in the small mill, the greater the degree of control it is likely to exercise over the mill's practices. It may give technical assistance in the operation of the mill and closely specify the product to be sawn. If the millman cannot make a go of his business as an independent or even as a contractor, the yard may need to take over his collateral, his mill and equipment, and put the millman on as an employee of the yard.

## SUMMARY

Marketing is that branch of production in which the title to commodities is transferred and the related functions of information, exchange, physical supply, and financial service are performed. Its importance in forestry stems from its growing costliness and from its role in setting material rewards and expenses in economic life.

Information as a marketing function: Many forest products, especially the raw products, are hard to describe and measure. Thereby marketing risks and other costs are increased and forest conservation discouraged. Furthermore, price and quantity reporting are made difficult at the lower stages of the market.

Exchange: In the markets for stumpage, roundwood, and rough wood products, the buyers often take the main initiative. Sellers commonly assume the lead in the higher stages of marketing.

Physical supply: Marketing generally involves concentration of the output of forest owners and subsequent dispersion of products toward consumers. The stage of greatest concentration, usually processing or wholesaling, is determined for each commodity by the opposing forces of scale economies and transfer costs.

Financial service: Marketing risks, of physical and of financial loss, may be attacked through insurance, countercyclical measures, market information, planning, and other programs. Credit is acquired from general sources mostly by the principal concentrators and is disbursed by them in both directions along the marketing chain.

Chapter 21

MARKETING
AGENCIES
AND THEIR
PRACTICES

THE AGENCIES of the market and their practices vary no less widely than the functions they perform. How greatly the agencies differ from place to place! How they change with time! Look around you at the timber economy and see what a complex of firms carries on the business of marketing.

However, let no one suppose that marketing agencies and their practices are simply a hodgepodge. Like everything else in our social organization, they are understandable and orderly and therefore approachable by the methods of science, if only one can find the right filing systems.

The character of the market is an adaptation, first, to the economy that the market serves, and second, to the resource with which it deals. Consequently in the economy and the resource—in the status of the timber economy—we should be able to find the subdivisions of a filing scheme capable of sorting out reasonably well the agencies and practices of the timber market. As the timber economy changes and matures, as it passes from one phase of development to the next, adaptive changes come over the timber market. One may speculate that it is largely because of the differences in developmental phase from one locality to another and the market influences that extend in varying degree between localities that agencies and practices in any one nation and era seem complex. If so, here is another opportunity to use the method of abstraction—of partial analysis—to simplify the story of the forest economy and make the story easier to grasp.

Let us, then, station ourselves in some characteristic, though uniform, forest area of the United States at an early period in its history and

340

watch what happens to timber marketing agencies and their practices as the years go by. Let us take the narrow viewpoint of the locality where we are stationed, and let us give particular attention to the lower stages of marketing: those situated nearer the woods end of the chain. Let us witness the arrival and departure of faces, firms, activities, systems—with little concern for whence they come or whither they go beyond the limits of the stage before us. This passing show will comprise six episodes:

1. Frontier period
2. Colonial period
3. Industrial period
4. Aftermath
5. Hiatus
6. Conservation period

As you study each period, see if you can think of some part of the country that is today approximately in this phase of its development. See if the marketing agencies and their practices are like those described.

And as we move from one episode to the next, remember that not every area experiences all six in just the form that we shall describe. In some areas, certain episodes may be telescoped or largely merged with others or even omitted. Or then again, conceivably the show may not be played out to the end in every area, however patiently we wait for the last act.

### IN FRONTIER PERIOD

In the frontier period, our area enjoys physical abundance of forest land and timber. However, in an economic sense these resources are not abundant, for transportation within the area and between it and the outside world is largely undeveloped. The area, therefore, is isolated, and its economy is self-sufficient. Outsiders who look at the area see inaccessibility. Insiders who peer out through its barriers see little opportunity for trade or commerce—for marketing—except of the most valuable commodities.

Within the area, the individual firms are characteristically self-sufficient. They have their own land, which they cultivate and from which they derive wood and other commodities for their own use. Marketing is a minor activity. There are few middlemen. Some of the firms operate sawmills or engage in other wood processing on a small scale, but when these firms produce commodities for others, they commonly do so on a *custom basis,* not taking title to the raw material or the finished goods. In return for their services, they may be given a part of the product.

Such selling and buying as are done, by barter or cash, are carried out on the basis of inspection. Timber raw materials have low value. The margin of availability rests near the surface of the resource and involves mainly the cream of it. Description and measurement are but minor functions of the market for raw material. Wood moves only short distances in the course of production and consumption. Its utilization is accompanied by a great deal of physical waste.

## IN COLONIAL PERIOD

The colonial period is distinguished from the frontier primarily in two ways: First, transportation facilities have become well enough developed to push the margins of availability deeply into the forest resource. The facilities in question may be tidewater or rivers and streams, in which case the colonial period may arrive very early in the whole life of the area. Second, the labor force is large enough and well enough supplied with the essentials of life to allow substantial exploitation of forests. On the basis of these advantages, the area is in position to sever great quantities of timber and ship them to the outside world.

The term *colonial* is used to name this period because at this time the economy of the area is like the great colonial economies created by the European powers in past centuries. The livelihood of the area comes chiefly from extracting natural resources. A large feature of life is trade with the mother country, which in our case may be simply the more mature, industrial sections of the United States. The firms headquartered in these mother sections may acquire blocks of natural resources in the area, and this development may be countered by the government, through acquisition or reservation in behalf of the nation at large. Capital for exploiting the resource comes principally through the mother firms.

Outsiders who look at the area in the colonial period see opportunities for access to raw material, perhaps to feed older manufacturing centers that have grown short of local supplies. Those on the inside see new ways for marketing their labor and new chances for resource development and trade. They see the area moving closer to the world at large. They see a growing agriculture, and outlets for the timber by-products of land clearing.

One of the great markets that develops is the market for forest land. Land is bought by timber manufacturers, loggers, dealers, speculators, farmers, and the government. Deals in timber land, based upon inspection, are serviced by the land looker and the timber cruiser, whose cursory methods are well proportioned to the low resource values.

However, it is the market for stumpage and for logs that comes closest to characterizing the era. By and large, the users of wood are not interested in forest land unless they must take it in order to get the trees.

Their interest is in seeing the logs move downstream and out through the other channels of supply. To facilitate such movement, they may themselves engage in buying stumpage and logs from timber owners and carry out the extraction and shipment of the raw material. Or they may contract for their needs with loggers and dealers, whose operations they will finance. Some loggers and dealers will have enough funds of their own to manage their business with a degree of independence, serving as concentrators and selling to numerous manufacturers. Supporting this activity is a labor force well versed in the many skills of the woods, stream, and loading yard.

Around water transportation and the work of log dealers there may develop an active log market, with facilities for storage, sorting, and dispersion, near the manufacturing centers. In any case, the measurement of logs and trees will be practiced. There may be some grading, too, to make possible the sale of logs by description. More commonly, buyers specify their minimum standards for raw material, thus in effect establishing two grades, merchantable and not. Where logs are dispersed to more than one kind of use—perhaps lumber and veneer—rules arise to guide the sorting. Users can set their quality standards high without fear that supplies will run short.

Timber-utilization practices entail a fair amount of physical waste. In the mills, there is little horizontal integration of enterprises, little close adaptation of the raw material to the end product. In the woods, creaming is common. Where transportation is by log drive or rafting, mixed forests are logged for softwood, and the hardwood is left standing. In any event, loggers direct their attention to the largest and highest-quality trees of the favored species. Thus are begun the changes in forest composition that perplex and challenge the silviculturist in later times.

## IN INDUSTRIAL PERIOD

In the industrial period, further development of the economy and improvements in transportation have drawn large wood-manufacturing plants into the area. The plants are users of logs and bolts—that is, they are *primary manufacturing* plants—attracted to the area by their orientation to the raw materials that economically are now the most abundant in the area's history. The characteristic industry is lumbering. Other mechanical processors of logs may be present also, such as makers of veneer and plywood. The pulp and paper industry is there if the industrial period has come to this area late in the whole development of the nation's forest economy. Remanufacturers, that use partly processed wood as raw material—that is, *secondary manufacturing* industries such as construction, furniture, and fixtures, which are market-oriented industries—are found if the area has become generally populated and industrialized. But it is the primary forest industry that characterizes the industrial period in our present sense.

Indeed, the industrial period in respect to the marketing of timber products has typically come to United States forest areas at a time when the areas' economies at large were still colonial: still big net importers of all sorts of finished goods.

Outsiders, even those who are far away, see the area as a large and dependable source of many wood products. Insiders feel that the area is an important part of the forest economy of the nation.

The marketing system—agencies and their methods—is highly consolidated and simple and relatively efficient. Much or all of the concentration phase takes place within the area itself, the big manufacturer standing at the apex of the pyramid. The tasks of concentration are much simplified by the fact that most of the tributary forest land is owned by the processors themselves or by the government. Only in the latter case is marketing involved, and the transactions are large and direct. Arrangements between industries for sorting and exchanging logs so as to make the best use of raw material are usually carried out directly by the firms involved. Some need is felt in this connection for standardized log grades.

In the first phases of production, therefore, quantity handling is the rule. Of course, there is some collecting of timber from smaller private holdings not owned by the processor, and this is commonly done through the user's procurement organization or independent dealers; but such channels are a negligible part of the scheme. There is also a part played by lesser operators, as in prelogging or relogging, the logging of unblocked parcels, and the lumbering of difficult situations with portable equipment, but in such cases the operator is often a part of the principal firm. Even the various product lines may be horizontally integrated within single firms, the enterprises being drawn together by economies of wood utilization, financing, selling, and diversification.

Beyond concentration and primary manufacturing, heavy volume still characterizes the dispersion lines of processing and marketing well along toward ultimate consumers. These lines lie for the most part outside the area, for the area is characteristically a big exporter, a source of products for a very wide territory. Some of the manufacturers, through their sales organizations, deal directly with large retailers and with large consumers such as building contractors and lumber remanufacturers. Most of them channel at least a part of their output to independent wholesalers. The latter include *yard wholesalers,* who take title to the commodities and stock them on hand for customers, and *commission wholesalers,* or brokers, who escape the financial burden of stock holding and merely buy and sell for the account of their principals. Many wholesalers engage in both types of business, and some follow a mixed sort of procedure: For example, we find today in the eastern lumber markets wholesalers who are continuously buying carload lumber on the West Coast and shipping it eastward. Most of the cars they are able to sell en route. Those that cross the continent unsold they unload at their yards. Such wholesalers may own and operate some of their western supplier mills, and with this arrangement we have run the whole circle, coming back to the vertically integrated manufacturer and sales organization, only that the parent enterprise in this case is marketing rather than processing. The parent enterprise may be the business descendant of an eastern firm that was a big manufacturer and exporter in the days when its locality was in the industrial period. Thus it is that individuals and families may stay in the same line of business and keep their roots in the same soil even though the industry of which they are a part has meanwhile migrated afar.

The area's whole dispersion system rests on selling by description and therefore on commodity grading. Grading rules are highly developed. So is the scheme for carrying out the grading, checking it, and guaranteeing its integrity.

Land markets may work briskly again in the industrial period. If there are still plenty of new forests for the industry to go to in other areas, it will dispose of its holdings as they are cut over, looking to prospective farmers or the general public as the purchasers. Firms establish subsidiary land companies to sell this by-product of their business.

And so in the industrial period the area sees the most intensive timbering and marketing activities in its history. Big operations are the keynote of the era, based upon concentrations of old-growth timber in the area. The capital for exploitation and marketing comes to a greater extent than ever before from within the area itself. And the area acquires its largest pool of labor skilled not only in extraction but also in the arts of fabrication and exchange.

## IN AFTERMATH

As the old-growth forest is worked out, the area enters the aftermath. The timber resource is now scanty, with light stocking of relatively small trees. The less wanted species and quality loom large in the forest inventory. Timber ownership is characteristically diffused. Farmers and other small-scale landowners hold much of the resource. Conservatively managed public forests of long standing are foreign to the aftermath in its simplest form; and so here let us abstract, picturing our area as enclosing little such forests. Some large cut-over or young-growth tracts remain in the hands of wood-using industry.

The area finds its livelihood now mostly in farming, or in industry other than primary wood manufacture.

Timber operators and many of the timber owners of the area want to market their products. They want to maintain the channels and contacts that were so strong and secure during the industrial period. However, the former big customers now are leery of the area as a source of supply. They find difficulty in getting the quantity they want, or the quality, or the guarantee of service. The area discovers itself reclothed in some of the old inaccessibility of frontier and colonial days.

The problems of the aftermath tend to produce a complex and varied marketing system. Because of the complexity, we shall need to devote much more space to the agencies and practices of the aftermath than to those of other periods. Let us first examine the circumstances with which the agencies are faced and then consider how the circumstances are met.

## CIRCUMSTANCES OF AFTERMATH

*One circumstance* is the sparseness and scattering of the forest resource. Timber procurement is a scavenging operation. It is socially costly, requiring either the existence of an underemployed class of rural labor that can subsidize it, or the services of workers with wider alternatives and therefore comparatively high wage rates. It is costly also in terms of risk to the wood user: risk that he will not get the quantity he is counting on, or the quality. The exacting user is inclined, therefore, to get his supplies from outside the area, and the area tends to be a net importer. The fact of importation, along with local costs, acts to raise the price level of wood within the area, especially of quality wood and wood in assured, substantial amounts. In this way the local margins of timber availability are pushed back more deeply into the resource. But between importation and self-sufficiency, between transportation cost and local extraction cost, a balance is struck that still leaves many of the area's wood users dependent for their supplies upon other areas that are in the colonial or industrial phase of their development. Within our area, the locational advantage is thrown mainly to three classes of timber consumers: (1) small-scale, unexacting firms such as farmers in need of fence posts, firewood, pigpen lumber, and the like; (2) larger firms that can adapt their requirements to the supply, such as railroads as crosstie users and pulp mills as users of cordwood; and (3) firms with exacting requirements, that can meet the supply situations with appropriate procurement and conversion measures—for example, the lumber wholesaler that can function as a concentration yard.

Now that we have enumerated the types of firms that are able to get wood from within the area, let us just glance at the predominating and contrasting case of the firm that cannot: the firm with exacting requirements that must be met largely outside the area. Consider, for instance, the manufacturer of quality furniture: His raw material is hardwood lumber and small dimension. He needs a lot of it; his requirements are specific as to sizes, grades, and moisture content; and his source of supply must be able to furnish what he wants on short notice. Now there is a great deal of scattered standing timber in the area that would yield the sort of material that this manufacturer uses. What are the manufacturer's alternatives? He could operate one or more small sawmills to provide himself with wood, but timber prospecting and lumbering are not his business. He is especially cool to the idea of *selling* lumber, which he would have to do, since he could not use all his own output. Furthermore, he rightly believes that, with hired labor paid on a competitive scale and involving such extra charges as the social security tax and workmen's compensation insurance, his costs would be inordinately high as compared with the family enterprises that set the tone of the market.

Alternatively, the furniture manufacturer could search out some mills —necessarily small mills—that might be capable of supplying his needs. This, however, is a difficult matter, for most such mill operators are unschooled in timber cutting and sawing for the grade lumber market, and even know little about grading. Besides, their operating schedules are irregular and their output uncertain. And then there is the credit problem. The manufacturer fears that he might end up in the lumber business.

And so this furniture maker turns to a dealer for his wants—a wholesaler, probably a yard wholesaler, who is accustomed to doing business in quantity and to guaranteeing his transactions. In the end, the costs are least this way. The supply of raw material is assured, the headaches of procurement are minimized, and the furniture man can devote his whole attention to his own business. The wholesaler, on his part, may get a little lumber occasionally here and there within the area. But to maintain his volume and quality, he depends largely upon big suppliers on the outside.

A *second circumstance* of the aftermath grows directly out of the sparseness and scattering of the forest resource. This is the characteristically small scale of operations near the woods end of the marketing chain. It takes small-scale operators to dig out the supplies, firms that are well acquainted locally and are probably doing their digging as a part-time sideline, not charging society as much for the service as a big, full-time firm would need to do. The little buyer, the little logger, and the small custom mill typify the scene.

A *third circumstance*, following necessarily from the first two, is that the area's marketing system, being organized for the immense task of concentrating many different timber products, appears complex and overstuffed. Aside from home-use commodities, nearly all wood produced within the area has to be concentrated. Much of the process is carried out separately for each class of product. Here and there diversified firms are found running parallel to those that are more specialized. The system not only is complicated but also is delicately hinged upon its requirements for financing, which must come mainly from sources further along the marketing chain.

A *fourth and last circumstance* is that the area has lost many of the skills that it acquired in the industrial period. Among the most important of these are the skills of commodity grading. In the absence of grading, the more exacting a buyer's requirements, the closer the personal attention he must give to procurement. And so the area's competitive position is weakened in supplying the needs of such a buyer.

## MARKETING TASKS IN AFTERMATH

How do marketing agencies meet the circumstances of the aftermath? Let us observe that the agencies have three great tasks to perform:

*First,* they have the task of importing wood into the area, mainly from regions that are in the industrial period. We have already taken note of the importing wholesaler whose firm was a manufacturer at the time when the area was in its industrial period. Other importers are large-scale processors, other big consumers, retailers, and the like.

*Second,* there is the task of dispersing commodities. In respect to dispersion, the aftermath is not essentially different from the industrial period in its agencies and methods, however great a difference there may be in volume.

*Third,* there is the overriding task of concentration. Let us have a look at some of the concentration schemes that typify the aftermath. As we do so, remember what was said earlier about the risk entailed in uncertain and fluctuating supplies, and note how such risk is reduced in each scheme by the function of storage at the appropriate stage of concentration.

## CONCENTRATING SINGLE COMMODITIES IN AFTERMATH

*One concentration scheme* is that used by pulping firms to obtain pulpwood from the so-called *open market*—that is, from lands other than those owned or leased by the firm. The problem is to keep a sufficient and reasonably steady supply coming in and to minimize the cost of the supply. Ordinarily the firm wishes to buy wood already cut and delivered, or loaded for shipment. Here its attitude is like that of the furniture manufacturer in wanting to stick to its own main business. Furthermore, it seeks to avoid becoming involved in controversy concerning title to standing timber, and it seeks to encourage independent procurement firms that are small enough to escape some of the taxes and fees that fall upon larger employers.

The pulp company's answer commonly is to get its requirements from dealers. Where the dealer is under contract to furnish the wood, he is often called a *pulpwood contractor.* Each dealer undertakes to find and buy stumpage and log it (or to buy wood from producers) and deliver or load the wood—or to subcontract for the purpose with still other dealers. This dealer system may have several layers, fanning out and reaching down ultimately to make contact with individual woodland owners. Generally the layers are most numerous in those parts of the procurement territory that lie furthest from the mill. Each layer is recompensed by a cut out of the price the pulp company pays. The company may make advance payments for wood in order to help with the financing. It may assign territories and make exclusive contracts with a dealer in each, the dealer on his part supplying no other wood user but this company; and the dealer may have similarly exclusive arrangements with such subcontractors as he may use. Or dealers may exercise more independence, supplying several buyers and determining their own territories. Contracts may be formal or, particularly at the lower levels, simply verbal. They usually state the amount of wood ("quota") to be delivered during a period, the species and other specifications, and of course the price. The pulp company may establish yards at principal railroad sidings and barge landings, where wood can be handled and loaded mechanically so as to save expense. Such yards serve as secondary storage points, supplementing the main storage facility, which is at the mill. So efficient is this whole scheme that pulping firms ordinarily use it even to procure wood from their own lands.[1]

*Another arrangement for concentration* is that followed by the yard wholesaler of lumber who takes the output of little sawmills. We looked into the practices of concentration yards in Chapter 20 (pp. 338–339).[2] Revealing of the problems of the aftermath is the fact that whereas the concentration-yard system has generally worked rather well in the softwood-lumber industry, it is not equally adaptable to hardwood. One cause is the fundamental difference between softwood and hardwood grade lumber. The former, used mainly for construction, is easy to produce. Most of the ordinary, rank errors that the little, unskilled operator commits in logging and sawing can be corrected at the concentration yard in the

[1] For descriptions of two somewhat different pulpwood contractor systems, see James, Lee M.: *Marketing Pulpwood in Michigan,* Michigan Agricultural Experiment Station Special Bulletin 411, East Lansing, 1957, pp. 30–39; and Duerr, William A.: *The Economic Problems of Forestry in the Appalachian Region,* Harvard University Press, Cambridge, Mass., 1949, pp. 212–215.

[2] For more on lumber concentration yards, see Duerr: Same reference, pp. 246–252.

course of seasoning and finishing. With hardwood lumber, on the other hand, used principally in manufacturing, most of the value is determined in the process of log making and sawing. Mistakes made then usually cannot be remedied later. Consequently the industry's skills must be focused upon the woods and mill.

*Still another concentration scheme* that typifies the aftermath is that employed by mines to get their props, headers, ties, lagging, and other timber. Much of the mine requirements are unexacting, but they are varied, and for some of the types of timber, size and soundness specifications are vitally important and must be closely followed in manufacture. Some mine timbers are sawed; others are produced by hewing; still others are used in the round. Ordinarily the mine must draw its supplies from many small woods owners and timber operators.

Three methods that are used in mine-timber marketing are described by Henry Webster.[3] In the first and simplest, the mine gets its timber direct from woodland owners who do their own cutting or from independent cutters who buy stumpage. In the second method, these agencies convey their output to the mine through a small-scale concentrator who operates a sawmill and also does some logging. In the third and most complex scheme, all the foregoing producers funnel their mine timbers through a dealer who performs substantial services of concentration and storage. The larger the mining firms and the smaller the woodlands, the more common is the third of these methods. In all the schemes, the mine attaches high value to continuity of relationship with its suppliers and to assurance of supply; it forecasts its needs and gives quotas to its suppliers. Where direct buying fails to afford the mine the assurances it wants, the mine ordinarily is glad to pay the higher prices necessary to get the services of a dealer.

## OTHER CONCENTRATION SCHEMES IN AFTERMATH

The preceding descriptions of concentrating agencies and their methods are principally a story of undiversified marketing firms. Here is a dealer who handles pulpwood. There is one who is concerned only with saw logs and lumber. Such one-track marketing is fostered by the specialized character of each industry and its wood requirements, and by the personal nature of the contacts between buyers and sellers in the marketing chain. However, the specialization of market agencies for a commodity as varied and widely adaptable as timber runs counter to the principle of devoting each piece of wood to its most profitable use.

[3] Webster, Henry H.: *An Economic Analysis of Mine-timber Marketing in West Virginia,* Northeastern Forest Experiment Station Paper 84, Upper Darby, Pa., 1956, pp. 6–13.

Society has much to gain from following this principle, and so does a marketing firm if it can economically overcome the attendant jack-of-all-trades hazards of diversification.

Some of the brightest opportunities for diversification in the aftermath come at the stage of concentration just preceding primary manufacture. And so we do occasionally find log and bolt dealers who maintain yards or decentralized facilities for receiving a variety of materials. These dealers sort, grade, and store the commodities and channel them into the uses from which the highest net returns can be derived. Such a dealer may, for example, be simultaneously a pulpwood and mine-timber contractor, a veneer-log agent, and a lumber producer with a concentration yard.

As a final example of concentration in the aftermath, let us mention *cooperative marketing.* The cooperative differs from the marketing schemes that have been described, not in the commodities it handles and not necessarily in the channels it employs, but rather in the form of organization of the firm. The firm is organized under principles that trace back to a group of enterprising weavers in Rochdale, England, who in 1844 banded together to strengthen their position as consumers. A cooperative is owned and is operated by and for the persons whose commodities it handles. Thus it is a means of vertical integration for the little firm. Organized as a corporation, it follows such rules as one-man-one-vote (as against the voting of stock), limited returns on capital, dividends to members on the basis of patronage, and open membership.

Long a successful institution in the United States in the marketing of farm products, the cooperative form of organization was first widely considered in the great rural depression of the 1920s and 1930s as a means of strengthening the hand of the little timber owner. Cooperatives were set up to handle their members' logs or Christmas trees or maple syrup. They could be found functioning as pulpwood contractors or as diversified log concentrators. They ran sawmills. These forestry cooperatives faced inherent handicaps such as infrequency of contacts with each member and the minor position of timber in most members' businesses. However, a few met with success and survived—primarily, as in any business, because of skillful management.[4]

## IN HIATUS

Beyond the aftermath, our area will, let us suppose, enter a conservation period which will represent the climax of its resource management

---

[4] You can learn about the history and principles of cooperative marketing in agriculture in any of the numerous books that have been written on the subject. One summary of the status of cooperation in forestry is that by R. N. Cunningham: *Forest Cooperatives in the United States,* U.S. Department of Agriculture, Forest Service Report 6 from Reappraisal of Forest Situation, Washington, 1947.

—a period in which the products marketed will have been deliberately grown for the purpose. But before the conservation period, there may come a hiatus while forest management is regrouping and timber growing stocks are being allowed to accumulate. This hiatus need not occur all at one time throughout a wide region. Typically, it will appear in spots or single forest properties here and there. But whatever form it takes, it brings distinctive changes in marketing.

Indeed, it brings virtually a cessation in the marketing of local timber. Where timber moves, it moves in as imports.

The land market, by contrast, may be active. Those wood-using firms that disposed of their holdings in the industrial period may enter the market again, this time as buyers. The public, too, may be buying forest land for timber production. There will also be a brisk interest in forest land for its watershed values and for recreational and game purposes and the like. Various levels of government from Federal to municipal will enter the land market with these values in view. Private individuals and corporations, too, will act upon their interest in the nontimber products of forest land.

An illustration of hiatus in timber marketing and of how it may occur area-wise has been observable in many pulp-company forests in the South. As the industry grew, its members acquired properties that would assure them a supply of raw material. In many cases they then set the properties aside to restock and come into prime yield condition. Meantime they garnered their pulpwood from the little holdings of the open market. It was the existence of these holdings, with their owners predisposed toward exploitive management, that made possible the ultraconservative forest program of the pulping firms with respect to their own lands. Thus existed side by side some of the most striking examples in the United States of destructive and of constructive private forest policies—each a child of the same industry and the same marketing phenomenon: the passing of the aftermath into hiatus.

## IN CONSERVATION PERIOD

Finally, let us suppose that our area finds itself in the conservation period. Timber is being grown under continuing programs on lands in all classes of ownership, even including the small privately held tracts. The products grown in abundance are being marketed under a system that is at once efficient and conducive to sustained abundance.

You will find in the United States no such examples of the conservation period. You may even question whether under our present institutions it is possible for forestry generally to take this final step. Nevertheless, it is essential that you think about the marketing problems of conservation and try to visualize the marketing agencies and methods that would foster intensive timber management. Try your hand at it.

[How, under conservation, can the area regain the marketing efficiency of its industrial period? What are its best approaches to the task of concentration? How go about routing each kind of wood into its most economical use? What, in summary, would be the needs in the conservation period for the marketing services of information, exchange, physical supply, and financing; and what agencies and procedures would be best adapted to giving these services?

[In areas where private timber management is in transition between liquidation and continuous production, as in the Douglas-fir region, one may find manufacturing firms, especially smaller firms, that are holding cutover or restocked forest lands, ostensibly as a long-term investment, but yet are reluctant to spend money on cultural practices such as pruning, noncommercial thinning, or even planting. These firms may foresee eventual returns sufficient to justify the outlays. Nevertheless, they look upon the expenditure as too risky, considering that they might need to close out their operations and sell their land before the returns from their practices materialized. They would rather make their investments in tractors, mill equipment, and other capital with a quicker (though not necessarily higher-rate) pay-out. What would be the characteristics of the ideal forest-land market in the conservation period, that would encourage firms to make promising forest investments with a substantially delayed return?]

## SUMMARY

One way to study timber-marketing agencies and their practices is to relate them to the status of the timber economy. In this historical approach, six developmental periods may be recognized. To see these periods and their marketing systems most clearly, in simplest form, one must do some abstracting, for no area of the United States today offers a perfect example of any one period. Every forest area is a somewhat mixed case, its timber marketing determined by mixed influences.

In its frontier period, an area is isolated by transfer-cost barriers. Its economy is largely self-sufficient. Wood enters little into transportation or trade.

In the colonial period, the area has become sufficiently accessible and populous to serve as a source of raw materials for other areas. The market for forest land and stumpage and the export market for logs and other rough products are well developed.

In the industrial period, the area's timber is abundant and highly accessible. Primary wood-using industries based on resource exploitation are at their fullest development. Both in the minor, concentration phase of timber marketing and in the major, dispersion phase, heavy volume is the rule. The marketing system is directed primarily toward exporting manufactured products. The system is simple and efficient.

In the aftermath, the timber resource is scanty and scattered and its ownership diffused. The area may be a net importer of wood. Its most elaborate timber-marketing efforts are those required to concentrate its own output of raw material. One finds, for example, the pulp company's dealer system and the concentration yards of the softwood lumber industry.

In the hiatus, which is a period of preparation for intensified timber management in the area, there is little marketing of local timber. The market for forest land, however, is active.

In the conservation period, the area is growing an abundance of timber. In the absence of American examples, it is important to speculate what agencies and methods consistent with conservation would best perform the essential functions of the market for forest products.

# Chapter 22

# GEOGRAPHY
# OF MARKETING

YOU REMEMBER an earlier statement (p. 327) that marketing can be explained in at least three ways. Marketing can be explained in terms of the things that are done in connection with it: the functions that are performed. Chapter 20 went at the subject in this way. Or marketing can be explained in terms of the persons who do it. This was the approach of Chapter 21. Finally, it is possible to explain marketing by talking about the places where persons carry out its functions. This locational, or geographic, view of marketing is taken in the present chapter.

Forestry and geography are mutually companionable subjects, because forest land, and to a degree the forest economy as a whole, is a manifestation of space, of position on the face of the earth. Furthermore, many of the agents of production in forestry and many of the products are highly sensitive to location, being either of low specific value or of low mobility for other causes. The subject of geography arises from the fact that resources are clustered, so that their distribution is "imperfect." The subject of forestry, as we implied earlier (p. 324), stems partly from the same imperfection.

All of us recognize the importance of the relationship between forestry and time. Equal recognition is seldom given, though it well could be, to the relation between forestry and place. An appreciation for the economic role of location and distance can be one of the forester's most valuable assets. For the forest-product maker and marketer, such appreciation is indispensable. We had an introduction to the economics of location in Chapter 11. What we shall take up now is, in a way, a continuation of that story.

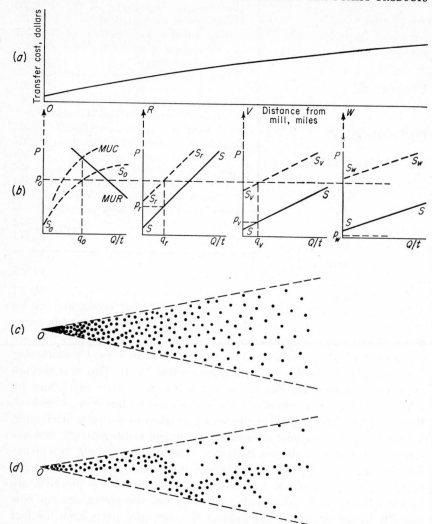

Fig. 40. Price and quantity structure of an isolated pulpwood shed: (*a*) Transfer-cost gradient. (*b*) Pulpwood supply and demand at the mill, and supply at points *R, V,* and *W.* (*c*) Output in a segment of the timber shed, assuming uniformity. (*d*) Output in the absence of uniformity.

The headquarters of sellers and buyers are always separated by distance. When a commodity changes hands, it is moved. What determines its movement? To answer the question, we could follow some unit of a commodity in its travels. Or we could observe a particular buyer and seller and try to explain the flow of the commodity between them. But however we went at it, we should soon find that in order to account for the commodity's origin and destination we should need to take into consideration its alternative origins and destinations. We should need to ask why it came from here rather than elsewhere, and why it went there instead of some other place. That is to say, we should have to study the processes of concentration and dispersion as a whole and understand the interrelationships among locations.

Let us, therefore, take the subject of market geography in three parts: Let us look first at the locational economics of concentration. Second, let us do the same with dispersion. Third, let us give attention at least very briefly to the whole complex of trade.

## ISOLATED TIMBER SHED: SUPPLY

Suppose that a single, uniform commodity is being concentrated at one location and that a uniform delivered price is paid for it, a practice that we shall call **delivered pricing.** To avoid soaring off into more abstractions than necessary, suppose the commodity is pulpwood and the point of concentration is the mill. To begin with, however, imagine that the whole territory from which the mill may gather its wood is perfectly homogeneous with respect to wood supply. This is like saying that forests are uniformly distributed, owners are alike in their supply responses, all points have equal access to transportation facilities, and demands for wood by users other than the mill are everywhere the same. The only differences from place to place are in distance from the mill and the differences arising therefrom.

The transfer-cost gradient for the mill's **timber shed** (wood-procurement territory) is drawn in Figure 40a. The horizontal axis, which is proportioned to distance, represents any radius within the timber shed, extending outward from the mill at the origin. Transfer cost increases with distance, but at a diminishing rate, so that the gradient is convex from above (compare Fig. 11c, p. 164). Location $O$ is the mill site, and locations $R$, $V$, and $W$, situated at increasing distances from the mill, represent all areas surrounding the mill.

Now consider the supply of pulpwood at the various locations. It is shown by the SS curves in Figure 40b. Supply per acre, by the terms of our assumptions, is everywhere the same, but total supply from all acres lying at a given distance from the mill varies with the distance. The amount supplied at any price is directly proportional to distance. For example, since there are twice as many acres situated 20 miles from the mill as 10 miles, then since pulpwood supply per acre is the same at both distances, the total amount supplied at any price is twice as great at 20 miles as at 10. (Note, however, that *elasticity* of the total supply at any price is unchanging with distance.)

The SS curves are the local supply—say, the amounts of pulpwood that sellers would be willing to deliver to the carrier at various local prices. The prices that would induce them to deliver these same amounts to the mill are the local prices plus the cost of transportation. Thus the supply of wood at the mill, the supply as it is viewed by the pulping firm, is represented by the curves $S_rS_r$, $S_vS_v$, and $S_wS_w$, each drawn at a distance above $SS$ equal to the transfer cost at that location. When all at-the-mill supply curves for the timber shed are added together, the resulting aggregate supply is found to be $S_oS_o$. This aggregate supply curve takes its position and shape from the fact that, as the pulping firm offers higher delivered prices, it can get more wood in two ways: First, it can get more wood than before from the same suppliers; second, it can get wood from new suppliers located further away. At each delivered price, the firm is confronted with two margins: One, the *intensive margin*, is the limit to which sellers are willing to carry their offerings of wood at that price. The other, the *extensive margin*, is the limit to which the firm can reach and still find sellers at that price. On the extensive margin, local price is so low that it just fails to call forth any offering: The seller's intensive margin is encountered at zero output.

## PRICE AND QUANTITY STRUCTURE OF ISOLATED SHED

Given the aggregate supply curve $S_oS_o$, which is the firm's average cost of wood, we may derive its marginal cost. The latter is shown as $MUC$ in Figure 40b. The quantity of wood that the firm will buy per unit of time, $q_o$, is determined at the intersection of this marginal cost curve with the corresponding marginal revenue curve. The delivered price, $p_o$, is the monopsonist's price, found on the aggregate supply curve at this quantity (compare Fig. 30d, p. 288).

At the delivered price $p_o$, sellers at $R$ will supply $q_r$, and the local price there will be $p_r$. Sellers at $V$ will supply $q_v$ at the local price $p_v$. Sellers at $W$ will supply nothing. The price is too low to attract them, and so they are outside the timber shed.

Figure 40b shows smaller total amounts of wood coming in from the greater distances. With delivered pricing and uniform supply per acre, we know that the amount supplied per acre will decrease with increasing distance from the mill. But the total amount supplied will increase with distance, up to a point, if supply is sufficiently inelastic or the transfer-cost gradient sufficiently flat or the delivered price high enough. Beyond this point, total amounts will decrease.

[Back in Chapter 11 we had the principle of relative transportability, according to which the commodities with higher specific value tend to move further. However, we have in Figure 40b what appears to be a contradiction: The wood that moves furthest is that of lowest value. What's wrong?]

Still keeping all our assumptions about the uniformity of the timber shed, if we look down upon the shed from above—or, say, a segment of the shed—we find that the geographic pattern of pulpwood marketings appears about as in Figure 40c, where each dot represents the approximate point of origin of a given quantity of wood. Here we have the *quantity structure* of the shed. Can you represent on this same graph the shed's local *price structure?* One way to do it is to map in the contour lines of price: the iso-price lines. You can now draw some analogies between the timber shed and a watershed. In the latter, water flows from the higher ground to the lower, emerging at the stream mouth. In the former, timber flows from the lower-price ground to the higher-, emerging at the mill. In the watershed, gravity is the ruling force. In the timber shed, it is the reward to be found in the market place.

At this point it is an easy matter to cast aside all our restricting assumptions save the one that permits us to view this timber shed as a single, isolated case: the assumption that demands for wood by users other than the mill are everywhere the same. Thus we can recognize the fact that forests may not be uniformly distributed over the shed, that owners may not all be alike in their supply responses, and that all points do not have equal access to transportation facilities. The resulting quantity structure, which comes far toward depicting what one actually finds in a pulpwood shed, is given in graph *d* of Figure 40. The concentrations of marketings are here determined not only by distance from the mill but also by the presence of a major line of transportation weaving eastward, by the loading points along this line, and by groupings of especially accessible forest lands bearing available timber.

## TIMBER SHEDS OF CLUSTERED CONCENTRATORS

In order to get rid of our last limiting assumption, that demands for wood by users other than the mill are everywhere the same, we need now to take the next major step in our analysis of the concentration process, studying the interrelationships among timber sheds.

How are timber sheds located in relation to one another? Is it usual for them to coincide, or to be entirely separate, or to overlap to some extent, or what? Actually all these different cases are to be found. The geography of the timber sheds within a region is determined by two things: the location of the concentrating firms and the size and shape of their sheds.

We have from Chapter 11 a general idea of the main principles governing the location of firms. For manufacturing firms, there were the three major cases, material orientation, market orientation, and intermediate cases such as location at a transshipment point or at a strategic junction of transportation routes. The same concepts apply to marketing firms. The log dealer is material oriented; the retailer, market oriented. The big concentrating wholesaler is often oriented to bottlenecks in the transportation system. Many of the principal concentrators of Appalachian hardwood lumber are to be found in Cincinnati, the first great railroad center on the northeastward path to the commodity's ultimate consumers. Cincinnati is referred to as the "market" for Appalachian hardwood lumber, and a market, in the same special sense, for southern hardwood is provided at Memphis, for southern pine at Atlanta, for central hardwood at Chicago, for Douglas-fir at New York City, and so on.

Where the concentrating firm is market oriented, either in the sense of Chapter 11 or in the immediately foregoing special sense, a good many firms are apt to be found together in one locality. The firms may even experience a mutual attraction, clustering closely around one another to gain certain advantages, such as being handy to customers who come shopping in the industry. Where concentrators are thus clustered, their timber sheds for any one sort of commodity tend to coincide. Indeed, the various sheds may be indistinguishable, for so long as a single delivered price prevails for each class of the commodity concentrated and so long as the commodity is accurately sorted and described as need be, it cannot matter to any concentrator from what parts of the shed he draws his supplies. The concentration efforts of the group might just as well be pooled so as to create in fact one timber shed. In practice, there is almost always a certain amount of product differentiation by local sellers, so that the various buyers are led to prefer this source or that. Nevertheless, the case here described is well illustrated by Figure 40. Of course, where the commodity being concentrated is not roundwood but a manufactured article such as lumber, the map of immediate sources may show more local variation and clustering than does graph *d*.

Now let us skip ahead for just a moment, so as to catch an advance glimpse of the case—in its simplest form, a hypothetical case—that is the opposite of the one just described in respect to price structure and certain other features. This is the case where concentrators are scattered, their sheds overlap but do not coincide, and there is *local pricing:* Uniform local prices prevail, so that every shipment of material from a different point of origin may be delivered at a different price. Keeping this case in the back of our minds, let us carry our reasoning along to it by easy steps. On the way, we shall consider the intermediate example of timber sheds that are entirely separate, with delivered pricing. To begin with, following the method of partial analysis, let us reach back and reinstate our earlier assumptions regarding the uniformity of the region, abandoning for the moment only the assumption that demands for wood by "other" users are everywhere the same.

## SEPARATED TIMBER SHEDS

We have given a little thought to the circumstances that may cause a clustering of concentrators. Let us next recognize that contrary circumstances may exist, under which concentrating firms are mutually repulsive and seek to get as far away from one another as possible, thus forming a more or less evenly scattered pattern over a region. In the forest economy, mutual repulsion is a rather general rule among firms in the material-oriented primary-processing industries. Pulp mills, for instance, tend to be mutually repulsive. The firm looking for a new mill site is inclined to search in places where other mills aren't: where there is untapped wood and power and good water and other essentials. Established mills have a way of spoiling the environment for others. Water pollution and timber depletion are obvious examples, but in general the spoiling takes the form of raising costs, and we shall soon see how this works in the case of pulpwood. Most primary wood concentrators share the tendency to raise their neighbors' costs.

To be sure, there are exceptions to the rule of mutual repulsion among material-oriented primary-processing plants. Local surpluses of timber may draw such plants close together, as they did, for example, in southwest Oregon after World War II and in all the other great centers of lumbering in years gone by. Similarly, large supplies of other raw materials and of labor may act as magnets. The more the concentrators are drawn together, the greater is the tendency for their timber sheds to merge into a single structure like the one that we have analyzed. But now let us take the clearly contrasting case where there is mutual repulsion unimpeded by any great clustering of productive agents.

Simplifying the problem by taking a commodity that is fairly uniform, let us again have pulp mills and their pulpwood sheds in the back of our minds. The main points are illustrated in Figure 41.

If the territory is uniform and the same delivered prices prevail at all concentration points, then timber sheds will be bounded by straight lines (map *a* of Fig. 41). These lines are the locus of points equidistant between pairs of concentrators, the locus of break-even points, where it is just as profitable for the shipper to consign his wood to the one concentrator as to the other. On either side of the line, shipment in one direction becomes clearly the better alternative, for one direction is the cheaper, and the higher local price may be gained by shipping that way. These straight timber-shed boundaries are the perpendicular bisectors of the lines connecting the concentration points.

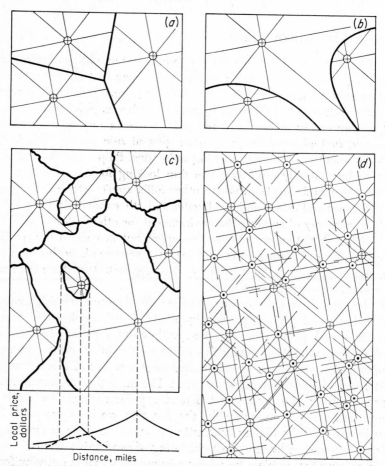

Fig. 41. Timber sheds of roundwood concentrators: (a) Where territory is uniform and delivered prices at all concentration points are the same. (b) Where territory is uniform but delivered prices differ among concentration points. (c) Where territory is not uniform and delivered prices differ, but there is no transfer-cost absorption. (d) Where there is transfer-cost absorption.

However, the case where delivered prices are uniform among sheds is a very special case. Usually some concentrators will have to pay higher delivered prices than others, because the supply of wood available to them is lower or because their demand is greater as a result of economies along lines other than wood supply. By paying a higher delivered price, they can get the extra wood they want by reaching deeper into nearby resources and by reaching further out.

[You should interpret the intensive margin encountered by the concentrator in terms of our supply analysis of Chapters 13 and 14. How can he get more wood by raising the price? What steps can he take in adjusting the quantity structure of his shed to resolve the conflict between his immediate wood requirements and those of the further future: the problem of time rivalry?]

Where does the timber-shed boundary lie between two concentrators with different delivered prices? Again the boundary is the locus of break-even points, of points where the concentrators' local prices are the same. If the territory were uniformly served by transfer routes and the transfer-cost gradients were straight lines, the boundary at a point between the two concentrators would be pushed over away from the one with the higher price, at a distance proportional to the price. From there, the boundary would bend back away from the high-price concentrator on each side, forming a hyperbola with the two concentration points as its foci. With curved transfer-cost gradients, the high-price concentrator is given even more elbow room. The shed boundary is pushed farther from him and bent back more sharply away from him (map *b* of Fig. 41). We shall see in a moment that it is possible for the boundary to be bent right around behind the low-price rival.

Now as we abandon our unrealistic assumptions concerning the uniformity of the territory, we begin to see the timber-shed boundaries as irregular lines (map *c* of Fig. 41). Their location is influenced not only by delivered prices and transportation rates, but also by the routes of transportation and by patchiness in the wood supply. The timber shed of the very low-price, small-scale concentrator near the center of map *c* is an *enclave* within the biggest shed. How such an enclave can exist is illustrated in the accompanying local-price profile. Give this a little thought. Do you see that there could be no enclave if the price gradients were not concave from above—that is, if the transfer-cost gradients were not convex? The big concentrator is able to enclose the little one because the big concentrator's marginal transfer costs are lower. He has a transportation advantage because he is located farther away!

[Considering that small concentrators can locate almost anywhere and get a supply of wood relatively cheaply, why do most pulping firms build such big plants that require stretching away out for wood? Indeed, why should any firm put itself in the position of having to maintain a large and costly timber shed? Many firms, as we know, do not. Why isn't their approach a sensible one for everybody?]

The firm that is contemplating more and more plant expansion to get scale economies in manufacturing finds that the acquisition and management of nearby blocked timber lands is a correspondingly brighter and brighter alternative to reaching for ever costlier open-market wood. For this among many reasons, the big wood user with long-term investments tends to make a conservative forest owner.

## OVERLAPPING OF SHEDS AND ITS CAUSES

It is seldom that one finds such sharp dividing lines between timber sheds, such strong elements of monopsony, as represented in Figure 41a, b, and c. Almost always, adjacent sheds overlap to some extent. That is to say, someone, either the carrier or the concentrator, discriminates between shippers at different transfer points by absorbing the transfer cost between the points. (Note that we use the term "absorbing" loosely, for part or all of the "absorbed" cost may be passed on to other parties to the transaction, after the principle of incidence.) The case where the carrier absorbs the cost we may call *transfer-rate discrimination*. The case where the concentrator absorbs the transfer cost, which he does by manipulating the local prices, we may term *geographic price discrimination*. Let us look into some instances of discrimination and the overlapping of timber sheds. Let us think of timber sheds in which identical products are concentrated.

An instance of transfer-rate discrimination is the zoning of rates. We saw in Chapter 11 (p. 166) that carriers commonly form their tariff schedules into steps rather than continuous gradients. With stepped rates, two sheds may not be separated by a line but may overlap along a broad zone within which it is a matter of indifference to sellers which way the wood is shipped.

Geographic price discrimination and overlapping timber sheds may result simply from change. Timber sheds are not static things any more than the lives of the concentrating firms themselves are static. As the firms expand or curtail their operations, shift their policies, establish new procurement contacts and relinquish old ones, and as supply and transportation conditions alter, sheds move and flow, their margins probing out here and drawing back there like restless amoebas. Firms that foresee expansion, or perhaps wish to forestall expansionist moves on the part of neighbors, will open new territory on the outskirts of their sheds, offering competitive local prices there and absorbing the extra freight. The concentrator must be prepared not only to advance with the trend but to meet the wood requirements of his seasonal and cyclical peaks. If he is to get the extra wood when he needs it, he must usually maintain continuous contact with the necessary suppliers. He cannot hope to do business with marginal suppliers simply on the basis of calling for their help when he needs them the most. Furthermore, the interior of the timber shed is subject to timber depletion, which may call for expansion at the fringe. In general, the tendency of every timber shed in the industrial period and aftermath is to grow bigger. Now if all adjustments to change were instantaneous, a sharp dividing line might still be maintained between adjacent sheds. But contractions come, by and large, more slowly than expansions, and so continuous overlap is normal in the process of change.

Another factor that we must recognize as contributing to price discrimination and timber-shed overlap is product differentiation. Although the timber specifications of all concentrators may be identical, the concentrators and suppliers themselves are not all the same. Some are easier to do business with than others. Some offer more attractive services. Certain concentrator-supplier pairs find that they can work especially well together. Such human relationships are no respecters of geographic lines. Concentrator A is happy to incur a little extra freight cost in order to gain the advantage of working with supplier C, even though the latter, strictly speaking, is located in concentrator B's territory. Perhaps both A and B use C as a supplier. In the absence of exclusive contracts, overlap is inevitable.

## PRICE DISCRIMINATION AGAINST INELASTIC SUPPLIES

Finally, let us take into account what is perhaps the most significant cause of all, leading to timber-shed overlap. This is the tendency of concentrating firms to practice geographic price discrimination in favor of suppliers whose supply is relatively elastic, and against those whose supply is inelastic.

Consider two local-price zones, C and D, within a timber shed (Fig. 42). Total wood supply in each zone is represented by the curves SS. At the uniform delivered price $p_o$, the total quantity of wood delivered from the two zones taken together is $q_c$ plus $q_d$, and the concentrator's total outlay for the wood is the aggregate area of a horizontal pair of the solid-line rectangles that corner on SS and the origin.

Suppose that delivered-price elasticity of supply is everywhere the same (section $a$ of Fig. 42). Let the concentrator lower the price a little in zone C, to $p_c$, so that the quantity of wood he gets from this zone falls to $q'_c$. And in zone D let him raise the price to $p_d$: just enough to keep his total receipts of wood ($q'_c + q'_d$) the same as before. His outlay for wood from zone C decreases, but his outlay for zone-D wood increases by no less an amount. He gains nothing from price discrimination. [Can you develop a general proof of this proposition?]

However, if delivered-price elasticity of supply is greater in one zone than the other, then geographic price discrimination will pay. If elasticity

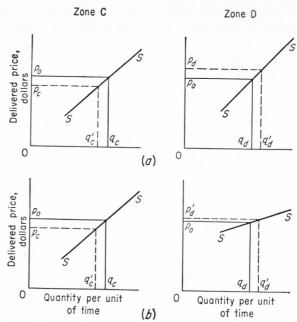

Fig. 42. Effects of geographic price discrimination between two zones of a timber shed: (a) Where supply elasticities are the same. (b) Where elasticities differ.

is greater in zone D (Fig. 42b), the concentrator can improve his position by discriminating in favor of this zone and against zone C. For a smaller total outlay than before, he can get the same amount of wood.

Now the delivered-price elasticity of supply commonly does tend to vary with distance from the concentration point. It tends to increase with distance, and thus to encourage price discrimination in favor of distant suppliers. One cause of increasing elasticity is increasing transfer cost. Turn again to Figure 40b (p. 356) and observe that delivered-price elasticities (of the broken supply curves) become greater with distance, even though local-price elasticities (of the solid curves) do not. A second cause of increasing elasticity is increasing competition from other concentrators. Competition is keen around the periphery of the shed; suppliers have relatively good alternatives, and so the elasticity of their supply is high. In the interior of the shed, close under the battlements of the concentrating firm, the opposite situation holds. The extent of competition in small timber sheds, which are composed more largely of peripheral areas, may be noticeably greater than in larger sheds.[1]

Thus, in general, supply conditions within a timber shed tend to favor

[1] Duerr, William A.: *The Economic Problems of Forestry in the Appalachian Region*, Harvard University Press, Cambridge, Mass., 1949, pp. 218–220. Most of Chapter VII of this book, pp. 203–230, concerns our present topic of market geography.

discrimination under which *local* prices are bent in the direction of equality over the shed, procurement activities are shifted toward the periphery, and heavy overlapping occurs. The outward shift of procurement may be furthered by the concentrator's desire to hold his protected, nearby sources for use in special emergencies and hard times.

## CLOSELY INTERMINGLED TIMBER SHEDS

Let us take into account all the foregoing influences toward overlapping of sheds for identical products, and add to them one more consideration. This is that in typical open-market country, the commodities being concentrated are not identical. Even concentrators of one type, such as pulp mills, are not all seeking just the same kind of wood. And then in the same region other types of timber concentration are going on, such as by sawmills, veneer plants, and perhaps mines and so on. Each concentrator is trying to accumulate wood that is partly the same and partly a little different from that in which his rivals are interested. And some of the firms may be moving their plants from place to place, and moving their timber sheds, in an effort to get the raw material they want.

It is clear, then, that with high rivalry for wood among a large number of well-distributed concentrators having varied requirements, where sellers also are numerous and their holdings rather evenly scattered, an intermingling of timber sheds is promoted. In such a region one may expect to find geographic price discrimination, and crosshauling, to the extent that a structure of delivered pricing may give way almost entirely to one of local pricing.[2] The map of a region so structured is sketched in Figure 41d (p. 362), where the crosses within circles represent one type of concentrator and the dots another. This map displays the geographic aspect of a somewhat perfect market, in which there is a high degree of atomization and a single local price tends to prevail for each commodity at any time.

[In timber sheds where there is local pricing, what do you suppose the quantity structure will look like? What will determine it?

[What do you judge are the effects upon land use and upon forest conservation, in timber sheds of the different types that we have talked about? What sort of price and quantity structure is most favorable to intensive forest management? In going at this question, assume that forest lands within the shed are variously owned—some by the concentrator, some by the public, others by private firms of different kinds, including farmers and nonfarm small holders.]

[2] Compare James, Lee M.: *Marketing Pulpwood in Michigan*, Michigan Agricultural Experiment Station Special Bulletin 411, East Lansing, 1957, especially pp. 54–57.

## SALES AREAS AND THEIR PRICE STRUCTURE

In turning, now, from the geography of forest-product concentration to the geography of dispersion, we find that the fundamentals are much the same—that the principal sorting and sifting of commodities is done by the cost of transportation, modified by geographic clustering of resources and people and by the state of competition. The counterpart of the timber shed on the side of dispersion is the *sales area*.

Concerned as they are with commodities of relatively high specific value, sales areas may be very large. In many cases they are international, or potentially so. As a consequence, two influences enter, about which we have had little to say in connection with timber sheds. One is long-distance water transportation, with its very flat cost gradient. Forest products coming from abroad may often be delivered about as cheaply to either coast of the United States. The other influence is public regulation of international trade, as through tariffs, quotas, subsidies, and the like. We shall touch upon these influences again in Chapter 29, when we consider world commerce.

Where the source of a dispersed commodity, notably an undifferentiated commodity, is strongly localized, prices tend to be uniform at the source (uniform f.o.b. the dispersion point) and to grade upward at delivery points according to their distance. Such a structure of uniform *f.o.b. prices* in a sales area is termed *f.o.b. pricing*. It is analogous to delivered pricing, with downward-grading local prices, in the isolated timber shed. Before World War II, when European mills were the dominant source of market wood pulp in the United States, delivered pulp prices were generally the same along both coasts and were higher inland, by the amount of the extra transportation cost.

A variant of f.o.b. pricing is *basing-point pricing* or *base-zone pricing*. Delivered prices grade upward, according to freight cost, from the basing point or zone, which is the place where the bulk of the dispersing firms are located and upon which the forces of supply and demand are therefore focused. For example, a system somewhat of this sort has been used in the newsprint paper industry. Under the leadership of the National Recovery Administration in the 1930s and the Office of Price Administration in World War II, the United States was marked off into zones, which were essentially freight-rate zones, each with an established, uniform delivered-price differential above the base price. The base zone, in effect, was New England and upstate New York, the source of most domestic newsprint. But the zoning also took account of the Pacific Northwest as a local source of newsprint. Ocean and Great Lakes ports were placed in a special price zone in recognition of their accessibility by water. Price-zoning systems are rather commonly followed in the dispersion operations of the paper industry.[3]

A system of f.o.b. pricing or of basing-point or base-zone pricing may create locational advantages for dispersing firms that are far from the dispersion center or base, and attract new firms to such distant areas. For delivered prices there are high, and if the firm can concentrate the necessary raw materials and other productive agents locally and its costs of production do not countervail, it will find itself in a profitable position to serve the local market. On the other hand, the firm would be disadvantaged in extending its sales area very far toward the base, for there it would encounter lower delivered prices and higher transfer costs, and consequently much lower f.o.b. prices. Thus the South and West are good locations for newsprint manufacture so long as the regions remain net importers of this commodity, but if firms must reach far for their outlets, they run into steeply rising disadvantages.[4]

If resource geography permits dispersing firms to move into the hinterlands of established sales areas and thus to overlap one another, the same thing tends to happen to price structure as in the case of intermeshed timber sheds: The structure shifts in the direction of uniform prices throughout the area. For the sales area, this means delivered pricing, which is thus analogous to local pricing in the case of the timber shed. All the factors relevant to the overlapping of timber sheds are relevant also to sales areas. One of them, product differentiation, is much more influential. Highly differentiated commodities, such as certain branded paper products, are often sold at uniform delivered prices throughout the United States.

## SALES AREAS FOR GRADES OF A COMMODITY

One aspect of market geography that is of particular interest in the study of sales areas is the question of how goods move that are different in respect to quality, or grade, or specific value generally. We have run into this question before, in connection with the principle of relative transportability. We should be in position now to reduce it to its simplest terms.

If you will talk with any lumber producer whose business is big enough to warrant his grading and channeling his output, you will prob-

[3] For maps of paper-price zones, see Guthrie, John A.: *The Economics of Pulp and Paper*, State College of Washington Press, Pullman, 1950, pp. 100–109.

[4] Brandes, Hans-Günther: "An Investigation of the Canada-United States Trade in Newsprint," doctoral dissertation, State University of New York, College of Forestry, Syracuse, 1955, pp. 195–196.

ably find that the sales areas for his various qualities of lumber are greatly different. The hardwood lumberman, for example, may dispose of most of his No. 3 common in the general vicinity of his mill. His best common lumber he may ship to buyers at considerable distances. His firsts and seconds and selects may go virtually anywhere in the world and are more apt to find advantageous markets far away than close by.

We have said that the geographical sorting of grades is carried out on the basis of their specific values: that the higher the specific value, the greater the transportation charge a commodity can bear. A product is shipped far because it has high value. Thinking a little further about the problem in terms of supply and demand, we can add that low-quality stuff—say, the lowest common grade of hardwood lumber—is comparatively ubiquitous, since it can be made from almost any sort of hardwood timber. That is to say, the supply of it is generally great and is also elastic. But demand, and therefore price, is low because the commodity is of limited usefulness. The opposite holds for the top grades. Anyone who wants very much high-grade lumber will probably have to reach out a long way to get it, and he will be willing to do so because his demand for transportation is inelastic, since transportation will represent in any case but a small part of his outlay. This explanation covers much of what we observe in the market areas for commodities of different quality.

But the explanation leaves some important gaps. Why, for instance, should a sawmilling firm ship its upper grades mainly to distant markets? Why not ship at least a good part of them to nearby markets and thus save on transportation? After all, this is what it does with its lower grades. Why penalize the higher grades? Let us try to state the principle of relative transportability in such a way that it will answer this question as well as the others about the geographical sorting of specific values.

### RELATIVE TRANSPORTABILITY REEXAMINED

Take a hypothetical example of hardwood timber that will saw out two grades of lumber. Grade I lumber will yield, per thousand board feet, a certain number of clear cuttings of specified length and width. Grade II will yield *half as many such cuttings per thousand feet*. The lumber is used by manufacturers, whose interest is in the clear cuttings: they buy the lumber for the cuttings. This example, though highly simplified, is entirely true to life. What distinguishes two grades of anything is that one contains more units than the other, of whatever it is that users want, be it measurable cuttings or imponderable satisfaction.

Let us suppose that the firm which produces and disperses this hardwood lumber sells all shipments of each grade at a uniform price f.o.b.

mill. The delivered price is this price plus the cost of transportation. Transportation rates are the same for both grades *per thousand board feet*. The f.o.b. price *per thousand board feet* is higher for grade I lumber than for grade II. Indeed, it is more than twice as high, so that the price *per cutting* is also higher for grade I than for grade II (Fig. 43). However, the transportation cost *per cutting* is higher for grade II lumber than for grade I, so that the delivered-price gradient for the former is steeper. As a consequence, moving out from the mill at O in Figure 43, one finds a break-even point, A, at which the delivered prices per cutting of grades I and II are equal. Between O and A, grade II is the cheaper and has the

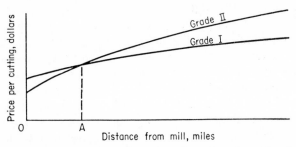

Fig. 43. Delivered-price gradients for two hypothetical grades of hardwood lumber in the sales area of a sawmilling firm.

advantage in use. But beyond A, grade I is the cheaper and has the advantage. Point A marks the boundary between the sales areas of the two grades. The seller ships grade I a long distance, not simply because it can bear the expense, but because it is the better buy for distant users, whereas grade II is better for those near at hand!

Turning this proposition around, we can express it in terms of manufacturers' orientation and thus relate it clearly to the ideas of Chapter 11. The remanufacture of grade II lumber is, compared to grade I, a strongly weight-losing process. Relatively speaking, users of grade II therefore are material oriented, while users of grade I are market oriented.

We also have now the basis for a comparatively simple statement of the *principle of relative transportability:* The lower a commodity's transportation rate per unit of value, the farther the commodity can be shipped.

But turning back to Figure 43, there is a fundamental point that perhaps needs more thought: Why is the f.o.b. price of grade II lumber lower, per cutting, than that of grade I? That is, why is grade I more than twice as expensive, per thousand board feet, as grade II? The answer is that (taking the supply and demand for transportation, the slopes of the gradients in Figure 43, as given) these are the relative grade prices required to clear the market of these joint products. If the relative price of grade II were any higher, its smaller sales area could not absorb the output at the higher price, and producers would benefit by cutting prices so as to push back both the extensive and the intensive margin of use. If the relative price were any lower, users within the enlarged sales area would bid the price up, so that all of them would use less of the lumber and users on the periphery would drop out altogether, allowing the sales area to contract.

We see, then, that, in the determination of relative grade prices, both an intensive and an extensive margin are involved, the former being the marginal quantity demanded by the user, the latter being represented by the marginal user at the edge of the sales area. Of course, this determination may be made in many sales areas simultaneously if there is a great deal of overlapping among them. In the ultimate case of overlapping, competitive conditions may produce a structure of uniform delivered prices. [Can you redraft Figure 43 to show the sales areas in the case where delivered pricing obtains?

[If you will take a sheet of paper and do some sketching of delivered-price gradients like those in Figure 43, you will observe that an increase in transportation cost (a steepening of both gradients by the same percentage) shrinks the sales area for grade II. Now you can see why lumbermen are so sensitive to freight-rate boosts, which hit them where it hurts the most: the market for the hard-to-move, critical lower grades. What do you suppose has been the relation between market geography and the rising trend in real prices that we observed in Figure 38, page 318?]

## INTERRELATION OF TIMBER SHEDS AND SALES AREAS

All the way through this study of market geography, concentration and dispersion have been kept apart as though they were two entirely separate processes. Keeping the two apart has been a helpful simplifying device, appropriate to partial analysis. But let us recognize now, by way of closing on a quite realistic note, that when marketing is viewed as a whole, concentration and dispersion are seen to merge considerably. The process in which lumber is shipped by manufacturers to wholesalers is at the same time dispersion, when viewed from one mill having numerous outlets, and concentration, when viewed from one wholesale yard where lumber is flowing in from many points of origin. The geography of the lumber market, which to the manufacturer seems like a sales-area question, to the wholesaler appears also in terms of a timber shed. Thus the ultimate analysis of market geography must be made not only in reference to interrelationships among areas and among sheds but also in consideration of the interplay between sales areas on the one hand and timber sheds on the other.

In Chapter 29 we shall have a look at the outcome of all the geographic interrelationships of the market: the actual flow of forest products within the United States and in international trade. Here, where our emphasis is upon the governing principles, let us merely summarize the analytical tools that we now have at hand for understanding what takes place. Among them are the principles of supply and demand, of the convexity of transfer-cost gradients (diminishing marginal transfer cost), of the orientation of manufacturing, and of relative transportability. We have practiced the use of all these analytical devices.

One further principle, which comes close to containing the others, is the *principle of comparative advantage.* According to this principle, each commodity is produced in the areas where its production is relatively profitable as compared with other commodities, and is shipped to areas where its production is relatively unprofitable as compared with other commodities. Notice that each line of production is located, not where it is absolutely most profitable, but where its relative position among alternatives is advantageous. The great value of the principle is that it takes the final step of putting the forest economy in the context of the whole.

Thus we see genetic production in the forest economy taking place where forests have comparative advantage under the principles of land use, each line of activity competing with others for space and for the use of cooperating productive agents. On the other side of the general economy, but not necessarily far removed in space, we see centers and scatterings of population in those places to which people are drawn by the sum total of opportunities for resource use and for the enjoyment of life. In between the two, both economically and geographically, and thus widely spread and clustered in complex patterns, we see the economic devices for bringing commodities and consumers together. Here we see primary wood processors attracted to the places where timber is abundant and still handy to transportation routes and to the necessary labor, power, water, sources of knowledge, and other agents. There we see wholesalers drawn to the strategic low-cost intermediate locations, and thus diverting through these locations the principal streams of commodities.

Concentrating our attention on the forest products, we see everywhere change and movement—often restricted movement, and very often movement by indirect routes—as the commodities are manufactured and remanufactured, sorted and resorted, brought together in sufficient quantity to be handled best, and then scattered again on their way to users. Looking beyond the forest economy, we see how its workings are controlled by the whole social effort to devote each place to those lines of production in which the greatest real values can be created, considering both the limited supplies of resources and the varied demands for commodities, communicated back to the production sites along the routes of transportation. Frequently we see the making and handling of forest products nudged aside by occupations of higher priority and bundled off to other spots where they can be carried out unmolested. We observe that the whole working of the system is greatly modified by political and other institutional barriers to freedom of movement, not only of goods, but also of people and other resources. And we observe that the whole structure is constantly changing as resources are attracted to less dismal necessities or to new or brighter opportunities.

## SUMMARY

Primary characteristics of a timber shed are quantity structure, price structure, and relation to other sheds. How these characteristics may vary is illustrated by the following timber-shed situations: first, the isolated timber shed of the single concentrator, with delivered pricing and with quantity per acre variable but generally diminishing toward the boundaries; second, the similar, merged shed of clustered concentrators; third, contiguous but separate sheds, with boundaries determined by delivered-price levels, transportation costs and routes, and location of supplies; fourth, overlapping timber sheds with price structure modified in the direction of local pricing, the overlapping caused by transfer-rate zoning, dynamics of the economy, product differentiation, or variations in supply elasticity; and, fifth, closely intermingled timber sheds with local pricing.

Characteristics of dispersing firms' sales areas follow analogous lines. Sales areas for grades of a commodity are in their simplest form concentric and exclusive, with the highest grades shipped to the furthest zones. In general, they follow the principle of relative transportability: the lower a commodity's transportation rate per unit of value, the farther the commodity can be shipped. Grade prices are determined in the process of geographic sorting.

The interrelation of timber sheds and sales areas may be analyzed in terms of comparative advantage: Each place produces the goods and services that it can produce most profitably and imports those in which other places have the advantage.

# Chapter 23

# APPRAISAL
# IN FORESTRY

APPRAISAL means estimating the value of something: stating its worth. Other terms that convey the same idea are valuation and assessment. The purpose of this chapter is to explain the aims and the methods of appraising forests and forest products, holding largely to fundamentals and mainly avoiding the details of procedure. The latter you can get by studying the appropriate manuals and books of instruction. Here let us see what lies back of the instructions.

The kind of *value* with which appraisal is concerned is, for the most part, value in exchange or some approximation or substitute thereof. Most commonly it is market value. If there is no market at hand though objects of the sort being valued are marketable, then value may be figured in a hypothetical market. But in cases where there is no market at all for commodities of the kind being appraised, another standard is substituted, such as the goods or services sacrificed by the firm in order to gain the commodity—that is, the commodity's opportunity cost.

This chapter is divided into two parts: The first part takes up the appraisal of things that are generally marketable in the United States. The second goes into the evaluation of things that generally aren't marketable here.

## APPRAISING MARKETABLE THINGS

Sometimes we hear it said that market value is "determined" by appraisal, as though the appraiser fixed the market. It may happen, of course, either by chance or by design, that if an appraised commodity is actually marketed, its sales value turns out to be the same as the appraisal. But in general, appraisers don't determine market value. Only the market can do this. All an appraiser can do is estimate, or approximate, or forecast market value. Of course many objects that are appraised are not put on the market at all, so that there is no test of these particular appraisals. Indeed, it is primarily because the thing appraised is not being bought and sold all the time that an appraisal of market value is necessary. If you want to know the market value of a certain corporate stock that is active on the exchange, you need not call in an appraiser.

The legal concept of market value in relation to appraisal is notoriously vague. This vagueness possibly stems from the effort to simplify the concept by treating it as a single idea. We know from our own studies that markets vary and that the unifying principle to be found in them is the interaction of supply and demand, not the invariable nature of the resulting value. Legal concepts are important in appraisal because appraisals are so often prescribed by law or reviewed by the courts. We shall be giving a little attention to the law of appraisals, though only by implication, when we sketch appraisal methods. To dwell on legal aspects would take us far beyond our scope. Let us just recognize at this point some legal terms that pop up so often in talk and writing about market value that we cannot ignore them.[1]

The appraiser of market value is commonly instructed to find the "full and true" value. It is hard to believe that there is any significant difference between full and true value and just plain value, though perhaps the phrase serves as a useful extra warning to persons such as tax assessors not to lop their estimates in half when they aren't supposed to. An appraiser is often told to estimate the "fair" value of something. Presumably this means that he is to couch his appraisal in terms of a competitive market. But what if the market isn't competitive? If you appraise the pulpwood in an isolated timber shed at the going market price, will the court send you back to figure out what the price would be if there were other buyers competing with the mill? Possibly not. In another phrase, one that carries related overtones, appraisers may be instructed to find the value that would be determined "as between a willing buyer and a willing seller." The phrase clearly implies that the appraiser is to assume that neither buyer nor seller is in distress to close the transaction. But what else are we to make of it? How willing is willing? We might answer in terms of supply and demand elasticities, but the court does not. Would there be other buyers and sellers in the market besides these

---

[1] Brief explanations of some of the legal aspects of appraisal are to be found in the articles on valuation, assessment of taxes, and related subjects in the *Encyclopaedia of the Social Sciences*.

two willing souls? If there weren't, who knows what the outcome of their bargaining would be. And even if there were, who knows. A hypothetical market has to be pretty rigidly defined if one is to estimate the price that would be found in it.

Now at least we have said enough to make it clear that the ideas lying back of market-value appraisal are not all cut, dried, and polished. And so far as procedures are concerned, there are a great many more questions than there are answers.

## PURPOSES OF APPRAISAL

Market value may be appraised for any of a number of purposes. Some of the principal purposes are as follows:

1. To guide a firm's selling or buying. Public timber is usually appraised before it is put on sale, and private sellers sometimes follow the same practice. The wood-using concern that is acquiring forest property commonly has it appraised before making an offer. The appraisal introduces greater knowledge into the market (compare Chap. 20, especially pp. 331–332).

2. To guide a firm in making other sorts of choice among alternatives. The firm contemplating an investment in forest planting must appraise the probable values to be derived. A firm selecting trees for harvest may estimate their value now and in the future so as to judge the best time for cutting (Chap. 16). Appraisal for such purposes is sometimes called *comparative valuation.*[2]

3. To establish the value of property or output for taxation. Appraisal for this purpose is termed *assessment.* We shall have more to say about it in Chapter 26.

4. To establish the value of collateral on which a loan is to be made. The collateral may vary from a forest property to a lumber retailer's plant and inventory. The subject of forest credit is taken up in Chapter 28.

5. To estimate damages. For example, privately owned hardwood bottomland that is to be condemned for flooding above a public dam may be appraised as a basis for compensation. Such appraisal guides the two parties toward a settlement, or the court toward a decision. A wood-processing plant is appraised for insurance or to settle a claim against an insurer (Chap. 28). Timber damage from trespass may be appraised to find the amount of someone's liability. Damage from fire or storm is estimated if the loss is an allowable deduction from taxable income (Chap. 27).

[2] Thomson, Roy B.: *An Examination of Basic Principles of Comparative Forest Valuation,* Duke University School of Forestry Bulletin 6, Durham, N.C., 1942.

6. Finally, it is best not to neglect one purpose of appraisals which, though minor, has an annoying way of bobbing up and presenting a challenge to some innocent forester when he least expects it. This is the purpose of demonstrating the "importance" of some industry or product —presumably to advertise it so as to win confidence or support for it. Thus the Mud County Chamber of Commerce may come out with the finding that forestry in the county is a million-dollar business.

Now as we check down through the foregoing purposes of appraisal, it is surely evident that though they all may call for estimates of market value, the concept of market value is not always the same. It follows that there are various approaches to appraising market value. Let us talk about four of them:

1. Direct approach
2. Three indirect approaches
   *a.* Capitalization approach
   *b.* Cost approach
   *c.* Conversion approach

## DIRECT APPROACH

The *direct approach* to appraising the market value of a thing consists of identifying the market where like things are bought and sold, and then studying the prices in this market with the object of estimating what price the thing being appraised would bring if it were put on the market, either as a whole or piecemeal. If you want to appraise some pulpwood, find out what pulpwood is selling for. If you want to appraise some forest land, find out what land of this sort is selling for in this locality. If you want to appraise the market value of New York's 2¼-million-acre State Forest Preserve—a feat that is in fact attempted for property taxation—forget the problem that there is actually no going market for such a big chunk of land and assume that the Preserve has the same value *per acre*, land category by land category, as do the smaller parcels of private property that are bought and sold.

The direct approach to market-value appraisal is used, on occasion, for every one of the six purposes outlined. It is of course very commonly used by firms as a guide to their selling and buying. It is also the standard approach to assessment for taxation. Let us talk about the assessment of forest land and timber by way of illustrating how the direct method works.

We shall learn in Chapter 26 that the job done by the tax assessor in setting a value upon forest property may vary a great deal from case to case, in method as well as in thoroughness and accuracy. Typically, however, all assessments follow the direct approach. Let us take a look at very superficial assessment and then at very thorough assessment. In so doing, we can see the range of possibilities of the direct approach.

The assessor setting out to do a superficial job goes armed with the general observations that have come to him over the years concerning the market for forest land and timber in his district. To the most barren and unpromising parcels in his district he assigns a value of, say, $1 per acre, mainly on the theory that if they have any value at all, they must have at least that much. At the other end of the scale, he appraises his best forest parcels at, say, $100 per acre, feeling that this is about the most that any human being would ascribe to another's mere greenery. If the property is a big one, the product of assessment per acre times the number of acres seems appallingly large, and he cuts it down. To the remaining forest parcels he assigns varying intermediate per-acre values according to the way they and their owners strike him.

## MANUAL FOR DIRECT APPRAISAL

At the other extreme, we find our assessor equipped with a manual for appraising forest land and timber.[3] The ideal assessment manual embodies the highest development of the direct approach to market-value appraisal. Dealing, as it does, with a complex case, it contains all the elements essential to any application of the approach. Let us see what such a manual might be.

The ideal manual is made up for a sizable territory and is based upon an ample accumulation of data on sales of forest property in the territory over a period of years. The data for each sale include the identity of buyer and seller; the circumstances, terms, and time of sale; the price; and all the attributes of the property that are relevant to price, such as the property's location, size, blockage, accessibility, and site quality, the characteristics of the timber, the forest assets other than timber, and the improvements. The data are handled—conceptually and in summary— somewhat as follows: They are sifted so as to eliminate the unrepresenta-

---

[3] Several states give pointed attention to forest lands in their assessment manuals, and a few have separate forest manuals. See, for instance, Washington State Tax Commission: *Appraisal Manual for Timber and Timberlands for Use by Washington Assessors,* Olympia, 1952. For an analysis of recent progress in forest assessment by the direct approach, see Williams, Ellis T.: "Tax Assessment of Forest Land and Timber Shows Improvement," *Journal of Forestry,* March, 1956, pp. 172–176. The same author reviews the status of forest assessment in the United States in *State Guides for Assessing Forest Land and Timber,* U.S. Department of Agriculture, Forest Service, Washington, 1956.

tive sales—those involving distress, sales within a family or between affiliated firms, and those where conditions were peculiar in other respects. Then they are subjected to some sort of correlation analysis, with price the dependent variable, so as to determine which of the sale conditions and property attributes are significantly related to price, and what the relationship is in each case.

The results of the statistical analysis are organized into tables, formulas, and rules that permit the estimation of market value for any property whose relevant attributes are known. These tables, formulas, and rules are put into the manual. They may, to use a simple illustration, set forth a standard, or normal, value per acre for some basic forest condition in each of the significant regions of a state and then list adjustment factors to be applied to the norm to allow for differences in assessment date, size and accessibility of tract, and forest site, type, and stocking. Thus the manual makes use of the same elements of value that might be employed by an experienced assessor working with the aid of judgment. The difference is that the manual formalizes and systematizes the judgment and vastly strengthens it by means of the statistical techniques.

Besides a section containing the tables, formulas, and rules, the ideal manual also includes an introductory section explaining how these guides were made and how they are to be used, and supplemental sections defining all the conditions and attributes recognized and instructing the user how to identify them in the field. For example, the manual may include pictures of the various forest conditions, and procedures for estimating timber volume. When assessors are given the manual, they may also be offered training in the use of it.

## INDIRECT APPROACHES

The direct approach to appraising market value is so straightforward and logical that one wonders, perhaps, why any other should be used. No doubt there is a growing trend toward the direct approach accompanying our growing knowledge of the markets in the forest economy and of the accurate description of forest commodities. Stumpage appraisal, long handled by other methods, may be the next large area of valuation to come under the direct approach.[4] And yet, because of our still limited knowledge of markets and products and the immensity of the research needed to build guides such as manuals, the direct approach is not always feasible. And in some cases where it is feasible, it may not be the best. Let us see, then, what the indirect approaches are.

[4] You should refer again, for their relevance to direct appraisal, to such works as that of Sam Guttenberg: *Influence of Timber Characteristics upon Stumpage Prices,* Southern Forest Experiment Station Occasional Paper 146, New Orleans, 1956.

## CAPITALIZATION AND COST APPROACHES

The *capitalization approach* to market-value appraisal, applicable to agents of production, is to estimate the value of an agent by discounting, or capitalizing, the anticipated net values of its products—that is to say, its probable net revenues. The resulting capitalized value is sometimes termed *expectation value.* This is the method explained in Chapter 8, pages 109 to 113, and applied to a problem of forest-land value in Chapter 16, pages 240 to 243. It is generally usable in enterprise planning: in guiding the decisions of a prospective buyer of productive property. It may be useful, too, in appraising loan collateral, for it stresses the very aspect of value in which lenders are most interested: the ability of the firm to amortize the debt. Capitalized value is used in forest property-tax assessment in some countries, but not in the United States.[5] The difficulty and the weakness of the method rest mainly in all the forecasting that must be done to carry it out: the forecasting of revenues and costs, the judgment of risk, and the choice of an interest rate.

A second indirect method of appraising market value is the *cost approach.* Like the first, it is applicable to agents of production, though one may use it also in evaluating products. The approach is common in damage valuation. A young forest plantation condemned for a public right-of-way may be valued at the *historic cost* of the site and the stand. An insurance company may settle for a burned-down sawmill on the basis of historic cost less depreciation and salvage value. In damage cases, value to the firm that has suffered the damage is ordinarily what counts, and so *replacement cost* may be more relevant than historic cost. If a sawmilling firm loses finished lumber in a fire, the relevant cost is not the cost of production, but the cost of replacement, which is the market value of the lumber, and here we come back to the direct approach to appraisal. Where a firm's productive plant (either machinery or growing stock) has been damaged, a part of the replacement cost may consist of losses arising from disruption of the firm's whole program of output and sales. In all these varied damage problems, the guiding *principle of the cost approach* is to appraise the least cost of restoring the firm to the position it held before the damage took place, allowing for any delay in the restoration.

[The relation between the capitalization and cost approaches is illus-

[5] In Oregon and Washington, the market value ("retail value") of mature timber, the cutting of which is to be deferred, in effect is discounted for the deferment period ("depletion period") as a means of estimating current ("wholesale") value for taxation. This procedure amounts to capitalization of income, though only the income from the first harvest. See Rothery, Julian E.: *A Study of Forest Taxation in the Pacific Northwest,* Industrial Forestry Association, Portland, Ore., 1952, especially pp. 15–32.

trated by the case of Firm N. This firm grows Christmas and ornamental trees on contract for a dealer. It incurs establishment costs of $20 per acre and sells the stand at age 10 for an average of $51.90 per acre. A neighbor, burning pasture one windy day, lets the fire get out of hand and burns up several acres of 5-year-old trees in Firm N's plantations. They go to court. Firm N claims damages of $40.70 per acre, the prospective value of the crop discounted for 5 years at what it considers a fair rate of interest—namely, 5 per cent. The neighbor agrees to the 5 per cent interest rate, but argues that the damages are only $25.50 per acre, which is Firm N's initial cost compounded for 5 years. The perplexed judge calls you in as a consultant to the court. What do you advise?]

## CONVERSION APPROACH

A third way of appraising market value indirectly is the *conversion approach.* This approach is applicable to many products and is the simplest of the three in its general outlines. Suppose you wish to appraise pulpwood piled at your local landing. Pulpwood in your locality is sold only delivered to the mill. The price there is $25 per cord. The cost of getting your wood delivered is $5 per cord. You therefore appraise your wood at $25 minus $5, or $20 per cord. The general form of the conversion approach is that the appraised value of a commodity at stage A is equal to its directly estimated sales value at stage B minus the cost of converting it from stage A to stage B.

The conversion approach is widely used to appraise public stumpage that is to be put up for sale. It is used to appraise national forest stumpage, which is generally sold, at no less than the appraised price, to the highest responsible bidder.[6] It may be used also by stumpage buyers to guide their market negotiations. Let us follow the traditional steps, taking saw timber as the illustration.

The starting point in our illustrative appraisal is the sales value of the lumber that the stumpage is expected to yield. This sales value is estimated by the direct approach. From sales value is subtracted the conversion cost: the estimated costs of logging, transportation, milling, and selling, other than those that fall under the heading of the operator's profit allowance. The result of this subtraction is called the *conversion return,* or *conversion value.* Then a profit allowance (an estimated margin for profit, risk, interest on borrowed capital, and income taxes) is subtracted from the conversion return. The final remainder thus determined is the appraised stumpage value.

[6] For the official description of the United States Forest Service timber-appraisal procedure, see the Forest Service *Timber Management Handbook,* chap. 2420.

Starting points in conversion appraisal of stumpage differ from case to case. In general, the starting point is the sales value of whatever the stumpage buyer produces and sells—commonly the first commodity beyond the stumpage stage for which value is clearly defined in the market. Saw-timber appraisal may begin with the sales value of saw logs if there is a well-organized market for logs, and in this event only logging, transportation, and selling costs need be subtracted to get conversion return. Appraisals of pulpwood stumpage ordinarily begin with the sales value of pulpwood. [Why do you suppose they don't begin with the sales value of pulp or of paper?]

Of the many difficulties of the conversion approach to stumpage appraisal (difficulties that we won't go into here), by far the most perplexing is that of estimating the profit allowance—that is, of dividing the conversion return between the seller and the buyer of stumpage. The task is not to "determine," or "fix," the profit, but to allow for it in an amount that is consistent with experience in the industry. This is ordinarily done by reference to past stumpage sales that are comparable to the one at hand—by observing what the profit margin was in those cases: a sort of direct approach.[7]

You should compare the notion of conversion return with that of conversion sulplus, discussed on pages 121 to 123. Note that conversion surplus is essentially a device for comparative valuation, and as such disregards fixed costs, whereas conversion return is a means to an "absolute" valuation and must therefore take all costs into account. Conversion surplus is equal to conversion return plus the fixed costs of conversion. That is, conversion surplus is larger than conversion return by the amount of the fixed costs.

[You should also compare appraised stumpage value with conversion surplus. In what way do they differ? Under what circumstances may the two be equal?]

## CONVERSION VERSUS COST APPRAISAL

Before we leave indirect appraisal methods, we need to study the relation of the conversion approach to the cost approach as applied to the valuation of a product. In the former, the appraiser reaches out toward the consumer to find a starting point for his estimates. In the latter, he reaches back toward the original producer. Why use one approach in preference to the other?

It is, for instance, sometimes contended that the traditional method of appraising stumpage value as the difference between end-product

[7] Alternative procedures are described and explained in the Forest Service *Timber Management Handbook*.

sales value and the costs and profits of conversion is unfair to the timber owner. It sets his return as a leftover, a scrap end. It makes him low man on the totem pole, whose interests are considered only after everybody else has been nicely taken care of. Actually, it is argued, the timber owner is not last but first in the chain of production, and his interests should be addressed first: Stumpage value should be appraised as the sum of the owner's production costs plus a reasonable allowance for *his* profit and risk. After all, runs the conclusion, if society wants his timber, society should be willing to pay him fairly for it.

One retort that is made to this sort of contention is that the timber owner's past costs are water over the dam: They are fixed with reference to his present alternatives and therefore irrelevant. Perhaps in the long run values tend toward costs of production, but this is as it may be. And anyhow, the costs of producing such a thing as stumpage are virtually impossible to figure.

A more thoughtful answer is as follows: Whether the cost or the conversion approach is more appropriate depends, first, on the purpose of the appraisal. If the purpose is to forecast a price (which is, in effect, the aim in the timber-sale case), then the appraisal must consider the conditions of supply and demand. In the stumpage market—which exists, as we know, in the stock-supply period—the price elasticity of supply is very low, whereas that of demand, which is derived from the demand for the end product, is relatively high. The seller is in position to determine the *quantity* of the sale, but only quantity, for once he has done so, *price* is set by demand. One must therefore go to the demand side of the market, to the price of the end product (the conversion approach) to appraise market value. If, on the other hand, the purpose of the appraisal is not to forecast price but to help fulfill a legal requirement, as in a damage case, that an owner be restored to some specified former condition, then the cost of the restoration becomes the issue, and the cost approach to appraisal becomes the appropriate method.

[To these thoughts, should we add that the cost approach is suited to price forecasting for markets where demand elasticity is very low and supply elasticity relatively high? What would be an example of such a market?]

Our four approaches can be boiled down into a single general *principle of appraising market value:* Begin by estimating directly the market value of the commodity at a stage that is as close as possible to the stage being appraised. Then, if the two stages are not identical, adjust for differences between them in respect to time (by compounding or discounting), place (by adding or subtracting transfer cost), or form (by adding or subtracting other costs of conversion).[8]

[8] The idea for this principle is stolen from Prof. Robert Seale of the University of Idaho.

## APPRAISING UNMARKETABLE THINGS

If your forestry career develops along normal lines, someone sometime is going to ask you what is the "value" of a wild duck on a chilly fall morning, or of a summer woodland scene, or of a gallon of snowmelt stored in the forest in spring. And if your questioner follows the norm for his species, he will grip you by the lapels and fix you with an eager eye, and you had better have an answer ready. The rest of this chapter is written with the purpose of priming you a little on the subject before this creature gets hold of you.

The assignment is hard. And yet what little we shall be able to say about it will not be hard to follow. Indeed, the principles are fairly simple and should not take us long to state, once we get the cluttered ground cleared so that we can lay them down. Then if sometime you need to rush out and set a "value" on duck hunting, at least you will have a general idea of what it is you are doing and what you are not doing.

We are going to be talking about the value of things that generally are not marketable in the United States. In doing so, let us shun the term "intangible" value. The term is meaningless. All value is intangible. If you find someone insisting that there is a logical distinction between things of the spirit and things that can be bought and sold, point out to him that ducks, trees, and water are perfectly tangible and that his highly marketable house provides him in large degree with things of the spirit. The meaningful contrast is the one we are using to divide this chapter: between things that are generally marketable and things that aren't.

Furthermore, we are going to be talking a good deal about money value. This is forced upon us by the fact that money value (or its equivalent, value in terms of other goods or of services) is what our insistent questioner is asking about. Notice particularly that the distinction between value in use (what we called "satisfactions" in Chapter 17) and value in exchange is not at issue here. All resources, whether marketable or not, have value in use, which lies behind the demand for them. But we are equally interested in the demand and the supply sides of value. We want to know about the interaction of supply and demand for goods and services whose supply and demand do not come together in a market. We are concerned with the nonmarket counterpart of exchange value.

Why is it that some things in our economy are not marketed? What sorts of things are they? They must be one of two sorts: First, they may be things such as most forest scenery, which, because they do not lend themselves to capture and control by individual firms or because our institutions disfavor such capture and control, are not owned. Since there is no title to these things, there can be no alienation of them. (We shall return to this point in Chapter 25, especially page 419.) Second, they may be things such as recreational facilities on many forest lands, which are owned but by custom are either given away or alienated for a nominal fee. In the United States forest economy, it is apparent that the things not generally marketable are, notably, goods and services of the forest other than wood and forage and that the value of these things is regarded as primarily of a public nature.

Now what can be the object of seeking the value of such things? And why, particularly, should anyone try to find the money value of something that is not valued in money? Using our earlier list of the purposes of appraisal (pp. 377–378) as a check list, we can at once eliminate many of the items. Appraisal is not needed to guide buying and selling where there is no market. It is not needed for taxation, credit, or insurance where these functions do not apply. As for damages, they can of course be traced where some firm has incurred a cost, but then we are dealing with market value, and there is no new principle. We seem to be left with a pair of purposes that require further study: the promotional purpose (number 6) and the purpose of comparative valuation to guide the firm's choices among alternatives (number 2).

### PROMOTIONAL APPRAISALS

As for promotion pure and simple, a guiding common-sense principle for valuation is to suit the appraisal to the audience. Take, for example, the values in sport fishing. If promotion in this area is being directed to participants and potential participants, one may wish to appeal to them in qualitative terms of the pleasures and other benefits of the sport and the feasibility of its arrangements and requirements for the ordinary man. This is what Izaak Walton did, and he can scarcely be accused of failure. If, on the other hand, the promotion is to be directed to the sporting-goods industry, then surely a commercial appeal is in order, perhaps a summing up of all the time and money that anglers have for spending on their hobby, and a tracing of trends in the outlays for licenses, equipment, travel, and so on.[9] To the social accountant, such a summing may involve fantastic double counting and a disregard for the existence of joint products. The fisherman may buy his boat not just to go fishing but also to take his family picnicking. But from the standpoint of the boat dealer, what matters is the existence of the buyer.

And what also matters, from our standpoint, is that the commercial summing up should not be mistaken for an appraisal of the value of fishing to fishermen, or to the public. One trouble with it as an appraisal,

---

[9] See, for example, *U.S. Anglers—Two Billion Dollars!* Sport Fishing Institute Bulletin 59, Washington, October, 1956.

aside from double counting, is that it is a measure of inputs, not outputs.[10] Other troubles will become apparent as we take up, now, the other and the major purpose of appraising nonmarket values: to help a firm, ordinarily the public, allocate resources.

## COMPARATIVE APPRAISALS

Let us study first, not a public firm, but the simpler case of a private firm, a hypothetical frontier family that is absolutely isolated, self-sufficient, and unspecialized. Among its various uses of resources, the firm cuts firewood for its own heating and cooking. It allocates a certain amount of its labor and facilities in each period to this purpose and to each of its other purposes such as producing food, making and mending clothes, maintaining tools, repairing the house, and enjoying rest and recreation. The firm makes its allocation decisions in the same way as the consuming firm that we studied in Chapter 17. If the firm is rational, it apportions its labor and facilities among its purposes in such a way that the last expenditures of labor upon each purpose promise to return the same satisfaction. To the extent that the firm fails of full rationality, it may fall short of the ideal allocation; but in any case its decisions are those of a sovereign and are final, and these decisions both reflect and determine the value of each of its purposes. Thus the marginal labor content—that is, the value—of a cord of firewood may be thirty hours of labor, and that of a bushel of corn may be ten hours. Or, to use corn as the standard, the value of a cord of firewood is 3 Bushels.

Now let us suppose that as time goes by, the family grows and subdivides. Separate firms are formed—separate households—and these become specialized. Corn is still exchanged for firewood, but no longer merely in the figurative sense that a little extra production of the one involves forgoing a little of the other. Some of the households no longer produce their own firewood. They grow more corn than they need and exchange some of it—literally—for the excess firewood made by others. The value of a cord of firewood is still 3 Bushels—or, let us say, the price of it is $3.

Prices do not stay always the same. In the year of the locusts, firewood falls to $2. When new, rich corn land is opened up, the price of wood rises to $3.50 per cord. The invention of a new woodcutting tool reduces the price to $2.50. Such changes in value are made by society in an effort to do just what the lone family did: rationalize its marginal rates of substitution so as to maximize its net satisfactions. The adjust-

[10] Black, John D.: "Values in Forest Wildlife," in Duerr, William A., and Henry J. Vaux (eds.): *Research in the Economics of Forestry*, Charles Lathrop Pack Forestry Foundation, Washington, 1953, pp. 273–280.

ments, however, are no longer so simple and direct. They are no longer put in effect by a single sovereign individual. The sovereign now is collective, the judgments social. They are carried out partly by trial and error, in a process of seeking the rational goal but never quite reaching it because economic circumstances are changing all the while and judgments are changing.

## COMMON VALUE: PRINCIPLE

At this point in the development of our little society, the collective judgment arises that it might be desirable to try maintaining a community park for meetings and public recreation. People want such a park for its facilities and for the pleasure of being in it and knowing that they have it. And so each household contributes some time, perhaps to a total of 1,000 hours per year from all the households, and a park is kept in running order. A sacrifice is here involved, to the tune of perhaps 100 bushels of corn. But it proves worthwhile in the judgment of the community, and in fact the decision is soon made to increase the outlay for park maintenance to 1,500 hours, or 150 Bushels. This is an inaccurate decision by the standard of rationality, but neither more nor less inaccurate than any of the other judgments by which the society allocates its resources. It is part of a process of trial and error, part of a common evaluation of all its inputs and outputs in which the society is continuously engaged. Society has, for the time being, established for the annual services of its park a *common value* of ₿150.

The park's common value changes, like any other, from time to time. It falls in the year of the locusts. It rises with the general technological advancement of the community. Common value, like the common law, expresses the public judgment of the fitness and appropriateness of institutions. It has, as perhaps the English common law has, the weakness of inflexibility, of looking rather more strongly to the past than to the future. Yet it has the strength of consistency and still is subject to revision by trial and error in accordance with changing resources and wants. One of the devices for regulating the life of the state, it is no better and no worse than the whole public policy system that the state has managed to create.

Now as our little illustrative society grows and elaborates still further, the time comes when other communities, just like the first one, want parks. There arises a widespread, and perhaps unwisely excessive, clamor for parks. Proposals are voiced by some influential groups for spending a great deal of public resources on these parks. And so, in the interest of rationality, the government passes a law authorizing, for park maintenance in each community, outlays up to an amount at which the last costs incurred are no greater than the benefits derived therefrom—just as in the Flood Control Act of 1936, as an example, the United States Congress recognized " . . . that the Federal Government should improve or participate in the improvement of navigable waters or their tributaries, including watersheds thereof, for flood-control purposes if the benefits to whomsoever they may accrue are in excess of the estimated costs. . . . "

To carry out the Park Maintenance Act requires appraisals of costs and benefits. To appraise the costs, which consist of items that have market value, is comparatively easy. But how appraise the benefits? What is the benefit—the value—of a community's use of a park for a year? We cannot find this value in any market. We can, however, find it in the record of social judgments of another sort: in the book of common value, where it is listed at ₿150.

Of course some of the communities may not accept the statutory ₿150 limitation upon their annual park maintenance. They may feel that it is in the public interest to go beyond this limit, and they may express their belief by chipping in, locally, an extra ₿50. Thus they express their judgment that the value of park service for a community of the given size and character is not ₿150 but ₿200 per year, and if their experiment is a success and their judgment becomes vindicated in the eyes of other communities that stand ready to follow their example, then new entries appear in the book of common value. And now, without any amendment of the Park Maintenance Act, the legal limit of government outlays in communities just like the first one is raised from ₿150 to ₿200.

Does the reasoning behind common value seem circular? (Compare Chap. 10, pp. 143 and 145–147.) It entails neither more nor less circularity than market value does. The two concepts, as we have seen, have identical bases. If you like market value, you are going to have to like common value.

## COMMON VALUE: PRACTICE

Now to review the foregoing thoughts unencumbered by the abstractions we have used in developing them, common value is that value which is not set down in terms of dollars in any market but is created, supported, and amended by manifold social decisions respecting resource use. Every time a decision is made respecting the use of public forest land—for water development, for recreation, or for other purposes or combinations of purposes—the social value of these purposes is implied in the decision. When society agrees to retain the whole of the Olympic National Park or the Adirondack Forest Preserve in its present use, the value of this use is implied in the market values thereby forgone. Admittedly these decisions are a weird compounding of political, economic, and other social forces; admittedly they are molded by conflicting pressure groups; but at least they express the public will. The problem is to have facts for judgment, so as to express the public will as clearly as we are capable of.

There is no use saying that the nonmarket values speak for themselves and are only degraded by quantification. We have seen in Chapter 4 (pp. 44–45) how the unmeasured values can be belittled and subordinated to market values in a business-oriented economy such as ours.

The requisites for a meaningful system of common value—one that will be more than just a series of somewhat unrelated decisions on resource use—are that it shall be consistent with those decisions of the past that have worn well and that it shall be sensitive to the changing needs of the future. Both these aims can be furthered by interpreting past decisions and prospective alternatives in terms of economic measures. Let us take as an illustration a land-use problem in California.[11]

## RECREATIONAL VERSUS INDUSTRIAL USE

William Atkinson, in a master's thesis[12] at the University of California, has worked out a "marginal method" of evaluating recreational versus industrial use of forest land, a method first proposed by Dr. Henry Vaux.[13] The method rests on the proposition that where a public forest tract is dedicated *solely* to recreational use, the lower limit of the tract's value in such use is the implied value represented by the opportunity cost of the timber output forgone in the dedication. That is to say, when society decides to use a certain timber property as a park, the decision implies that society places a higher value upon the recreation to be derived than upon the timber that would otherwise have been produced. Then, the reasoning continues, if one can analyze a number of comparable forest tracts, of which some are used for timber and others for recreation, and for each of these tracts calculate the ratio of timber value per unit of recreational use, he may be able to discover the particular ratio that represents the break-even point between timber and recreation. If past decisions were rational, the break-even point becomes a guide to rational use of other, comparable tracts, whether for recreation or for

[11] This illustration of the common-value principle is selected for its simplicity in dealing with single resource uses. For some ideas on value in multipurpose use, see Gregory, G. Robinson: "An Economic Approach to Multiple Use," *Forest Science*, March, 1955, p. 13.

[12] Atkinson, William Allen: "A Method for the Recreational Evaluation of Forest Land," master's thesis, University of California, Berkeley, 1956.

[13] Duerr, William A., and Henry J. Vaux (eds.): *Research in the Economics of Forestry*, Charles Lathrop Pack Forestry Foundation, Washington, 1953, pp. 261–263.

timber production. It also becomes an index of the value of recreational use per unit. And we might add that in any case the break-even ratio would be helpful if it served as a guide to consistency in land-use decisions.

Mr. Atkinson represents value of timber output by the total value of stumpage on a tract. Not altogether happily, he measures recreational

*Table 31. Ratios of timber value per man-day of recreational use during 1955 for thirty-four forest holdings in California*

| Type of holding | Value ratio | Type of holding | Value ratio |
|---|---|---|---|
| | *Dollars* | | *Dollars* |
| Timber properties: | | Parks (continued): | |
| Lumber company | 8,667 | Wilderness area | 554 |
| Lumber company | 7,585 | State park | 154 |
| Lumber company | 5,668 | State park | 149 |
| Lumber company | 5,520 | Wilderness area | 133 |
| Lumber company | 4,170 | State park | 121 |
| Lumber company | 3,151 | State park | 81 |
| Lumber company | 2,290 | State park | 81 |
| Lumber company | 2,240 | State park | 44 |
| Lumber company | 1,300 | State park | 39 |
| Plywood company | 1,127 | State park | 22 |
| Lumber company | 1,089 | State park | 17 |
| Lumber company | 845 | State park | 14 |
| Diamond Match Co. | 736 | State park | 9 |
| ⟶ "Margin" | | State park | 8 |
| Parks: | | State park | 7 |
| Wilderness area | 728 | Memorial grove | 4 |
| State park | 619 | State park | 2 |
| State park | 571 | State park | 2 |

SOURCE: Atkinson, William Allen: "A Method for the Recreational Evaluation of Forest Land," master's thesis, University of California, Berkeley, 1956.

use in terms of man-days per year. Then he selects 34 tracts in California, 21 of them state parks or national forest wilderness areas and 13 of them industrial forest properties. For each of the 34, he estimates stumpage value and obtains the record of man-days recreational use in 1955. He then computes the ratios of stumpage value per man-day of recreational use and arrays them as in Table 31, coming out with a break-even ratio of about $730 per man-day. Applying this ratio as a guide to land use, he examines an illustrative forest tract being considered for state acquisition as a park, forecasts stumpage value and recreational use as of 1960, by which time recreational facilities and use habits would have been developed, and finds a ratio of $5 per man-day, clearly justifying acquisition. He also derives what we might call a common value of $36.50 per man-day of forest recreational use by taking 5 per cent interest on his $730 break-even ratio. (The latter is in terms of capital value and must be converted to terms of annual output.)

[Why do you suppose Mr. Atkinson's ratio so perfectly sorts the two classes of lands in Table 31? Does this perfect sorting mean that the land-use decisions concerning these tracts were perfectly rational?]

## SUMMARY

Appraisal means estimating the value of something: assessing it.

Marketable things are appraised to guide a buyer or seller, to evaluate a firm's alternatives, to determine a property-tax assessment, to establish the value of loan collateral, to estimate damages, or to support a promotion. Four approaches may be taken to such appraisal. One is the direct approach, which may be guided by a manual. Then there are three indirect approaches: the capitalization, cost, and conversion approaches. The conversion approach is ordinarily better suited to stumpage appraisal than is the cost approach, but the direct approach has advantages over both.

Unmarketable things are appraised for promotional purposes or to guide public allocation of resources (comparative appraisal). Promotional appraisal may be carried out in any way that is suited to the interests of the audience. Comparative appraisals of unmarketable things may be made by the common-value approach. Common value is the social opportunity cost of a good or service, determined by public decisions that have worn well and amended by new decisions to meet new circumstances. The common-value approach is illustrated in the problem of recreational versus industrial use of forest land in California.

# Part Four

# INSTITUTIONS
# OF THE FOREST
# ECONOMY

# Chapter 24

# CENTERS OF INFLUENCE IN THE FOREST ECONOMY

As WE adventured out of Part Two and through Part Three of this book, we came by stages from the province of the individual firm into the realm where we began our studies: the economy as a whole, the sum and the context of firms. This realm, this macroeconomics of forestry, will be our prime interest throughout the rest of the book. In the present chapter and the next four, which form Part Four, we shall explore some of its institutions.

*Institutions* are the practices established by society for living—the customary or legal forms, that we tend to take for granted, but which are peculiar to our place and time and make up our distinctive manner of life—such as the ways of the home as we know it, our educational ideals and system, the practices of the church, the rights to property, the use of money, the usages of business, the form of our government. Notice that institutions, as we use the term, refer broadly to the man-made guides to social life and not narrowly to the instruments of guidance such as colleges or court buildings. Disraeli once said that institutions alone can create a nation. And by the same token, it is institutions that create an economy. We are going to look at a very few of the institutions that underlie the forest economy of the United States in the twentieth century.

## POWER SYSTEM: EXAMPLES

The first institution we shall look at is the pressure, or power, system wherein *centers of influence* affect the governance of our lives, including

395

our economy. Big business and industry is one center of influence, or group of such centers. Labor is another. Still another is agriculture, and to agriculture at times are attached some of the units of little business. And then of course there's government, which is a center of immense influence. Beyond these are many others, including such relatively weak or ill-defined centers as the consumer, the conservation movement, and the professions, even our own. You should be able to name still more influence centers, particularly ones that bear mainly on the forest economy. As an institution, the system of influence centers is of special interest because one of its functions is to mold institutions, even including the power system itself.

Suppose that within one of the forested states there are sizable tracts of pine in state ownership. The policy is to grow primarily saw timber and sell it to the loggers and mill operators, mostly little fellows. The pulp industry of the region, pressed for raw materials, sees these lands, now largely inaccessible to the industry, as a potential resource. Through its trade association, which has allies in the legislature, the industry gets a bill introduced that would put up the public forests for sale in large blocks "in order to restore the property to private, tax-paying ownership, give to the dependent communities the benefits of efficient business management of the lands, and uphold the American free-enterprise system." As word goes out that the bill has been referred to committee, two groups spring into action against it. One is the state conservation department, the administering agency, which is concerned with possible damage to the public interest and to the department (in the department's eyes, the two are synonymous). The other is a farm organization some of whose members are part-time loggers and sawmill operators; they view the legislative move as an attempted "land grab." The friends and members of these organizations visit legislators and influential citizens or ply them with telegrams, some of which, unfortunately, are identically worded. Now the state association of commerce enters the contest in support of the bill, and so does the principal newspaper in the state capital. Both these centers of influence identify themselves with the public and claim to speak in defense of its interest. Thus the power system gets into motion.

Or suppose that in the Federal government there are strong stirrings toward some form of public regulation of private forestry practices. The executive departments involved and some of the labor unions and conservation groups have come out in favor of such action. There may be enough affirmative sentiment among the general public to make the step possible. The brunt of the defense against this proposal falls to organized wood-using industry, which feels that it has the most to lose from regulation. Among many defensive measures, industry tries policy advertising in the national magazines. The company name is displayed beneath bright pictures of polished forests watched over by ruddy-cheeked, tin-hatted men in well-creased trousers. Any fool can see that public forest regulation would be superfluous and can confirm his impression by reading the crisp and heartening description—straight from sylvan Madison Avenue—of the company's management program.

These hypothetical examples of influence centers and their doings, you may say, are merely illustrations of the democratic system at work. True. Or at least they show a facet of our social system in the midst of the twentieth century. But there is nothing mere about it.

## VISIBLE HAND—UNNATURAL ORDER

In Chapter 4 (p. 40) we talked about eighteenth-century liberalism and the natural order. We mentioned Adam Smith and the invisible hand, the automatic working of the economic system of markets and prices. The automatic controls of our economy and our forest economy are immensely important and perhaps paramount. The thoughtful man never ceases to marvel at the prodigies of economic organization and adjustment that are achieved socially without conscious social planning. Think of the goods and services that you enjoy in the course of a year and consider how they are brought to your door through the efforts of a far-scattered multitude of persons working largely independently, without central direction. Let us not belittle the natural order, or at least not the invisible hand.

Nevertheless, as we turn to our cursory study of influence centers, we are forced to concede that there is represented here an unnatural order, a highly visible and deliberate hand in economic and political affairs. For in his whole dissatisfaction that leads to striving, the individual is not content nor obliged to wait for an automaton to satisfy his hopes and fill his wants. He can grasp time by the forelock, strike out on his own or band with others who have the same destination, and take comprehensive action to gain his ends sooner or more fully than automatic forces would allow. That is to say, he can create or join a center of influence, which has as its primary function to further the objectives of the persons with whom it identifies itself. The influence center then teams with others or vies with them, according to whether the goals are compatible or conflicting. It strives to promote the gain of its members and to defend them from loss and from the encroachment of other aggressors. Here we have intimations not of atomism but of aggregation in economic life. The aggregates may grow great and their strivings become a battle of giants.

## STRUCTURE OF POWER SYSTEM

Each major center of influence comprises secondary centers, and sometimes these, in turn, still others. So the United Brotherhood of Carpenters and Joiners of America, the great woodworkers' international labor union, old AFL, with a membership of some 850,000, is made up of seven major districts, each of them broken down into state councils, which again are made up of district councils covering groups of counties, these in turn comprising locals, which are the ultimate units.[1] The International Paper Company is made up of geographic divisions, and these, in turn, of the communities where the Corporation's plants are located. The Forest Service in the United States Department of Agriculture divides its field activity into national forest regions and experiment station territories, the ultimate subdivisions of which are the ranger district and the work center, respectively. In all these examples we are speaking, of course, of administrative organization—of the organization chart. The point is that each structure is significant both in reference to production, or supply, and in reference to the conscious regulation of the economy. That is to say, each structure is significant in both individual and social planning.

The memberships, or groups of affiliates, of different influence centers are not always mutually exclusive. Individuals, families, and neighborhoods may belong or be kindred to more than one influence center, and even to influence centers that have conflicting objectives. Why, indeed, should any American in good health pass up any chance to join an organization? In Chapter 4 (p. 42) we noticed that the objectives of an individual may be partly conflicting. An individual may have divided loyalties. A firm may have divided loyalties. And so, through its affiliated individuals and firms, may an influence center. The ultimate case of divided loyalty is that of the center which does its own private planning and is also engaged—necessarily, as a center of influence—in social planning.

Every one of us is caught up in the power system. We are not only individuals—some would say, not even mainly individuals. We are parts of groups in whose power we seek shelter and security, position and advancement, defense against the contrary gains of other groups. This state of affairs is different from traditional American ideals. It is certainly different from Kipling's Victorian ideal: He travels the fastest who travels alone. It is different from the political ideal of freedom, from the economic ideal of atomism, from the religious ideal of individual dignity, from the moral ideal of individual responsibility. We create an institu-

---

[1] You can read about this union, the fifth largest in the United States and the spokesman for many loggers and mechanical-conversion mill workers, in Robert A. Christie: *Empire in Wood*, Cornell Studies in Industrial and Labor Relations, vol. VII, Ithaca, N.Y., 1956.

tion to seek our wants, shield us against strife, assure our security. In return, as serfs did, we pledge our fealty. But in many ways the age of feudalism was a happy time for human beings.

## ORIGIN AND MEANING OF POWER SYSTEM

The origins of our own happy time are ancient and complex. The relation to the Industrial Revolution is of special interest.[2]

Our modern economic life is unusual. Of course, one always seems unusual to oneself, but this is more than seeming. So far as is known, the world has never before witnessed a time when resources were being used and created at such a rate as now, or when the rate was rising to the extent that it is now. We inquired into some of the circumstances in Chapter 3.

The modern economic era appeared with the so-called Industrial Revolution, which was not really a revolution, since it came into life gradually some time between the invention of the wheel and that of the steam engine (more nearly the latter) and is active still. In the Industrial Revolution, production technology was changed—ways of making things—processes and machines and the power to run them. Percapita control over resources and power increased many, many fold, and so far always faster and faster. Man has had to devise ways of using all this power, of connecting it up: not just belts that would link steam engines to factory equipment, but social belts that would link the new technology to the people for whose interest or detriment it might be used. The inventions brought forth to fill the need comprise our contemporary institutions.

Among the institutions created in response to the Industrial Revolution is the modern corporation. The corporation is a device for assembling and managing quantities of labor, productive equipment, money, power, knowledge, and other resources. It is a device for making the assembly and management humanly possible, for concentrating and centralizing authority, for unifying the direction of things. It is a center of power, social, economic, and political—the counterpart of nuclear devices as a center of physical power. It is a center of influence.

Not only is the corporation a center of influence, but also it is in a sense the prototype of influence centers and the progenitor of power systems. Big technology, big business, big war, big government, big labor, and the big strivings of the other entities in our society have begotten one another amid the din of the Industrial Revolution.

In the prototype of influence centers, and therefore to a degree in all

[2] You may wish to do some reading on the Industrial Revolution, a great chapter in economic history which cannot be analyzed here. A good place to start is the brief article on the subject in the *Encyclopaedia of the Social Sciences*.

such centers, we find authority proceeding from the peak of the pyramid toward the base, and responsibility from the base toward the peak. These are the directions of flow of authority and responsibility that are necessary in order to capture the forces of the Industrial Revolution and lock them under centralized control. They are the directions characteristic of a center. Within a group of allied centers, we find again that authority proceeds down from the peak pyramid in the pyramid, and responsibility up from the pyramids at the base. The term for a social system so organized is *fascism*. Fascism is different from democracy, a system in which authority flows from the base of the pyramid toward its peak, and responsibility from the peak toward the base.[3]

There are persons who believe that one of the great issues today in American society is the issue between fascism and democracy. They believe that the fascist goose was by no means cooked in World War II but that it lived to prosper and fatten in the burgeoning postwar world. They point to what they regard as a growing tendency of the American people to delegate their authority to their representatives in the influence centers—to abdicate their authority in favor of the peak, and thence of the peak of the peaks of the peaks. . . .

However, there are others who take a contrary view concerning at least the ultimate significance of aggregation in our economy. One school of thought points to the fact that the aggregates, though often large individually, are also numerous—that they vie and compete with one another while maintaining always a balance of power that prevents the ascendancy of any one of them—and that government then is in position to step in as referee, deciding each issue in the public interest. This explanation of the social arrangement is known as *pluralism*. It represents an analogy to the atomistic ideal of eighteenth-century liberalism, in which the atoms are replaced by aggregates and the market by government.

This great contemporary social issue deserves our earnest attention—primarily, of course, because of its dominant influence upon our lives and incidentally because of its relevance to our understanding of the centers of influence in our forest economy.

## AIMS OF INFLUENCE CENTERS

We can better understand the influence centers by studying more fully their objectives. Let us, therefore, turn to the question of objectives, after which we shall conclude this chapter with some consideration of the means used to reach objectives.

[3] Compare Brady, Robert A.: *Business as a System of Power*, Columbia University Press, New York, 1943, p. 217.

Since centers of influence are an institution partly economic, their aims may be expected to include economic gain—increasing net revenues, getting tighter control of more resources, exercising monopolistic and monopsonistic power. In what follows, we shall mostly take this sort of aim for granted. We shall dwell upon three sorts of aims:

1. Bigness and strength
2. Ascendancy over rivals
3. Unanimity

Then we shall discuss, in passing, such special aims as political reform and revision of specific public policies.

## BIGNESS AND STRENGTH: IN GOVERNMENT

One of the common goals of an influence center is to increase its own size and strength. The goal is common because size and strength are every aggregate's means and measure of success. They may enhance the efficiency and monopoly power of the center, and they contribute to the aggrandizement of its leaders.

In respect to government as a center of influence, the growth of the executive bureaus, particularly of the Federal government, has become a mark of our times. With the Federal Forest Service, notable as it is among the bureaus in having no major regulatory responsibility, growth has been relatively slow and has followed primarily the needs of national forest administration and of research. Wartime, which has brought some temporary regulatory responsibilities, and depression, leading in recent instances to countercyclical government expansion, have resulted in spurts of growth. In the growth of regular activities and the congressional appropriations to support them, there tends to operate a sort of ratchet effect, in which last year's level becomes this year's minimum, and deliberation centers upon the question of increases.

Although the role of the Forest Service respecting the national forests contributes vitally to its position as a center of influence, especially in the West, it is probably the research activities of the Service that in general carry the greatest weight. As a part of research or an adjunct to it, the Forest Service has two powerful and steadily growing activities that merit special note. One is the nationwide forest survey, a regular program authorized by the McSweeney-McNary Forest Research Act of 1928—a program of resource fact finding and analysis. The other is less clear-cut as to authorization but presumably comes partly under the forest survey and partly under the Service's general mandates. It is to make periodic, comprehensive reviews of the forest situation in the United States, including a setting of goals for the forest economy, an interpretation of resource trends in relation to these goals, and, commonly, the recommending of an appropriate action program for public agencies and private interests.[4] Immense energies are poured into these activities, to which the Forest Service organization is uniquely suited. And great authority is derived from them, and great influence upon the thinking of the nation concerning its forest resources. As one industry spokesman[5] puts it:

> The Forest Service somehow has developed an invulnerable prestige among many members of Congress and with other national leaders. It is not unusual, therefore, for such people to quote the Forest Service regarding the condition of our national timber budget. When the Forest Service issues gloomy statements on our future timber situation, we find them echoed by these leaders. This, in turn, sets the stage for action on legislation or on forestry programs. . . .

With the rise of private forestry and with the growth of immense research campaigns outside the forest economy, the sentiment for public forestry research has deepened. These developments augur well for the size and strength of government influence centers in forestry, even though these centers as a whole continue to have little regulatory power.

## IN BUSINESS

In business circles in the United States, the search for bigness and strength took on its modern form only after the time of the Civil War. That was when the Industrial Revolution came into full being in this country. In the 1860s, 2 industrial trusts were formed (by the combination of previously competing concerns); in the 1870s, 4 more; in the 1880s, 18 more; and by 1900 there was a total of 183 industrial trusts.[6]

As you know, there was a great deal of resentment at that time against the growing centralization of power in industry. Various measures were taken to combat the trend of concentration. Here is a story of influence centers vying one with another. One of the measures was antitrust legislation. The Sherman Act, declaring combinations in restraint of interstate trade illegal, was passed in 1890. Such legislation, at first not altogether

---

[4] The latest of these reviews, known as the Timber Resource Review, was reported in preliminary nine volumes in 1955, revised and published finally in 1958. Before this came the Reappraisal, on which the final report was released in 1948. The next earlier review by the Forest Service was that which led to the Copeland Report, 1933. We shall have more to say about these studies in Chaps. 31 and 33 when we talk about social planning and problem analysis.

[5] Nelson, A. Z.: "The Great Guessing Game," *The Freeman*, December, 1956, p. 20. Quoted by permission.

[6] McCrary, Alvin J.: "Another View of National Incorporation Needs," *American Industries*, Oct. 1, 1904, p. 13.

effective, has become increasingly significant in the economy. Today, large firms are careful not to expand beyond that percentage of their industry's total business that the government regards as allowable—not in restraint of trade. As they approach the limit, they may find themselves earnestly solicitous of their competitors' economic health and well-being.

In the face of hostility, business interests early turned to a variety of forms of aggregation, and to some emphasis upon the less obvious forms. The *trade association* was one of these, a relatively loose arrangement for concerted action by the major firms in an industry. Several trade associations were put together within the forest economy at that time. The Minnesota White Pine Association, an organization of lumbermen and perhaps the earliest durable combination of this sort in the industry, was founded in 1888. In 1893, a similar association was formed in Wisconsin. The first important and lasting group of lumbermen in the South, the Southern Lumber Manufacturers Association, was organized in 1890. The peak organization in the industry, the National Lumber Manufacturers Association, was brought together in 1902 as an association of associations.[7] This is a story of searching after legal devices for bigness and power. The associations were not always big in terms of membership. But they were comparatively big in terms of business volume represented, for they included in almost all cases the larger and more stable firms in the industry.

Today there are well over one hundred trade associations in the forest economy.[8] There are, for example, in the pulp and paper industry, the American Paper and Pulp Association (APPA) and the American Pulpwood Association (APA), both with headquarters in New York City, where the principal offices of many of the member firms are situated. The National Lumber Manufacturers Association (NLMA) still thrives and is managed from Washington, D.C., a strategic spot for any influence center. In the plywood industry, a major group is the Douglas Fir Plywood Association, in Tacoma. Illustrative of the many groups active in other wood-using industries are the American Wood Preservers Association, located in Washington, and the Railway Tie Association, with headquarters in St. Louis, the great tie market. And among associations in the marketing field are the National-American Wholesale Lumber Association, New York, and the National Retail Lumber Dealers Association,

---

[7] Compton, Wilson: *The Organization of the Lumber Industry,* American Lumberman, Chicago, 1916, pp. 52 and 57. Dr. Compton's book has some interesting sections on the early doings of the lumber associations. See, for example, his discussion of their price-fixing efforts, pp. 129–143.

[8] U.S. Department of Agriculture, Forest Service: *Lumber-manufacturing, Wood-using, and Allied Associations, 1955,* Washington, 1955.

Washington.[9] And haven't these many and divers combinations themselves attempted to combine in the interest of a still further centralizing and strengthening? The manufacturing associations have indeed—and successfully—as we shall see later on.

## IN LABOR MOVEMENT

As compared with business, labor in the United States was slow to achieve bigness and strength. Our *labor-union* movement in general lagged behind that in Europe. In our early history, there was plenty of unclaimed land, so that workers' status was strengthened by their ever-ready alternative of becoming independent proprietors, and there was correspondingly less need for unions. In general, our high levels of living in this country had the same retarding effect upon unionization, and at the same time frequent sharp depressions of economic activity served to arrest or set back such organizing as was successful in the interim. National rivalries brought over by immigrants made it difficult for the groups involved to get together. For years, government hostility was a powerful influence against unions. And then there was the Horatio Alger myth, that the worker who was zealous in his independence and ambition advanced to become the boss—that is, joined the ranks of management. The myth is kept alive today by such devices as the annual Horatio Alger award, voted by college students across the country to the candidate with the most outstanding success story.

The prosperity of the labor movement that we see nowadays in the United States is of comparatively recent origin, traceable largely to the New Deal of the 1930s.

In the forest economy, the labor movement has had less than average success. Among the unions that recruit woods and mill workers are the mammoth United Brotherhood of Carpenters and Joiners of America, mentioned previously, and the International Brotherhood of Pulp, Sulphite, and Paper Mill Workers, both old AFL. Then in the old CIO group there are the International Woodworkers of America (IWA), covering logging and much of the mechanical processing industry, and the United

[9] It will not be possible here to go into the interesting story of individual trade associations. If you can manage it, you should select an example or two and read about them to get better background for studying this chapter. The trade journals are a source—as the *Paper Trade Journal* for the pulp and paper industry, the *Southern Lumberman* (see, especially, recent Christmas issues) for the lumber industry. Among books and bulletins there are, concerning the lumber industry for instance, Wilson Compton's work cited earlier, the *Report of the Federal Trade Commission on Lumber Manufacturers' Trade Associations*, 1922, and Stanley F. Horn: *This Fascinating Lumber Business*, The Bobbs-Merrill Company, Inc., Indianapolis, 1943.

Furniture Workers of America. Across the old AFL and CIO lines, two unions in the paper industry have joined to form the United Papermakers and Paperworkers. Finally, let us mention one independent union which today is very small and seldom noticed, but which, forty-odd years ago, was an active and militant group in the forest economy and played an important part in labor history: the Industrial Workers of the World (IWW).

Though there are unions that may be joined, it appears that only about 15 to 20 per cent of the laborers in the forest economy are union members. Aside from the general factors we have recognized, the minor position of unions in forest industry is perhaps attributable also to some special circumstances of the industry: its migratory character in times past, its individualistic psychology, and, above all, the smallness and wide scattering of its firms and the part-time character of many of them. Like trade associations, labor unions find it difficult to reach the multitude of little fellows in the industry. Their mainstay is the class of larger and more stable units. And so in the forest economy we find the greatest unionization in the pulp and paper industry and in West Coast logging and lumbering.

One contribution of the IWW was to the principle of the *industrial union,* as distinguished from the *craft union.* The union organized purely along craft lines tends to be a small union for the labor elite. The growth of huge corporations employing many crafts, as well as noncraftsmen, under one management called for an appropriate countervailing concentration of labor influence. The answer was found in the industrial union, a native American invention. Between the time of its founding in 1905 by secessionists from the AFL and its virtual retirement after World War I in the face of strong government and public disapproval of its radicalism, the IWW organized across the board in many a lumber camp and sawmill, demonstrating a new device for bigness and strength in the labor movement.

The United Brotherhood of Carpenters and Joiners of America, traditionally and nominally a craft union, is actually a mixed form containing large elements of industrial unionism. Its form is the result of evolution in the construction and allied industries, and the union's aggressive strivings for size and power. Carpenters once did nearly all the work associated with house building. Their craft was in wood, and wood was almost the exclusive building material. Carpenters selected and felled the trees, sawed and seasoned the lumber, and worked it through to the finished structure. The carpenters' union arose and throve, despite the coming of machines and mills and unskilled workers and substitutes for wood, by virtue of militant adaptation. The union enlarged its jurisdiction to encompass the laborers other than carpenters who came to work with wood.

They fought for jurisdiction over all that is made of wood . . . or that was ever made of wood. . . . [10]

## ASCENDANCY OVER RIVALS: BUSINESS VERSUS LABOR

Almost a corollary to an influence center's objective of bigness and strength is a second objective: gaining ascendancy over rival centers, and perhaps defeating and overthrowing them. The tendency for business to strive against labor, for union to compete with union, is the sort of tendency on which the pluralists base their hope for the future. As fine friendship and the spirit of compromise and unity replace the fire of rivalry, the pluralists lose hope. However, there is still competition among centers, and plenty of it in their historical traditions. Let us take business as a case in point.

The traditional adversary of the center of business influence is the labor union. When the great peak association of business, the National Association of Manufacturers (NAM), was formed in 1905, its overriding aim soon became the suppression of labor organization. The thesis used for presentation to the public was that the employer, not the labor union, is the natural leader of workmen. "The real and ideal union," said an NAM bulletin, "is the one between employer and employee."[11] One of man's essential rights is freedom to choose and pursue his work. Labor unions, by substituting group for individual action and by engaging in such tactics as strikes, deprive their members of "freedom of labor." Today we find state legislation to curb labor unions being referred to by its designers and supporters as "right-to-work" legislation. Each aggregate cherishes the right of others to be divided.

In the early days, all conceivable tactics were used to fight unions, from gentle persuasion and injunction to the billy and gun. A Special Conference Committee was organized by the NAM in 1919 to formulate and promote a uniform "labor relations" program in industry. The guiding spirit of the program was Parryism, a radically harsh doctrine named after an early NAM leader who believed that "organized labor knows but one law and that is the law of physical force—the law of Huns and Vandals, the law of the savage, . . . "[12] and advocated fighting fire with fire.

The general attitude of business toward labor has changed immensely

---

[10] You can read about the development of unionism in the United States in *Brief History of the American Labor Movement,* U.S. Department of Labor Bulletin 1000, 1950.

[11] Brady: Work cited, p. 276.

[12] National Association of Manufacturers: *Proceedings, 8th Annual Convention,* Apr. 14–16, 1903, report of David M. Parry, president.

since those times. By the 1930s it was evident that unionism was an established institution that would have to be lived with. As unions grew older and larger, they became more conservative, more ponderous, and more congenial. They became more respectable—that is to say, more like business organizations. We find the president of a labor union sitting on the board of trustees of a forestry college.

Not that the rivalry has vanished: It has subsided. The spirit of the times within the forest economy can be sensed clearly in the following trade-journal editorial,[13] which incidentally brings out a significant difference between the mechanical and chemical conversion industries:

At a recent meeting of the International Woodworkers of America, President Hartung of that organization called attention to the large number of mergers of large paper companies and lumber companies during 1956 and stressed the desirability of one big organization of workers in the paper and lumber industries. "The companies," he said succinctly, "are integrating and consolidating; so must we." He also expressed the view that these corporate mergers might have as one of their objectives the hope that "they can be more effective in their labor relations dealings as industrial giants than they have been able to do as smaller companies," in urging the paper workers and lumber workers to get together in one big union.

It seems to be admitted that the attempt to unionize the sawmill labor of the South has been a flop. Most of the lumber manufacturers are of the rugged individualist type, inclined to resist the regimentation of their workers, and the workers themselves have not shown much enthusiasm for the unions. Most of the big paper companies, however, are accustomed to such organization of their labor, and it is entirely possible that the development of this giant industry in the South might make it easier for the unions to accomplish their objectives. Certainly a renewed effort will be made in this direction, and developments should be closely watched.

### BUSINESS VERSUS GOVERNMENT

However, since the onset of the New Deal, business influence centers have become more and more inclined to regard big government, rather than labor unions, as their chief adversary.[14]

In general, business dislikes government regulation, except that which clearly protects it from itself. It fears more regulation. It wants what it sometimes calls industrial self-regulation, not regulation by government, and particularly not by the Federal government. It wants to stop what it refers to as "government interference in business." You are aware of the

---

[13] *Southern Lumberman*, Apr. 1, 1957, p. 20. Quoted by permission.
[14] For some recent history written by one who knew both sides of the business-government rivalry, see Greeley, William B.: *Forests and Men*, Doubleday & Company, Inc., Garden City, N.Y., 1951, especially chaps. XIII, XV.

issue concerning Federal regulation of private forestry practices, an issue that arouses passions and elicits strong language from the centers of business influence:[15]

The growth of private forestry enterprise is the sum total of the growth of . . . individual enterprises. It has not been, and we know it never can be, a consequence of government dictatorship. The timber famine philosophy built up . . . by the Forest Service could lead to such dictatorship.

Business influence centers generally want to see trends reversed with respect to government, with government playing a diminishing part in our national life and levying correspondingly lower taxes. In their opinion, taxes are too high, and Federal income taxes for the individual are too progressive: The rates rise too steeply with the income bracket.

## BUSINESS VERSUS BUSINESS

But the adversaries of business, even of its influence centers, are not all in labor and government. Some of them are other centers of influence within the business community. One of the battles of the lumber industry is its eternal struggle with the industries that produce competing materials. We saw in Chapter 19 (pp. 317–321) that the lumber industry is a rising-cost industry and that its concern over substitute materials is more than ordinarily keen and real. It has seen steel, cement, glass, and many other construction materials enter its domain and take possession. It has found the influence centers representing the rival materials to be aggressive, shrewd, and well financed. It has tried every defensive expedient—product research and development, as at the Teco laboratory in Washington; lobbying for favorable building codes; encouraging better production methods in the industry; influencing consumers' tastes and preferences. The words of a 1938 president of NLMA[16] are still relevant today:

Our industry can well learn a lesson today from world affairs. . . . Preparedness and propaganda are the order of the day. Power in world affairs, as in an industry, means organization, brains, energy, and money. . . . Within the American industrial field we see small groups very strongly organized and sufficiently financed to both protect and to promote their interests. Between industries, as between nations, those that are unprepared, timid, and willing to drift will certainly be pushed out of the way by those which are well organized, well financed, and well prepared to defend their place in the sun.

[15] Nelson: Work cited, p. 22. Mr. Nelson is an employee of the National Lumber Manufacturers Association.

[16] McNary, James G.: *President's Address at Thirty-sixth Annual Meeting*, National Lumber Manufacturers Association, Chicago, Nov. 15, 1938, p. 4.

## UNANIMITY

Besides bigness and strength and ascendancy over rivals, there is a third objective, common to all influence centers: unanimity among members. Unanimity is the most essential feature of a successful aggregate. In unity lies all manner of strength, and through it a loosely knit organization may be able to achieve some of the same power wielded by the large single firm centrally managed. Unanimity does not necessarily mean identical action on the part of every unit in the combination. It means identity of purpose and such action as is suited thereto. To take an example from business, unanimity does not necessarily mean uniform sales prices for all firms. It may mean simply the maintenance of prices—say, within regions—to the extent of the law. It may mean the avoidance of price cutting on the part of "selfish," "acquisitive," competitive-minded individuals, so far as this can be achieved legally. It may mean mutual agreement concerning the wisdom of avoiding "overproduction" that might force price cutting. Unanimity may mean that all members of the organization think alike regarding whether a certain legislative measure is good or bad, a certain political candidate "sound" or not, a certain policy desirable or not. "Unit thinking" is a term sometimes used to cover the immense and vital point here involved. Unit thinking is presumably the forerunner of unit action. Both are acts of sacrifice made by the organization man in return for supposedly much greater gains that he will share with his group.

Through the founding of the NAM, according to one of its presidents, "notice was . . . given to the world . . . that the American manufacturing industry . . . would speak with one voice on every occasion of common defense and on all occasions pertaining to its general welfare."[17]

Again, one finds in the constitution of the NLMA the principle of unanimity variously stated. One purpose of the association is expressed thus: "To unify conflicting interests and eliminate elements of friction." One element of friction that the lumber industry has tried hard to curb is the small-mill segment, with its inelastic or even backward supply responses (compare Chap. 13, p. 208). Another purpose of the Association is: "To gather and disseminate reliable statistics showing the annual production and consumption of the various kinds of lumber manufactured in this country, cooperating with and aiding other associations along this line." For unit thinking and unit action to mean anything, the organization must first have the facts from which to judge what action is right. Still another NLMA purpose is: "To strengthen the bonds of fellowship and inculcate more friendly relations among those engaged in the same

[17] National Association of Manufacturers: *Proceedings, 34th Annual Meeting,* October, 1929, pp. 14–15.

calling and occupation, whose interests are common and lie along almost parallel lines." In the interest of unanimity on a broader scale, NLMA has joined with the two major trade associations in the pulp field, APPA and APA, to establish a forest policy-coordinating body, the Forest Industries Council.

## SPECIAL AIMS OF INFLUENCE CENTERS

Besides the three major objectives of influence centers that we have now analyzed, we should recognize that every center or allied group of centers has special goals that shape its actions.

For instance, some labor unions have had the aim of changing our form of government. The IWW leaders were socialists, and the organization was pledged to the "abolition of the wage system." It was this aim of the union that contributed to the scorn and hatred widely bestowed upon it and thus to the physical violence and strife that marked labor relations in lumbering during the IWW era.

Many unions, on the other hand, stand aloof from social issues, devoting their energies largely to "pure and simple unionism," which consists of striving for higher wages (and related benefits) and better working conditions.

Somewhere between the foregoing two extremes is the aim of effecting moderate political reforms. Most influence centers, of whatever sort, hold such an aim. They want to see the friendly party in power. They hope for a sunny political climate, with perhaps just enough patches of shade to meet the needs of their opponents.

Centers of influence in the business sector of our economy have generally advocated a protective tariff, a substantial tax upon imported goods, which would shield United States industry from foreign price competition. It was fear of foreign, particularly Canadian, competition that brought the regional lumber manufacturers' associations into conclave in Cincinnati in 1897, to enjoy a mutuality that led to founding the national association five years later.[18]

Many influence centers in the forest economy have published statements on forest policy—statements enumerating the public and private forestry programs and measures that they advocate. We have seen how Federal Forest Service policy is taken partly from the Service's periodic reviews of the forest situation. Conservation groups, labor, and industry may also use the Forest Service findings to shape their widely varying

---

[18] The story of early tariff activities of NLMA is to be found in *The Lumber Industry, Part IV: Conditions in Production and Wholesale Distribution Including Wholesale Prices*, U.S. Department of Commerce, Bureau of Corporations, 1914, pp. 50–70.

policies or to justify them. Among labor unions, the industrial unions, with their fresher militant tradition, are more forest-policy-minded than the craft unions. The IWA has been especially active in forest policy. Among business groups, the lumber and allied industries have been more closely oriented to the forest and to forest policy than have the paper and allied industries, whose thoughts are turned more largely toward the market. You may be sure that a center of influence will have policy statements or a clear policy position on all matters that it regards as vital to its aims. This is the first essential for unit thinking and unit acting.

Now there are three most common methods for an influence center to use in carrying out its objectives: One is political action. The second is direct action. The third is—to use the euphemistic jargon—education.

## GAINING AIMS: BY POLITICAL ACTION

We have spoken already of political objectives. These may be sought by any of the methods, including political action. For its part, political action is one way of furthering almost any objective that an influence center may have. Let us look at political action aimed at obtaining certain laws or rulings, or at avoiding or getting rid of certain others.

The use of the polls is a form of political action in which we place much confidence for the long run. It is inapplicable, however, to the day-to-day business of gaining ends. Furthermore, many centers of influence find it ineffective in any case, since they have few votes. The persuasion of legislators and public officials—or lobbying—then comes to hand as a good approach to the problem. The way that prospective lobbyists can feel about their avocation and about any restriction of their activities is illustrated by the following statement, written from the viewpoint of "private forestry enterprise":[19]

> The proposed new lobbying act may put America in the hands of bureaucrats. A bill, S. 2191 . . . , regarding the regulation of lobbying, tightens up registering and reporting requirements for persons who influence or attempt to influence legislation. The bill . . . provides stiff penalties for failure to register or to report.
>
> We have always maintained that it is a citizen's right and privilege to influence legislation—more than that, it is his duty.

Alas, that citizenship is not granted to centers of influence! Be this as it may, we find, as the thesis is enlarged, that it is not the requirement of registering and reporting but the denial to lobbyists of the privilege of claiming a tax deduction for their work that hurts most. Continuing with our "citizen,"

[19] *What's Happening in Forestry,* a report to private forestry enterprise by Albert G. Hall, forestry relations counsel and consulting forester, Washington, June 16, 1957.

If he attempts to influence legislation in order to protect his business from the invasions of federal competition or control, he should be able to consider such activities and related expenditures as legitimate business expenses. This is especially equitable when he must pay taxes to support those who seek to compete with him or to control him, and to pay for all their efforts to lobby and otherwise influence legislation directed against him.

The point made here is that employees of the Federal bureaus, such as the Forest Service, get paid for talking to congressmen, whereas our citizen gets nothing for his pains but the tax bill, sans deductions. As the story goes on, we learn that our citizen is no casual lobbyist: He spends $300 or more per three months putting his ideas across:

Under the proposed legislation, however, he may still spend money to protect himself, but he cannot deduct it as a legitimate business expense if he spends as much as $300 in any calendar quarter.

Here's what can happen—and probably will. Some day, we'll again have a federal program for regulation of private forestry. Federal supporters can and will publish propaganda, lobby in the Halls of Congress, take congressmen on junkets—all expenses of which are added to the forest landowners' tax bill. But if the landowners try to tell their story in the same way, they'll be unable to consider it a business expense for tax purposes.

So, we advise our readers—before the bill becomes law—to engage in some really high-powered lobbying in order to retain the right to influence legislation.

Readers, or at least the citizens among them, may have taken this advice to spend while the deducting was good. At any rate, Senate bill 2191 did not become law. This little tempest in a teapot helps us to understand the workings of our economy.

Speaking of bureaucrats taking legislators on junkets, one may judge that the other camps, too, have learned their lessons well. Here, for example, is the account of a representative of business:

At regular intervals we invite groups of state politicos and members of the . . . delegation to Congress to visit our plant and our hunting lodge. . . . We have found these to be tremendously helpful. On those occasions when we feel it necessary to discuss proposed legislation, which we believe might affect us adversely, with our state and national representatives, we have always received an attentive hearing. In complete fairness I should point out that some of our legislative friends are more impressed with our hunting lodge facilities than they are with our several manufacturing units or our forestry program.

## BY DIRECT ACTION

As for direct action, which is a second means that influence centers may employ to reach their goals, we shall deal with it here in passing.

Instead of working for a law to permit price fixing, or in addition to working for such a law, the center figures out a way to fix prices anyhow. Besides persuading the public that it is dangerous to enter the forests at times of high fire hazard, the center closes the roads. Apart from legal and "educational" efforts made to defeat a labor union's membership drive, steps are taken to see that the organizers leave town.

Some of our plainest examples of direct action are from labor history. Some of our roughest are from the history of the IWW. To get the picture of those times, you can read about such episodes as the so-called Louisiana Lockout of 1911, in which the Southern Lumber Operators Association fought the union with whiskey and gunpowder.[20]

Of course, direct action needn't involve physical violence. And anyhow, times are changing. [Is society becoming more civilized, or more subtle, or what do you think is happening?]

Whatever the ends, or the means, one may confidently expect that "no tactics [will be] used other than those generally recognized as proper in such cases."[21]

## BY "EDUCATION"

We turn finally to a third method for influence centers to gain their ends: education, leaving off the quotes from now on, but understanding that the term is used in a special and highly inclusive sense. Much of what we shall call education seems to bear only the faintest likeness to the present process in which we fancy we are engaged as teacher and student. And yet, is the difference so great? What is happening in any case is a struggle for men's minds. The difference is presumably in the degree of objectivity. But beware the man who claims objectivity. He is after you, with your allegiance the prize in view. Beware television, radio, the spoken word, the picture, the guided tour, the printed page, including this one.

Ours is an age of education, in a country that is obsessed with the idea anyhow. Thomas Jefferson proclaimed the need for education if democracy is to work. Education is required to safeguard freedom. Or, to look at the matter the other way, it is to the extent of our freedom that we have this education bestowed upon us. The annual $10 billion of advertising that bombards us is a compliment to our freedom of choice. If we were utterly in bondage, there would be no point in it. So we enjoy annually $10 billion worth of this kind of freedom. "Don't ever think,"

[20] See, for instance, Jensen, Vernon H.: *Lumber and Labor*, Farrar & Rinehart, Inc., New York, 1945, pp. 87–91.
[21] Letter of Apr. 19, 1909, from J. E. Rhodes to F. E. Weyerhaeuser, quoted by U.S. Department of Commerce, Bureau of Corporations: Work cited, p. 65.

writes an adviser to the pulp and paper industry, "it's time to ease off on educating the public."[22]

Education as it is practiced by the centers of influence is primarily a long-run device. An effort is made to imbue the public with those ideas which will lead it to vote right in forthcoming elections, think right concerning the issues that really matter, act right when it comes to a choice, and in general help develop the sunny social climate. Only secondarily is education used to smooth the way for immediate action. Education is an investment.

One of the outstanding conceptions in education in the forest economy is the peak association of associations in all wood-using business, the American Forest Products Industries (AFPI), of Washington, D.C. Formed in 1938 mainly to stem the tide then flowing toward Federal regulation of private forest practices, this organization has built unhurriedly and with great pains a comprehensive program in defense of the business interest and the business point of view. Among many activities, the AFPI sponsors the "Tree Farm" program, whose powerful educational value—in its name, its idea, and its statistics—is scarcely overshadowed by its accomplishments in forest conservation. The AFPI publishes attractive pamphlets on pertinent subjects, including the timber-resource situation nationwide and state by state ("Forest *Facts*"). Here it takes its data, of necessity, mostly from the Federal Forest Service, but the sunny interpretation is its own. Its bright literature goes into the secondary schools, for the benefit of young minds.[23] Its authoritative releases find a friendly press. Through its capable field men in all the forest regions of the country, it looks in on doings—on people, firms, and government—it learns, and gently advises and arranges.

We must recognize, too, the stars of lesser magnitude in the educational world. Every trade association has education as a purpose, often explicit. So does every labor union. *Research, information,* and *public relations* are some of the terms applied to activities clearly educational in our sense. Forestry and conservation associations, public agencies, and professional societies stress the education side of their struggle for success. For all these groups, education fills the role of the interference runner on the football team. The Federal Forest Service has its Division of Information and Education, charged with the duties of writing, talking, photographing, promoting Smokey Bear, and making friends. Of course everyone in every organization must make friends. What is conceptually a very personal privilege has been made an obligation to the group.

[22] *The Rice Barton Cellu-Letter,* Worcester, Mass., May, 1957.
[23] See *Youth and the Forest Industries: A Progress Report by American Forest Product Industries, Inc.,* Washington, 1956.

## ADVERTISING AS "EDUCATION"

One cannot leave the subject of education without at least touching upon the overworked topic of advertising. America's advertising budget has been growing recently at the rate of 10 per cent per year, compounding an already dominant social institution. You are being diagnosed and operated upon by the world's most energetic brain surgeons. Your tastes have been investigated, and your preferences, your weaknesses and fears, your skin condition, and the toilet training you received as an infant. You are now being remolded nearer to the heart's desire, made a finer person, more loyal to Peough. That is, unless the other outfit undermines my work. Or my psychologists turn out to have used the wrong theory. Or you get too sophisticated.

During World War II, when goods were scarce and everything buyable was being snapped up, there was no use advertising wares. And yet firms wished, against the future, to keep their names before the public. They did so, in advertisements that featured description or praise of themselves, or general sentiments that people would like and for which they would remember the company pleasurably. Thus policy advertising, the advertising of ideas rather than goods, was given its big trial. Apparently it was judged successful, for it continued to be widely employed. It is liked by wood-using industry (compare Chap. 20, p. 335). Look through some of the national magazines and notice the industry's advertising. Observe in how many cases the product is mentioned only incidentally if at all.[24] [How do you explain such advertising?]

## SUMMARY

The system of influence centers—aggregations of power in business, labor, government, and other fields—is one of the institutions that determine our forest economy. Influence-center activities are a part of conscious economic planning, as distinguished from the automatic operation of the economy. Their modern form has been shaped by the Industrial Revolution. Collectively they constitute a power system in which elements of fascism are represented, but in which there may still be enough competition to safeguard public interests.

Influence centers have many objectives besides the immediate one of

[24] A famous example is Weyerhaeuser Timber Company's eight-page spread in *The Reader's Digest* for February, 1956, an outstanding advertisement in respect to size and cost. The ad describes and attractively illustrates an industry program of forest management, utilization, and research, merely footnoting the name of the company and a list of its products. Such advertising, termed *public-service advertising* in the trade, is of service primarily to the industry.

economic gain. Among major objectives are bigness and strength, triumph over adversaries, and unanimity among members. Individual centers also have many special goals.

The means that influence centers use to carry out their objectives include political action, direct action, and "education," a part of which is advertising.

# Chapter 25

# THE TENURE INSTITUTION

YOUR FRIEND Mr. O owns a nice tract of land not far from town. The property is largely wooded, but there are clearings, and a comfortable house, and a little stream that comes down the cove and flows out through the meadow. Mr. O enjoys the rural life and puttering with forestry. When he wakes up of a fine morning and lays his eye against the green hill, he is king in his castle, the monarch of all he surveys.

Now let us, quietly so as not to disturb Mr. O's good spirits, inquire into the nature of his kingship. We need to do so, not only as part of our obligation to take the joy out of life, but also in order to understand more clearly the relation between man and resources, which is the subject of our studies.

## RIGHTS IN LAND

With a little research, we find that when Mr. O bought his place, he was short of cash. Most everyone is, of course, and for the most part it is a good thing: An economy in which everyone relied in financial matters entirely on his own devices would be the last word in inefficiency. At any rate, Mr. O got a mortgage loan from the bank, in return for which he bound himself for a period of ten years to maintain insurance on the house, keep it in repair, manage his land conservatively, get the bank's permission before cutting any timber, and repay the loan, with interest, in annual installments. If he fails to carry out his part of the bargain, he is in for a bad time and may even lose his real estate through foreclosure.

Clearly, Mr. O is not an absolute monarch. He shares the rights in his

417

land with others. In this particular case, the bank holds some of the rights. Then there are other individuals and groups who invariably and always hold rights in everybody's real estate—namely, society, represented variously by Mr. O's neighbors, his local and state governments, the Federal government, and the general public. Mr. O must pay an annual tax on his property, toward the support of state and local government services. Failure to pay may lead to the same consequence as failure to live up to the covenant with the bank: foreclosure. In fact, the two obligations are alike in many ways, though that to society has precedence and is perpetual. The neighbors, too, have rights in Mr. O's land, for he may not use it in any way that will cause them harm. He may not do anything that would be in the nature of a public nuisance. He may not divert the water from the stream or otherwise materially change the character of this community asset. The Federal government levies an income tax upon Mr. O—not, to be sure, upon his property, but the tax represents a claim upon any proceeds from the land, and the form of it affects his management of the land. The general public enjoys many rights, such as to travel through Mr. O's holding along the road, to rest their eye on his green hill, perhaps to enter the estate for such purposes as recreation, and in any case to use the air corridors above him. And beyond all such rights, there is society's right of *eminent domain,* exercised through government and permitting seizure of property (under due process of law and after just compensation) for purposes that are in the public interest.

Now, truly, we begin to see that there are many rights in Mr. O's property and that they are widely shared. But we have just begun the list of right holders. Mr. O is renting one of his fields to a neighboring farmer, who has thus acquired various rights of entry and use. The electric company has a right of way over in one corner for constructing and maintaining its power line. The former owner of the property has reserved a perpetual right of access to a family cemetery on the hillside. The tradesmen, mechanics, and utility companies with whom Mr. O does business have various temporary rights on his place, and if he does not pay his bills, they may extend their rights to the point of obtaining a lien upon his property.

You will be able to think of other social and individual rights that may be held in the land by others than Mr. O himself. Some of these rights are explicit in law; others are implicit in the custom of the community.

### OWNER'S RIGHTS

But what about the owner, Mr. O? What are his rights? They are easier to list than the others, and it is already obvious that they are neither so numerous nor so full as we are sometimes inclined to assume.

One is the right of *possession:* the right to occupy the place. If Mr. O leases his property, he may lose this right nearly completely, though he will still be the owner. Another right that may be heavily suppressed through leasing is the right to waste: to deplete the inherent productivity of the estate. But like the right of possession, the right to waste is not in any case an absolute right. No owner has the right to commit waste which will harm others or create a public nuisance, such as to burn his own property in a manner that will lead to the burning of others. Here we have a restrictive principle of high significance, for in our closely integrated society the others who are affected by a landowner's act are far-flung in space and time. We have noted how the bank regulates Mr. O's timber depletion. Society may do the same thing in the interest of "neighbors" and their descendants. Fire, wildlife, water, perhaps with soil in it —these things can move physically across ownership lines and thus tend to socialize the incidence of waste. But *any* sort of waste can move *economically* across ownership lines, and across the barriers of time as well.

Another sort of right that the land owner has, and perhaps the most fundamental and characteristic of all, is the right of *alienation:* the right to transfer the property to another owner. The right of alienation somehow seems essential to the concept of ownership. And yet this right, too, is limited. There are certain persons and groups to whom society forbids Mr. O to sell or otherwise transfer his holdings. There are certain circumstances under which Mr. O is entirely deprived of the alienation right —for example, if he holds his property for life under the terms of a will which gives the estate ultimately to others.

[Can you think of any right in real property—say, in forest land—that owners in the United States today invariably hold? Can you think of any right that is invariably held by society? What conclusion do you draw, so far, about the nature of property rights and right holding?]

The holding of property rights—the whole circumstance of right holding, which is a relationship among persons, an institution—is called *tenure.* We shall study here the subject of tenure in *real property,* or *real estate:* land and the things affixed to it; and our interest, of course, will center upon forest land. But before narrowing our attention to forestry, let us try to understand, at least sketchily, the historical background of what we witness today in the United States. How did the complex human circumstances surrounding Mr. O's land come into being and become accepted as a part of the ordinary business of our lives?

## ORIGINS OF TENURE RIGHTS

The current meaning and forms of land tenure in our country as expressed in law and custom are the result of trial and error and of amendments and revolutionary developments marching upward from the earliest history of Western civilization. In today's land-tenure arrangements, the ancient, often revised, and complex rights of tribe and king, feudal lord and vassal, church and state, individual and society, rural and urban dweller are all to be found intermingled, modified, and reexpressed in forms believed to be appropriate to our social system. The direct line of descent of these institutions in the United States is from colonial America and so principally from Britain.

The human notion of belonging and of ownership is far older than history. It arose, perhaps, in the relation of the individual to his family. Its earliest examples were probably personal property: clothing, weapons, utensils, livestock, slaves. Here ownership was signified and determined in the fact of possession. The possessor was in some cases the individual and in some cases the family—or its representative, the head of the family. And so ideas of both individual and social ownership, and perhaps also of intermediate forms, must have existed from the start; and along with them there must have existed the concept of property rights and a recognition that such rights vary in character and are vested in various individuals and groups, for varying periods of time.

Real property, too, was owned—originally by the group or its representative rather than the individual. In Britain, as late as the beginning of the Anglo-Saxon period, all land was the property of the people: *folcland*. Subsequently, Anglo-Saxon custom began to allow land holding by individuals, whose grants of *bocland* were conveyed by a kind of deed, or *book*. At first, such individual land holding was for a term only; later it was for life; still later, in perpetuity, with rights of devisal. Since land was immovable, it offered ready opportunities for separating possession from ownership and hence for elaborating tenure rights.

In the course of the Anglo-Saxon era—say, from the fifth century until the time of the Norman invasion in the eleventh century—there was being developed in Britain and modified from abroad a *feudal* type of social organization. Feudalism took shape in the Western world in response to the need for new order when the old order of the Roman Empire had broken down. That was a time of social chaos, of strife, brigandage, and unpunished wrong. It was a time of danger, insecurity, and fear for the many families who still retained a tradition of order, law, and civilized living. No man was safe alone. What should he do? He sought safety in alliance with someone else, preferably someone stronger. And so a social arrangement took form, crystalizing the populace around the community leaders, and groups of these in turn around the strongest of them, and so on up the pyramid and perhaps to a king at the top. The relationships between leader and led within this hierarchy, the bonds by which society was reestablished, were personal relationships. The leader, or lord, granted the protection of his laws and military strength, as a father might do. The led, or vassal, standing in the position of the son, pledged loyalty and the performance of service. The feudal contract was impressively sealed as the vassal knelt before his lord and placed his hands between his lord's hands. And to this personal contract were adjoined some material considerations, chief among which was land.[1]

## FEUDAL TENURE

Today, many nations are attaching a diminishing significance to land. They are accumulating the preponderance of their capital in forms other than land. Since the Industrial Revolution they have become less dependent upon land as they have redirected their economic effort away from farming and raised their agricultural efficiency. New developments in the technology of war have also tended to deemphasize land. But in the feudal era of which we are thinking, the holding of rights in land assumed peculiar and central importance because of land's permanence, its role as wealth and as the site of production and as the locus of populations, and the evidence it comprised of power and position. Man's rights in general and his rights in land were closely identified.

Land, therefore, filled an important place in the feudal contract. As the lord granted protection in return for service, so also he granted property in return for the care and management of it; and this property, or fief, was usually land. The king held the land, presumably, from God. This land he could divide among his immediate vassals, who, as lords, could subdivide it in support of the next feudal layer, and so on down to the meanest vassal who worked a plot of ground.

It would be a mistake, however, to make the feudal system seem systematic. At best it was a chaotic system. It varied a great deal from fief to fief. It varied in respect to the laws and customs that determined personal and property relationships, and it varied more and more widely in the lower ranks of the hierarchy. In England alone, almost every known form of land tenure existed in some locality in the course of the feudal age.

British feudalism reached its fullest development under the Norman kings, during the century and a half preceding Magna Carta. The lines of authority and responsibility that connected the social layers were then strongest and most nearly uninterrupted. Rights were most highly centralized. Let us look briefly at the major forms of land tenure that existed then, and at the duties of the land holder to his lord.

[1] For fuller background on feudalism, see the article in the *Encyclopaedia of the Social Sciences*. For detail on land tenure under the feudal system, see Harris, Marshall: *Origin of the Land Tenure System in the United States*, Iowa State College Press, Ames, 1953, especially chaps. 2, 3, and 21.

The forms of land tenure were, in general, two: free tenure and villein tenure. The former was held in return for services appropriate to the free man, notably military service. Tenure by knight service was the highest type of free tenure, and there were also lesser military tenures, including those which no longer involved actual personal service by the land holder, but an annual money payment in lieu of such service. Then there were nonmilitary free tenures, in most of which the payment of a money rent had come to be substituted for the direct service. In the case of tenure by church bodies, however, there was no money substitution: rent was taken in the form of spiritual services. These free tenures were all relatively secure and of long duration. In general, they allowed the holder to bequeath or otherwise transfer his rights. They were the forerunner of our modern ownership in *fee simple.* Villein tenures, on the other hand, held for service regarded as menial, especially the cultivation of the land, tended to be inferior in certainty and in duration. The copyholder had a sort of third-class fee-simple ownership, while the bondsman and laborer had tenures which at best resembled those of today's *tenants* (renters) and sharecroppers. Over villeins of the lower ranks the lord held absolute power in all matters save of life and limb.

As for the duties of the land holder to his lord, we have already taken note of the principal material one: service or a money payment in place of service. The main thing to notice is that, as time went by, payment was substituted more and more for personal service and thus the system gradually changed from an organization of persons to one of property. Today, instead of lord, we say "society," or "state," or "government." And our payment in lieu of service we call a tax.

We have also taken note of the principal intangible duty of the land holder during the full flower of feudalism: fealty.

Besides service and fealty, there were a number of other duties, often burdensome ones. These duties were rights of the lord with respect to all or certain classes of his vassals. The lord collected a "relief" from the heir to property at the time of accession. Relief was originally paid as a sort of bribe by the likely successor to a title that had been granted only for the life of the grantee. Today we have it in the inheritance tax. To make sure of his relief, and of other duties as well, the lord had the right to take possession of the land until the duty was paid. The lord had also the right to levy a fine for the alienation of land. This payment, originally made for the purpose of disposing the lord favorably toward a proposed new occupant of his land, has come down to us in the form of the tax upon deeds. Again, under the arrangement known as *escheat*, the property of a traitor, a felon, or a decedent without heirs reverted to the lord. Today, there is reversion to the state in the last of these cases. These were some of the rights and duties with respect to British feudal land that have close counterparts in current practice in the United States.

## REVISION OF FEUDAL TENURE

Beginning with Magna Carta in the year 1215, and through a series of acts of nearly equal importance during the next four hundred years and more, rights in land were gradually reallocated. Many were taken from the lord. Some were vested in the tenant. Some, however, were placed in the sovereign in such forms as the state and the public, and others became lodged in various additional parties to the tenure arrangement. Our tenure heritage in the twentieth century still vests a substantial sheaf of rights, and all ultimate rights, in society and widely distributes the remainder.

In the years between Magna Carta and the Declaration of Independence, most of the feudal rights in their personal form were abolished. As it became possible for more individuals to hold an interest in a given piece of land, laws were formulated to prevent waste, as by minor tenants or those with passing interest. Whereas on the one hand the concern of society for land resources was made more effective, on the other the freedom of the individual owner was in some respects enlarged. As individual freedom was enlarged, emphasis seems to have been shifted more and more toward the individual's rights and away from his responsibilities. Mechanisms for alienation and devisal were elaborated and clarified. At the same time, renters and laborers upon land were given higher status.

The Western Europeans who settled America brought with them most of this heritage of tenure institutions, and took their own steps to bend these institutions to their needs. They found the country occupied by Indians who had quite other ideas about rights in land. The Indian ideas and the economy they suited were shouldered aside by the land rights and economic ways that traced back across the water. Soon very little was left of the native schemes. [What are rights, anyway? How do they come into being?]

In this country, of course, as in modern Britain and generally in the Western world, the holding of land is no longer feudal, but is *alodial.* That is to say, a man may hold land in his own right and not under obligation of rent or service to another. However, he is still under obligation to serve the public interest, though the nature of the obligation and of the public interest is in continuous question and evolution, as it is with respect to the use of all resources.

Indeed, land-tenure laws and customs, like all our institutions, have reached their current form in the course of man's never-ending search for ways of social coexistence. Tenure arrangements, therefore, are always changing. And they vary more or less from place to place. They may be greatly different between one nation and another, and even within our own country they vary widely in detail.

Let us come back, now, to the forest for a look at some of the major holders of tenure rights.

## HOLDERS OF RIGHTS IN FOREST LAND: GOVERNMENT

Government for one—local, state, and Federal—holds tenure rights in our forest land. *One* of the most direct and obvious is the right to levy taxes against the value of the land or its products. This right, like most rights, is not unlimited. It is often restricted by law, and even the land-owner himself has a voice in the exercise of the right. Not simply property taxes but any kind of tax that the government levies may affect land use and thus constitute a form of tenure. We shall see in Chapters 26 and 27 the effects of various taxes.

A *second* right of government is the right to condemn—the right of eminent domain. A *third* is the right to police and to regulate. Forest regulation by state government may be exercised under the police power, as affirmed in the case of Washington's forest-practice act by both state and Federal supreme courts in 1949. The Federal government may perhaps exercise the right under its authority respecting interstate commerce, but this has not been tested. The police authority of the states, which may be delegated to local governments, includes the right to zone the use of forest and other rural land. Some of the same regulatory rights that governments possess are held also by quasi-governmental bodies such as drainage districts and soil conservation districts.

A *fourth* right of governments is the right to exert control over land by spending money. Governments carry on a number of forestry programs, the administration of which represents an exercise of tenure rights —taking a hand in the use of forests. Such are programs of public education, of technical assistance to woods owners, of fire control and other forms of forest protection, and of direct subsidy. Not only government but also various private interests have programs of this sort and thereby acquire tenure in forest land.

Where are we led by the foregoing line of thought? If tenure is the holding of rights in land, and if rights are interpreted to include the right to influence land management, then, since land management is influenced in some measure by virtually all the values throughout the economy, one comes to the unhelpful conclusion that forest-land tenure rights are held by everyone and are exercised simply within the general scheme of economic relativism. No doubt there is something to be said for this path of reasoning. It suggests, for example, that the study of influence centers in the forest economy, as in Chapter 24, may be regarded as a study of forest tenure—and indeed, that any part of forestry economics may be so regarded. The answer to the problem here implied is the same that we reached in Chapter 2 when we puzzled over a definition of the forest economy. When one studies a system in which there is universal interdependence, as there always is in social science, one must apply a rule of reason and judgment in analyzing the behavior of any part of the system: One must concentrate on the most direct influences, giving less attention to the less direct, by way of abstraction.

## OTHER HOLDERS OF RIGHTS IN FOREST LAND

The general public, including you yourself, hold some important rights in forest land. The right to enjoy the scenery, to walk or hunt on the land under certain circumstances, to use water from the land—all these are tenure rights. The air corridors above forest land are mostly for the use of the general public, though such tenure is restricted in certain cases, such as over some wilderness areas owned by the public itself. Mining rights on the national forests are a form of tenure held by the public.

[Why should an urbanite be concerned with forest-fire control and be confronted by pictures of Smokey Bear in the bus advertisements? Is this evidence of the city dweller's forest-land tenure?]

Renters of land hold numerous rights. Forest land is often leased, with rights extending to the subsurface, or the surface, or the timber, or all of these. Owners sometimes lease hunting privileges on forest land. On the farm, the tenant (renter) may have certain rights in the woods, such as the right to cut timber for farm use, or the right to remove dead trees.

An interesting example of forest tenure, one that is important to the management of small forest holdings in many parts of the United States, is the tenure of the timber buyer or operator. This man is customarily granted numerous rights: rights of entry, the right to choose within limits the time of cutting, the right to determine logging methods, and even to decide which trees to cut. It is not unusual for the owners of small woodlands to forfeit to the timber operator some of their most influential management rights at the time of cutting, which is generally the most critical time in the culture of the forest.

Creditors hold rights in forest land. As we observed in the case of Mr. O, such rights may range from a voice in management to the right of foreclosure.

## OWNERS OF FOREST LAND

We began our study of tenure with the forest-land owner; let us conclude it with a few more thoughts on the subject of ownership.

Clearly, the idea of forest *ownership* must be approached with care and forethought. The significant thing about forest ownership is the rights that go with it, and these vary greatly with time, place, and circumstances. All that we know for certain about any forest owner is that he holds a legal title of some sort. The title may be to all the attributes of the land or only some part of them, such as the surface. The title may rest upon any of the widely varying forms of deed, or upon inheritance. And in any case the owner's rights are limited, explicitly and implicitly, by those of many other individuals and groups. We have seen how complex is the structure of these tenure rights. The tenure system represents part of the effort of our civilization to weigh social and individual interests and give expression to its current conclusions.

Nevertheless, in our society, with its emphasis upon property, the owner is still in most respects the dominant figure among right holders. Economically the most meaningful single glimpse that we can get of forest lands and timber in the United States is the glimpse of who owns them (Table 32). Despite the unquestioned interests of others, it is generally these owners who determine resource management. They are the producing firms to which we have devoted a large part of this book. Their ideas about production functions, costs, and revenues set the decisions and the status of forestry.

Our nation has seen a good many changes both in the distribution of our forest land among classes of owners and in philosophy about the distribution. One of our early ideals was individual, small-scale proprietorship of rural lands. This ideal had much to do with shaping the policies for disposing of the public domain. And despite occasional reversals and misgivings, we still persist in this ideal. We are predisposed toward atomistic operation of rural land resources, toward the sort of scheme represented in Figure 41*d* (p. 362).

As you know, the *original public domain* was acquired by the United States during the years extending until roughly the time of the Civil War. In this era, public ownership of forest land reached its greatest extent, though such ownership was for the most part regarded as only a passing phase in the national development. The twenty years centering on 1900 saw the principal amassing of the national forests out of the public domain. The national forest and other public forest systems were then greatly enlarged during the rural depression of the 1920s and 1930s. The enlargement was brought about by purchase of private lands and by their reversion, through tax delinquency, into a *new public domain.* The era of enlargement ended with World War II. But shifts still continue between the categories of public forest ownership, particularly shifts of commercial forest land into park or wilderness status.

## PRIVATE FOREST OWNERS

Meanwhile private ownership of forest land, generally increasing trendwise, has exhibited a varying complexion.

*Table 32. Ownership of commercial forest land and saw timber in the United States, 1953*

| Item | North | South | West | All regions |
|---|---|---|---|---|
| Commercial forest (thousand acres) by type of ownership | | | | |
| Private: | | | | |
|   Lumber manufacturer | 3,955 | 18,517 | 12,215 | 34,687 |
|   Pulp manufacturer | 9,224 | 12,188 | 1,864 | 23,276 |
|   Other wood manufacturer | 924 | 2,818 | 677 | 4,419 |
|   Farm | 61,394 | 90,143 | 13,680 | 165,217 |
|   Other | 66,118 | 52,943 | 11,609 | 130,670 |
|     All private ownership | 141,615 | 176,609 | 40,045 | 358,269 |
| Public: | | | | |
|   Federal | 13,094 | 14,196 | 75,834 | 103,124 |
|   State | 12,546 | 1,857 | 4,766 | 19,169 |
|   Local | 6,786 | 626 | 635 | 8,047 |
|     All public ownership | 32,426 | 16,679 | 81,235 | 130,340 |
| All ownership | 174,041 | 193,288 | 121,280 | 488,609 |
| Private commercial forest (thousand acres) by size of holding | | | | |
| Less than 100 acres | 69,338 | 48,315 | 3,370 | 121,023 |
| 100–500 acres | 37,608 | 52,449 | 7,825 | 97,882 |
| 500–5,000 acres | 10,214 | 27,428 | 8,736 | 46,378 |
| 5,000–50,000 acres | 8,279 | 20,140 | 6,400 | 34,669 |
| More than 50,000 acres | 16,176 | 28,277 | 13,714 | 58,317 |
|   All size classes | 141,615 | 176,609 | 40,045 | 358,269 |
| Saw timber (billion board feet) by type of ownership | | | | |
| Private: | | | | |
|   Farm | 102 | 144 | 62 | 308 |
|   Other | 132 | 178 | 462 | 772 |
|     All private ownership | 234 | 322 | 524 | 1,080 |
| Public: | | | | |
|   Federal | 17 | 31 | 853 | 901 |
|   State | 11 | 3 | 50 | 64 |
|   Local | 4 | 1 | 7 | 12 |
|     All public ownership | 32 | 35 | 910 | 977 |
| All ownership | 266 | 357 | 1,434 | 2,057 |
| Number of private holdings by size | | | | |
| Less than 100 acres | 2,316,089 | 1,476,478 | 82,526 | 3,875,093 |
| 100–500 acres | 224,935 | 322,414 | 39,118 | 586,467 |
| 500–5,000 acres | 12,259 | 26,605 | 7,462 | 46,326 |
| 5,000–50,000 acres | 563 | 1,367 | 409 | 2,330 |
| More than 50,000 acres | 75 | 156 | 62 | 283 |
|   All size classes | 2,553,921 | 1,827,020 | 129,577 | 4,510,499 |

SOURCE: U.S. Department of Agriculture, Forest Service: *Timber Resources for America's Future*, Forest Resource Report 14, 1958, table 163, p. 291; table 164, p. 293; table 168, p. 298. The South is as defined in our Chap. 3, p. 23; North is all else east of the tier of states from Montana to New Mexico, except the Black Hills; West includes coastal Alaska.

Much of the original public-domain forest was intentionally conveyed into the hands of large firms, such as railroads, and a good deal more found its way into possession of big lumbering concerns and other large owners. The concentration of forest ownership in the United States appears to have culminated at about the time of World War I, when perhaps four-tenths of all privately held timber was in the hands of fewer than two hundred owners. Shifts in private ownership since then have been the result mainly of two kinds of influence.

First, the influence of *nationwide* depression, which hit the lumber industry in 1920 and deepened until the mid-1930s. This was an era of retrenchment, liquidation, and disaggregation of private land ownership. We shall come back to the story of these times, and to the changing philosophies about forestry problems, in Chapter 33.

Second, the influences of *regional* development and transition from the colonial into the industrial period and thence into the aftermath and toward the conservation period. As we saw in Chapter 21, where the idea of these periods was introduced, the industrial period in each region generally brought an increase in the concentration of private forest ownership; the aftermath, a decrease; and subsequent development toward conservation, an increase again. Thus the South in the mid-1930s and the West Coast in the mid-1940s entered eras of heavy forest acquisition by large private firms. And it may be true for the nation generally that we are living in a time of gradual and steady concentration of private forest ownership (compare pp. 25–26, 316).

The trend toward concentration is contrary to our ancient ideals for rural land ownership. But our ideals are changing, and also our tolerance of contrary trends. Many foresters believe that the big, well-integrated timber-products corporation such as leads the concentration movement is the only inherently "strong" private forest owner: strong in the sense of being able to hold timber land and growing stock over the long term.

Our own studies of forestry economics are leading us to much the same conclusion. Respecting the weakness of the little owner we have had some discussion already, especially in Chapter 10 (pp. 155–156). Some weakness, too, extends into the class of intermediate-size forest owners, such as the closely held family lumber companies that own up to 20,000 or 30,000 acres of forest land. Often these concerns are not small enough to enjoy marked overhead advantages, nor large enough to launch into cost-saving diversification. If inheritance-tax payments are in prospect, they may need to hold back on reinvesting net revenues so as to stay highly liquid. Or the oncoming generation of owners may have no great interest in the business. Handicapped in competing for timber in the open market or for more forest land, these intermediate firms may face at least a moderately uncertain raw-material position. But with their well-blocked holdings and going operations, they make a choice addition to the properties of the big firm. In the South and Pacific Northwest, especially since World War II, many a concern of intermediate size has sold out to the big fellows.

Respecting the strength of the big processing firm, pieces of evidence have come to our attention repeatedly and insistently: the firm's comparatively low alternative rate of return for forestry (pp. 149–150), the premium that the firm can place on timber quality (pp. 136, 331), other sources of efficiency in integration (pp. 228–230), economies of scale (p. 220), marketing advantages (pp. 330–339), incentives toward self-sufficiency in timber supplies (pp. 363–364), incentives for research and development (pp. 294–297)—to mention a few. In Chapter 27 we shall find that there are tax economies of scale in forestry and in corporate consolidation. And beyond these matters one must reflect that we are speaking of an era of general inflation, that land buying is a hedge against inflation, and that the big corporation that uses timber raw material is most able to afford such a hedge.

It is the inevitable logic of economics that resources tend to move into the hands of those firms that can make the most of them, and thus forest land from weak into strong ownership.

[How would you summarize the advantages and disadvantages of the various classes of private forest owners? What are some of the pros and cons of a national policy fostering concentration of land ownership? How far is any concentration trend likely to continue? What factors would change the trend?]

## SUMMARY

Forest-land tenure is the holding of rights in forest land. There are a great many such rights. They are held by owners, government, the general public, creditors, renters, timber operators, and numerous other individuals and groups. The rights that are held, the persons who hold them, and the manner and duration of right holding are determined by law and custom, which vary with time and place. Tenure, like all institutions, at the same time that it is shaping circumstances, is forever being adapted to them. The principal tenure customs and laws of the United States today derive from colonial America and, more remotely, from Britain in the era of feudalism.

Forest ownership in the United States has always been shifting and changing. Two trends are noteworthy: One is the long trend that led to establishment of public forest systems. The other is the recent tendency toward concentration of private forests into strongly held corporate properties.

# Chapter 26

# FORESTRY AND THE GENERAL PROPERTY TAX

IN THIS chapter and the next we shall give thought to a few of the many kinds of taxation that bear upon the forest economy. This chapter will treat of general property taxation.[1] The chapter following will deal with special property-tax plans designed for forestry, and with excise and income taxation. We shall not talk about the inheritance tax, though it does have a bearing upon forestry.

*Taxes* are an ancient, if not always honored, device of governments for raising revenue (shifting resources from individual to collective use) or for regulating economic affairs. They stand near the center of both political and economic life. "The purse of the people," wrote Thomas Jefferson, "is the real seat of sensibility. Let it be drawn upon largely, and they will listen to truths which could not excite them through any other organ." As the small but sharp reflection of public authority, taxes are a symbol of the whole issue between eighteenth- and twentieth-century liberalism, and between these on the one hand and authoritarianism on the other. And as a drain upon everyman's resources and livelihood, taxes symbolize hatefully all costs and risks. To tax and to please are as improbable a pair as to love and to be wise.

In the United States, all levels of government have taxing authority, but each uses somewhat different forms of taxation for its revenue raising

[1] Parts of the chapter appear also as a paper given before the Division of Forest Economics and Policy at the 1957 annual meeting of the Society of American Foresters. See Duerr, William A.: "Forest Tax Problems—How Serious and for Whom?" in *Proceedings Society of American Foresters Meeting 1957*, Society of American Foresters, Washington, 1958, pp. 125–128.

(Table 33). The Federal government places chief reliance on the income tax and does not levy a property tax. Local government (counties, townships or towns, cities, and other units such as school districts and road districts) gets most of its revenue from the property tax. The states rely chiefly on still other forms of tax.

## GENERAL PROPERTY TAX

The property tax that we shall take up first, in this chapter, is the so-called general property tax. This term comes from the time when the

Table 33. Taxes collected by the three levels of government in the United States, fiscal year 1953

| Tax | Federal | State | Local | All governments |
|---|---|---|---|---|
| | Million dollars | Million dollars | Million dollars | Million dollars |
| Individual net income | 29,816 | 969 | 96 | 30,881 |
| Corporate net income | 21,238 | 810 | 7 | 22,055 |
| Inheritance, estate, gift | 881 | 222 | 4 | 1,107 |
| Property | — | 365 | 9,016 | 9,381 |
| General sales | — | 2,433 | 431 | 2,864 |
| Tobacco | 1,655 | 469 | | 2,124 |
| Alcoholic beverage | 2,781 | 545 | | 3,326 |
| Motor fuels | 906 | 2,019 | 287 | 2,925 |
| Amusement | 416 | 19 | | 435 |
| Other selective excises | 5,010 | 809 | | 6,106 |
| Other | 92 | 1,894 | 519 | 2,505 |
| All taxes | 62,796 | 10,552 | 10,361 | 83,709 |

SOURCE: *The Commission on Intergovernmental Relations* ("Kestnbaum Commission report"), U.S. Government Printing Office, Washington, 1955, p. 105.

tax was virtually the sole support of the states and their subdivisions and was broadly based upon nearly all classes of property. The term is still used today, even though the tax is now limited mostly to real estate.

The *general property tax* is a direct annual tax upon the value (*ad valorem*) of the property. Since property, and especially real estate, is fairly easy to describe and somewhat difficult to conceal, it makes a convenient tax base, especially if, as is certainly true of farm real estate, it yields a yearly income. The annual feature of the tax traces basically to the yearly cycle of the agricultural harvest. In the administation of the tax, let us recognize arbitrarily five steps.

## STEPS IN TAX ADMINISTRATION

1. Assessment. The size of the *tax base* is estimated by assessors, who are elected or appointed officials. They place a valuation, which is an attempt to approximate either the full value or some fraction specified by law, upon each tax parcel on their tax rolls. Some of the real property in their territories, such as most of the public land, is not on the rolls, since it is not taxable. A *tax parcel* is a tract of land, part or all of the holding of a single owner, and the taxable property located upon it. The assessment of each parcel is brought up to date annually or at longer intervals, depending upon the law and upon the local procedures. In any case, the assessments are subjected to local *review*, so as to make them comparable from parcel to parcel, and to local and state *equalization*, for comparability as among assessors. The methods and problems of placing a value upon property were considered in Chapter 23.

2. Budgeting. Officials of each *taxing unit*—state, county, school district, and so on—forecast in a budget its outlays for the coming year or other fiscal period. With its various sources of revenue in mind, they then decide what amount shall be raised through the general property tax in the year ahead. This decision, of course, involves such approval by the voters or their elected representatives as is provided for by law.

3. Setting the *tax rate.* For each taxing unit a tax rate is determined for the year by dividing (*a*) its total proposed property tax, as determined in the budgeting, by (*b*) its total tax base, which is the sum of the (reviewed and equalized) assessed values of taxable property within its boundaries. For example, suppose that the total tax base within a certain school district is $10,000,000. That portion of the school budget that is to be met through the property tax is $20,000. The tax rate for this school district is then $20,000 divided by $10,000,000, or 0.2 per cent. This may be referred to as a *millage rate* of 2 mills, meaning 2 mills per dollar, or $2 per thousand, of assessed valuation. The tax rate that applies to any tax parcel is the sum of the rates of all the taxing units within whose boundaries the parcel is situated.

Sometimes we find the budgeting and rate-setting steps just reversed from usual order. The government officials apply an accepted, customary tax rate to the total assessed value. The result is the amount of money they can afford to spend. In some cases the officials must work within a maximum allowable tax rate set by law.

4. Billing the taxpayer. The amount of tax on each parcel is calculated by multiplying the (reviewed and equalized) assessed value of the parcel by the total tax rate. Thus, for example, the tax in fiscal 1960 on Parcel P (Table 34) is $24,000 multiplied by ½ per cent (a 5-mill rate), or $120. The taxpayer's total bill is the sum of taxes on all the parcels he owns.

A little reflection will convince you that, if this scheme is followed, the total of all the tax bills sent out will equal the total property tax budgeted for all the taxing units involved, and furthermore that exact provision is made for the budget of each unit individually. Receipts under the general property tax, unlike those from most other forms of tax, thus are highly predictable. From the standpoint of the taxing unit, particularly the small unit, this fact is a strong point in favor of the property tax.

5. Dealing with *tax delinquency*. Of course, not everyone will pay his taxes—at least, not on time. When economic conditions are hard and

*Table 34. Calculation of general property tax on Parcel P, fiscal year 1960*

| Item | Rate | Amount |
|------|------|--------|
| | *Mills* | *Dollars* |
| Assessed value of Parcel P | — | 24,000 |
| Tax: | | |
|    State | 0.5 | 12 |
|    County | 2.0 | 48 |
|    Town | 1.5 | 36 |
|    School district | 1.0 | 24 |
|     All taxing units | 5.0 | 120 |

people are short of ready cash, many may fail to meet tax bills. Or sometimes the property owner may purposely turn his back on the tax gatherer, as when he has liquidated a forest and intends to abandon the land anyway. The government may try to forestall delinquency by offering discounts for promptness or payment in advance. It may exact mounting penalties for tardiness. Owners who are long delinquent have in some cases been tempted back to the tax office by special offers of partial forgiveness of their taxes and penalties—a rather neat form of suicide for the taxing authority. Or eventually the property may be taken over by the state or local government and either operated publicly (as state or county forests, for example) or sold to some other prospective taxpayer. If the old owner later comes after his former property with a change of heart and a refilled wallet, he can often get it back. In any case, governments are vividly conscious of the virtue of keeping property on the tax rolls—of maintaining their tax base, which is, after all, their livelihood.

## SIZE OF A TAX BILL

With the foregoing sketch of taxing procedure in mind, we are now in position to see what determines the size of a tax bill, which is what makes the taxpayer run. Every normal, red-blooded taxpayer thinks his taxes are too high. Well, what would it take to lower them?

Since the tax bill depends in the first instance on assessed value and tax rate, we can look back of each to find ultimate causes. The thing that is important about the assessed value of your property is not the absolute amount of it but the amount of it in comparison to that of other properties in your taxing units. If all assessments were doubled or all cut in half, it would not affect your tax: It would simply require a halving or doubling, respectively, of the tax rate, leaving your tax unchanged. Assessors seem to have a tendency, which in some states is given the force of law, to underassess everyone's property, keeping the friendship of the taxpayer and passing the buck to those responsible for setting tax rates. Perhaps people feel less unhappy about a high rate than about a high assessment.

What does matter about your assessment is whether it is high or low— measured, say, in percentage of full value—in comparison to the assessments of your neighbors and the other taxpayers in your taxing units. With a given assessment on your property, your tax is higher, the lower the assessments on the other properties. Consequently the real issue about assessment is the issue of fairness, or equity, as among the tax parcels in a unit. We shall take up later how to pin down the idea of equity.

Following the other leg upon which the tax bill stands, the tax rate, we recall that this is the ratio of the budget to the tax base. The budget in question is set by the cost of government and the proportion of this cost that must be defrayed through property taxation. The tax base depends on the size of the taxing unit and its economic development. Thus your tax bill is reduced, other things being equal, by the cutting of government cost or reliance upon the tax, or by an increase in the size or wealth of your taxing unit. [Consider, as a much-discussed example, the consolidation of local governments, such as towns or counties, where the units are overly small. How might such a merger benefit you as a taxpayer?]

It is normal and fashionable for the taxpayer to express himself as fed up with the high cost of government. While granting all due deference to the cause of government economy, we must nevertheless recognize that much money is better spent—and much of our resources better allocated—by society than by individuals. So long as taxation takes from the people funds which will benefit them more when spent by the government than by themselves, the taxation is surely justified. The fact that people growl about it simply illustrates the divergence of the individual from the social interest.

In summary, the two outstanding influences upon your property tax bill are the fairness of the assessment and the cost of government in proportion to its tax base and its other revenue sources.

## HISTORY OF FOREST TAX PROBLEM

Now let us turn from the property tax in general toward the tax specifically upon forest land. The property tax has, over the years, been much more of an issue in the forest economy than elsewhere in rural United States. It is our task to explore this issue and understand it. Let us do so with as much sophistication as we can muster, recognizing especially that the forest property tax is not an isolated event, that it must be studied against the background of property taxation and government finance in general. Does the tax upon forest property seem unduly high? Is it a burden upon the forest owner who is saving his growing stock and postponing his revenues? Does it, in fact, work against forest conservation and thus damage the public interest as well as the private? What can be done to make the forest property tax a good tax—supposing optimistically that any tax can be good? Let us not be so foolish as to imagine that the answers to such questions lie just within forestry and within forest taxation.

Concern over forest property taxation in the United States goes back at least a century and a half. In those days forest depletion, for firewood and construction materials, was spreading out from the population centers in the East. This depletion hadn't advanced a great distance, but it was causing a scarcity of wood because transportation was so poor. Thoughtful citizens turned over in their minds the exploitive actions of the forest owners and lit upon the general property tax, then by far the biggest of all taxes, as a major cause. Poor, benighted forest owners! We find over the years a chronic rash of explanations for their doings—ignorance, carelessness, preoccupation with things other than forestry, exploitive attitudes—and now comes the forest property tax as another suggestion.

At any rate, it appeared to the thoughtful citizens of the time that the tax when levied on forest property was more than just another disagreeable tax—that there was something peculiarly burdensome about it, something not encountered in the tax as applied to other kinds of property, something which, in its effect on resource management, ran against the good of the general public and of forest owners.

Interest in the property tax and alarm over its influence on the forest grew as the decades went by, with perhaps occasional lulls during especially prosperous times. Always the alarm was tied in with general fear of timber depletion, or the wish to encourage tree conservation. Thus concern deepened during the rapid westward spread of forest exploitation in the years up through World War I. Then came the crash of 1920, and rural United States entered bad times, to be followed at the end of the decade by the rest of the economy. During this great interwar depression, forest-product prices suffered the steepest and longest decline in their history; forest-land owners had a disastrous loss of income, and as a lifesaving measure pushed timber liquidation to the limit of the sagging market; tax delinquency grew to be a national problem; and the nation became more aroused over the issue of forest taxation than ever before—or since.

## FOREST TAXATION INQUIRY AND LATER DEVELOPMENTS

The early 1920s witnessed a growing conviction in Federal government circles that there was need for a sharp counter-attack upon the forestry ills of the times. In 1924, the Congress passed the Clarke-McNary Act, one section of which called for a nationwide study of forest taxation. Under the title Forest Taxation Inquiry, this study during the next several years was a major project of the Forest Service's Branch of Research. The Inquiry was notable not only for its contributions toward progress in forest taxation but also for the fact that it was one of the first large research jobs in forestry economics in this country, and the men who worked on it organized our first generation of forestry economists.

The final report[2] of the Forest Taxation Inquiry, a monumental work, was brought out in 1935. It described forest taxation in the United States, both the general property tax and certain other taxes. It analyzed the effects of the property tax upon forest practice. It reviewed the problems of local government finance, of assessment, and of tax delinquency. And it made suggestions for better forms of taxation for forests, better assessment, and other improved procedures. The report today is still the basic reference in the field.

The ideas of the Forest Taxation Inquiry did not take hold at once, and even the best ideas were slow to catch. Meantime the national mood changed immensely. Even in 1935 it was beginning to change, and new circumstances were coming to surround forest taxation. The property tax itself, which had been rising since time immemorial, leveled off. Relatively, it shrank in importance as other forms of revenue grew and, later, as inflation set in. The United States climbed back out of the Depression, and after World War II the nation at large and American forestry prospered as never before. This was no time for wailing over forest taxation, especially since the biggest tax of all, the Federal income levy, was now working, in ways that we shall see in Chapter 27, to the immense advantage of the forest owners, particularly the larger ones. And the smaller owners, to whom income-tax favors meant less, commonly now had good

[2] Fairchild, Fred Rogers, and Associates: *Forest Taxation in the United States,* U.S. Department of Agriculture Miscellaneous Publication 218, 1935. A helpful condensation was written by Hall, R. Clifford: *The Forest-tax Problem and Its Solution Summarized,* U.S. Department of Agriculture Circular 358, 1935.

outside sources of regular income to help with their taxpaying. Furthermore, their multiple interests in their forest land represented just so many strong incentives for tax payment. To reinforce these effects, administration of the property tax began to be improved. It was not surprising, then, to find only here and there real distress and a sense of urgency over forest taxation.

Through the years, three issues have seemed to stand out concerning the general property tax in its effects on forest land use and forestry practice: the *amount of the tax,* the *form of the tax,* and partly underlying these, the *fairness of the tax* as between one property and another. Let us have a look at each of these three issues.

## EFFECTS OF HIGH TAXES: CONFISCATION

As for the amount of the tax in its effect upon forest property, the most drastic possible effect is, of course, confiscation. A property tax is a **confiscatory tax** when it promises to be as high as the property's net income before the tax—in other words, when it promises to extinguish the value of the property. For forest property, confiscation results when the tax is high enough to wipe out just that part of the value that cannot be liquidated. Then the owner's tendency is to abandon the land or find another use for it, after liquidating any merchantable timber. An example will help to make these points clear.

Consider an average acre on a forest property that has a production function as shown in Table 35 when managed under annual sustained yield. Assume that all growing stock and growth has a sales value of 10 cents per cubic foot. And assume that the owner's alternative rate of return is 4 per cent. Suppose that the stand is managed with a growing stock of about 1,500 cubic feet per acre, this being the best stocking so far as we can tell from the data at hand.

Now, leaving costs other than interest out of the picture for the moment, let us figure the capitalized, or expectation, value per acre of this forest. Using formula 2a from Table 9 (p. 110), and taking $r$ in this formula as the gross return, we find

$$V_0 = \frac{r}{i} = \frac{10.25}{0.04} = \$256.25$$

This is the value of land and timber together. The merchantable timber, at 10 cents per cubic foot, has a *liquidation value* of \$150. The remainder, \$106.25, is the value of the land (along with any unmerchantable growing stock). In the largely costless situation we are studying, \$106.25 is the ceiling price of the land. The ceiling rent is 4 per cent of the ceiling price, or \$4.25. The rent arises by virtue of the excess of annual revenue

($10.25) over cost (4 per cent of $150 = $6.00)—that is to say, the excess of the average growth rate over the alternative rate of return—which is the same as saying the excess of average over marginal timber growth.

However, forest properties cannot be operated for nothing. Let us suppose that in this case there are anticipated management costs $(S)$, in-

**Table 35.** *Timber production function and revenues of the average acre*
*in a hypothetical forest property*

| Timber volume | Annual growth | Total annual revenue | Marginal revenue |
|---|---|---|---|
| (1) | (2) | (3) | (4) |
| *Cubic feet* | *Cubic feet* | *Dollars* | *Per cent* |
| 1,000 | 76.0 | 7.60 | |
| | | | 6.3 |
| 1,100 | 82.3 | 8.23 | |
| | | | 5.8 |
| 1,200 | 88.1 | 8.81 | |
| | | | 5.3 |
| 1,300 | 93.4 | 9.34 | |
| | | | 4.8 |
| 1,400 | 98.2 | 9.82 | |
| | | | 4.3 |
| 1,500 | 102.5 | 10.25 | |
| | | | 3.8 |
| 1,600 | 106.3 | 10.63 | |
| | | | 3.3 |
| 1,700 | 109.6 | 10.96 | |
| | | | 2.8 |
| 1,800 | 112.4 | 11.24 | |
| | | | 2.3 |
| 1,900 | 114.7 | 11.47 | |
| | | | 1.8 |
| 2,000 | 116.5 | 11.65 | |

cluding administration and protection, of $1 per acre annually, and property taxes $(G)$ also amounting to $1. We will leave out of consideration as a cost the income tax, which would affect our figures, but not the principle. Now we can get a better estimate of value:

$$V_0 = \frac{r - S - G}{i} = \frac{8.25}{0.04} = \$206.25$$

The ceiling price of the land alone is $56.25, and its ceiling rent is 4 per cent of this, or $2.25.

Thus we find that the effect of annual costs is to subtract directly from the ceiling rent of the land. If the costs were $3, the ceiling rent would be $1.25. If the costs were $4, the rent would be 25 cents. And if the costs were $4.25 or more, ceiling rent (and ceiling price and land value) would be wiped out. And these costs would be confiscatory, for property value would become

$$V_0 = \frac{r - S - G}{i} = \frac{6.00}{0.04} = \$150.00$$

which is the same as timber value alone. That is to say, the owner might just as well sell his timber and quit forestry as continue to manage such a property.

We have here the working of what we may call the *principle of choice in timber management:* If the expectation value of a firm's timber property exceeds the liquidation value, the firm has an incentive to grow timber; but if liquidation value equals or exceeds expectation value, the firm tends to liquidate. This, you will observe, is simply an extension of the obvious rule that the firm tends to choose its most valuable alternative.

And so we conclude that a forest tax (or *any cost*) is confiscatory if it extinguishes land value—if it is as high as the ceiling rent before the tax.

The amount of tax that it takes to be confiscatory varies immensely with the quality of the land. And just how heavy a tax a given tract of forest can bear is as hard a question as what will forestry pay—in fact, it is nearly the same question, and one that will continue to stump foresters for many a long year. However, we have all seen poorly productive lands for which almost any tax would be confiscatory. Most such lands are necessarily off the tax rolls, in public ownership. On the other hand, reasonably productive forest sites that bear a well-regulated growing stock can stand a surprisingly high tax. In our principal timber regions, on the better lands intensively managed, assuming 1958 prices and cost rates, it would probably take an annual tax of $5 to $10 per acre to limit the net return to a bare 4 per cent on growing stock alone.

## OTHER EFFECTS OF HIGH TAXES

As taxes go up, and well before they become confiscatory, their height may be a cause of trouble. There seem to be mostly two kinds of trouble: One is increased risk, resulting mainly from the threat of still higher taxes, and perhaps of confiscation. The other is the sheer difficulty of paying the tax, especially if the taxpayer's main source of funds is a forest that needs building up.

So far as the risk is concerned, it resembles that arising from any other sort of cost. By raising the alternative rate of return, it militates against capital-intensive forestry and long-term investments. It leads the taxpayer toward practices with a quick return, even liquidation. When property taxes are on the uphill climb, such risk is especially serious. When the tax is believed to have reached a plateau, it carries less risk. Furthermore, increasingly orderly and stable tax administration and better public understanding of the administrative procedure also help to lessen risk.

So far as the difficulty of paying the tax is concerned, its effect upon forestry is not necessarily bad. We hear of owners who resort to some liquidation of timber in order to meet their taxes. But we hear also of owners who, for the same purpose, intensify their timber-growing business or add nontimber enterprises—for example, leasing of hunting privileges. One is a little inclined to infer that these owners follow their best alternatives, regardless of the tax. Perhaps the tax nudges them into seeking more vigorously their best combination, whatever this may be, just as any other type of cost carries with it incentives to economize. Thus we can see the power of taxation as a governmental device for regulating land management—or, for that matter, land use.

[How would the foregoing effects of taxation be modified if the taxpayer were able to escape part of the tax by passing it on to timber buyers in the form of higher prices? Are timberland owners able to do this?]

All these effects of high taxes vary with the type and scale of ownership of the forest. For the very small-scale owner, there may not be much absolute difference in total between a high tax and a low one. In the case of the small absentee owner, his income and his diversified interests in his forest patch may make the tax seem an easy load. For the farmer, the tax on the woods is often but a small part of his total, perhaps not even distinguishable on the bill. Hardships do indeed cause these little owners to cut down growing stock, but it is probably rare that taxes make the hardship. If a real burden from high taxes is to be found anywhere, it is more likely to be on the big holdings.

The effects of high taxes vary, too, with alternations of prosperity and depression. As a given amount of tax is more of a burden on poor forest sites than on good, so it places more burden on any forest in hard times, when incomes are low and alternative rates of return correspondingly high. And it is more of a burden when money is scarce, when commercial interest rates are high. It is at such times that the adverse effects of a high tax upon the forest show up—when presumably the tax problem is demonstrated. What is demonstrated, however, is not only the tax's adverse effects, if any. Indeed, what is shown is primarily the effects of low incomes and high commercial interest rates, which are of themselves adverse to forestry, tax or no tax.

It looks as though the issue concerning the amount of the property tax comes down to the familiar issue about the size of any cost item—at least, of any annually recurring item. And among such items, the property tax is not generally first in size. That place would usually be taken by the item of interest on investments (Chap. 8, pp. 104–105). This is not, of course, to deny that cost reduction, even to the secondary items, is a good thing. Firms usually work at cost cutting through raising their efficiency. In the case of the property-tax cost, this may mean modernizing local government finance and operation, as through mergers and internal streamlining. Some progress in this direction is being made. For example, the total number of governmental units in the United States declined a fourth between 1942 and 1952. The reduction was mainly in school districts and townships.

## EFFECT OF THE FORM OF TAX

We have been looking at the amount of the property tax. Let us turn now to the second of the three outstanding issues in forest taxation: the form of the tax in its relation to forestry. We will touch upon two cases: that in which the tax is a fixed cost and that where it is a variable cost. To analyze the influence of a tax upon forest practice, we will use our customary approach through a study of the firm's best combination. But let us use additionally a device for general thinking that is often very useful in tracing the influence of costs upon people's actions: Let us reason that people dislike costs and therefore tend to adjust their affairs so as to reduce their costs if possible, according to the principle of economizing productive agents (p. 89). Thus, they seek to cut their tax payments if they can—that is, they try to hide from the tax collector.

For instance, we know from Chapter 10 (p. 149) that an income tax tends to favor building up the forest, since it reduces the alternative rate of return. Now, if we like, we can reason that when a tax is put into effect upon income from the sale or cutting of timber, forest owners will find a way to hide part of their assets from the tax gatherer: They will cut a little less timber and let growing stocks accumulate for a while. They will not, of course, cease cutting and escape the gatherer altogether. That would be chopping off their noses to spite their faces. What they will have a tendency to do is postpone cutting until a new combination has been reached that is best in light of the tax.

Thus in Table 35, a new income tax, or a higher income-tax rate, such as would lower the alternative rate of return from 4 to 3 per cent, would raise the best stocking from 1,500 to 1,700 cubic feet per acre and call for about two years' postponement of the cut.

Now, to apply this sort of reasoning to the property tax, imagine, first, a tax that is administered in such a way that the assessment is never brought up to date or changed but is just recopied in the books from year to year. This old-fashioned method is going out of style but is still followed to some extent. The assessor is freed from the chore of examining the property and can devote his time to other work or just take life easy.

*Table 36. Timber production function and revenues of the average acre in a hypothetical forest property, assuming annual management costs of $1 and fixed property-tax costs as stated*

| Timber volume | Annual revenue before tax | $1 annual tax | | $2 annual tax | |
|---|---|---|---|---|---|
| | | Net annual revenue | Marginal revenue | Net annual revenue | Marginal revenue |
| (1) | (2) | (3) | (4) | (5) | (6) |
| *Cubic feet* | *Dollars* | *Dollars* | *Per cent* | *Dollars* | *Per cent* |
| 1,000 | 6.60 | 5.60 | | 4.60 | |
| | | | 6.3 | | 6.3 |
| 1,100 | 7.23 | 6.23 | | 5.23 | |
| | | | 5.8 | | 5.8 |
| 1,200 | 7.81 | 6.81 | | 5.81 | |
| | | | 5.3 | | 5.3 |
| 1,300 | 8.34 | 7.34 | | 6.34 | |
| | | | 4.8 | | 4.8 |
| 1,400 | 8.82 | 7.82 | | 6.82 | |
| | | | 4.3 | | 4.3 |
| 1,500 | 9.25 | 8.25 | | 7.25 | |
| | | | 3.8 | | 3.8 |
| 1,600 | 9.63 | 8.63 | | 7.63 | |
| | | | 3.3 | | 3.3 |
| 1,700 | 9.96 | 8.96 | | 7.96 | |
| | | | 2.8 | | 2.8 |
| 1,800 | 10.24 | 9.24 | | 8.24 | |
| | | | 2.3 | | 2.3 |
| 1,900 | 10.47 | 9.47 | | 8.47 | |
| | | | 1.8 | | 1.8 |
| 2,000 | 10.65 | 9.65 | | 8.65 | |

The amount of the tax may change with changes in the tax rate, but these changes are unrelated to the condition of the forest. In other words, this tax is a fixed cost so far as forest practice is concerned. How hide from the tax collector?

Aside from going out of the forest business—which, generally speaking, is a sensible move only if the tax threatens confiscation—there isn't any way to escape the collector. Since the tax is unrelated to the condition of the property, nothing that the taxpayer can do to the forest will help him lighten the tax. Short of confiscation, the tax may rise or fall without having one whit of effect upon forest practice. This is certainly what we would expect of a fixed cost—that it would have no bearing on the best combination.

The foregoing principle is illustrated in Table 36, which gives more data for our same illustrative forest property. With the assumption that annual management costs are $1 per acre, annual revenue before the tax (col. 2) is taken as $1 less than the value of the annual growth (Table 35, col. 2) at 10 cents per cubic foot. Net annual revenues from the timber stand are then computed, assuming first a tax of $1 (Table 36, col. 3) and then a tax of $2 (col. 5). The tax certainly affects this total revenue, but it has no effect at all upon marginal revenue (Table 36, cols. 4 and 6, and Table 35, col. 4). Consequently, the alternative rate of return being unchanged, there is no influence upon the management program.

## VARIABLE VERSUS FIXED-COST TAX

Suppose, now, that this old-fashioned tax administration is given a good overhauling—for, after all, the property tax is supposed to be an ad valorem tax, and there is no good reason why the amount of the tax should be the same for a stand of 2,000 cubic feet per acre as for one of 1,000. Suppose that assessment practice is modernized so that the assessment is made to move with changes in property value. Confronted with such a tax, the forest owner now can find a place to hide from the tax gatherer. He can escape part of the tax by reducing his property value a little. That is to say, this tax favors forest depletion. And if tax rates go up, the pressure upon the forest increases. This characteristic of an ad valorem property tax literally administered is fundamental and significant. Let us examine the working of it in the case of our illustrative forest, taking the tax as a variable cost, first at a rate of 4.85 mills on an assessment equal to net property value and next at a rate of 9.70 mills. The first rate (actually 4.848 · · ·) is chosen as that which gives a tax of $1 on the stand of 1,500 cubic feet. The other is taken as double the first.

In order to see what effect the tax has on the best combination, let us figure the marginal revenues under each of the two tax rates (Table 37). We begin by computing the value of the property, so that we can work out the tax. Notice, now, that with the tax expressed as a rate $(g)$ on net property value—that is, value *after* the tax, $V_a$—value and tax are mutually interdependent, and the former must be found by the relationship

$$V_a = \frac{r - S - gV_a}{i}$$

which boils down to

$$V_a = \frac{r - S}{i + g}$$

You should give some careful thought to this formula for value, since it helps reveal the workings of an ad valorem property tax. What it says is that net property value is equal to net income before the tax, capitalized at a rate equal to the interest rate plus the tax rate. In other words, in

Table 37. *Timber production function and revenues of the average acre in a hypothetical forest property, assuming annual management costs of $1 and variable property-tax costs as stated*

| Timber volume | Annual revenue before tax | Tax rate 4.85 mills | | | | Tax rate 9.70 mills | | | |
|---|---|---|---|---|---|---|---|---|---|
| | | Property value | Tax | Total net revenue | Marginal revenue | Property value | Tax | Total net revenue | Marginal revenue |
| (1) | (2) | (3) | (4) | (5) | (6) | (7) | (8) | (9) | (10) |
| *Cubic feet* | *Dollars* | *Dollars* | *Dollars* | *Dollars* | *Per cent* | *Dollars* | *Dollars* | *Dollars* | *Per cent* |
| 1,000 | 6.60 | 147.16 | 0.71 | 5.89 | | 132.80 | 1.29 | 5.31 | |
| | | | | | 5.6 | | | | 5.1 |
| 1,100 | 7.23 | 161.21 | 0.78 | 6.45 | | 145.48 | 1.41 | 5.82 | |
| | | | | | 5.2 | | | | 4.7 |
| 1,200 | 7.81 | 174.14 | 0.84 | 6.97 | | 157.15 | 1.52 | 6.29 | |
| | | | | | 4.7 | | | | 4.2 |
| 1,300 | 8.34 | 185.96 | 0.90 | 7.44 | | 167.82 | 1.63 | 6.71 | |
| | | | | | 4.3 | | | | 3.9 |
| 1,400 | 8.82 | 196.66 | 0.95 | 7.87 | | 177.48 | 1.72 | 7.10 | |
| | | | | | 3.8 | | | | 3.5 |
| 1,500 | 9.25 | 206.25 | 1.00 | 8.25 | | 186.13 | 1.80 | 7.45 | |
| | | | | | 3.4 | | | | 3.0 |
| 1,600 | 9.63 | 214.72 | 1.04 | 8.59 | | 193.77 | 1.88 | 7.75 | |
| | | | | | 2.9 | | | | 2.7 |
| 1,700 | 9.96 | 222.08 | 1.08 | 8.88 | | 200.41 | 1.94 | 8.02 | |
| | | | | | 2.5 | | | | 2.2 |
| 1,800 | 10.24 | 228.32 | 1.11 | 9.13 | | 206.05 | 2.00 | 8.24 | |
| | | | | | 2.1 | | | | 1.9 |
| 1,900 | 10.47 | 233.45 | 1.13 | 9.34 | | 210.68 | 2.04 | 8.43 | |
| | | | | | 1.6 | | | | 1.4 |
| 2,000 | 10.65 | 237.47 | 1.15 | 9.50 | | 214.30 | 2.08 | 8.57 | |

order to account for the capitalization of a tax, one may either subtract the absolute amount of the tax from the numerator, as we did previously, or add the tax rate to the denominator.

[Why bother with this new formula? Would it not be simpler just to work, as before, with the absolute amount of the tax?]

For the same timber volumes and before-tax revenues as in Table 36, we use the formula to determine property value under each of the two tax rates (Table 37, cols. 3 and 7). Thus, for example, the value $147.16 in the first line of column 3 is computed by dividing $6.60 by 0.04485. The absolute amount of the tax (cols. 4 and 8) is then derived by applying the tax rate to these values. And the net revenue (after tax) in the next two columns is the before-tax revenue minus the tax. Finally, marginal revenue (cols. 6 and 10) is worked out from the successive differences in total revenue, expressed in per cent of the $10 increase in timber value. The alternative rate of return being 4 per cent, the best program for this forest property when the tax is a variable cost at 4.85 mills is 1,400 cubic feet, 100 feet less than when the tax was a fixed cost. And if the tax rate is doubled, a still further reduction of growing stock is indicated.

[Notice that the total net revenues in Table 37 turn out to be 4 per cent of the property values. Why?

[Also observe that doubling the tax rate does not double the tax. Why not?

[Was it correct to compute marginal revenue by expressing the increase in total revenue as a percentage of the increase in timber value? Why not express the former as a percentage of the increase in *property* value, thus recognizing the very real fact that the tax serves to check the rise in property value as timber stocking goes up? Try recomputing the marginal revenue, using this latter approach. Observe the interesting figures that you get. Can you explain what they mean?]

## FAIRNESS OF A TAX: PARCEL BIAS

The two forest-taxation issues that we have talked about, the amount and the form of the property tax, are partly reducible to the third and last one, to which we now turn: the tax's fairness. By *fairness* let us mean equitable treatment of all properties, forest and nonforest—placing commensurate burdens upon them—for example, in terms of the percentage of property income or value taken by the tax. At the same time, let us grant that definitions of fairness may vary. To some, a fair tax may be one that subsidizes certain classes of property. The fairness then presumably consists in satisfying the community interest in such subsidy. In any case it is the privilege of every taxed group to define fairness and attempt, as an influence center, to put its concept into use.

We know of the long-standing indictment of the general property tax as unfair to forest owners. The corn stalk, it is said, walks up to the collector's office just once, whereas the tree is obliged to march there countless times, borrowing all the while on its credit. This certainly sounds unfair.

However, the unfairness of the forest property tax does not follow necessarily from the fact that trees take a long time to grow. What it does follow from is a bias in the tax assessment, coupled in some cases with other special circumstances. There seem to be two different sorts of bias that lead to an unfair tax.

One sort of bias is that which results in under- or overvaluing a property or group of properties in relation to the rest. Let us refer to this kind of bias as *parcel bias,* since it directly entails comparison of one tax parcel with another. An example is the tendency toward *regressive* appraisals: too high assessments on low-value properties and too low on those of high value. Here the result often is to work a particular hardship on the owners of forest parcels. In general, bias may arise from the fact that assessors are less familiar with forest property than other kinds and less skilled in appraising it. There is reason to believe that parcel biases are prevalent and substantial, providing a fairly ready opportunity for bettering tax assessments.

### TIME BIAS

The other sort of bias leads to an unfair tax upon forest properties where forest capital is being either accumulated or depleted over at least several years. This bias is exerted by assessments through the manner in which they are changed from time to time, and so let us call it a *time bias.* The most ordinary example of a time-biased assessment is the one we analyzed on pages 443 to 445: the assessment that was modernized so as to move closely with changes in property value. If the assessment for any ad valorem property tax has a time bias, then the tax will be unfairly high on forest properties being built up and unfairly low on properties being depleted. Fairness, here, is in comparison to properties that are on sustained annual yield. If either the owner of the corn field or the owner of the woods is lucky enough to get a rather constant annual return from his property, then he will be fairly treated by the property tax, even if the assessment practice tends toward a time bias.

To dig a little deeper into the foregoing propositions, let us study examples of two forest properties, one on annual sustained yield and the other whose yield is delayed. Let us figure the tax burden on each property and attempt to grasp the why of it.

We already have in Table 37 the data for a property on annual sustained yield. What is the burden of the 4.85-mill tax on the optimum stand of 1,400 cubic feet? If a property owner's objective is in terms of net income, then the tax burden can be measured, as suggested earlier, by the extent to which the tax reduces net income. The reduction, expressed in per cent, is called the *tax ratio.* The tax ratio ($R$) may equally well be thought of as the percentage reduction in property value. That is,

$$R = \frac{100 \times \text{capitalized tax}}{\text{value before tax}}$$

Since in the 1,400-cubic foot case (Table 37) the property value before tax ($8.82 capitalized at 4 per cent) is $220.50 and the capitalized tax is $23.84,[3] the tax ratio turns out to be 10.8 per cent. That is to say, this 4.85-mill property tax puts the same burden upon the firm as would a 10.8 per cent income tax.

## DELAYED-YIELD EXAMPLE OF TIME BIAS

Now contrast this case with that of a 4.85-mill tax upon a delayed-yield property—say, one that produces an income only at 20-year intervals and has just produced in the past year. Let us suppose that the anticipated gross periodic revenue per acre is $292.39, so that $V_b$, the current property value *before* taxes (but after other costs: $1 per acre each year) is the same as in the previous example:

$$V_b = \frac{292.39}{1.04^{20} - 1} - \frac{1}{0.04} = \$220.50$$

Here the periodic return is capitalized by formula 3a (p. 110) and reduced by the amount of the annual costs capitalized by formula 2a. Value now is at the low point of the cycle, and the tax, which is in proportion to value, is also at its low. During the next two decades, both will rise as yield time approaches. They will reach a high point just before the harvest and then fall, to begin another cycle.

To find the present tax ratio for this property, we compute the *after-tax* value by incorporating the tax rate into the same formulas as above:

$$V_a = \frac{292.39}{1.04485^{20} - 1} - \frac{1}{0.04485} = \$187.30$$

We subtract this after-tax value from value before tax to find that the capitalized tax is $33.20. We then determine the tax ratio as 33.20/220.50, or 15.1 per cent. Thus the tax ratio on this particular delayed-yield property is nearly four-tenths greater than the ratio on the annual sustained-yield property.

And if you will draw up further examples for yourself, making sure that they are comparable by using the tax rate of 4.85 mills and the interest rate of 4 per cent, you will find that the ad valorem property tax will always lay a burden greater than 10.8 per cent on delayed-yield for-

[3] Some of the calculations here and in other places in the chapter cannot be checked perfectly, because after they were made the fractions were rounded off.

ests—any forests on which the growing stock is being built up. On the other hand, you will discover that the tax is relatively favorable to accelerated-yield forests, such as those being depleted or liquidated or those on periodic sustained yield which are close to yield time. For instance, the property that we have just studied, the one on a 20-year cycle, will have a value before taxes of $492.20 in the year just before the harvest, and an after-tax value of $458.14, so that the tax ratio will be 6.9 per cent.

When we search for an explanation of the relatively heavy tax burden on delayed-yield forests and turn again to our examples of delayed yield and annual sustained yield, we may well be struck by the fact that here are two properties with identical before-tax values and identical tax rates, and yet quite different taxes. On the annual-yield property the tax is 95 cents each year. In the delayed-yield case, the tax is 91 cents this year and will rise to $2.22 in the year before the harvest. The latter program takes nearly a 40 per cent larger slice out of property value than does the former program. Clearly, if this is supposed to be a tax upon value, there is an error somewhere.

## ASSESSMENT AND TIME BIAS

Taking the annual-yield case as the standard and accepting the idea of uniform tax rates, one comes directly to the only room for error, the assessment of the delayed-yield property. The assessment is too low (!) by virtue of being based on the assumption that assessments and therefore taxes will subsequently rise. If today's assessed value takes into account the expected yields, and then if the assessment is later increased along with the rise in property value, double counting becomes involved, for these expected increases in value were already reflected in the original assessment. Thus the time bias is introduced. The equitable assessment, in our example, is the value before tax minus a capitalized constant tax:

$$V_a = V_b - \frac{G}{i}$$

and the equitable tax is this assessed value multiplied by the tax rate:

$$G = g\left(V_b - \frac{G}{i}\right) = \frac{giV_b}{g+i}$$

Solving for $G$ in the delayed-yield example gives 95 cents, which, as we know from the annual-yield case, means a tax ratio of 10.8 per cent.

[Does it seem to you that this reasoning is wrong? Does it strike you that wherever forest yields are irregular, one has a choice between a tax that is constant over time and a tax ratio that is constant: that one cannot have both? And therefore that the problem of equity may be insoluble? Consider, for instance, the example (p. 448) of the property that is on the verge of a periodic yield. Its before-tax value is $492.20, and the equitable tax, by our formula, is $2.13. How will the owner of this property feel a year hence when his harvest has been made and he has a delayed-yield business on his hands just like his neighbor—save that the neighbor will be paying a 95-cent tax while he is paying $2.13? Can you find equity in this situation?]

If the general property tax is unfair to forestry, then there are the two alternative approaches toward equity: One is to change to some special form of property taxation that will be less sensitive to the timing of revenues. This may well mean altering the tax in the direction of a levy on income—for example, setting up a yield tax. The other approach toward equity is to accept the property tax essentially as it stands, but to modify assessment practice so as to lessen its biases. We will take up these measures briefly in Chapter 27.

Meanwhile we must understand that fairness in any case is only a general goal: that complete precision in the matter is beyond the reach of both a special property tax and a modified assessment. For one reason, the attainment of fairness is finally an administrative rather than a technical problem. Some errors and deficiencies are put up with simply because further refinement would not justify its marginal cost. For another reason, the concept of fairness under the property tax must, by the nature of this tax, be interpreted for the average situation rather than for the individual taxpayer. The tax is, after all, levied on property, not on persons, though admittedly the latter become involved. A property tax cannot be expected to individualize fairness, as personal income taxation seeks to do. To give general effect to a highly refined concept of fairness would require abolishing the property tax altogether—which, happy as the thought may be, is probably a little too much to hope for.

## SUMMARY

Ad valorem taxes are levied, mainly by local governments, against real estate, including forests. These general property taxes have long caused public concern by supposedly creating special problems of forest management. National concern, however, has greatly diminished since its peak at the time of the Forest Taxation Inquiry.

Today three issues regarding the tax seem especially noteworthy. First, the amount of the tax: This is a function of government cost and, for each property, of relative assessments. A high tax makes for risk and other difficulties and ultimately may be confiscatory. Second, the form of the tax: Administered so as to be a fixed cost, the tax is more favorable to forest conservation than when it is a variable cost, though in any case the general property tax is discouraging to forestry as compared with a tax upon income or net yield. Third, and partly underlying the other two issues, the fairness of the tax: The general property tax may work a special hardship upon the forest owner because of bias in assessment, of two sorts. Parcel bias is that which directly over- or undervalues one parcel in comparison to others. Time bias is that which leads to over- or undervaluation through the manner in which the assessment is changed from time to time.

# Chapter 27

# SPECIAL PROPERTY TAXES AND TAXES ON OUTPUT

Y OU MAY well imagine that with all the hue and cry after the general property tax and the bad odor in which the tax has so miserably existed over the years in forestry circles, there have been plenty of schemes for changing it to soften its supposedly harsh effects.

Let us recognize three types of *special property tax* as applied to forests. *First,* there is a relatively primitive type, in which the form of the general property tax is unchanged but the amount of it is altered directly by specifying a ceiling or providing for the taxpayer an exemption, bounty, prize, or rebate. *Second,* there is a comparatively sophisticated type, in which again the general form of the tax is unaltered but the amount is indirectly adjusted in the interest of equity through modification of the assessment, the tax rate, or the timing of payments. *Third,* there is a type in which the form of taxation is fundamentally changed by substituting, as in a yield tax, output for capital value as a basis for the levy. We shall consider, in turn, each of these three sorts of special property tax.[1]

We shall then take up two other types of forest taxation: the severance tax and the income tax.

[1] The account is based largely upon the following references: Fairchild, Fred Rogers, and Associates: *Forest Taxation in the United States,* U.S. Department of Agriculture Miscellaneous Publication 218, 1935, pp. 341–404, 552–618; Williams, Ellis T.: *State Forest Tax Law Digest 1956,* United States Forest Service, Washington, 1957; Marquis, Ralph W.: *Forest Yield Taxes,* U.S. Department of Agriculture Circular 899, 1952.

## EXEMPTIONS, BOUNTIES, REBATES

As for exemptions, bounties, prizes, rebates, and ceilings, the honor perhaps falls to the State of Massachusetts for passing the first law of this sort: an act of 1819 to provide "premiums and encouragement" for growing and conserving ship timber. From this quiet New England beginning that was only vaguely connected with forest taxation, up through the first decade of the twentieth century, marched a procession of such acts. The people of the prairie and plains states, with their keen awareness not only of timber scarcity but also of alleged forest influences upon climate, led the parade in the later years. The first exemption law was that of Nebraska Territory in 1861. A typical law of this kind is that of Iowa, passed in 1906, requiring that planted trees (but not the land) be exempt from property taxes. An example of a tax ceiling (in this case a *specified tax*) is found in Wisconsin's Woodland Tax Law of 1953, setting a levy of 20 cents per acre per year upon small tracts that have been offered and accepted for classification under the law. The great majority of such special legislation has fallen into disuse or been repealed. In some cases the enthusiasm that once attended the idea has died. Or the laws proved unpopular or ineffective or even unconstitutional. Or the concessions allowed the taxpayers proved too expensive.

Today some fourteen states have tax laws of the type under discussion. Most are exemption laws, and most of these are *mandatory* rather than *optional* in application—that is, responsibility for taking the initiative to put eligible lands under the provisions of the law rests with the public officials and not with the property owner. Some of the laws have a regulatory feature: They provide that, in order to be eligible for the special tax treatment, the taxpayer must follow specified management practices and perhaps pass periodic inspections by public forest officers.

[How effective would you expect such tax measures to be? How large an exemption, bounty, prize, rebate, or tax reduction would be necessary to get taxpayers to put land into forest use or to follow certain management practices? What would be the effect upon intensity of management of forest lands? Under what circumstances would the provisions of the law represent the abatement of a fixed cost (fixed in relation to output), and under what conditions the abatement of a variable cost—and what would be the difference in result?]

Quite apparently, special property-tax legislation pointed directly to the amount of the tax has some weaknesses. It has weaknesses apart from limited effectiveness. It makes no rational provision for fairness and may overshoot the mark by as much as the general property tax may fall short. Where it specifies the tax, it introduces rigidity that is totally out of keeping with the dynamics of economic life. Furthermore, it often constitutes a thinly disguised *subsidy* to forestry—that is, a gift or grant to promote forestry practice or forest-land use. The subsidy feature is commonly called bad by the experts. [How do you feel about it? Is it wrong to use a tax as a vehicle for subsidy in the public interest? If so, what is wrong about it—subsidy in general, or using the tax? Why?]

Now let us turn from the first type of special property tax, that works immediately upon the amount of the tax, to the second type, that works more subtly through assessed value, the tax rate, or the timing of tax payments. There exist few going examples of this second type. The type is important and interesting mainly because it includes all three alternative tax modifications recommended by the Forest Taxation Inquiry. For their historical interest and for the light they throw upon forest property taxation, let us review very briefly these three proposals: the adjusted property tax, the deferred timber tax, and the differential timber tax.

## ADJUSTED PROPERTY TAX

The *adjusted property tax* is designed to come as close as practicable to perfection in the sense of producing the same tax ratio for all properties regardless of the timing of revenues. The adjustment in question is in the assessment of the property, the other features of the general property tax being untouched. The assessment is adjusted so as to remove its time bias. It is permitted to change with unexpected changes in revenue or cost rates, such as log prices or the cost of labor for logging. But it is not permitted to change with expected changes in value—namely, those arising from (1) the approach of yield time, which increases value, (2) the payment of costs, which also raises value, and (3) the receipt of incomes, which reduces value. From this ideal, the Forest Taxation Inquiry then proposed two practical departures.

First, the Inquiry proposed that assessments should be allowed to rise as a result of the payment of costs other than taxes. Thus assessments on delayed-yield properties would gradually revert to unadjusted levels over a period of years. This fact would help solve some long-range problems that might otherwise come up, as when a delayed-yield property was converted to sustained yield and was permitted to retain its old tax advantage, an advantage that sustained-yield properties of long standing would not have. Again, the provision for letting assessments rise with cost payments would encourage property owners to get onto a basis of sustained yield so as not to be susceptible to damage from time bias. And it would let assessors escape the administrative problem of keeping track of costs other than taxes.

Second, the Inquiry proposed that assessors should overlook any part of earnings that would cause a net downward adjustment of the assessed value. This procedure would dodge various troublesome administrative issues. For example, it would eliminate the necessity for lowering the assessment on cut-and-get-out properties. It would also eliminate the need for lowering the assessment on annual sustained-yield properties, a lowering that otherwise would follow inevitably from the omission of some cost payments from the adjustment.

### DEFERRED TIMBER TAX

The *deferred timber tax,* like the adjusted property tax, represents an approach toward the ideal. It differs from the adjusted property tax mainly in two respects: First, taxes on delayed-yield properties are adjusted toward an equitable ratio, not by scaling down current payments, but by postponing them. Second, and as a consequence, the burden of financing the payments to local government is borne not by the forest owner but by the state—that is, the burden is shifted from particular taxpayers to all taxpayers.

Under the proposed plan, assessments of forest properties are made each year in two parts, the timber and the remainder of the value. (This remainder, termed "land," of course includes *any* forest values not reflected in timber value.) Tax rates are calculated in the usual way, in relation to total property value, and taxes also are figured in the regular way, but in the same two parts. The tax on the "land" is billed to the taxpayer. The tax on the timber, however, is billed to a state timber-tax fund, which pays this part of the tax for the property owner. Then, when the property yields an income, the owner repays to the fund, without interest, what has been advanced in his behalf. Payments to the fund at harvest time are limited to a fraction of the total stumpage value of the harvest—say, 30 per cent, and any remainder due the fund is carried along on the books until the next harvest. Provision is made for cases of hardship, where the owner has suffered a large loss of timber, as from fire. Such cases are met by limiting the owner's liability to the fund at any time to the current assessed value of his timber. Thus a part of the risk of loss is transferred from the individual owner to taxpayers at large.

The deferred-timber-tax plan requires a much larger participation, and even control, by the state than does the adjusted property tax. We refer here not merely to the existence of the state timber-tax fund. We refer to the fact that, since payments from the fund to local governments would be assured, there might well be a tendency on the part of the governments to let their costs get out of hand and to up their assessments or tax rates immoderately. To check this tendency, it would probably be necessary for the state to step in with controls. You will note that this necessity arises basically from the fact that the scheme of taxation has put an insulating strip between the local tax and the local taxpayer, so that the latter is no longer motivated to play his customary role as watchdog over the financial doings of his community. This is a disadvantage of all forms of deferred, or yield, taxation.

On the other hand, the taxpayer gains relief from financing taxes in advance of earnings. And the local government reaps the benefits of an undisturbed flow of receipts.

## DIFFERENTIAL TIMBER TAX

The *differential timber tax* is, in effect, a highly simplified plan for roughly approximating an adjusted property tax. As in the case of the latter tax, such correction as is made for time bias is made by scaling down current tax payments. This scaling down, however, is accomplished through lowering the assessment by use of a blanket reduction factor rather than by adjustments appropriate to the individual property.

Timber and "land" are assessed separately. Then the assessment on the timber—except for old growth currently being operated (on accelerated yield)—is reduced by a percentage factor. The reduction factor is worked out, preferably as a single figure to apply state-wide, so that the resulting tax will represent a fair tax ratio for typical or representative or average forest properties. Where the period of income deferment for forest properties is typically twenty-five years or more, the reduction factor will probably be about 50 per cent. It will be correspondingly less for shorter periods of deferment, and possibly nil if the period is typically less than five years. In effect if not in principle, the assessment is handled somewhat as it is in the Rothery "wholesale-value" method footnoted on page 381. At any rate, after timber assessments have been appropriately reduced, the plan follows the standard procedure of the general property tax. If necessary in order to soften the transition in local finances, the assessment reduction factor is brought into effect over a period of years, by steps. Provision is made for decreasing the reduction factor if forest practice progresses enough to shorten the prevailing periods of income deferment.

The differential timber tax will not, of course, give everyone an equitable levy. The best it can do is aim generally for the average, whatever that may mean. On the other hand, once an assessment reduction factor has been agreed on, the plan has the great merit of simplicity.

All three recommended plans of the Forest Taxation Inquiry have met with an uncommonly dull reception. Few persons today remember the names of the plans or even know what they mean. We look through the state statute books almost in vain for instances of adoption of the plans. We find in Ohio a kind of differential tax on forests, which, however, was

first set up in 1925, before the Inquiry made its recommendations. It is an
optional plan and is now in effect on less than 2 per cent of privately
owned commercial forests in the state. We find in Washington a sort of
deferred-timber-tax law, enacted in 1941, optional, and nowhere in effect.
And this is the story.

That the Inquiry's recommendations have done so poorly is perhaps
partly the fault of the times, as suggested in the historical review in
Chapter 26; partly the fault of the plans themselves, and the fact that the
first two are too complicated for people to grasp; and partly the result of
sound public thinking about assessment problems in general. For, after
all, the working of any of the three plans would be only as good as the
tax assessment, and there is nothing inherent in any of the schemes that
assures a good assessment. The schemes are designed to correct time bias
in assessment and will produce a good result only if the assessment first
has its parcel biases scrubbed out of it. Now time bias is a complicated
thing that relates mainly to one class of property, whereas parcel bias is
relatively simple and obvious and concerns everyone. So far as assessment practice is concerned, better lick the problem of parcel bias first—
so the thinking goes, and so the popular sentiment runs. This line, by the
way, is by no means counter to the sense of the Taxation Inquiry report.
At any rate, we find growing emphasis in recent years upon improving
assessments in respect to parcel bias.

## YIELD TAX

We find also in recent years, by way of attack upon time bias, a continuing interest in the third type of special property tax (p. 451): the
*yield tax.* This tax is like the deferred timber tax in postponing levies
upon growing timber until the time of harvest, but it bases these levies
upon the value of the cut, not of the property. Interest in the yield tax is
of long standing. It arose in reaction against the exemption-bounty-rebate
sort of approach to forest taxation. The idea was advanced, it is said, in
Michigan about 1890 by John Hubbell, a man experienced in land surveying and timber cruising. His proposal was soon being widely debated
in the East. It was many years before constitutional questions could be
resolved and legislation passed. A Michigan act of 1911 was the first but
was very soon followed by acts in other states. Nineteen states have had
yield-tax laws at one time or another.

The development of the yield-tax idea is understandable. For the yield
tax largely escapes the hard issue of assessment. And it seems to get almost directly to the goal of giving forestry a fairer break: the goal of
equity in terms of the percentage of income taken away. (The tax misses
the goal in being levied upon gross income rather than net, with consequences that we shall discuss later in this chapter.) The yield tax gives

every impression of being superior to the adjusted property tax in simplicity and workability, to the deferred timber tax in the basis used for determining the amount of the deferred payment, and to the differential timber tax in not seeming to grant bargain rates to a favored class of property owners. This is to look at the matter only partially, and to stress the points of contrast. Anyhow, it is really no wonder that in the mid-1950s fourteen states had yield-tax statutes.

The gist of the yield tax is that "land" and timber are treated separately; that the former is taxed annually, ad valorem; and that the latter is taxed at the time of cutting, on the basis of output. Among going examples of the yield tax, the details of the scheme vary to some extent. The tax upon the "land" is in some cases specified; in others, the assessment is fixed or a ceiling placed on the tax rate; or the "land" may be exempted from tax. The tax upon the timber is levied in at least one state as a specified amount per unit of measure of the product, but in most states it is a percentage of stumpage value harvested. The percentage is usually fixed, though in some cases it is arranged to increase with time, and in others, to diminish. Products cut for home use are commonly exempt from the tax.

In most of the states, the yield-tax plan is optional: The property owner makes the decision whether to stay under the general property tax or try for classification under the yield tax. The legislation is mandatory, bringing all specified forest land under its provisions, in five states— Louisiana, Mississippi, New Hampshire, Oregon, and Washington— though in the last two the law is administered as though it were optional. Many of the optional plans have eligibility requirements about the forest practices to be followed. Such requirements are presumably set up in the public interest in return for the favors of the yield tax: postponement of the tax, greater certainty regarding its amount, and in some cases preferential treatment for forest holdings as compared with others. However, there are some yield taxes that put a heavier burden on the forest than the general property tax does. [Can you offer any explanation or justification for such a yield tax? Can you think of circumstances in which a forest owner would wish to have his property classified under such a tax plan?]

Some of the yield-tax laws recognize the danger that local governments whose tax base is largely depleted forest may suffer for some years a serious loss of revenue because of the yield tax. The commonest remedy is to have the state make up the loss, or part of it. A fund may be set up, as in the deferred-timber-tax plan. If the fund runs low, it may have to be replenished by upping the rate of yield taxation, at least temporarily. This was the story in New Hampshire, and it may be regarded as part of the inevitable process of trial and error with a new form of tax. In any case, it is inherent in the yield tax that the state takes over from the forest owner a share of the risks of forest-land management, and a larger share than with the deferred timber tax.

The preponderant, optional form of the yield tax has come in for severe criticism. If a tax scheme is worthy of adoption at all, critics say, it is worth applying to everyone. A state legislature has the responsibility to decide what form of tax is best, and to require it. Furthermore, the presence on the books of two or more alternative plans of taxation makes for unnecessary trouble.

Typically, when an optional yield-tax law is first passed in a state, those forest owners who have supported it or taken an active interest apply to have their lands classified. Within a short time, a small fraction of forests in the state, usually 1 or 2 per cent, has been signed up. Thereafter there is little further classification. The rest of the owners hold off for one reason or another. Many of them do not know about the law. Many others do not understand it. Some know of it and would take advantage of it were it not for all the trouble and complication of getting signed up. Some attempt unsuccessfully to have their lands classified, meeting strong resistance from the reviewing tax officials, who hate to see property taken from the general tax rolls. Some sit tight and use the yield-tax option merely as an implied warning to the assessors that they should be reasonable. Some are repelled by regulatory features of the law. Some fear criticism from their neighbors that they are seeking favored treatment. Some foresee no advantage for themselves, especially if they are going to harvest much timber soon. Many are ineligible because their forest tracts are too small or for other causes.

Establishing a yield tax on forest property, whether optional or mandatory, does not in itself solve the problems of forest taxation. There is still the issue of government cost, and there may be a new problem of variable or pinched revenues. At the same time, as with the deferred timber tax, there is a built-in anesthetic for the taxpayer, to dull his pain and blunt his insistence upon economy. There is usually still the need for painstaking, unbiased assessment of forest land and the problem of setting an equitable tax rate upon the yield, and there is need for frequent reviews of assessments and rates. And furthermore, the yield tax, so far as it is a tax upon gross income, has possibly an adverse effect upon forest conservation. This effect of a gross-income tax we shall see as we turn our attention now to severance taxation.

## SEVERANCE TAX

The *severance tax* on timber is a levy upon the output or product at the time of cutting, similar to a tax upon minerals severed from the earth. The timber-severance tax seems at first glance much like the yield tax, but on closer study we find that it is clearly different.

While the yield tax is a special form of property taxation, a substitute for the general property tax shaped to fit the needs of forestry, the severance tax is a separate and additional revenue measure applied to the exploitation of natural resources. Of the six states that have severance taxes on timber, three also have a yield tax.

The severance tax is usually levied as a specified amount per unit of measure of the product. The timber operator is the one primarily responsible for paying the tax—not the forest owner, unless he happens to be the operator too. Thus severance taxes apply to timber cut from Federal lands, which ordinarily would never pay a yield tax. The severance tax is further distinguished in the fact that it is always mandatory and in the fact that it does not concern forest land as distinguished from timber. The law usually exempts timber cut for the owner's home use.

Revenues from the timber-severance tax are in most cases earmarked for forest protection or other public forestry programs. In this way the tax may favor intensive forest management. Or it may be neutral if it is simply a substitute for the sources of revenue that would otherwise support the same public programs. Or it may hamper public forestry programs if it is made the chief source of support and if it shrinks or fluctuates a great deal.

In other regards, too, the timber-severance tax has mixed effects upon forestry. Let us try to analyze some of these effects. In doing so, let us have in mind the incidence of this tax—that is, who bears it, who pays it in the last analysis (see Chap. 18, p. 281). Although the logger or manufacturer actually pays the tax bill, he may be expected to pass the cost back to the forest owner in the form of lower stumpage prices. Operators would find it difficult to pass the cost on to consumers so long as there was an interstate market for forest products and other states had no severance tax. The tax, then, tends to subtract from timber prices.

We may now analyze the effect of the severance tax in the same terms in which we analyzed the effect of product price upon the practice of forestry (Chap. 14). *First,* the tax will lower the margins of timber availability, so as to discourage the harvest of younger or poorer or less accessible timber and the making of intermediate cuttings. This is in part the effect that we would expect from any income tax—that it would lead to some refraining from the receipt of income. In Minnesota, it was found that the severance tax on iron ore had little influence on the output of the higher grades but that it sharply curtailed low-grade production. In Oregon, the severance-tax law provides special relief in cases where the state forester finds that the tax is discouraging salvage cutting.

*Second,* the tax will tend in the short run to discourage inputs other than capital, such as labor outlays for silviculture, and will tend in the long run to discourage forestry investment.

The effects of the timber severance tax are traceable to two characteristics of the tax: One is that the tax is limited to the output of the forest. It thus fails to exert many of the conservative influences of an income tax that is general in application. The other is that the tax hits gross, rather than net, income.

In ordinary cases, such as the input of labor (not capital) in forestry, we think of a net-income tax as having no effect upon the best combination. Whatever combination maximizes net revenue before the tax will maximize it after. That is to say, the tax has no effect upon either marginal revenue or marginal cost in the range where they equate, because in this range the extra net revenue is nil and the extra tax therefore is nil. Thus the tax must be irrelevant to the best combination, since such a tax, even when progressive, is always designed to allow some extra income after the tax for every increase in income before the tax.

A tax upon gross income, however—upon the value of the product— acts differently. It does bear upon the best combination. It reduces marginal revenue or raises marginal cost and hence tends to curtail operations. For example, if the firm is permitted to take in only 90 cents of every gross-revenue dollar, then to be rational it must stop the process of intensification at the point where the last 90 cents of input returns a dollar of gross revenue. This is the effect of the severance, the yield tax, and certain other levies, such as perhaps the payments in lieu of taxes upon public forests. For the national forests, the gross-income levy is 25 per cent. For some of the other Federal forests it is as high as 75 per cent. [If you were the manager of a public forest, would you think it rational to let such deductions influence inputs? Or would you hold that since the money is taken from one public pocket and put into another, the transfer should have no bearing on forestry outlays?]

## FEDERAL INCOME TAX

The impression that we keep getting of net-income taxation, that as taxes go it is kind to forest conservation, is well borne out. Let us turn our attention to the tax upon personal and corporate income, taking the Federal tax as the example—and a mighty one, you will recall, amounting to more than six-tenths of all taxes raised by all levels of government in the United States (Table 33, p. 431). To simplify the assignment, let us stress the effects of the tax upon management, and primarily upon timber management.

The Federal *income tax* is authorized by the Sixteenth Amendment to the Constitution, ratified in 1913. It is a levy upon individuals' and corporations' taxable income for each year. Taxable income is the difference between certain gross receipts and various allowable deductions and exemptions. What receipts are relevant and what subtractions are allowable are determined by the Internal Revenue Code as amended by the Congress from year to year, and its interpretation by the courts and the Internal Revenue Service. The understanding of these matters, the calculation accordingly of income and tax, and the weighing of alternative actions in their effect upon future taxes seem to be for many an individual and firm a major aspect of modern American life.

We will sketch the Federal income-tax computation by first defining gross receipts; second, characterizing the subtractions allowed for computing taxable income; and third, describing the application of tax rates to income. So far as possible, we will talk about individual and corporate income taxes together. Where the procedures for the two are different, this fact, if not clearly implied in the context, will be recognized explicitly. But remember that what follows is necessarily condensed to an extreme. It is sufficient for our present needs. It is not intended, though, for the specialized student of taxation, nor for the person seeking specific guides to making a tax return. And frequently we will depart from the official terms used by the Revenue Service.

## TAX COMPUTATION: GROSS RECEIPTS

*Gross receipts* are the bulk of receipts from professions, vocations, trades, commerce, sales, dealings in property, interest, rent, dividends, securities, the transaction of business, or any other source. They include payments made, not to the taxpayer, but for his account—for example, employers' payments of union dues, insurance premiums, or withheld taxes. They include the value of rights exercised by the taxpayer, such as an employee's right to buy the employer's securities at less than market price. Gross receipts include only the actual realization of the taxpayer, whether in money or in kind: They do not include such revenues as the mere increase in value of property or the intangible benefits derived from the use of property. Furthermore, some types of actual realization are excluded, such as gifts (but not bonuses paid by an employer), legacies, repayment of debts, certain tax-exempt revenues, and proceeds from the payment of damages for personal injury or from life or health insurance.

## DEDUCTIONS AND EXEMPTIONS

The allowable *deductions* and *exemptions* by which gross receipts are reduced to taxable income may be divided for our convenience into two sorts: business deductions and other subtractions.

Business deductions are in general all those necessary and usual expenses paid or incurred by either an individual or a corporation in mak-

ing or collecting income, or for managing and maintaining property held
for income. They include current expenses and losses. They include depreciation and obsolescence of property that has a limited useful life, and
also depletion of minerals, other natural deposits, and timber by virtue
of extraction or harvest.

Business deductions include also losses from sale or exchange of capital
assets. Such *capital losses* by a corporation are deductible only to the
extent of its *capital gains.* An excess of loss over gain in any year may
be carried forward for use as a deduction from net capital gains in any of
the next five years. For an individual, the rule is more lenient, allowing
deduction of capital losses in each case up to the amount of gain plus
$1,000. Where capital gains are made on assets that have been held more
than six months (*long-term capital gains*), allowable deductions for the
individual taxpayer include 50 per cent of any excess of such gains over
capital losses, both long- and short-term.

Business deductions include the net operating losses of a corporation.
Such losses in any year may be deducted from any net profit reported in
the three preceding years and an amended tax return submitted to the
Revenue Service, or they may be carried forward for deduction from
any net profit in the next five years.

Business deductions specifically exclude expenses ruled to be of a personal nature—for instance, the family living expenses and depreciation
on the private dwelling of the individual taxpayer. Such personal expenses as are deductible we will include under the heading of other subtractions.

Other allowable subtractions from gross receipts include gifts, up to
certain percentages of income, to domestic governments for public purposes and to nonprofit charitable, educational, religious, and certain
other organizations.

Other subtractions also include certain expenses and losses of a personal nature incurred by the individual taxpayer, which are the counterpart of some of the business deductions of individuals and those of corporations, and are taken in addition to the former. For example, interest
on personal indebtedness is deductible. So are many taxes, including
virtually all state and local taxes, that represent a personal expense.
Losses of a nonbusiness character from bad debts, from theft, and from
casualties such as fire, storm, and accident are deductible within specified limits. Net capital losses and net long-term capital gains enter into
deductions along with, and under the same rules as, those of a business
nature incurred by the individual.

Finally, other subtractions include certain special deductions and exemptions that are permitted the individual taxpayer: personal exemptions
for self, spouse, and dependents in a prescribed amount per person; cer-

*Table 38. Marginal and average tax rates and total taxes on incomes up to $250,000, by steps—for single persons other than heads of households—1958*

| Total taxable income* | Marginal income | Tax rate on any part of marginal income | Total tax | Average tax rate |
|---|---|---|---|---|
| (1) | (2) | (3) | (4) | (5) |
| Dollars | Dollars | Per cent | Dollars | Per cent |
| 0 | | | 0 | — |
| | 2,000 | 20 | | |
| 2,000 | | | 400 | 20.0 |
| | 2,000 | 22 | | |
| 4,000 | | | 840 | 21.0 |
| | 2,000 | 26 | | |
| 6,000 | | | 1,360 | 22.7 |
| | 2,000 | 30 | | |
| 8,000 | | | 1,960 | 24.5 |
| | 2,000 | 34 | | |
| 10,000 | | | 2,640 | 26.4 |
| | 2,000 | 38 | | |
| 12,000 | | | 3,400 | 28.3 |
| | 2,000 | 43 | | |
| 14,000 | | | 4,260 | 30.4 |
| | 2,000 | 47 | | |
| 16,000 | | | 5,200 | 32.5 |
| | 2,000 | 50 | | |
| 18,000 | | | 6,200 | 34.4 |
| | 2,000 | 53 | | |
| 20,000 | | | 7,260 | 36.3 |
| | 2,000 | 56 | | |
| 22,000 | | | 8,380 | 38.1 |
| | 4,000 | 59 | | |
| 26,000 | | | 10,740 | 41.3 |
| | 6,000 | 62 | | |
| 32,000 | | | 14,460 | 45.2 |
| | 6,000 | 65 | | |
| 38,000 | | | 18,360 | 48.3 |
| | 6,000 | 69 | | |
| 44,000 | | | 22,500 | 51.1 |
| | 6,000 | 72 | | |
| 50,000 | | | 26,820 | 53.6 |
| | 10,000 | 75 | | |
| 60,000 | | | 34,320 | 57.2 |
| | 10,000 | 78 | | |
| 70,000 | | | 42,120 | 60.2 |
| | 10,000 | 81 | | |
| 80,000 | | | 50,220 | 62.8 |
| | 10,000 | 84 | | |
| 90,000 | | | 58,620 | 65.1 |
| | 10,000 | 87 | | |
| 100,000 | | | 67,320 | 67.3 |
| | 50,000 | 89 | | |
| 150,000 | | | 111,820 | 74.5 |
| | 50,000 | 90 | | |
| 200,000 | | | 156,820 | 78.4 |
| | 50,000 | 91 | | |
| 250,000 | | | 202,320 | 80.9 |

* Assumed to include no long-term capital gains.

tain medical expenses; wages received while on sick leave under certain conditions; and so on.

When *taxable income* has been computed by subtracting all the allowable deductions and exemptions from gross receipts, the amount of the tax may be figured.

Table 39. *Marginal and average tax rates and total taxes on incomes up to $250,000, by steps—for corporations—1958*

| Total taxable income* | Marginal income | Tax rate on any part of marginal income | Total tax | Average tax rate |
|---|---|---|---|---|
| (1) | (2) | (3) | (4) | (5) |
| *Dollars* | *Dollars* | *Per cent* | *Dollars* | *Per cent* |
| 0 | | | 0 | — |
| | 25,000 | 30 | | |
| 25,000 | | | 7,500 | 30.0 |
| | 25,000 | 52 | | |
| 50,000 | | | 20,500 | 41.0 |
| | 25,000 | 52 | | |
| 75,000 | | | 33,500 | 44.7 |
| | 25,000 | 52 | | |
| 100,000 | | | 46,500 | 46.5 |
| | 25,000 | 52 | | |
| 125,000 | | | 59,500 | 47.6 |
| | 25,000 | 52 | | |
| 150,000 | | | 72,500 | 48.3 |
| | 25,000 | 52 | | |
| 175,000 | | | 85,500 | 48.9 |
| | 25,000 | 52 | | |
| 200,000 | | | 98,500 | 49.2 |
| | 25,000 | 52 | | |
| 225,000 | | | 111,500 | 49.6 |
| | 25,000 | 52 | | |
| 250,000 | | | 124,500 | 49.8 |

* Assumed to include no long-term capital gains.

### RATE AND AMOUNT OF TAX

For individuals, the tax rates are *progressive* and the rate of progression moderately steep. For example, consider the tax rates upon income in calendar year 1958, for single persons other than heads of households. These rates were set by the Internal Revenue Code of 1954. They started at 20 per cent on the first $2,000 (or less) of taxable income and rose to a maximum of 91 per cent on any income above $200,000 (Table 38).

Different rates were effective for married couples who filed a joint return and for others who were heads of households. The tax rates published by the Internal Revenue Service (col. 3) were marginal rates, applying only to the increments of income (col. 2). Thus, for example, the total tax (col. 4) on an income of $4,000 (col. 1) was 20 per cent of the first $2,000, or $400, plus 22 per cent of the second $2,000, or $440, which made $840 altogether. It follows that the average tax rate (col. 5) on incomes above $2,000 was always less than the marginal rate.

For corporations, the 1958 tax amounted to 30 per cent of the first $25,000 of taxable income and 52 per cent of any additional income. Thus here, too, the rates were progressive (Table 39), though not so steeply as those we have just examined.

Even after the tax has been computed, there may still be adjustments. The one that concerns us here is the one that individual and corporate taxpayers may make for long-term capital gains. An individual taxpayer may calculate an alternative tax by applying a flat 50 per cent tax rate to that part of his income which consists of taxable excess of long-term capital gains over all capital losses. If the alternative tax is lower, it becomes the effective tax. In other words, the 1958 tax rate on the long-term net capital gains of individuals (remember that half of these gains are deductible) is limited to a maximum of 25 per cent. The same limit applies also to corporations, and for them represents a preferable alternative regardless of their income.

[How large an income would the single taxpayer of Table 38 need to have in order to benefit from the 25 per cent tax-rate limit that applies to long-term capital gains? Note: the income at which the average tax rate reaches 50 per cent is about $41,370.]

With the general mechanics of Federal income taxation in the back of our minds, we can now have a look at some of the effects of the tax within the forest economy. We will suggest eight principal effects.

## TAX EFFECTS: INTEREST AND CAPITAL GAINS

1. The Federal income tax tends to lower the taxpayer's alternative rate of return. It does this in three ways: *First*, as we recognized in Chapter 10 (p. 149), the tax is like a transfer cost. It sets up a barrier against shifting resources out of forestry into other investments. If the return on other investments is 8 per cent and is taxed at a 50 per cent rate, forestry need return only 4 per cent in order to be competitive; and this 4 per cent, then, is the alternative rate of return. The tax rate that governs is the marginal rate. *Second*, the tax lowers the alternative rate by putting many investments other than forestry at a comparative disadvantage, in ways that we shall see. *Third*, the tax lowers the rate by reducing the

riskiness of forest investments—again, in ways that will be evident as we go on. Notice that all three influences on the alternative rate of return are of greater force, the higher the tax rate, and consequently this effect of the tax is in general more powerful the larger the taxpayer's income. The result of the lower alternative rate of return is in the shorter pull to encourage capital-intensive forestry, and in the longer pull to promote forest investments in general.

2. The Federal income tax subsidizes forestry by its definition and treatment of long-term capital gains. This phenomenon, a dramatic one, is of fairly recent origin. True, capital gains have been specially recognized in tax procedure for a long while. By way of example, the taxpayer who sold timberland that he had bought more than six months before could treat the resulting income as a long-term capital gain. He could figure the gain by subtracting the cost of the property reduced to allow for any depletion due to his cutting, from the sales price of the property reduced for costs of sale. On this capital gain, he could enjoy such preferential tax rates as were in effect at the time—just as he could do with capital assets of any sort. But of course if he cut timber, that was ordinary income, taxed at the regular rate.

Then in 1943 Congress amended the Code—Section 117(k), which became Section 631 in the 1954 code—so as to make more room for forest owners at the cozy capital-gains hearth. Long-term capital gains were redefined to include the gains resulting when timber held longer than six months is sold, not simply outright, but also on a "pay-as-cut" basis, as in scale transactions. Long-term capital gains were further redefined to include gains represented in the value of standing timber held more than six months before the beginning of the taxable year and cut by the taxpayer for sale or for use in his own business, as for manufacture into lumber or pulp.[2] Here we find all the forms of timber harvest and revenue that are most significant in the practice of forestry blanketed under the capital-gains provisions of the tax law and thus taxed at preferential rates. The rates in question, speaking of 1958, are 25 per cent for the corporation and, for the individual, half of the marginal rates that would apply to ordinary income, but in any case not more than 25 per cent. Here is a happy boon, and for the individual taxpayer, the bigger he is, the happier the boon. By virtue of it, forest land looks a lot better as an investment, and forestry, as a business. Some people say that the capital-gains feature of the Federal income tax has been the greatest single

[2] For the details of these and other forest provisions of the tax law discussed from the practical standpoint of making a tax return, see Williams, Ellis T.: *The Small Timber Owner and His Federal Income Tax*, U.S. Department of Agriculture Handbook 52, 1953. A briefer statement by Mr. Williams on the same subject is his *Federal Income Tax Tips for the Small Woodland Owner*, published occasionally by the United States Forest Service.

factor in the rise of private forest management in the United States since World War II.

## EFFECTS THROUGH EASING COST BURDENS

3. The Federal income tax increases the taxpayer's incentives to incur conservation costs. Aside from the influences already discussed, the tax favors certain conservation expenditures by allowing them as deductions from gross receipts. Such expenditures may include the employment of foresters—surely a splendid thing—road building and maintenance, outlays for protection, for watershed and other land-management improvements, for silvicultural practices, for improvements in utilization, for research, for the granting of scholarships at forestry schools, and so on—even for advertising Smokey Bear and his sage sayings, if you will admit him as an item. By making such outlays deductible from taxed income, the law provides, in a sense, that the public will share in the cost to the extent of the marginal tax rate. The resulting gains are most obvious in the case of the high-bracket individual taxpayer. His revenues from forest operations will be taxed, for the most part, at the preferential rate, as 25 per cent in 1958. His costs, on the other hand, commonly are deductible at a higher rate. True, some of them, such as planting costs, must be charged over a period against capital gains (must be "capitalized"). But most of them are allowable as deductions from ordinary income (may be "expensed"), and thus are subsidized to the extent of the ordinary tax rate so long as the taxpayer has ordinary income, current or carried over, against which these costs may be offset. Adding a processing enterprise widens the forest taxpayer's opportunity for taking advantage of this tax provision.

4. The Federal income tax tends to lighten the burden of the property tax. The burden is lightened in two ways: *First,* the income tax may be regarded as partly and indirectly a substitute for the property tax; if the income tax were lower, some of the public costs now borne through Federal taxation would have to be carried locally, and the property tax would need to be higher. And remember that an income tax is generally less of a handicap to the forest economy than a property tax. *Second,* the income tax helps with the payment of property taxes in the same way that it takes some of the sting out of other costs, by recognizing them as deductions.

## OTHER EFFECTS

5. The income tax tends to favor the absorption of unprofitable corporations by profitable ones, through mergers. This tendency arises from

the provision in the tax law for carrying losses forward. A corporation that has suffered heavy losses within five years can be a real asset to the profitable corporation that merges with it and uses its losses as deductions. Typically the upshot of such a merger is more conservative forest management, closer timber utilization, and the strengthening of business influence centers. (Compare Chap. 25, pp. 428–429.)

6. The income tax, as a result of steeply progressive rates upon individual income, may have the effect of limiting the entrepreneurial zeal of individual proprietors and the size of noncorporate enterprise in the forest economy. We have characterized the income tax generally as neutral toward best combinations. There is, however, one way in which a progressive tax may conceivably affect the best combination: by taking so much of the enterpriser's last prospective increments of income that leisure becomes more attractive to him than the work necessary to earn these increments and the net rewards of the work. If this occurs to any extent in the forest economy, some of the secondary effects that may be expected are a rise in contracting and subcontracting, as in logging and timber procurement, and a rise in the proportion of all activity carried on through corporations. In the forest economy, with its traditional heavy reliance upon individual enterprise, the result can be a hastening of broad changes in the character of economic life.

7. The Federal income tax tends to accelerate the forest-land-acquisition programs of large-scale private forest owners. Such programs would ordinarily be counted on to meet with automatic resistances, or governors, in the form of rising prices and other costs of acquiring property. Most such costs, however, are capitalized into the depletion basis which may go to reduce the gain chargeable against the owner's timber-cutting operations on other lands. Thus the tax arrangements postpone the application of brakes to forest-acquisition programs in boom times. And in general they encourage the holding of forest lands by industry as a raw-material backlog and by individuals as an estate.

8. Every one of the foregoing tax effects is heightened by higher tax rates on ordinary income. It is therefore more pronounced for the high-bracket taxpayers—the large-scale forest owners, especially in good times. Furthermore, the tax effects are generally in the direction of more intensive and more conservative forestry. Consequently the broad result of Federal income taxation appears to be to strengthen the advantages of scale in the forest economy, particularly since it is the large owners and operators who have the greatest incentives and the fullest means for taking advantage of the complicated provisions of tax law. Thus the tax relatively deepens the great conservation problem of the little forest owner and the little operator, and underscores the threat of economic depression to forest-land management and use.

## SUMMARY

Three kinds of special property-tax schemes have been offered as remedies for some of forestry's problems under the general property tax: Exemptions, bounties, rebates, and tax ceilings, stressed in the nineteenth century, have been largely ineffective. The proposals featured by the Forest Taxation Inquiry—adjusted property tax, deferred timber tax, and differential timber tax—have some advantages in principle but have never been given a real trial. The yield tax has some appeal and has been adopted, at least as an optional plan, in many states. It admittedly leaves unsolved problems, notably of government finance, tax assessment, and rate setting.

The timber-severance tax is in force in six states. As a levy upon gross income, this tax may have some adverse influence upon forestry by discouraging the harvest of inferior timber and the input of labor and materials in forest management.

The Federal income tax generally encourages forest conservation. It helps lower the alternative rate of return. Its capital-gains provisions make forest investments attractive and thus favor stable forestry and forest industry. It tends to ease the burden of various costs. But by emphasizing advantages of scale, the Federal income tax relatively deepens the problems of the small landowner and the small operator in the forest economy.

# Chapter 28

# CREDIT AND INSURANCE

E VERY TIME we have talked about economic objectives and the winning of them—when we have spoken of finding the best combination— we have involved ourselves in the implicit assumption that the objectives or the combination could be financed. So it was back in Chapter 5: We assumed that Hawkins's firm would have the wherewithal to pay the eight-man crew. You will remember that on the revenue side of Hawkins's job we used an estimate of the per-tree value of timber-stand improvement. The estimate was made by discounting, to the present, the expected future gains of the cultural operation. This discounting was, in effect, an allowance for the cost of tying up working capital during the years until harvest. Or, you might say, it was an allowance for the cost of borrowing in order to get or to replenish this working capital. We assumed that Hawkins's firm would be able to find a lender, or at least successive lenders, who would be willing to make funds available for the necessary stretch of time. And we assumed that the firm would be willing to go in debt to the extent required.

So again in Chapter 11 concerning land use: We implicitly assumed financing when we worked out the best intensities of land management. And in Chapter 13 we made the assumption that the lumber retailer would find the financial means to hold his stock.

Broadly speaking, credit is essential to the whole economic development of our modern world. For imagine what the world would be like if there were no credit and thus every enterpriser had to rely on his own cash resources. Picture how at times he would be thwarted in his efforts at profitable expansion. And how at other times he would sit with idle

470

funds in his hands. His life would be spent compromising between these two disadvantages.[1] Hawkins would not, in general, achieve his eight-man force, nor the landowner his full management intensity, nor the lumber retailer such great size and variety of stock. It would be a cramped and inflexible existence.

An economy's *credit* system is an institutional scheme for meeting one man's investment opportunity with another's idle resources—for clearing society's shortages against its surpluses, and so providing for full and growing resource use. The credit system not only gives borrowers access to the existing funds of savers and would-be lenders, but also normally furnishes through banks a supply of new funds appropriate to the promise of new output. Thus the monetary system is given the elasticity necessary to meet the problems and opportunities of a dynamic economy.

## CREDIT INSTITUTIONS

The credit system of the United States is centered around its banking. This, in turn, is centered on the Federal Reserve System, which includes in its membership all the national banks and many of the commercial banks chartered by the states. The commercial banks, national and state, receive funds in the form of demand deposits (checking accounts) and in most cases also time deposits (savings accounts). Funds are lent out to merchants, industrialists, farmers, and consumers. As with all loans, these are made on the basis of some sort of *security* offered by the borrower as a pledge of repayment: real estate, other property or goods, or perhaps simply the signature, or symbol of personal integrity, of the borrower. Most of the lending is *short-term credit,* for periods up to a year, as when credit is advanced to the storekeeper to buy goods, to the farmer to hire pickers, or to your family to get a car. Some of the lending is *long-term credit,* to be repaid over ten years or more, as when the bank invests in home mortgages or government bonds of distant maturity. *Intermediate credit,* too, is advanced by the commercial banks in the form of term loans, mostly to businesses for the purchase of moderately durable equipment. Commercial bank credit is ordinarily provided in the form of bank money—that is, accounts on which checks may be drawn.

There are other kinds of banks besides commercial banks. For instance, there are savings banks that take time deposits exclusively and normally offer a larger share of long-term credit. And within the comprehensive public credit system designed to meet the special needs of agriculture, there are the Federal land banks. These banks, established in 1916, got

---

[1] Compare Hawtrey, R. G.: "Credit," in *Encyclopaedia of the Social Sciences,* New York, 1954, vol. 3, p. 549.

their funds originally from the government. They lend to individual farmers on terms up to forty years and have been instrumental in widening farmers' borrowing opportunities and lowering the interest rates.

But there are many more credit institutions besides the banks. One example is the cooperative building and loan and Federal saving societies, which take time deposits and buy mortgages and other such investments. Another example is the insurance companies, notably life insurance. We are not inclined to think of them as credit institutions, but they may amass huge sums of money in premiums, to the point that their main energies must be given to investment—i.e., lending. The stock exchanges and the related system of brokerage houses and investment banking establishments put a wide range of savers directly or indirectly in touch with the demands of corporations for equity and bond financing. Many institutions have grown up for providing short-term credit in special forms: the factor, the discount house, even the merchant, as when he offers prepayment to his suppliers or accepts delayed payment from those to whom he sells (compare Chap. 20, pp. 338–339).

Indeed, it may seem as though no nook or cranny of our economy remains unlighted by the beams of credit, for no sooner has some dark corner been discovered than special steps are taken to throw financial light upon it. And yet complaints over inadequate credit facilities are still heard in many a special field of production, and one of these is forestry.

## WANT OF FOREST CREDIT

Capital requirements in the forest economy are clearly immense. Aside from the usual complement of mills, equipment, supplies, and goods, and the obligations of producers that call for the use of working capital, there is the land and its timber growing stocks and other resources. These last, because of long periods of production and often low rates of return on investment, are uncommonly large items in proportion to income. Here, then, is a wide field for the use of credit. The need for credit would appear to be particularly great in timber management, where capital costs are the major costs (compare Chap. 8, pp. 104–105). We have seen in Chapter 9 how strong an effect upon management intensity is exerted by the rate of interest. We have seen in Chapter 10 that timber-resource depletion goes hand in hand with high rates and with low incomes. Both the rate and the income problem may in turn be attacked through credit.

However, it is in the area of forest management that credit facilities are least developed. In manufacturing and marketing—except for the little operators, who are something of a special problem—the forest economy enjoys the ample arrangements that service economic activity generally. But how are the purchase, holding, and care of forest lands financed? For the public forests, the financing comes through the general income and credit sources of government. The corporate forest owners, nearly all of whom are mainly engaged in some business other than woods forestry, also have their own general sources of credit. In the case of individuals, who hold the lion's share of forests in the United States, it appears that resource ownership and management, such as it is, must be financed almost entirely by the owners themselves. We do not, therefore, altogether need to speculate about what the world would be like if there were no credit. We can get an inkling by looking at the small woodlands.

Our situation in this country with respect to the financing of forest management is in marked contrast to that in Scandinavia and some other parts of Western Europe, where special forest-credit arrangements have been in effect for years.[2]

The fact that in the United States it has been difficult or impossible to borrow money on the basis of forest land as collateral is mainly the result of high risk. Bear in mind that risk is real and meaningful to the degree that it enters into people's judgments, whether justifiably or not. As we saw in Chapter 20 (p. 337), three sources of risk are relevant:

1. Risk of physical loss. Bankers and other potential lenders have tended to look upon forests as a tinder box that would be reduced to ashes if fire should strike. They have also greatly feared the dangers of insects, disease, and trespass. All such fears are of course magnified with the length of term of a proposed loan. Furthermore, their effect has been decisive because forests have not (until very recently) been insurable at reasonable premiums. Institutional lenders are accustomed to require that insurance be carried on assets used as security for loans.

2. Risk of financial loss. Paralleling the risk of physical loss is the risk of loss from changes in value over time. The risk of this sort that has perhaps loomed largest has been the risk of general inflation, which would undermine the worth of any loan repayable in dollars. Such risk could be judged very great in the case of extra-long-term credit (say, fifty years or more) of the sort that might be needed for forest regeneration or the care of young growth. Lenders, especially those familiar with the risks of farming, have also stressed the danger of "overproduction" that would cause timber values to fall and thus impair the ability of the collateral to repay the loan. This may seem ridiculous to foresters, but that is beside the point.

3. Risk of technical misjudgment. Most potential lenders have been unfamiliar with, and somewhat baffled by, the problems of forest measurement. Timber cruising for appraisal purposes has seemed to be filled

---

[2] See, for example, Kissin, R.: *Forestry Credit*, Imperial Forestry Bureau Technical Communication 3, Oxford, England, 1945.

with uncertainty. So have the forecasts of timber output that would enter into both the appraisal and the plan for repayment of the loan. At best, lenders have been inclined to deduct a big safety factor from volume and growth estimates.

## FOREST CREDIT PROPOSALS

Thoughtful foresters have for years advocated that special forest-credit arrangements be set up. The discussion has been confined largely to timber credit—based upon land and trees as security and aimed toward producing wood. Partly in recognition of the risks—discouraging, as they were, to private enterprise—many of the recommendations, especially before World War II, leaned toward a public credit system. The social interest in forest resources (the reasoning ran) carries with it a low alternative rate of return. This implies long-term loans at low rates such as might be made available through public credit. The long term is, of course, an essential feature of any loan that must be repaid in part from the proceeds of long-delayed yields. And the low rates would be justifiable in view of the importance to society of the many forest values that cannot be captured, and therefore may tend to be neglected, by individuals. Furthermore, it has been the belief that forest credit, to serve the needs of immature and depleted properties as well as those on sustained yield, must provide for a degree of flexibility in repayment schedules such as may be difficult for private sources to offer.

A public credit system was favored by a Society of American Foresters subcommittee reporting in 1920.[3] Again, it was with a public system in view that the subject of forest credit was given prominent billing in the United States Forest Service's comprehensive problem analysis of 1933, *A National Plan for American Forestry.*[4] The need for forest credit has been emphasized in reports by the Department of Agriculture, in the American Forestry Congresses, and by other weighty spokesmen. Forest credit bills have been introduced into the Federal Congress.[5]

One proposal for public credit which is illustrative, even to the point that action was never taken upon it, is that of a special committee, appointed in 1945 by Governor I. W. Duggan, of the Farm Credit Admin-

---

[3] "Report of Subcommittee on Forest Leasing, Forest Loans, and Forest Insurance," *Journal of Forestry*, March, 1920, pp. 260–274.

[4] See pp. 1125–1134 of the publication, Senate Doc. 12, 73d Cong., 1st Sess.

[5] For example, the Fletcher bill, S. 3417, 74th Cong., 1st Sess., 1935; the Pierce bill, H.R. 3458, 77th Cong., 1st Sess., 1941; the McNary bill, S. 47, 78th Cong., 1st Sess., 1943; the Hook bill, H.R. 6221, 79th Cong., 2d Sess., 1946; the Cooley bill, H.R. 8724, 84th Cong., 2d Sess., 1956; the Stennis bill, S. 1229, 85th Cong., 1st Sess., 1957.

istration.[6] The Committee was chairmanned by Professor M. R. Benedict of the University of California and was made up of one other agricultural economist and two foresters.

The Benedict Committee proposed a Forest Credit Bank, which was to be a centralized Federal bank with regional branches, set up as a division of the Farm Credit Administration. The bank would have a capital fund of $100 million and authority to issue bonds and make loans up to 10 times its capital and surplus. The activities of the Bank would tie in with those of other Federal lending agencies, such as the Federal Farm Mortgage Corporation, and the bank would also work through, encourage, and develop private lending channels.

The Forest Credit Bank would deal primarily in commercial loans— that is to say, loans on acceptable commercial security, and with no element of subsidy. And it would deal mainly with medium- and large-scale forest owners. Several types of loans would be made. It will be helpful for us to review the types proposed, for they represent the main continuing categories of need for forest credit.

There would be first-mortgage loans, for terms up to 60 years and in amounts up to 50 per cent of "normal appraised value" (a conservative appraisal based on the dollar values that existed in a stated period just before World War II) to be repaid at "suitable intervals," for such purposes as refinancing existing indebtedness, restocking open lands, holding immature stands, orderly utilization of mature timber and the holding of it in depressed times, land purchase, and development of roads and facilities. There would be second-mortgage loans, also of long term, in amounts that could bring total indebtedness up to 75 per cent of value, for the same purposes plus the easing of pressure from a first mortgage. There would be short- and intermediate-term loans, up to five or ten years, covering logging equipment, rolling stock, mill machinery, working capital such as that required for holding lumber stocks, and other such purposes. And there would be special, experimental loans to individuals and small corporations.

The Benedict Committee advocated or discussed a number of programs complementary to that of the Forest Credit Bank. A Forest Fire Insurance Corporation could provide essential insurance services. Again, the need was recognized for credit for small forest holdings. It was felt that such credit could best be offered through the land banks and other established agencies equipped to deal with many small borrowers. Consideration was given to the special problems of the small, low-income forest owner, and the thought advanced that loans might be made to him on

[6] Black, J. D., S. T. Dana, L. K. Pomeroy, and M. R. Benedict: *A Suggested Plan of Organization for a Forest Credit System for the United States,* Preliminary Report, U.S. Department of Agriculture, Farm Credit Administration, Kansas City, Mo., 1946.

the basis of the hours of labor which he would devote to the improvement of his woods. The report advocated a program of public education and of technical assistance in forestry to parallel and strengthen the credit and insurance programs. And it emphasized the need for promoting private lending activities in forestry. (One way for a public lending agency to encourage private credit is to offer guarantees for private lending, as the Farm Security Administration did in the case of farm credit.)

## SOURCES OF FOREST CREDIT

As forest credit has actually begun to develop in the United States, it has taken more largely the form of private enterprise than was envisaged or recommended by many of its early advocates. The system that has so far evolved falls substantially short of the goals that have been set, especially in its failure to service the little owners and operators and the holders of property the yields from which will be long delayed. Let us mention the activities of three types of credit institution.[7]

1. Federal land banks. The banks of Columbia, South Carolina, and New Orleans, Louisiana, began to lend money on forest security in 1944. It is significant that this was a southern development. Much of the demand for forest credit on the smaller holdings and much of the response in the form of facilities has been in the South. But the two pioneering banks as of mid-1956 had fewer than 900 outstanding loans based primarily on timber security, in a total amount of less than $7½ million. Their average loan covered about 560 acres of forest. In general, the land banks lend for a term limited to forty years, in amounts up to 65 per cent of "normal value," at interest rates that have usually been a bit lower than those of other agencies—4 per cent until 1956 and 5 per cent for a while thereafter, at one bank in the South. The required repayment schedule calls for annual or semiannual payments of interest and of the principal prorated over the term, except that minimum payments may be arranged for a period when no income is planned, these payments consisting of interest and a smaller fraction of the principal.

The land banks make loans only to individuals and to family farming corporations. To qualify as security for a loan, a forest property must be located in an area where the feasibility of sustained forestry practice has been demonstrated on representative private tracts. The property must be readily salable in normal times. It must yield a sustained income in sufficient quantity to repay the loan with interest and to cover the owner's living expenses if he does not have other sources. It must in any

[7] For more detail on the programs of these and other lending agencies, see Resources for the Future, Inc., Committee: *Forest Credit in the United States: A Survey of Needs and Facilities,* Resources for the Future, Inc., Washington, 1958, pp. 53–71.

case bear a substantial amount of merchantable timber. And the owner must agree to follow forestry practices that are acceptable to the lender: He must have a mutually approved plan of management that assures desirable practice and also provides for harvests and income such as may be needed to service the loan. This feature of forest credit, that it is granted on the basis of a plan, may be regarded as an outgrowth of the standard practice in agriculture and many other types of business. It is widely regarded as well suited to forestry, and in fact as a means of directly promoting forest conservation.

2. Life insurance companies. In the late 1940s, three of the large insurance companies began very active study of the possibilities of making loans on forest security. All three soon began their programs of forest credit, and other companies followed their lead. The insurance companies in the 1950s were by a wide margin the largest source of forest credit, their outstanding loans reaching probably more than $100 million. They have been drawn into the field by such developments as more complete fire control and the adoption of more intensive forestry by the corporate owners, who are their principal customers. At the same time, however, the apparent prospect of continued timber shortage in the United States has been heartening to them as prospective lenders. The insurance companies go in for large loans, $25,000 to $50,000 as a minimum, so as to hold down the costs of negotiation and of keeping tabs on loans. Like other credit institutions, they require a satisfactory plan of management. The plan agreed on is introduced as a covenant into the mortgage that the lender takes. Most of the mortgages apparently have been for periods of 20 to 30 years. Interest rates have ranged mostly from 5 to 6 per cent.

3. Commercial banks. In 1953, at the instigation of both forestry and banking interests and after careful study of the trends in forestry risk, Congress amended the Federal Reserve Act in such a way as to permit national banks to take a first mortgage on forest property. The result was to bring them to some extent into this area of credit, and perhaps also to stimulate forest lending by state banks, which had already been making such loans on a small scale. In making forest loans, the national banks are limited to a maximum ten-year term, and to properties well protected and managed for continuing yields. What with the shortness of the term, the limitation of the loan to 40 per cent of timber value, and the great caution exercised by the banks in entering the forest-credit field, the amount of the business is not great. Loans are more apt to be used to finance timber purchase, harvesting, and conversion than forest improvement. Indeed, the banks tend to limit their service to the choicest properties, those in the best and most merchantable condition and least in need of improvement. Of course, all lenders choose, if they can, to do

business only with the owners of tracts that are the strongest security. As Ogden Nash says, "One rule which woe betides the banker who fails to heed it, never lend any money to anybody unless they don't need it."

## CREDIT FOR SMALL OWNERS AND OPERATORS

Credit for those who need it the most, although perhaps a contradiction in terms, is still mainly an unsolved problem in the forest economy. The small timber operator has but unattractive security to offer in either his logging business or his little mill. Merchant credit (pp. 338–339) is his best bet, though this is apt to cost him 15 to 18 per cent when more reliable borrowers are paying their bankers 5 to 6. The owner of the small, raggedy woodland is even less well off, for he is shunned by all lenders in their right minds.

How to deal with the credit problem of the small forest owner is a question that many have had answers for—verbally. We have noticed what the Benedict Committee said.[8] Others have advocated, very possibly without consulting the principals, that this little countryman should be looked after by his neighbor, the country bank. Again, one hears the thought expressed that the credit should be issued through consulting foresters, who could take responsibility for setting up a plan and carrying it out. Again, some say that the little fellows don't want credit; they don't need it: They do their own woods work; and anyhow, they hate to be in debt. This may very well be true of some of them. Often, when we speak of small-owner credit, we are really referring not to what the owner wants but to what society wants for him.

Two questions are critical when it comes to the use of credit for improving small-owner forestry. First, how to get the credit to him, how solve the problem of administrative cost. Second, how to put the credit in a form which will either raise the forest value growth per cent or lower the alternative rate of return, one or the other of which is, as we have seen, essential to changing forestry practices so far as they are based on timber value. Look for a moment at this second question. For the many small owners whose alternative rates of return are based on consumption alternatives, credit will not lower the alternative rate unless the funds are added to consumable income. But if credit is used for consumption, how will the loan be repaid? It is conceivable that credit might be offered to small owners in return for their accepting strong restrictions upon their management practices. But then would there be a demand for loans? Perhaps after all, as some authorities insist, the problem of depleted

<hr>

[8] The ideas were mainly those of Prof. John D. Black of Harvard University and are expressed more fully in his "The Role of Federal, State, and Local Governments in Promoting Forestry," *Proceedings of the American Philosophical Society*, July, 1945, pp. 438–439.

forest capital is generally, for the small-woods owner, a problem of sub-sidy rather than of credit.

Both for the small owner and for all other forest owners, credit cannot be translated quickly into the form of timber growing stock, as in other industries it can be translated quickly into productive capital goods. Only the slow and largely inexorable processes of nature can create growing stock. Forest credit can ease the financial burden, permit the application of labor to forest land, finance planting, and so on, but it cannot fill quite the same role in forestry as it can in the steel industry or the shoe industry or even in farming.

One is forced to the conclusion that on the small holdings where credit developments lag, as on the larger ones where progress now is stirring, satisfactory financing can only follow more fundamental improvements in the economic and institutional climate for forestry. A report published in 1958 by Resources for the Future helps to spark our thinking on this question.[9] Prepared by a committee of foresters, economists, and bankers, the report urges more vigorous extension of public and private credit to the little forest owners. But it emphasizes the concurrent need for generating forest practice, the incentives for such practice, and thus the demand for credit—by means of education, technical assistance, market development, forest insurance, and direct public subsidy. And the report particularly stresses the requirement that the holdings be organized for the practice of forestry so as to overcome the handicaps inherent in small-ness (see Chap. 10, p. 155)—as through consolidation or joint manage-ment arrangements for the nonfarm tracts.

## FOREST FIRE INSURANCE

From credit, it is an easy step to the closely kindred subject of insur-ance. We have taken a look at the central credit problem, that of risk. We have seen how risks of physical and financial loss have frightened lenders away from forest property. Insurance is a means of reducing risk. If a wishful borrower can insure himself against loss of collateral, he is much more apt to succeed in using the collateral to attract willing lend-ers. Insurance and credit go hand in hand. It will be apparent, too, as we go on, that insurance has other values besides those associated with credit.

Let us talk about insuring forest property, notably standing timber. Here lies whatever special interest the subject of insurance holds for us: Insurance elsewhere in the forest economy is pretty much the same story as insurance in general. And let us talk about insurance against fire. This type of protection has proved to be the first step in forest insurance in the United States. A study of it will reveal to us the principles that apply

[9] Resources for the Future, Inc., Committee: Work cited, especially pp. 82–94.

to other types of coverage that may some day be extended to forest property, such as storm and theft, insects and disease.

To sweep away any possibility of misunderstanding, let us remind ourselves that fire *insurance* is not a device for preventing or stopping fire. The existence of an insurance program may, as we shall see, cut fire losses. However, the purpose of the program is to reimburse the timber owner after loss occurs and in this way to erase this particular element of his risk. To erase risk sounds like a job for a magician. Actually, the social view of it is not an erasure but a spreading of risk, and ordinary persons are capable of doing it. Let us see how.

Suppose that you are the owner of 1 million acres of timberland. Your land consists of some 10,000 parcels averaging about 100 acres each, some contiguous, some separated, and the whole widely spread in a belt paralleling the coast. Every year you have fires. A few parcels are hit hard by real conflagrations. Many are burned over less heavily, with comparatively little mortality loss. Some are touched by fires but not burned far. The experience varies a little from year to year with the weather, the status of the forest, the causative circumstances, and the fortunes of fire control. Your records show that on the average—and a rather steady average it is—0.4 per cent of your acreage burns over annually and 0.05 per cent of your value is destroyed beyond the possibility of salvage. You predict that these same percentages will hold in future, and consequently you budget the 0.05 per cent of value, or currently an average of 6 cents an acre, as a yearly cost due to fire damage: a *loss cost.*

Because your fire loss is highly predictable, there is little risk attached to it. The loss cost is pretty much an everyday affair in your timber-growing business, like the cost of salaries and marking paint. It stands at 6 cents an acre, we may suppose, because that is the best combination: The marginal cost of reducing it at all would exceed the reduction, and conversely any attempt to save on fire-control costs would result in a more than proportional rise of loss cost. The risk of an exceptional fire year being, let us suppose, altogether negligible, you have no need for insurance. You are, as the term goes, a *self-insurer.* The reason why you can insure yourself against this cost is perhaps twofold: First, you know how much the cost is going to be and when it will occur. Second, you have the financial resources to meet the cost when it occurs. We might say that in this case of the self-insurer there is a very high probability of a certain small loss—small, that is, in relation to the resources at stake.

## HOW INSURANCE WORKS

Now imagine that the 10,000 forest parcels, instead of being held in a single ownership, are owned by 10,000 individuals. Let's see what difference this makes to the problem of risk and the need for insurance, and how the individual owners may go about reducing their risk through insurance.

Although one can still predict with great certainty what fire will do to the whole million acres, he cannot by any means predict what will happen to any one parcel. Supposing that losses on the whole forest will still run 6 cents per acre per year on the average, it unfortunately doesn't follow that the individual owner of a 100-acre parcel can count on an annual loss of $6. The chances are he will have no loss at all. On the other hand, it is just conceivable that this very year he may be wiped out —to the extent that fire is capable of doing. Unless he is in the very peculiar position of having other extensive assets for which the *hazards* (circumstances that affect loss) are like those of the forest and among which he can spread all the risk, he cannot economically insure himself. He does not know what the cost is going to be or when it will occur. And the chances are that he does not have the financial resources to stand a maximum loss. There is a low probability of a large loss, and the owner can benefit from insurance against this loss. [Incidentally, we have seen how the need for insurance stands in the case where there is a big chance of a small loss and where there is a small chance of a big loss. How about the case where there is a big chance of a big loss? Or where there is a small chance of a small loss?]

If the 10,000 forest owners can find some way of getting together co-operatively they can insure themselves just as you did, when you were the sole owner, taking advantage, as you did, of the so-called law of large numbers. They can set up a kitty, or pot, and each year each of them can put in 6 cents for every acre that he owns. Whenever one of them suffers a fire loss, he can dip into the pot for recompense. So long as everyone is honest and the averages hold and nearly everyone stays in the organization, the scheme will work, and there will always be enough money in the kitty to pay off the losses when fire strikes. The 10,000 owners have, in effect, set up a mutual insurance company.

Of course, in practice even the mutual company will need to ask its members to chip in more than 6 cents an acre. For one thing, they will be sensible to sweeten the pot at the start with a reserve that will cover the possibility of early heavy losses. Whereas the self-insurer can generally afford to owe himself any losses that may temporarily run above his budget, the individual insured owner can probably not afford to have his losses owed to him. The chances are he would resent such a situation and react to it in ways that might lead to dissolving the company. Besides the cost of carrying a reserve, there will be other administrative costs. It will surely be necessary to hire people to manage the kitty, to work with the members, to arrange for the annual payments (*premiums*), and to appraise and settle losses. These people will need an office to work in and will run up various other expenses such as of travel. Perhaps it will be necessary for the members to assess themselves 10 cents an acre annually. [Basically, what factors will determine the amount?]

Other forms of organization are possible besides the mutual form. The group can achieve self-insurance by placing the affair in the hands of its representative, the government. Government insurance is more appropriate, the greater the percentage of the people that will be insured. Social security is the ultimate example. In our country, however, much insurance is handled in still a different way, by ordinary profit-making stock companies. Particularly where there is a chance of very large single losses and the need for maximum spreading of the risk, such insurers may band together into a pool, sharing both the premiums and the responsibility for meeting losses.

Whatever form the insurer takes, there are certain minimum essentials to the success of the scheme. The losses against which individuals would be insured must be largely unpredictable for the individual but largely predictable for a group. There must be enough individuals who stand ready to buy insurance, or can be sold on the idea, to form a group having this characteristic, that its aggregate losses will be highly predictable. Furthermore, the predicted loss costs and the administrative costs must be within the range of the premiums that the group is willing to pay for insurance service. And under the heading of costs must be included allowances for carrying a reserve against early and heavy losses, for the net returns of a profit-making insurer, and for such extra risks of insurance writing as may be involved if the line is a new one, with meager loss experience or loss data, as is true of forest fire.

## SETTING A PREMIUM

Up to this point we have pictured our insured forest owners as paying an annual premium of 6 cents or 10 cents or some such flat rate per acre of their holdings. We must now step back and refine our ideas about the premium. In practice, it cannot very well be a uniform percentage of the insured value. The reason for this is of course that forest acres vary greatly in the probability that there will be fire and in the probability of heavy loss if there is a fire. Differences from acre to acre arise in differences in exposure to fire-causing factors (effectiveness of prevention in the area, nearness of the tract to traveled roads, use of it for recreational purposes, etc.), differences in forest conditions that affect fire behavior (timber type, size class, and stocking, condition of undergrowth, presence of logging slash, etc.), and differences in the circumstances of fire control (accessibility of tract, type of control setup, etc.).

Thus if forest fire insurance were offered at a uniform premium in per cent of insured value, forest owners with hazardous situations could be expected to be overly represented among the buyers, and the premium would prove too low. Such *adverse selection* is avoided—and the chances accordingly bettered for a good spreading of the risk—by suiting the premium to the hazard. One way of doing this is to set a standard premium for average situations and then reduce the premium for properties that enjoy conditions that lower the hazard and raise the premium where there are especially hazardous conditions.

One other point about premiums needs mentioning. If a premium is set on the basis of the probable percentage loss in property value as a result of fire, then the insurer will be able to pay the full amount of losses only if the properties are insured at full value. For example, take our earlier simplified case of a uniform 0.05 per cent premium, based on an average 0.05 per cent loss of value. Reflection will quickly convince you that the premium pot will contain enough money to pay off the losses only if everybody insures his property at full value—that is, pays a premium equal to 0.05 per cent of full value. Reflection will also make it clear that the reason for this is that almost all fire losses are partial losses. The issue would not arise if a fire always reduced a property entirely to ashes. If forest owner Q, with a $10,000 property, decides, in view of the good chance that he will not be wiped out by any fire, to play it smart and insure for $5,000 and thus get by with a premium of $25, the only way the company can make a go of it when Q has a $1,000 loss is to consider him a coinsurer for half the amount and to pay him only $500. Of course it is conceivable that Q would want to be a coinsurer; if he does, he may, and for a reduced premium. [Under what circumstances might such insurance be desired?]

## FOREST INSURANCE HISTORY

In the United States, the topic of forest insurance has been under discussion for a long while, though mainly by foresters and not so much by insurance people. The advantages of forest insurance and the need for it have been widely proclaimed and generally accepted within our profession. And yet little insurance has been written, and virtually none until just the past few years. As late as 1949, Ellis Williams, in the introduction to his monograph on the subject,[10] was able to compare forest insurance to the snakes of Ireland, of which there aren't any.

In this respect as in others, our experience runs counter to, or at any rate later than, that in Europe, where there was forest insurance in effect

[10] Williams, Ellis T.: *Forest Insurance,* Northeastern Forest Experiment Station Paper 26, Upper Darby, Pa., 1949.

INSTITUTIONS OF THE FOREST ECONOMY

at least as early as 1870,[11] and where this class of insurance is today well tried and matured, especially in the Scandinavian nations. An early venture in the United States was that of the Timberlands Mutual Fire Insurance Company, organized in New Hampshire in 1917 specifically to write forest insurance. After running, apparently not unsuccessfully, for a mere seven months, this insurer turned over its business to a general fire insurance stock company.[12] Other stock companies have dabbled in forest insurance from time to time, but the dabbling never grew into a substantial interest. Many proposals have been made for the government to write forest insurance. No use was ever made of a 1944 law authorizing the Federal Crop Insurance Corporation to insure standing timber on a trial basis. Standing timber insurance by the War Damage Corporation was limited to the event of enemy attack in World War II.

The bleak history of forest insurance in the United States can be explained by many factors of supply and demand. The slow development of private forestry is one. Another has been the lagging of fire control in many areas, though the difficulty of gaining accurate knowledge of fire losses and their determinants has been equally crucial. The same technical complexities that have given pause to the lenders have affected the insurers as well. With little insurance being written, risk spreading was meager.[13] This situation made for high premium rates, commonly from 2 to 10 per cent. Such rates sent all but the most eager insurance seekers back home. It was a vicious circle. So, too, was the relationship between credit and insurance: Credit's skinny status can be blamed on the want of insurance, but lines of causation ran in the opposite direction also.

[Suppose that forest-fire-insurance rates were prohibitively high, not because of poor risk spreading, but simply because loss costs were large. And suppose that fire control was being managed at the best combination, in the sense explained earlier in this chapter. What would be the answer to this dilemma?]

## RESEARCH IN FOREST INSURANCE

In the 1930s, Harold B. Shepard, of the United States Forest Service, made a bright mark upon the history of our forest insurance with his studies of insurance possibilities on the Pacific Coast and in the Northeast.[14] Like the Forest Taxation Inquiry, these studies were authorized

---

[11] "Forest-fire Insurance in France," *Forestry Quarterly*, March, 1914, pp. 111–112.

[12] Averill, C. C., and L. M. Frost: *Some Factors Underlying Forest Fire Insurance in Massachusetts*, Harvard Forest Bulletin 17, Petersham, Mass., 1933, pp. 10–11.

[13] Williams: Work cited, p. 31.

[14] Shepard, H. B.: *Forest Fire Insurance in the Pacific Coast States*, U.S. Department of Agriculture Technical Bulletin 551, 1937; also *Forest Fire Insurance in the Northeastern States*, Technical Bulletin 651, 1939.

by the Clarke-McNary Act of 1924; the necessary funds, however, were not appropriated until a few years later. Mr. Shepard concentrated his energies upon what was the most needful and difficult part of insurance research: the analysis of loss experience and the calculation of premium rates. He spelled out a comprehensive schedule of losses, and he proposed rates according to locality and all the various forest conditions significant to the hazard. On the Pacific Coast, he found an average loss expectation for all forest regions of 0.082 per cent per year (8.2 cents per $100 of value), and his recommended premiums averaged 45 cents per $100 of value. In the Northeast, the calculated average loss turned out to be 13.5 cents per $100, and the premiums suggested were again proportionately higher. The rate schedules proposed by Mr. Shepard were intended not only to cover the payment of losses, cost of providing the service, and a "fair profit" on the business but also to include a safety factor against the inevitable indeterminate elements of early trial. Chief among these he listed incomplete reporting of losses, errors in computations, uncertainty regarding the effect of adverse selection, and an insufficient allowance for conflagration hazard.[15] He foresaw that after an active insurance program got under way and lived through its experimental period and the insurers worked up a sizeable business, the premium rates would be cut.

## ONE INSURER'S PROGRAM

It was through such careful studies as those by Mr. Shepard and through the gradual warming of the whole climate for forestry that a sharply directed and possibly permanent insurance program got under way in 1955. The insurer that came into the picture then—and has since been followed by at least one other—was, in effect, a pool of some eighteen established companies. Within two years, they were insuring more than $200 million worth of timber—merchantable timber only—against fire and lightning. Most of the insurance was issued in the Far West, and most of the remainder in the South. The coverage was written mainly in connection with life-insurance-company loans on large forest holdings. One policy was taken out by a logger who, in his contract, had accepted liability for fire in the tract. Let us take a brief look at the premium rates as of 1957, for what they may tell us about the fundamentals of forest insurance.

First, standard rates were set up for each state. The highest was for Mississippi: $2.24 per year per $100 of value. Rates between $1 and $2 were established for Florida, Texas, Tennessee, and Louisiana. The rate for Alabama was 72 cents, and for Georgia and South Carolina, 56 cents.

[15] U.S. Department of Agriculture Technical Bulletin 651, pp. 41–42.

In all other states, the rate was 50 cents per year per $100 of value. [Why do you suppose the South shows up so poorly here?]

Next, credits were established for conditions or practices believed to be associated with lower hazard. For example, if the insured firm supplemented public fire control by keeping fire-fighting equipment on hand, the standard premium was reduced by 5 per cent. If the firm had fire fighters ready, it was given an extra 10 per cent credit. Credits of from 2 to 5 per cent were allowed on large timber, dense stands, fire-resistant species, light underbrush. Interestingly, if the property was a registered tree farm, a 20 per cent credit was granted. Altogether, it was possible for an insured firm to earn a total reduction of 44 per cent of his standard premium. [What effects would you expect these terms to have upon the actions of owners seeking insurance?]

Finally, on the other side of the scoreboard, extra charges were made for things linked with higher hazard. The standard premium was boosted 5 to 10 per cent if there was a turpentining operation in progress on the insured property or if there was a railroad or paved public highway nearby, or a commercial recreational development. Extra charges were made, too, for steep terrain, heavy underbrush, and the presence of logging which was not part of a sustained-yield program. Other special hazards might result in a 50 to 100 per cent charge. The owner of a tract not covered by the state-Federal fire-control system would have to pay an extra 50 per cent of the standard premium—if he could get insurance at all. You can see from all these requirements that in the writing of the insurance, the companies would certainly have to be represented by foresters skilled in forest surveying as well as appraisal.

Looking back over the general character and the specific terms of forest insurance, one sees clearly that its effect would be to make forests more valuable and to intensify the practice of forestry, the effect being more pronounced the wider the insurance coverage. On balance, fire insurance could be expected to strengthen the incentives for effective fire control. It could be expected to reduce risk, lower the alternative rate of return, and so encourage conservation. It would intensify forest management also in the stock-supply period, for a threat of fire loss is much like the expectation of a falling price in prompting a positive supply response, or reduction in growing stock (compare Chap. 14, pp. 215–216). It would open the possibilities for credit programs. It would, by its premium bonuses and penalties, steer forest practice in conservative directions.

Programs of forest insurance, like those of credit, will march with the advances in private forestry. So long as times hold reasonably good and the advances continue, we may expect to see fire insurance extended so as to cover losses of unmerchantable timber and of forest productivity.

We may look forward to the growth of insurance into hazards other than fire and to the spread of both credit and insurance coverage.

## SUMMARY

In the United States forest economy, problems of credit and insurance center upon the woods. For the rest of the forest economy, the credit and insurance story is much the same as that in the economy at large.

Forest credit, like all credit, is necessary for economic efficiency. A suitable program, however, has been slow to develop, mainly because of risks of physical and economic loss and of technical misjudgment of forest collateral. Among credit proposals, those for a public forest-credit agency have been prominent. Actual developments, however, have been mainly along other lines: Most of the lending being done on forest collateral is by Federal land banks, life insurance companies, and commercial banks. Amid these developments, little progress has been made with the credit problem of small-scale forest owners and operators.

Forest insurance, a close companion to forest credit, is a social device for applying the law of large numbers to forest hazards in such a way as to reduce risk by redistributing losses. Like credit, insurance has been eagerly advocated by foresters. But it has been slow to come into being, mainly because of slow progress in forest protection, in other forest practices, and in knowledge of losses. Advances in private forestry and painstaking research into insurance possibilities have led a few companies since 1955 to offer forest fire insurance at premiums within the reach of some buyers.

The growth of credit and insurance facilities is likely to accompany or follow forestry development rather than bring it about.

**Part Five**

**OPERATION
AND PLANNING OF
THE FOREST ECONOMY**

Chapter 29

# FOREST ECONOMY OF THE WORLD

As we begin this fifth and last part of our story, we reenter, for a better look, the ground sketched in Chapter 2 in the Introduction: the workings of the forest economy at large. As in that chapter, so here in this group of chapters we start with the whole spectacle of resources and their management, then inquire about the purpose, the ends, of what we see, and finally go on to the question of adapting means to ends—and ends to means. The book concludes on the same note respecting social management as did Part Two respecting that of the firm: planning, which is the most comprehensive economic act.

In this chapter we study the forest economy of the world, taking up first the geography of world forest resources and industry; second, national forest economies; third, the movement of wood and its products in the course of trade.

## FOREST AREAS

There are some 37 billion acres of land on earth, or excluding the polar regions, some 33 billion acres. Of the latter area, perhaps 40 per cent is physically capable of bearing forest cover (compare the United States figure: 50 per cent), while 25 per cent is by nature grassland, and 35 per cent desert.

Nearly three-tenths of the nonpolar lands are actually forested, about the same proportion as in the United States. These 9½ billion acres are strongly concentrated. The main body of coniferous forest occurs as a belt around the earth below the arctic tundra, with projections southward along the east and west sides of North America and of Eurasia (Fig. 44a). Temperate hardwoods are more widely scattered, but tropical hardwoods occur principally in three great concentrations: the Amazon basin, central and western equatorial Africa, and southeast Asia together with the outlying islands (Fig. 44b). Thus vast stretches of the earth are open and largely treeless: central North America, the northern half of Africa and its southern end, the Middle East and the steppes and deserts that extend thence across central Asia. Australia is a bald head with a fringe.

About half of the world's 9½ billion forest acres are classified as accessible for timber use, and about a third are actually in such use.[1] The inaccessible forests are located mostly in the remote interior of the U.S.S.R., Canada, and Alaska, and in parts of Asia and Latin America. The accessible forests not in timber use are found mainly in Canada, Latin America, and Africa. Whether used or not for timber purposes, most of the forest performs a protective function of great value. Furthermore, much of it is in use for recreation and in many cases is reserved for that purpose. About half of the forest not in timber use is regarded as a likely source of timber for the future. Percentages of total forest acreage in timber use in the major subdivisions of the world are as follows:

| | |
|---|---|
| Europe | 96 |
| U.S.S.R. | 47 |
| Asia (except U.S.S.R.) | 44 |
| North America | 34 |
| Pacific area | 20 |
| Africa | 13 |
| Latin America | 9 |

Lying back of regional and national differences in the timber economy are great differences in the character and management of the forest, only a few of which we have space to discuss. One that we need to stress arises from the contrast between conifers and hardwoods. Coniferous timber, or softwood, is what may be called general-purpose wood; it is readily usable for construction, pulping, and other ends. Hardwood, under present technology, is more suited to special and limited uses: oak for flooring, furniture, cooperage; mahogany for furniture, paneling; balsa for floats, carvings. Although coniferous forests make up only a third of the total forest area, they form more than half of the acreage in use for timber. Look again at Figure 44 and see what this contrast between soft-

---

[1] The terminology and most of the data here and following are those of the Forestry Division, FAO, United Nations. See United Nations, FAO, Forestry Division: *World Forest Resources*, Rome, 1955. Also United Nations, FAO, Forestry Division: *Yearbook of Forest Products Statistics*, Rome, 1957. Supplementary reading is to be found in Haden-Guest, Stephen, and others (eds.): *A World Geography of Forest Resources*, The Ronald Press Company, New York, 1956.

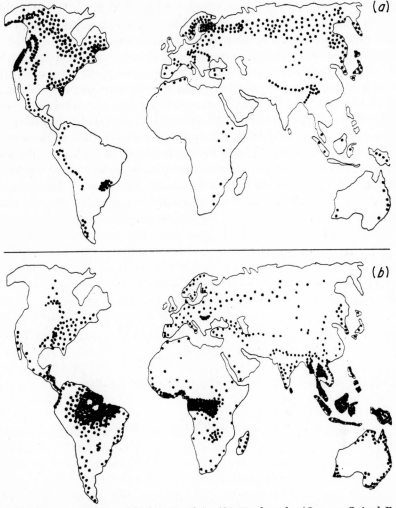

Fig. 44. Forests of the world: (*a*) Conifers. (*b*) Hardwoods. (*Source: Oxford Economic Atlas of the World, Oxford University Press, 1955, shortened ed., p. 40.*)

woods and hardwoods signifies. Notice the countries that control most of the world's softwoods and thus are preeminent today in timber resources. Notice the hardwood areas—especially the tropical hardwoods, which amount to half of all the world's forest acreage. These vast potential resources await developments in wood conversion and use.

A little less than a fourth of the earth's accessible forest area is in private ownership. The remainder is held by the public. Private ownership is most extensive in North America and Europe, where in both cases it represents about half of the accessible forest. Also on both continents, the little private holding, about which we have had much to say in this book, is common. A nation in point is West Germany, where 42 per cent of the private forest is in holdings of less than 25 acres.

The forest areas that are in use for timber vary greatly in respect to the status of timber management. In Europe, perhaps 40 per cent of the forest is managed under working plans. At the other extreme, in Latin America, Africa, and the Pacific area, the proportion of forests so managed is of the order of one-tenth. A survey of the opinion of public forestry authorities in Europe finds that they classify 95 per cent of the forest area as subject to "good" or "fair" cutting practices. In Latin America and Africa, 60 per cent of the cutting is judged "poor or destructive" by local officials. Conscious management of the world's forests for watershed and other nontimber values is no doubt generally less intensive than the timber management.

### TIMBER INVENTORY

Data on the quantity of standing timber in the world are so incomplete and so variable in their meaning from nation to nation that they are difficult to summarize. It has been estimated that total growing stock in all forests in timber use amounts to some 3,600 billion cubic feet (with bark), of which 55 per cent is softwood. This would mean an average of about 1,300 cubic feet per acre (compare the United States average: 1,100), varying as follows among the major world subdivisions:

| | |
|---|---|
| Latin America | 1,800 |
| Asia (except U.S.S.R.) | 1,400 |
| U.S.S.R. | 1,400 |
| Europe | 1,100 |
| Africa | 1,100 |
| North America | 1,000 |
| Pacific area | 800 |

Growing stock per acre is a function of silvicultural treatment and age distribution, but above all of climate. In the tropical rain forests (e.g., Belgian Congo, Madagascar, French Equatorial Africa) it may reach 4,300 to 5,700 cubic feet; in temperate zones (Switzerland, Austria, Chile) 3,000 cubic feet is not uncommon; 700 to 850 cubic feet per acre is typical for countries like Finland, Norway, and Canada; in the savanna forests of Central Africa the figure may fall as low as 300 to 400 cubic feet.[2]

From forest growing stocks and other timber, a total of some 56 billion cubic feet is being harvested annually. Somewhat more than half of this

[2] *World Forest Resources*, p. 12. The original is given in terms of cubic meters per hectare.

is softwood. The Forestry Division of FAO estimates that in the world's forests used for timber, taken as a whole, the harvest of softwood is about equal to the net growth while that of hardwood is substantially exceeded by growth. At the same time, however, it is recognized that for resource maintenance in the long pull, the current allowable harvest is generally less than the growth, either because growing stocks are below the desired norm or because, as in the case of many hardwood forests, much of the growth is of species and quality unusable with today's technology. Over-cutting in relation to allowable harvest is considered to be widespread. It is very common in those regions of the world where the level of living is close to bare subsistence and where the practice of forestry is undeveloped. But it is found even in Europe: There in the mid-1950s the total harvest exceeded the allowable cut by one-sixth.

## FOREST PRODUCTS AND INDUSTRY

The total timber harvest reported to FAO for the year 1956 was proportioned as follows among major uses, in per cent of log volume:

| | |
|---|---|
| Firewood | 41 |
| Industrial wood: | |
|     Logs for lumber, veneer, and cross-ties | 37 |
|     Pulpwood and mine props | 16 |
|     Other industrial wood | 6 |
| Total | 100 |

The two forest industries—lumber and pulp—which used most of the industrial wood are mapped in Figure 45. One is struck by the overwhelming concentration of these industries in the earth's North Temperate Zone. Such concentration, of course, is not peculiar to wood-using industry but holds for industrial development generally. Viewed in relation to Figure 44, the industrial pattern of Figure 45 underscores our observations about the underutilization of tropical hardwoods and the world's heavy reliance upon softwood. North America, Europe, and U.S.S.R., the three predominantly coniferous regions, contain a third of the world's population and two-fifths of its forest land; yet they harvest 70 per cent of all the timber, saw 85 per cent of the lumber, and make close to 95 per cent of the wood pulp.

Much in contrast to the closely clustered lumber and pulp industries is the case of firewood, which is the world's most nearly universal timber product. Wood is used the world over for burning, the geographic pattern of its use (Fig. 46) following roughly that of forest occurrence. In point of timber volume, as we have seen, the reports to FAO put firewood in first place among forest products. Firewood is hard for nations to keep

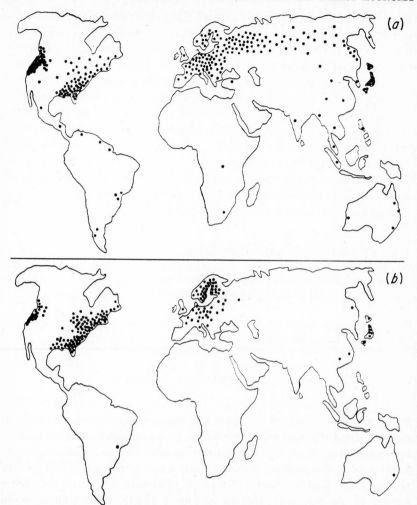

Fig. 45. Output of two wood-using industries, 1956: (a) Lumber. (b) Pulp. Each dot represents about 500 million board feet of lumber or 500 million pounds of pulp produced within the indicated region. (*Source: United Nations, FAO, Forestry Division: Yearbook of Forest Products Statistics, Rome, 1957, tables 13, 25.*)

track of statistically, and therefore the reporting of it is relatively incomplete. If the facts were known, we might well learn that the quantity of this product substantially exceeds that of all others combined. Many an industrially underdeveloped nation burns nearly all the wood it harvests.

Even from the foregoing highlighted sketch of world forestry, it is obvious how greatly the situation varies from region to region. Let us look a little further into this variability, dividing the nations of the world into relatively uniform groups and briefly studying the forest economy of

Fig. 46. Output of firewood, 1956. Each dot represents about 100 million cubic feet produced within the indicated region. (*Source: United Nations, FAO, Forestry Division: Yearbook of Forest Products Statistics, Rome, 1957, table 1, adjusted.*)

each group. The seven groups recognized are mapped in Figure 47. Data for illustrative nations in each group are given in Table 40.

## SOUTHERN, TROPICAL, AND BORDER NATIONS

At the southern end of the earth, lying mainly in the Temperate Zone, is a group of rather lightly forested, agrarian countries, the *South-temperate nations*. Linked to Western Europe by cultural, political, or economic ties, these nations have adopted some of Europe's ideas about the practice of forestry. They have in some cases a strong interest in tree planting, both on forest areas and as an afforestation measure for timber and protective purposes. Moderately high standards of living and limited forest resources make most of the nations timber-product importers. The extent of importation can be judged from a comparison of the figures in Table 40 on per-capita timber harvest and consumption, both of which are stated in like terms of roundwood raw material. The position of the timber economy in the nation—measured, say, by per cent of employment or income—varies a good deal within the group. In the Union of South Africa it is negligible; in Australia it perhaps approaches 10 per cent. The Table-40 data on per-capita harvest are a rough index of importance of the timber economy—to be tempered, of course, by such considerations as the degree of development of industry in general and of wood processing.

Most of the nations within the tropical-hardwood zone of the earth may be grouped together. These *tropical-hardwood nations* are industrially underdeveloped, and their forest economy is colonial: Their wood exports run heavily to logs and squared timbers, and firewood makes up a very large share of their total harvest (see Table 40). Some of them are heavily forested, though particularly in Africa the forest may be localized: French West Africa, for instance, is but one-fourth forested. A good deal of the forest is still inaccessible, and only by virtue of low population density do some of the nations show moderately high acreages of

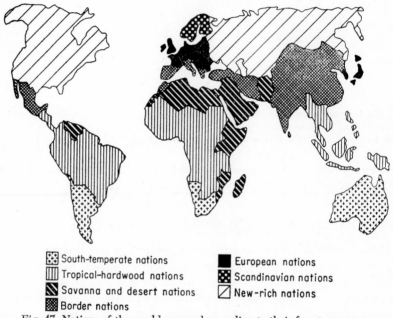

|  | South-temperate nations |  | European nations |
| --- | --- | --- | --- |
|  | Tropical-hardwood nations |  | Scandinavian nations |
|  | Savanna and desert nations |  | New-rich nations |
|  | Border nations |  |  |

Fig. 47. Nations of the world grouped according to their forest economy.

accessible forest per capita. Tropical hardwoods grow in bewildering variety. In Indonesia, for example, it is estimated that there are some 3,000 different tree species that reach timber size; in Malaya, 2,500; in the Amazon basin, 2,500. The few species whose qualities are known and whose special uses are well established may be far between, so that commercial logging is a picking and choosing process, yielding but a very small harvest per acre. The harvest per capita, however, is comparatively high, and in some of the nations the timber economy provides substantial employment and income. With few exceptions, the practice of forestry is undeveloped, as is knowledge of the timber, its silviculture, and its utilization. Here is a great world forest surplus, but so far only in potential.

The third group mapped in Figure 47, the *savanna and desert nations*, are also industrially underdeveloped. Most of them are nations of the

Table 40. Measures of the timber economy in illustrative nations, 1955–1956

| Nation | Forest land | | Annual timber harvest, cubic feet | | Annual timber consumption, cubic feet per capita | Firewood harvest, per cent of total |
|---|---|---|---|---|---|---|
| | Per cent of all land | Accessible acres per capita | Per accessible acre | Per capita | | |
| South-temperate nations: | | | | | | |
| Argentina | 25 | 7.8 | 3 | 23 | 28 | 80 |
| Union of South Africa | 3 | 0.2 | 12 | 3 | 7 | 14 |
| Australia | 5 | 4.0 | 14 | 58 | 69 | 32 |
| Tropical-hardwood nations: | | | | | | |
| Brazil | 57 | 5.1 | 3 | 63 | 62 | 87 |
| Belgian Congo | 45 | 2.2 | 6 | 14 | 10 | 88 |
| Indonesia | 54 | 1.9 | 12 | 23 | 24 | 93 |
| Savanna and desert nations: | | | | | | |
| Libya | 1 | 0.9 | 10 | 9 | 9 | 99 |
| Iraq | 4 | 0.4 | 1 | 1 | 2 | 74 |
| Kenya | 2 | 0.2 | 9 | 2 | 2 | 37 |
| Border nations: | | | | | | |
| Mexico | 13 | 2.0 | 2 | 4 | 13 | 29 |
| Spain | 25 | 1.1 | 12 | 13 | 12 | 65 |
| India | 22 | 0.3 | 4 | 1 | 1 | 75 |
| European nations: | | | | | | |
| United Kingdom | 6 | 0.1 | 29 | 2 | 22 | 12 |
| Austria | 38 | 0.9 | 61 | 60 | 18 | 27 |
| Japan | 62 | 0.6 | 42 | 26 | 24 | 46 |
| Scandinavian nations: | | | | | | |
| Norway | 24 | 4.8 | 19 | 90 | 79 | 5 |
| Sweden | 56 | 7.8 | 27 | 208 | 91 | 15 |
| Finland | 71 | 12.1 | 28 | 335 | 169 | 32 |
| New-rich nations: | | | | | | |
| Canada | 38 | 20.6 | 11 | 222 | 107 | 9 |
| United States | 33 | 2.6 | 27 | 68 | 75 | 17 |
| U.S.S.R. | 34 | 5.3 | 11 | 59 | 56 | 37 |

SOURCE: United Nations, FAO, Forestry Division: *Yearbook of Forest Products Statistics*, Rome, 1957.

Arab world. They have little forest land, commonly less than 5 per cent, and so are extremely deficient in respect to this resource. Their imports, however, are small, and their per-capita wood consumption is the lowest of any group (refer again to Table 40). Thus their timber economy is negligible, though locally trees have great protective value.

The *border nations* are on a borderline, not only geographically in relation to the earth's North-temperate forest regions, but also economically, with but generally slight industrial development and a heavy pressure of population upon land resources. Having rather little forest land, mostly 10 to 25 per cent of their total area, they are all timber-deficit nations. Some of them are large importers. A few have brought professional forestry concepts from Europe, as Turkey from Germany and India from Britain, but for the most part, outside of occasional reserved forests, the woodland capital is run down as a result of long exploitation for wood and for forage to supply the livestock that abound throughout most of the region. Conservative land management is difficult where people and animals weigh heavily upon the soil, where climate is marked by long dry seasons and where these may be interspersed by serious flood and erosion periods. Forests have a big protective role, mainly in potential.

## NORTHERN NATIONS

As we turn now to the last three groups of nations recognized in Figure 47, we enter a part of the world which is markedly different from the rest. We have already seen that these North-temperate nations have something of a corner upon wood-using industries and softwood timber supplies. We know that most of them have a highly developed economy. Turning again to Table 40, we can observe that they are distinguished also by rather consistently high forest acreage, large output of timber per acre and per capita, and heavy consumption of industrial forest products. You should keep your eye on Table 40 as we move on through this regional review.

The *European nations*—including Japan as essentially European in its forest economy, but excluding from the group certain border and northern nations as mapped in Figure 47—have forest lands that are more largely accessible than those of any other group. Consistently high population density results in a very low forest acreage per capita. Heavy requirements for forest products, a surplus of labor, and, on the continent, a policy of national self-sufficiency to meet the continual threat of war led these nations early to undertake intensive forest production. Their timber output per acre today is the highest in the world, and represents most nearly the physical capacity of the land to grow wood continuously. All the nations are brisk traders in forest products, mostly amongst themselves. In general, those toward the east are in a surplus position and are net exporters, while those toward the west are timber-deficient and do a good deal of importing. The position of wood in the economy similarly ranges from east to west. In France and Germany, perhaps 5 per cent of income and employment arise in the forest economy, while in such nations as Austria the proportion is substantially higher, but in the United Kingdom it is almost negligible.

In the *Scandinavian nations*—here stretching the term to include Finland, but dropping Denmark, which is more like Western Europe—we find the heaviest dependence in the world upon forests and forest industry for a livelihood. Finland is said to derive one-half of her national income from wood products. Sweden, more largely industrialized, derives possibly one-fifth. All three nations in the group consume enormous amounts of wood per capita and export large additional quantities to the rest of the world. Backing up this utilization and trade is an intensive program of timber management strongly supported by social controls, under which these northern lands are made to yield in the necessary measure.

The *new-rich nations*—Canada, United States, and U.S.S.R.—are characterized by general resource abundance, fast-growing industrial economies, and considerable dependence upon forests and timber. The United States gets about 5 per cent of her income and employment from timber products; Canada, about 15. Canada and U.S.S.R. have large acreages of forest land, inaccessible at present, that represent a world reserve of softwood. Both nations have an exportable softwood surplus, and the United States, too, was until recently a timber-surplus nation and still has a substantial supply of untapped old growth, particularly in Alaska. In all the nations, localities have rather recently witnessed eras of lavish resource use and depletion. Out of this experience the nations have developed programs, suited in each case to their institutions and economic circumstances, that strive to place forestry upon permanent footing. We find today in all three a concern—again variously expressed—for setting regional and national forestry goals and for working out ways to meet goals. In Chapter 31 we shall have a look at the problem of goals for the United States.[3]

## TRADE IN FOREST PRODUCTS

Now that we have completed a sketch of forest resource geography, we are in position to talk a little about timber *trade*. Our main interest is in the trade among nations. Yet we cannot confine our attention to international trade, for this is simply part of the whole trade in timber, most of which occurs within national boundaries. Let us try to see the picture of trade in the large, first reviewing the principles and then going on to intranational and international movements of wood products.

In Chapter 22 we gave some thought to the tools for analyzing market geography—the principles of supply and demand, of diminishing margi-

[3] You will find supplementary reading on the timber situation in the United States in *Timber Resources for America's Future*, U.S. Department of Agriculture, Forest Service Forest Resource Report 14, 1958, especially pp. 102–109, 1–102.

nal transfer cost, of the orientation of manufacturing, of relative transportability, and, blanketing these, of comparative advantage (p. 373). We
can expect timber or its products to move out of areas where there is
much accessible timber of useful kinds and where the alternatives to
forest employment are not relatively so good as to draw capital, labor,
and enterprise largely away from the woods and mills. The Philippines
are an example of a raw-timber exporter; Canada, of a processed-wood
exporter. Or we can expect forest products to be exported from places—
Singapore, for instance—which, though not themselves supplied with timber locally, are advantaged in wood manufacture because of their low-
cost situation with respect to raw material and other agents of production
and which are in position to furnish the marketing services that buyers
demand.

On the other hand, we can expect wood in raw form to flow into areas
of the latter sort that are not well supplied with forests, and into areas
with a high demand for raw wood as an end product, such as fuel or
mine props. And we can expect processed timber products to be imported by other deficit areas where consumers have a preference for such
products and the means to acquire them, ordinarily in the form of exports
of other goods or services. Many a timber-deficit area, as in the savanna
and desert nations, fails of such means for forest-product importation. At
the same time, some areas that are well supplied with timber import it
because they are better occupied in other lines. In Chapter 19 (p. 317)
we gave attention to the fact that the United States shifted from a
timber-export to a net import position about the time of World War II.
Foresters are inclined to attribute such a shift exclusively to physical
resource depletion. In doing so, they fail to examine the other side of the
shield: the burgeoning of alternative economic opportunity. [Turn to
Figure 38 (p. 318) and the discussion accompanying it. What do we learn
there about the history of comparative advantage in the lumber industry,
and its causes?]

When we apply the concepts of comparative advantage beyond national borders, we need to take note of some special institutional sources
of cost. One may be national customs and prejudices concerning trade
with this or that other nation. American hardwood lumber exporters have
a traditional advantage in the British market, an advantage that weakens
in favor of such other nations as Yugoslavia and France only in the face
of marked shifts in relative price. Another institutional source of cost in
trade may be restrictions placed by governments upon the use of foreign
exchange. Still another may be tariffs and other taxes upon trade. During
its high-tariff era centering in the 1920s, the United States placed substantial import duties upon forest products. Since then, such duties in
general have been much reduced. We noticed in Chapter 24 (p. 410)
that influence centers may play a part in determining duties. News-

paper publishers, a highly influential center, strive to hold down the tariff on newsprint paper, which the United States imports in great quantities from Canada. Hardwood plywood manufacturers in the United States take a favorable attitude toward tariffs upon the product that comes in from Japan and other foreign nations. To uphold a low-tariff policy and still protect domestic manufacturers, a nation may set up import quotas, as the United States has done in the case of Japanese hardwood plywood.

In passing, we must recognize that institutional barriers may be set up, not only against international trade, but also against a nation's internal trade. For instance, in the United States, the states have erected a good many small barriers to the free flow of commerce across their borders, such as regulations concerning the type, operation, and loading of trucks.

## UNITED STATES INTERNAL TRADE

Now to take a look at the actual flow of trade, and to begin with that which occurs within nations (*internal trade*) let us use the United States as a case in point. As we know from our previous work on the principle of relative transportability (pp. 167, 371), such raw timber products as firewood and mine timbers are highly restricted in their movement, whereas pulpwood and saw logs are more mobile, and poles and piling, which have tight specifications and a heavy demand at the particular spots where they are required for use, move very great distances. Processed products, by and large, are shipped much more freely than are raw products. Lumber enjoys comparatively wide mobility, and paper is extremely mobile.

The basic physical fact behind our internal trade in wood is our forest geography: concentrations of big softwood timber along the West Coast and in the Inland Empire; the concentration of smaller softwood in the Southeast and parts of the West; the fact that nearly all the hardwood is in the East, widely scattered; the virtual absence of forests from the central and western prairies, plains, and deserts. Another factor is the population pattern, relatively dense in the East. Another is the eastern concentrations of industry and commerce, which tend to create importing centers both because of their large use of forest products and because they place local production at a relative disadvantage. New York State, highly industrial, with plenty of rural land, half forested, but with a comparative scarcity of labor, imports eight-tenths or more of the wood she uses. Let us observe the movement of lumber within the United States as an illustration of how the various forces bear upon trade.

The history of our lumber distribution has been one of gradually increasing transportation distances and *interregional trade* (internal trade, between regions of the country). As the center of lumbering moved from the Northeast successively into the Lake states, South, and West, lumber production and consumption on the whole grew further and further apart. Today close to nine-tenths of United States population is east of the Rockies, but the West has two-thirds of all the standing saw timber and four-fifths of all the softwood saw timber.

However, an economy may at length rebel against the penalty of rising transportation cost, for such cost represents a rising advantage of local production. Recently we have evidence of some stemming and even reversal of the growing trend in interregional trade—evidence of a movement toward greater local self-sufficiency. Apparently a smaller percent-

*Table 41. Characteristics of three major regions of the United States with respect to domestic lumber trade; average data for early 1950s*

| Item | West | South | North |
|---|---|---|---|
| Per cent of total U.S. lumber production | 43 | 43 | 14 |
| Per cent of total U.S. lumber consumption | 26 | 30 | 44 |
| Intraregional lumber movement | Southward—e.g., fir to Calif., pine from Idaho | Pine eastward, northward, especially from La., Tex., Ark. Hardwood inland from coast and rivers | Mainly local; Appalachian hardwood and New England pine into Middle Atlantic states |
| Exports to other regions, per cent of production | 40 | 20 | Exports little |
| Destinations of exports | Northeast; elsewhere in North; little to South | Mainly central states (Ill.-Mo. to Ohio-W. Va.); some throughout North | Imports 60 per cent or more of consumption |

age of total lumber output is crossing state lines than formerly. The per-capita consumption of lumber, generally declining, is dropping faster in the deficit states. At the same time, these states, such as California and many of the states in the East, are increasing their output by opening up new areas or cultivating their second-growth timber.

A summary of lumber trade in recent years among three principal regions of the United States is given in Table 41. The regions are the same as we have used earlier in this book (e.g., p. 427). In general, the West is a heavy net exporter, the South is also a net exporter, while the North is a heavy net importer. No state of the Union is totally self-sufficient in respect to lumber. Every state has varied species and quality requirements, and none has a corresponding variety of forests. And then there is always local shipment of lumber across the line into states which are concurrently exporting lumber of the same kind. Even Oregon, with the nation's biggest lumber production, imports Douglas-fir lumber from Washington, redwood from California, pine from Idaho, and hardwood from West Virginia, Arkansas, Michigan, and other parts of the East.

## EXPORTING AND IMPORTING NATIONS

Just as in the United States since World War II (Fig. 35, p. 311), so among the nations generally the output of wood products has been on the increase. But in the world at large there appears to be no trend toward national self-sufficiency; rather, a growing trade as institutional barriers are lowered, standards of living rise, and the more remote forests are brought within reach. In the mid-1950s, close to a fifth of the world's harvest of industrial wood was shipped across international boundaries at some stage in its utilization. Let us study this *international trade*, using data from the year 1955.

The total value of forest products that entered international trade during the year is estimated by FAO at $5.4 billion. The estimate does not include much of the trade with, or within, the Soviet world, but this omission, by all appearances, is comparatively small. Four-tenths of the total value is logs, bolts, and lumber; three-tenths is paper and paperboard; two-tenths, pulp; and one-tenth, mechanically processed wood other than lumber.

The regions of the earth where national forest economies depend most largely upon the export trade are Africa and Europe. In the Pacific area and U.S.S.R., on the other hand, national exports as a percentage of all industrial wood output are very small:

| | |
|---|---|
| Africa | 40 |
| Europe | 39 |
| North America | 16 |
| Latin America | 15 |
| Asia (except U.S.S.R.) | 8 |
| U.S.S.R. | 3 |
| Pacific area | 3 |

In absolute terms of the total volume or value of exports, the story, as we may well imagine, reads quite differently. Here the northern hemisphere takes the upper hand by virtue of its immense total timber activity. The value of all national exports (omitting those of the Soviet world) is distributed as follows among the major subdivisions of the earth (the figures are percentages of the 1955 world total; the Pacific area, with less than ½ per cent, drops out):

| | |
|---|---|
| Europe | 50 |
| North America | 40 |
| Asia | 4 |
| Latin America | 4 |
| Africa | 2 |
| Total | 100 |

Africa's poor showing here is partly attributable to the fact that the timber exports of African nations are largely in the form of logs, while those of European nations are chiefly processed products, with much higher unit value.

First among the world's forest-product exporters is Canada, with about three-tenths of the total value. Then come Sweden and Finland, with another three-tenths between them. If now we add to the list the United States, Austria, Norway, France, and Brazil, we have accounted for more than 80 per cent of the world's total value of exports. We begin to see how strongly concentrated is the international trade in wood, and as we turn now to the import side of the picture, the fact of concentration becomes even more sharply established.

Europe and North America are the leading wood importers in terms of the percentage of 1955 total world value. Each of them exceeds the rest of the free world put together:

| | |
|---|---|
| Europe | 51 |
| North America | 29 |
| Asia | 7 |
| Latin America | 6 |
| Africa | 4 |
| Pacific area | 3 |
| Total | 100 |

The principal importing nations are the United States, with slightly more than a fourth of the total value, and the United Kingdom, with only a little less. West Germany, France, Italy, and Australia together import another fourth.

Thus the bulk of international trade in forest products flows from Canada into the United States and secondarily to the United Kingdom, and from Scandinavia into Western Europe, chiefly the United Kingdom.

## COMMODITIES IN INTERNATIONAL TRADE

Of what commodities does the trade consist? The answer is spelled out in Table 42. The basis for the table is the volume of roundwood raw material represented in each commodity. The figures in the table are percentages of the total volume in all commodities. As we should expect, processed products dominate the trade. Of these, three loom above all the rest: softwood lumber, wood pulp, and newsprint. Here are the commodities that make up most of the shipments between the great trading nations identified in the preceding paragraph. Notice that they are all

*Table 42. Percentage of the total volume of international trade in forest products, by commodity, 1955*

| Commodity | Per cent | |
|---|---|---|
| Roundwood: | | |
| Pulpwood | 7 | |
| Hardwood logs | 4 | |
| Mine props | 3 | |
| Softwood logs | 1 | |
| Poles, piling, posts | 1 | |
| Firewood | 1 | |
| All roundwood | | 17 |
| Mechanically processed wood: | | |
| Softwood lumber | 34 | |
| Hardwood lumber | 4 | |
| Boxboards | 1 | |
| Veneer and plywood | 1 | |
| Crossties | 1 | |
| All mechanically processed wood | | 41 |
| Pulp products: | | |
| Wood pulp | 22 | |
| Newsprint | 13 | |
| Other paper | 5 | |
| Paperboard | 1 | |
| Fiberboard | 1 | |
| All pulp products | | 42 |
| All commodities | | 100 |

products of the much-sought-after coniferous forest. Let us examine more closely the trade in each of these three commodities, and then consider a fourth, hardwood logs, which will illustrate the part played in commerce by the forests of the tropics. The story is told for the year 1955 in Tables 43, 44, 45, and 46.

In international trade in *softwood lumber* (Table 43), Canada among exporters holds the lead by a wide margin, originating more than a third of the total shipments. The United States and United Kingdom together import half of the world total. Among the other major importers, the two that are not European are South-temperate nations.

*Table 43. International trade in softwood lumber, 1955*

| Importing nation | Exporting nation | | | | | | |
|---|---|---|---|---|---|---|---|
| | Canada | Sweden | Finland | Austria | U.S.S.R. | Others | All |
| | Million bd ft | Million bd ft | Million bd ft | Million bd ft | Million bd ft | Million bd ft | Million bd ft |
| United States | 3,420 | * | * | — | — | 110 | 3,530 |
| United Kingdom | 860 | 930 | 650 | 10 | 490 | 500 | 3,440 |
| West Germany | * | 300 | 160 | 540 | 40 | 180 | 1,220 |
| Benelux | 10 | 410 | 260 | 120 | 190 | 100 | 1,090 |
| Italy | * | 10 | * | 560 | 30 | 100 | 700 |
| Australia | 140 | 20 | 10 | — | — | 150 | 320 |
| Union S. Africa | 150 | 30 | 10 | * | — | 130 | 320 |
| Denmark | — | 190 | 70 | — | * | 10 | 270 |
| Others | 200 | 290 | 420 | 210 | 240 | 1,490 | 2,850 |
| All | 4,780 | 2,180 | 1,580 | 1,440 | 990 | 2,770 | 13,740 |

* Less than 5 million board feet.

SOURCE: United Nations, FAO, Forestry Division: *Yearbook of Forest Products Statistics*, Rome, 1957, Tables 17 and 18.

*Table 44. International trade in wood pulp, 1955*

| Importing nation | Exporting nation | | | | | | |
|---|---|---|---|---|---|---|---|
| | Sweden | Canada | Finland | Norway | U.S. | Others | All |
| | Thousand metric tons | Thousand metric tons | Thousand metric tons | Thousand metric tons | Thousand metric tons | Thousand metric tons | Thousand metric tons |
| United Kingdom | 810 | 280 | 480 | 440 | 180 | 110 | 2,300 |
| United States | 170 | 1,700 | 140 | 10 | — | 10 | 2,030 |
| France | 280 | 40 | 160 | 70 | 30 | 50 | 630 |
| West Germany | 240 | 20 | 100 | 50 | 60 | 80 | 550 |
| Benelux | 230 | 20 | 50 | 70 | 20 | 30 | 420 |
| Italy | 150 | 10 | 40 | 10 | 20 | 100 | 330 |
| Others | 460 | 120 | 360 | 70 | 260 | 90 | 1,360 |
| All | 2,340 | 2,190 | 1,330 | 720 | 570 | 470 | 7,620 |

SOURCE: United Nations, FAO, Forestry Division: *Yearbook of Forest Products Statistics*, Rome, 1957, Tables 29 and 31.

In the *wood-pulp* trade, we find much the same group of countries playing the principal roles (Table 44). Here, however, the United States appears not only as a major importer but also as an exporter of sorts. Her exports of pulp go to a long list of nations, including those of Latin America. The trade in *newsprint paper* (Table 45), is engaged in by

### Table 45. *International trade in newsprint, 1955*

| Importing nation | Exporting nation | | | | | | |
|---|---|---|---|---|---|---|---|
| | Canada | Finland | Sweden | U.S. | U.K. | Others | All |
| | *Thousand metric tons* | *Thousand metric tons* | *Thousand metric tons* | *Thousand metric tons* | *Thousand metric tons* | *Thousand metric tons* | *Thousand metric tons* |
| United States | 4,560 | 120 | * | — | — | 10 | 4,690 |
| United Kingdom | 260 | 80 | 50 | — | — | 20 | 410 |
| Australia | 70 | 10 | 20 | — | 90 | 30 | 220 |
| Brazil | 20 | 30 | 30 | 20 | — | 30 | 130 |
| West Germany | 20 | 30 | 10 | 10 | — | 40 | 110 |
| France | 20 | 10 | 20 | 20 | — | 30 | 100 |
| Others | 290 | 190 | 70 | 140 | 50 | 250 | 990 |
| All | 5,240 | 470 | 200 | 190 | 140 | 410 | 6,650 |

* Less than 5,000 metric tons.

SOURCE: United Nations, FAO, Forestry Division: *Yearbook of Forest Products Statistics*, Rome, 1957, Tables 33 and 34.

### Table 46. *International trade in hardwood saw logs and veneer logs, 1955*

| Importing nation | Exporting nation | | | | | | |
|---|---|---|---|---|---|---|---|
| | Philippines | French Equatorial Africa | France | Ghana | British North Borneo | Others* | All |
| | *Million cu ft* | *Million cu ft* | *Million cu ft* | *Million cu ft* | *Million cu ft* | *Million cu ft* | *Million cu ft* |
| Japan | 59 | — | † | — | 7 | 1 | 67 |
| West Germany | † | 10 | 4 | 4 | 1 | 15 | 34 |
| United States | 5 | † | † | 2 | † | 15 | 22 |
| Benelux | — | 6 | 13 | 4 | † | 5 | 28 |
| United Kingdom | — | 2 | † | 4 | 1 | 9 | 16 |
| France | — | 11 | — | † | — | 4 | 15 |
| Argentina | — | † | † | — | — | 9 | 9 |
| Italy | † | † | 2 | 2 | † | † | 4 |
| Others | 3 | 4 | 6 | 2 | 8 | 10 | 33 |
| All | 67 | 33 | 25 | 18 | 17 | 68 | 228 |

* Including Nigeria, Indonesia, Belgian Congo, Sarawak.

† Less than ½ million cubic feet.

SOURCE: United Nations, FAO, Forestry Division: *Yearbook of Forest Products Statistics*, Rome, 1957, Tables 7 and 8.

many of the same countries but differs from the other commodities we have examined in that it is overwhelmingly dominated by shipments from Canada into the United States, which make up seven-tenths of the total volume. Indeed, the Canada-United States trade in newsprint is the largest single item of international trade in forest products and makes up some 10 per cent of the total value of such products entering world commerce. The trade arises from our inordinate demands for the product in the United States (compare Chap. 3, pp. 26–27) and from Canadian cost and profit advantages that have attracted much of the North American industry to that country.[4]

As we turn to consider *hardwood saw logs and veneer logs* (Table 46), a largely new cast comes on the stage. Among the first five ranking exporters—and, indeed, among the first nine—only one is other than a tropical hardwood nation. The main importer is Japan, whose shipments from the Philippines make up a fourth of the total commerce in this commodity.

## SUMMARY

The earth's 9½ billion forest acres occur mainly as an intensively utilized conifer belt, interspersed with hardwoods, through the North Temperate Zone, and three great blocks of comparatively remote and lightly used tropical hardwoods. Firewood, which makes up at least four-tenths of the world timber harvest, is produced almost everywhere that trees grow, but wood-processing industry is heavily concentrated in the northern belt.

Nations of the world may be classified into seven groups on the basis of their forest economy. In the southern and central regions of the earth are the South-temperate, tropical hardwood, savanna and desert, and border nations. In the northern region are the European, Scandinavian, and new-rich nations.

Trade in forest products follows the principle of comparative advantage. In the United States internal trade in lumber, the West is the chief exporting region, the South also is a net exporter, while the North is a large net importer. International trade in forest commodities is dominated by shipments of softwood lumber and wood pulp from Canada to the United States and United Kingdom and from Scandinavia into Western Europe, and of newsprint from Canada to the United States.

[4] Brandes, Hans-Günther: "An Investigation of the Canada-United States Trade in Newsprint," doctoral dissertation, State University of New York, College of Forestry, Syracuse, 1955.

# Chapter 30

## SOCIAL PLANNING FOR THE FOREST ECONOMY

FROM WHAT we know of any of the nations of the world, we can deduce that the national forest economy is not a perfectly efficient machine. Often its resources are underemployed, its system wasteful, and its output low. It leaves some wants ungratified and satisfactions unmaximized. It may permit large inequalities in the possession and use of forests. It commonly neglects opportunities to raise labor productivity by means of better education, housing, and distribution and use of leisure. It may tolerate many social costs of private enterprise, such as those that stem from high interest rates. Its lifeblood, knowledge, is anemic and poorly circulated.

What seems to be the matter? The difficulties boil down to perhaps two: One is the divergence of the individual interest from that of the public—in our country, the failure of the automatic market economy to achieve social norms—for such causes as we studied in Chapter 4. The other is the frailty of deliberate devices for planning and pursuing public goals, and in many cases the hesitancy of society to use such devices: limitations of human wisdom and foresight and the imperfections of politics. Social goals and planning are the subject of our remaining chapters.

## CHARACTERISTICS OF SOCIAL PLANNING

There is no sharp distinction between social planning and planning for the firm. Such distinction as may be found is not to be drawn on the basis of who does the planning. You may remember that when we talked about planning for the firm in Chapters 15 and 16, we used a public agency, a state park board, as one illustration. At the same time, many private firms engage in social planning. For example, we find studies of the national timber outlook in the United States being sponsored, not only by the Federal government, but also by the Weyerhaeuser Timber Company.[1] Nor is the division between social planning and planning for the firm to be made according to the plan's scope. The plans for some corporations cover a wider territory and range of considerations than do many social plans. Social plans can be narrow, for social planners can be narrow.

Let us try differentiating *social planning* on the ground that it ordinarily has three characteristics: *First,* it takes as its main objective the fulfillment of the public interest. *Second,* its primary concern is for the effects of planned measures upon society and the economy, rather than vice versa. *Third,* it implies deliberate action on the part of firms other than the planning firm in order to carry out the plan—that is to say, the planning is *for* other firms.

To illustrate, we may contrast social planning with planning for the firm, using lumber production as an example. *First,* the social plan deals with the problem of keying the total output of an area to the general need of consumers for the product and for resource maintenance and employment; whereas for the firm's plan the chief objectives are to maintain the firm, to hold its position in the industry and the market, to earn a net revenue, and so on. *Second,* the social plan is apt to stress the influences of the lumber industry upon consumer satisfaction, general income and employment, the construction and remanufacturing industries, and other conditions on the outside; but the plan for the firm probably considers such conditions primarily in their bearing on the firm's costs and market and is concerned for the community principally because the firm's "relations" with the community affect its habitat. *Third,* the social plan for lumber production, unless it just happens to recommend continuance of the present status or trend, cannot very well be carried out unless the programs of firms are bent to its purposes by some deliberate means such as the firms' voluntary cooperation with the plan, public regulation of their output, taxation or subsidy to effect it, or "education" of the industry regarding conservative practices; whereas the implementing of the plan for the firm is under the firm's control and will affect others only to the extent that all events are generally interconnected.

As a corollary to the three characteristics that we have stressed for social planning, such planning may have still other features. For instance, it may extend to very far horizons in time. Senate resolution 148 (Eighty-

[1] Stanford Research Institute: *America's Demand for Wood 1929–1975,* Weyerhaeuser Timber Co., Tacoma, Wash., 1954.

fifth Congress, Second Session) calls for extending the planning horizon in cost-benefit computations for Federal dam-building proposals from fifty years to one hundred years. Again, social planning may be heavily involved in appraisal of nonmarket values. The sort of public comparative valuation that was treated in Chapter 23 (pp. 387–392) is essentially a function of social planning. Still again, social planning may need to consider more sorts of cost and revenue than planning for the firm. For example, the costs of labor may be given for the firm but not for society. The social plan that contemplates reduction of the number of workers in an industry may not be able to disregard the question of where the displaced workers will go.

## PUBLIC INTEREST

Now we have said that social planning takes as its main objective the fulfillment of the *public interest*. This concept, the public interest, is variously called the social, general, common, public, community, or national good, welfare, interest, well-being, and other such terms. It is to be found throughout human law and custom. In the United States, it is embodied in the welfare clause of the Constitution and enters into the mores of forestry through such terms as greatest good to the greatest number in the long run. The idea of the public interest is surely as old as society itself, as old as man. It cannot have failed to arise the first time the security of the primitive family was threatened by the action of some member. From such a beginning, the notion of public interest has been defined, shaped, and redefined in each society by successive generations in their endless search for a workable social arrangement. The process of shaping the public-interest idea is analogous to that of forming the common-value concept or other social institutions. And like them, the public interest is a function of place and time.

What is the meaning of public interest today? A general definition does not exist, and perhaps cannot. Each group in society has its idea of public interest. Each situation where the public interest comes into question may give rise to a specific definition. What comes closest to a general definition is to be found in the whole body of laws, customs, and social usages. A common theme runs through the idea as it is applied in the Western world, though there is much variation from country to country, and in particulars even from one community to another.

In Britain, we find the Restrictive Trade Practices Act of 1956 setting out the principles that are to guide the courts in deciding whether a given restriction is in the public interest—for example: Does it protect the public against physical injury? Does it benefit consumers? (Even though a business practice does harm to retailers, the court may approve it if it benefits consumers.) Does it afford protection against a monopolist within the trade? Does it afford protection against overmighty buyers and sellers? Does it protect the community from unemployment?[2]

We find a United States president philosophizing in these terms about the social objectives of government:[3]

. . . to increase the security and the happiness of a large number of people in all occupations of life and in all parts of the country; to give them more of the good things of life; to give them a greater distribution, not only of wealth in the narrow terms but of wealth in the wider terms; to give them places to go in the summer time—recreation; to give them assurance that they are not going to starve in their old age; to give honest business a chance to go ahead and make a reasonable profit; and to give everyone a chance to make a living.

The meaning of public interest in forestry, as in general, has never been comprehensively spelled out. Where, then, shall we turn for a crystallization of this vague but vital idea? Perhaps the best place, for our purposes, is to the beginning and end of economic life, the wants of the sovereign consumer. The embodiment and measure of the public interest in forestry for us is found in our community and national and world goals for the output and consumption of wood and its products, of the means for forest recreation, of the services of forest watersheds, and of the other values of forest land. Thus social planning for forestry, which begins with the public interest, is at the same time the process for determining the public interest, and we are again involved in the dilemma of circularity (compare pp. 143, 145–147, 389). The circle is broken by the means that we explored in Chapter 23, in our discussion of common value—means that we shall study more fully in the two chapters that follow this one.

In defining the public interest, who speaks for the public? Anyone who has a mind to may do so, though of course all the voices are not heard with the same clarity or equally heeded. In general, it is the centers of influence that in our society shout the loudest and with greatest effect. The power system described in Chapter 24 may be regarded as a system for defining the public interest: a system for social planning. Governments and trade associations, professional societies and labor unions are all, under our system, social planners. Some of the groups appear not to recognize this fact, for they sometimes apply the term derogatively to their bedfellows.

[2] Albery, Michael, and C. F. Fletcher-Cooke: *Monopolies and Restrictive Trade Practices,* Stevens and Sons, Ltd., London, 1956, pp. 43–51.
[3] *The New York Times,* June 8, 1935.

## STAGES OF SOCIAL PLANNING

The steps in social planning are the same seven steps that we traced in Chapter 15 (pp. 226–227). And just as in planning for the firm as we discussed it there, so in social planning the process is bracketed by policy, taking its guides from policy at a more general level and in turn guiding policy at a more specific level. To recognize explicitly these connections between social policy and planning and to emphasize the process of public review to which social plans are subjected, let us think of the seven steps of social planing as comprising the first stage, and then again the last stage, of a four-stage process:

1. Planning the *goal*
2. Describing the existing *situation*
3. Defining the *gap* between situation and goal: problem analysis
4. Planning the *measures* for altering the situation in the direction of the goal

Take for example the planning of water-resource management in a watershed or region. In the *first stage*, the general goals of management are established, commonly for a specific future date. The potential development of population, industry, and agriculture, with their respective demands for water in terms of quantity and quality, are weighed against the prospective supplies, or costs, of the water. The weighing may follow meticulously the seven steps of planning, beginning with a definition of the public interest as the objective. Or it may need to be carried out very roughly and with a large element of general judgment. The result of it in any case is a goal. Similarly, goals are set for permissible flood occurrence in terms of severity and frequency, for power production, for navigation, and for other services of the watershed.

In the *second stage*, the conditions in the planning region are described —as of today, or perhaps as of the future reference date under the assumption that present trends continue. Clearly, in practice, the second and first stages must be carried out together, for the existing situation is necessarily a major determinant of the goal, particularly on the supply side. This is especially true of those inelastic elements in the supply such as climate and the fundamental hydrology of the region. The report on the planning may, in fact, reverse the order of the first and second stages.

In the *third stage*, the goal and the situation are compared. The gap between them defines the character and severity of the water-resource problem. The gap is described in terms of inadequacies in quantity and timing of water supplies, the existence of water impurities and pollution, flood damages, soil erosion, local waste and overuse of water, impediments to navigation, conflicts between water users in different localities and between different types of use, and so on. This *problem analysis* constitutes the justification for the measures that will be proposed and is a necessary part of the political process of getting public action.

## MORE SPECIFIC STAGES

In the *fourth stage,* the steps of planning are again carried out, this time for the purpose of outlining specific measures for meeting the goals. For instance, alternative locations and types of dams may be weighed. Or upstream measures such as forest planting and stand improvement may be planned. Here again it is clear how closely interlocked are the planning stages, for the setting of goals in the first stage cannot be carried through without at least some general assumptions regarding the feasibility of measures for reaching these goals. In practice, therefore, we must think of the four stages as representing equations for simultaneous solution.

The fourth stage in public planning may in turn become the first stage in a new, more specific, process for which it sets the goal. Where, for example, the stage has to do with upstream measures of forest improvement and land-use adjustment, it may be followed, in a new round of planning, by detailed description of forest and land-use conditions (second stage) and analysis of forest and land-use problems (third stage) in light of the specific goal. Then follows a new fourth stage, in which measures are planned perhaps for each minor watershed, or even property by property. Thus with the successive rounds, social planning may merge into planning for the firm. You should compare this chain of goals and measures with the chain of ends and means described in Chapter 5 (pp. 53–54). [Would you say that the two chains are in fact the same? Why, or why not?]

Observe that the whole process of social planning is, in effect, a process of *criticism:* in our case, criticism of the forest economy. How is criticism carried out? Suppose you are to criticize the manuscript of an article that a colleague has written for the *Journal of Forestry.* For a constructive job, you begin with a standard of judgment, a norm. You then describe the work that you are criticizing. Next you show how the work meets or departs from the norm: You analyze its successes and failures. Finally, you may offer suggestions for improvement. Do you see that we have here the four stages of planning? Just as many a book review is given over mainly to a mere retelling of the story, so many a pseudo social plan is largely just a statement of how things stand, which is the second stage. This is a vital part of the work but is the easiest and is apt to drag on. Unless the planner has plenty of fuel, his fire may burn out before he gets any further.

## KINDS OF SOCIAL PLANNING

In Chapter 15, we recognized three types of planning for the firm: enterprise, organization, and operation planning (pp. 227–232). The same classification may be applied to social planning, especially at the more specific levels. However, for our purposes it is more generally useful to subdivide social planning on a different basis, into two kinds: First, there is *program planning*, dealing primarily with a particular commodity such as water or wood or recreational service, or at most with a sector of the economy such as forest industry. Second, there is *area planning*, which stresses the whole life of an area or some major part of its life. To be sure, each kind of planning implies the other, and there is a middle ground where the two can scarcely be told apart. Nevertheless, the distinction is basic and is a good one for organizing our story. Program planning is the subject of Chapter 31; area planning, of Chapter 32.

## SUMMARY

Social planning is done by both public and private agencies. It may be distinguished from planning for the firm in that it has three basic characteristics. First, it is pointed to the public interest. Second, its orientation is from the plan toward the economy at large. Third, it is done for a number of firms.

The public interest to which social planning is directed is in the last analysis the interest of consumers in satisfying their wants for goods and services.

Social planning comprises four stages: planning the goal, describing the situation, analyzing the problem, and planning the measures to solve the problem and reach the goal. This four-stage process may be repeated at successively more specific levels of planning. The first and fourth stages involve the same steps as does planning for the firm.

Two kinds of social planning are program planning and area planning.

# Chapter 31

# PLANNING
# PUBLIC
# FORESTRY
# PROGRAMS

SOCIAL PLANNING, as we saw in Chapter 30, comes in two parts. Let us get on with the first, which is program planning: the planning of a program as distinguished from the planning of a whole economy.

Now program planning can be exceedingly specific, to the point where it is more individual than social in character. Such planning is of the sort outlined at the close of Part Two of this book. Toward the other end of the scale, program planning can be very general—broad as the blue sky— the planning of goals in a wide sense. To planning of this sort let us give our attention here. Let us first catch a glimpse of national goals for some of the forest's services and then take a longer look at goals for timber production.

## PLANNING FOR OUTDOOR RECREATION

What about a goal for forest recreation in the United States? Is there such a goal? And if so, what is it, who did the planning, and what method was followed?

Not forest recreation specifically, but outdoor recreation in general is a workable unit for broad program planning. The public interest in outdoor recreation is recognizable, but in many cases the distinction between what is associated closely with the forest and what is not is immaterial. And so let us think about outdoor recreation, of which a good part will necessarily and fittingly take place in a woodland or forest setting.

A great many national agencies, both private and public, have an

**518**

active interest in planning for outdoor recreation. In 1958, the Congress created a National Outdoor Recreation Resources Review Commission, with a broad mandate and with the obligation to produce a plan by 1961. Before this development, one agency took the principal leadership in drawing up comprehensive plans and goals for the United States: the National Park Service in the Department of the Interior. Its authority for such planning derives from an Act of Congress of 1936. Let us study the Park Service's most recent major analysis of the recreation problem, published in 1941.[1] The analysis was made in cooperation with state and local agencies, and concerns that predominant part of outdoor recreation which, it assumes, must be serviced by the public.

Three considerations are suggested as the basis for planning a recreation system:[2]

1. The recreational requirements of the population to be served, by kind and quantity.
2. The kind and quantity of land needed to meet those requirements.
3. The lands available and suitable for the kinds of recreation to be supplied and not more valuable for uses other than recreation.

Though the National Park Service does not explicitly do so, we may interpret the recreation planning problem here set forth as one of relating demand and supply: The first of the three considerations is the demand for services. The second is the derived demand for land—and, presumably, the necessary improvements. The third covers the supply of land and improvements, and clearly recognizes the governing principle of opportunity cost. Demand and supply are to be considered for the future: predicted. The goal is to be set far enough ahead so that there will be time for substantial accomplishments. No specific target date is fixed, but we may infer that the planners are reaching into the future at least a couple of decades.

## DEMAND FOR SERVICES AND FACILITIES

The analysis of demand for services—of recreational wants—begins with a study of mankind's ageless, inherent needs for refreshment of body, mind, and spirit through capture and constructive use of leisure time. The analysis is then brought down to twentieth-century America in an examination of the trends in influential demand factors: population, its total size, its geographic and age distribution, its urbanization, as bearing upon the amount, type, and location of demands; leisure time and its

---

[1] U.S. Department of Interior, National Park Service: *A Study of the Park and Recreation Problem of the United States,* 1941.

[2] Same reference, p. 41.

occurrence over the day, week, and year, as affecting recreational opportunities; national income and its distribution as determining the effective demand for the different forms of recreation, with the varying expenditures they require; the development of roads and auto travel in its relation to allowable distances between points of residence and places for recreation; and consumers' tastes and preferences, learned by interview and from attendance records at parks, for the various types of outdoor recreation such as touring and sightseeing, picnicking, water sports, hunting and fishing, hiking, winter sports, nature studies, camping, and so on.

Demand for services is then translated into demand for land and improvements. The translation is carried out in general terms. Uniform standards for recreational facilities, such as guiding ratios of population to park acreage, are specifically rejected as unsuitable because the quality of land and of demand varies from place to place and with the form of use and because demand itself is partly a function of the means provided for recreation.[3]

. . . recreation cannot be measured quantitatively, because it is a quality of living. Who can say when our living is good enough? Yet there are published statements that the present acreage of parks is all that the country will ever need. . . . The struggle to improve our living is a never ending one. . . . Present indications are that we can afford to live more generously than we have realized.

In the end, however, demands are quantified at least to the extent of analyzing the attributes of desirable recreational areas of the various types. And a great deal of attention is given to the geography of demand: to wants of city children for neighborhood playgrounds and of city people of all ages for parks accessible for daily use; and to people's wants for areas of other sorts that can be situated within a successively widening range of travel.

### SUPPLY IN RELATION TO DEMAND

On the supply, or cost, side (following, still, our own economic interpretation of the Park Service report), the planners study the occurrence of areas suited to recreational use within the natural geographic regions and the metropolitan regions of the United States. They review the facilities currently in existence. They speculate that about a fifth of the nation's land area will not be needed for farming, timber production, and other commercial and residential uses; that most of this fifth is a potential recreational resource; and that some of the remainder, too, may be

---

[3] Same reference, p. 39. [Compare the analysis in Chap. 23 concerning recreational versus industrial use of forest land, and the man-day measure of recreational use there employed (p. 391). Can you suggest a better measure?]

tapped for recreational purposes, as on the national forests in conjunction with timber growing. They give a great deal of attention to the costs of acquiring, developing, and operating recreational areas, and offer rules for cost reduction, for example:[4]

In choice between sites of comparable character capable of serving approximately the same populations, that one should be chosen which can supply its intended uses at the least cost for acquisition, development, and operation, . . . The history of park acquisition . . . is full of instances of the ultimate costliness of cheap land, or land acquired by gift.

A single site which will serve a variety of recreational uses is preferable—acquisition costs being approximately equal—to several sites which, taken as a group, may appear capable of providing for those uses.

Examples of satisfactory park plans are spelled out—illustrating for us that a general planning of goals implies a specific planning of measures (compare Chap. 30, p. 516). Other cost or supply matters considered are park administration and financing.

Concerning what we may think of as the meeting of supply and demand, the planners lay down the principle that[5]

Any area devoted to recreational use of any type may be said to have been wisely selected for its purpose when selection has been determined by the logical relating of needs, on the one hand, to the capacity of the area to supply them at reasonable cost, on the other. Admittedly, in the case of an area selected because of its possession of exceptional inspirational qualities, "need" is the great imponderable, and a decision as to selection may often have to be based on some such determination as this:

Here is an area possessing qualities so inspiring, so satisfying to the human spirit, that we are justified in acquiring it and protecting its inherent values, even though it may not be visited by the thousands—perhaps could not be without destroying the very qualities that make it worth public possession. We shall do this in the profound belief that the return to the individual visitor, and to society as a whole, provided by such an area as this, will be sufficient to justify our acquiring it for the benefit of those sensitive and appreciative persons who will seek it out.

You will find in this philosophy the same ingredients that enter into the common-value idea.

## HIGHLIGHTS OF RECREATION PLAN

The whole work culminates in a park and recreational land plan for the United States. The plan indicates[6]

[4] Same reference, p. 41.
[5] Same reference, p. 43.
[6] Same reference, p. 122.

. . . what provision of lands and waters is required in order to meet adequately the recreational requirements of the American people—a provision which at the same time will give full and fair consideration to all other land-use needs. . . . The consummation of [the plan], under the American form of government, cannot rest upon a single agency but instead will require the combined and coordinated efforts of all agencies, at all levels of government, which deal with any phase of recreation.

The principal types of public development that the plan then proposes and discusses are as follows:

1. Within urban boundaries, accessible to the people for their frequent use—neighborhood playgrounds, neighborhood playfields and centers, community parks big enough to escape overintensive use, and stream-beautification projects such as parkways.

2. Within easy reach of persons living in cities and other heavily populated areas, for holiday and week-end use, parks that provide means for picnicking, water sports, camping, hiking, and the like in uncrowded surroundings.

3. Small parks designed and located so as to give rural people recreational advantages comparable to those planned in items 1 and 2 for the urban population.

4. For vacation use by all the population, extensive holdings such as national and state forests and parks featured by tree cover, rugged terrain, or lakes and streams; and also appropriately developed vacation lands in the prairies and plains.

5. Frontage on major lakes and rivers, and particularly on the ocean—amounting to perhaps 10 per cent of the total national shore line—for the public enjoyment of scenery, water, and wildlife without undesirable crowding, or encroachment by private enterprise.

6. Other areas containing scenery of great distinction, the preservation of which calls for public ownership.

7. Areas having outstanding historic, prehistoric, or scientific significance.

8. Special-use areas important to the rounding out of state and Federal recreational systems: parkways, trails and trailways, routes of water travel such as the abandoned canals and the Intercoastal Waterway, and waysides along roads. For the pleasure of the recreationist, control of outdoor advertising and measures to preserve roadside beauty are also recommended.

## PLANNING FOR WATER RESOURCES

Turning now from the subject of recreation to that of water, we find another case where program planning belongs only partly in the context of forestry.

Responsibilities for program planning in respect to water resources are about as widely diffused as for any resource or activity of nationwide scope. Some private concerns and a multitude of state and local public agencies have a share. The Federal government has a large part because of its interstate obligations and also because of the immense cost of many water-resource projects. At least eight Federal departments and independent commissions have been given functions to perform in water-resources planning. As a result of this diffusion and the lack of effective means for coordinating the agencies, the national accomplishments in planning are neither neat nor simple to describe. They represent a profusion of methods somewhat matching that of planners. More often than not, the planning of specific measures has proceeded without very much planning of general goals: Many local and single-purpose projects have been developed without the benefit of comprehensive planning for the river basin and for the multiple uses of the water resource. The Watershed Protection and Flood Prevention Act of 1954 stresses planning for small watersheds by local groups and is essentially a piecemeal approach to resource development.

At the same time, national policy in late years has increasingly considered the problem of coordinating the planning agencies. It has also given some recognition to the idea of the river system in all its aspects as the primary unit for planning and development. Among recent unifying documents that hold special interest for us here are one that offers standards and procedures for cost and benefit appraisal[7] and reports of two presidential commissions on water-resources policy. The latter documents[8] propose interagency organizational arrangements for water-resources planning. They suggest principles to guide the planning and also the necessary collection and analysis of data. They consider the various water uses and problems, the growing national importance of these, and the outlook with respect to them. They do not, however, offer a national plan, even in the broad sense represented in the Park Service plan for recreation. In fact, they specifically reject a national approach to planning and emphasize the river basin, or for some purposes the region, as the planning area. [Can you explain why the river-basin approach is preferred to the national approach in the United States?]

Comprehensive river-basin planning has advanced in the last few decades. For the Tennessee River, we have the unique example of unified

[7] Federal Inter-agency River Basin Committee, Subcommittee on Benefits and Costs: *Proposed Practices for Economic Analysis of River Basin Projects*, U.S. Government Printing Office, Washington, 1950.

[8] President's Water Resources Policy Commission: *Report*, 3 vols., U.S. Government Printing Office, Washington, 1950; Presidential Advisory Committee on Water Resources Policy: *Water Resources Policy*, U.S. Government Printing Office, Washington, 1956.

Federal responsibility under a single agency, the Tennessee Valley Authority. In other basins, such as the Missouri, Columbia, and Colorado, the Federal Inter-Agency River Basin Committee, a voluntary organization, has set up regional committees for planning.[9] The tendency is growing for such regional agencies to take a broad view of their responsibilities, looking beyond merely water resources and thus approaching the scope of area planning.

## PLANNING FOR TIMBER GOALS, OR REQUIREMENTS

In the planning of goals for timber production in the United States, we find no such bevy of agencies as in the case of water resources, but rather a strongly centralized responsibility. Because of the varied national pattern of forests and population, and the resulting large internal trade, the planning of goals for either output or consumption of timber, beyond the individual firm or its immediate community, almost inevitably takes on national scope. National planning has become the accepted procedure. Here, among Federal agencies, the Department of Agriculture's Forest Service has been given the main responsibility, notably through the Mc-Sweeney-McNary Forest Research Act of 1928. Section 9 of this act authorizes and directs the Secretary of Agriculture to cooperate with state officials or with private or other agencies

. . . in making and keeping current a comprehensive survey of the present and prospective requirements for timber and other forest products in the United States, and of timber supplies, including a determination of the present and potential productivity of forest land therein, and of such other facts as may be necessary in the determination of ways and means to balance the timber budget of the United States.

Here is broad authority to carry out a continuing nationwide forest survey, not merely to take inventory and to find the amount of growth and removal, but also to learn about national *requirements* for forest products —that is, to plan goals for the timber economy.

## IDEAL TIMBER GOAL

What is the purpose of a national goal for the timber resource, and what are the problems of setting up such a goal? Let us attempt to define some of the characteristics of an ideal goal.

---

[9] For an illustrative river-basin plan, see New England–New York River Basin Committee: *Land and Water Resources of the New England–New York Region*, Senate Doc. 14, 85th Cong., 1st Sess., 1957, especially part 1.

1. The goal is stated in any of four forms: First, it may be stated as a forest-products *consumption goal,* the total annual quantities of these products to be taken by ultimate consumers or used by producers of end products. Second, it may be stated as a stumpage *production goal,* the domestic-standing-timber equivalent of the consumption goal—that is, the total amount of domestic standing timber to be cut annually. Third, a net timber *growth goal* may be stated as the amount of annual growth required to meet the production goal. Fourth, a timber *growing-stock goal* may be estimated as the quantity of growing stock that would permit attainment of the growth goal. It will help us to understand these four forms of a national timber goal if we note how they differ. Suppose that all timber and wood is measured in total cubic feet. Then:

The consumption goal is equal to the production goal *plus* goals or allowances for imports *minus* goals or allowances for exports *minus* allowances for wood lost in logging and processing *minus* allowances for building up stocks of harvested timber or products on hand *plus* allowances for reducing stocks.

The production goal is equal to the growth goal *plus* allowances for the use of dead and cull timber *minus* allowances for timber knocked down or killed in logging and left unused in the woods *minus* allowances for building up the growing stock *plus* allowances for decreasing the growing stock.

And the growth goal is equal to the growing-stock goal times the annual growth per cent of the timber, this per cent being figured net of all mortality and cull losses from insects, disease, fire,[10] and other agencies.

2. The goal is not merely expressed as a national total, but is also broken down into its significant subdivisions. For instance, in the case of a consumption goal, these subdivisions may include commodities and types of use. For a production goal, the breakdown may consider species, quality, and location.

3. The goal serves to guide public and private policy. It fulfills the first stage in the four-stage process that we described on pages 515–516, culminating in the planning of measures. The goal is therefore a forecast of consumption or production. But it is not a mere *descriptive forecast* of what is likeliest to happen, as in the absence of planning. Rather, it is a *normative forecast* that assumes special efforts to satisfy the public interest with respect to forest products.

[10] You may wish to delve a bit into the problem of determining allowable fire losses. The problem amounts to that of planning fire control. It illustrates one facet of the comprehensive planning of measures that accompanies the ideal job of timber-goal planning. For the purpose, see Hayes, G. L., and T. F. Marburg: "Optimum Intensity of Protection from Forest Fires," in Duerr, William A., and Henry J. Vaux (eds.): *Research in the Economics of Forestry,* Charles Lathrop Pack Forestry Foundation, Washington, 1953, pp. 98–105.

4. The goal may be set for any future target date; or a series of goals may be proposed for a series of dates. However, considering that the cycle of production in forestry ranges from perhaps twenty years to one hundred years or more, the vital long-term adjustments that may be desirable for the timber resource must guide the planning of any goal, near or distant. The planning must be done in recognition of the long time it will take for management changes in existing forests to bear fruit or for new forest land to begin yielding timber. Thus if goals are set up for the near future, they are to be regarded as bench marks on the way to further goals.

5. Progress toward any long-term goal depends upon meeting the intermediate bench-mark goals. To have enough growing stock in the far future requires forbearance in the cutting of stocks meanwhile. That is to say, all goals—very distant ones and the possibly long series of bench-mark goals—are related to one another according to the principle of time rivalry that we studied in Chapter 13 (pp. 205–206). The higher the distant goal, the greater its cost in terms of forbearance meantime. To attain both near and distant high output goals may be physically impossible.

6. The time series of timber goals is interconnected, not only through the relation of stock to growth, but also because of the effect of current wood consumption upon the future demand for it.[11] If wood is scarce in period A, consumers tend to respond by shifting their consumption technologies in favor of other materials. Then in period B, even if wood becomes abundant, the decline in demand will result in a lower consumption than would have taken place in the absence of the earlier scarcity. Of course, in period C the demand may pick up again. Nevertheless, the tendency is for high actual consumption to favor high consumption goals for subsequent target dates, and for low consumption to depress goals. Observe that this linkage represents a sort of *time jointness,* working in opposition to time rivalry.

7. The goal, whether stated in terms of consumption or of production, represents an equating of demand and supply, or of marginal revenues and costs. It is keyed not simply to the dreams of consumers but to the comprehensive social problem of resource allocation. Ideally, the planner relates demand and supply to the determinants with which they are most strongly correlated.

8. The goal has an error, comprising all the customary errors inherent in forecasting. The further the goal, the greater the likelihood of error. This realization has led some critics to disparage long-term goals and to

[11] Vaux, Henry J., and John A. Zivnuska: "Forest Production Goals: A Critical Analysis," *Land Economics,* November, 1952, p. 325.

advocate emphasis upon short-term forecasts. On the other hand, as we have seen, the short forecast, if normative in character, is simply a bench mark that implies all the errors of the longer range. And if it is not normative, and thus escapes such errors, it has at the same time little value in guiding policy, which is its purpose. Long-range policy decisions have to be made every day. Either they are based on the best long-range guides that can be provided, however fraught with uncertainty, or they are irrational. The surest timber-requirements estimate is the one for *now*, but it has the least value.

9. Planning for the goal, like all planning, requires a great many facts. Four kinds of facts (and accompanying forecasts) are particularly useful. First, facts and forecasts concerning the general measures of economic activity: population, income, employment, and so on. Second, facts and forecasts relating especially to the demand for forest products, such as tastes and preferences, including the technology of consumption. Third, facts and forecasts regarding timber production functions and the technology of product conversion and distribution. Fourth, facts and forecasts concerning the nontimber by-products of timber management: the recreational, watershed, and other forest values that will flow from a constructive timber program and should be credited to this program. To the extent that such facts are uncertain or unknown, the errors in the goal are increased.

## REQUIREMENTS ESTIMATES: EARLY PLANNING

The ideal job of timber-goal planning has never been done. Perhaps it will never be done. However, during the better part of the past century in the United States, from rude beginnings, foresters have made immense progress in developing and sharpening the concept of the goal and in improving the methods for planning it.

When, in the 1870s, some foresighted persons began to point out that we were fast losing our comfortable surplus of standing timber and began to advocate national efforts to foster the growth of new timber, they were implying that the nation should have a goal in such matters.[12] The implied goal was simple and open-ended: Grow more than we are growing. The 1897 act establishing the national forests "to furnish a continuous supply of timber for the use and necessities of the citizens of the United States" presented the challenge of determining the extent of these necessities.

[12] See, for example, Hough, Franklin B.: *Report upon Forestry*, 2 vols., U.S. Government Printing Office, Washington, 1878, 1880.

In the early decades of the present century, as rough forest statistics came to be available, the practice grew of comparing current timber growth with depletion, using the difference or ratio between them as a measure of the forest problem. The comparison is often made today. Sometimes it has been made with the implication that if the ratio were one to one, all would be well. Here is a sort of goal: to grow the same quantity of timber that will currently be used or destroyed—to hold the timber inventory constant, perhaps regardless of the amount of it. Not much of a goal! But yet it was a recognition of the need for national planning. As an early example, we find in the Bureau of Corporations Report of 1913 the statement that the rate of growth in forests of the United States was only about a third of the timber cut.[13]

### GOALS IN CAPPER AND COPELAND REPORTS

The Capper Report of 1920—named for the senator who introduced the resolution requesting it and representing principally the work of Mr. Earle Clapp of the Forest Service—contains one of the first plain statements of a goal for the United States timber economy. Under the heading Future Trends in Requirements and confining himself to lumber as the principal timber product, Mr. Clapp made a forecast based primarily upon past trends in per-capita consumption in the United States and Europe. He considered also the general economic outlook:[14]

The United States is still a new country. We still have large areas of undeveloped agricultural land. In much of our territory first construction was of such a character that replacement on a larger and better scale will be desirable if not absolutely necessary. Our population is growing rapidly and there is no reason to believe that it will not continue to grow. Industrial development in many sections has hardly begun. . . .

Even with large allowances for the substitution of other materials for timber, it seems hardly possible that our annual demand for lumber for years to come will fall below 35 billion feet. . . . Any future lumber production falling below approximately 35 billion feet, unless we can make up the difference by imports, will result in hardship to many classes of consumers and to many industries. . . .

In the last sentence quoted, you will recognize the explicit interpretation of the public interest. [What do you think of the timber goal suggested in the Capper Report?]

[13] U.S. Department of Commerce and Labor, Bureau of Corporations: *The Lumber Industry*, Part I, *Standing Timber*, 1913, p. xviii.

[14] U.S. Department of Agriculture, Forest Service: *Timber Depletion, Lumber Prices, Lumber Exports, and Concentration of Timber Ownership*, 1920, pp. 36–37.

As we turn now to the Forest Service's next major planning document, the Copeland Report of 1933, we discover the idea of timber requirements somewhat elaborated. The purpose of requirements analysis, the report states,[15]

. . . is to review past experience and to evaluate current trends in the consumption of wood and other important forest products in the United States, in order to throw as much light as possible on what the Nation's normal needs for such products, translated into terms of timber, may be in the future. . . .

[The term] "requirements" is used, not to denote irreducible needs, but as a measure of use by consumers afforded a reasonable latitude of choice of materials.

We gather from the subsequent detailed analyses and forecasts that consumers' reasonable latitude of choice means, generally and simply speaking, that it will be assumed that forest-product prices will bear the same relation to prices of other commodities as they did in the recent past. This assumption continued to guide the requirements forecasts made by the Forest Service during the 1930s for construction lumber and other specific commodities and uses. And it was retained also, along with the same general definition of requirements, in the Forest Service's comprehensive Reappraisal of the timber situation following World War II.[16]

### REAPPRAISAL TIMBER GOALS

In the Reappraisal, the target date, or period, 1950 to 1955 was chosen for one set of timber goals. These were then worked out, commodity by commodity. For some commodities, including paper, past consumption was related to gross national product (GNP) and then predicted on the same relationship, assuming that GNP in the target period would reach $200 billion in terms of 1944 prices. For other commodities, various devices—the ones considered most appropriate and reliable in each case—were used to project past consumption trends. A second set of goals was then daringly estimated for the furthest target date yet taken in any requirements studies: the year 2000. The forecasts were guided mainly by predictions of population and per-capita consumption.

So far, none of the timber-goal planning took much account of the relation between the amount of the goal and the prospective cost of reaching it. The planners assumed, in effect, that timber supply is highly

[15] U.S. Department of Agriculture, Forest Service: A National Plan for American Forestry, 2 vols, 1933, p. 245.

[16] See U.S. Department of Agriculture, Forest Service: Potential Requirements for Timber Products in the United States, Report 2 from a Reappraisal of the Forest Situation, Washington, 1946.

elastic with price. Partly because of criticism on this ground, of which we shall catch a glimpse a little later on, efforts were made in the most recent national appraisal, the Timber Resource Review (TRR), to give some consideration to cost. [As we sketch the story of timber requirements from the TRR, see if you can spot any of the places where cost is given new attention. Note that the relation of *output* to cost is still not pointedly analyzed.]

## GOALS IN TIMBER RESOURCE REVIEW

The TRR Report offers a comparatively sophisticated, cautious definition of requirements. It even rechristens them under the name *projected timber demand*, a name that we must interpret as signifying consumption or production, but not demand in our sense of the word:

> Estimates of potential demand for timber products at specified future times under various sets of assumed conditions are termed "projected timber demand." Such estimates are not to be regarded as forecasts of actual future consumption of timber products. They are somewhat analogous to the potential demand estimates frequently made by large manufacturing concerns to serve as guidelines for planning their marketing and production facilities.

The role of supply as well as of demand in goal forecasting is then recognized, and the possibility admitted that supply may be less than perfectly elastic. But the assumption that wood-products prices will show a substantial further rise in relation to the general price level is rejected as inappropriate to social planning:[17]

> Prospective demand higher than prospective supply indicates a probability of upward movement of timber price, but higher and higher relative price for one of the Nation's basic raw materials would not be conducive to continued improvement in the general standard of living. It would not be good public policy to base forestry programs for the future solely upon estimates of either potential demand that assumes a further substantial increase in the relative price of timber products or future timber supplies less than the Nation can reasonably grow.

[What do you think is meant by "prospective demand higher than prospective supply"? What are the circumstances that might lead to a low prospective supply? See Chapter 19, pages 311–321.]

Two target dates are set up for requirements planning in the TRR,

---

[17] U.S. Department of Agriculture, Forest Service: *Timber Resources for America's Future*, Forest Resource Report 14, 1958, p. 15. The summary statement concerning requirements is given on pp. 7–22; the detailed statement, on pp. 357–471.

1975 and 2000. For each, the "assumed conditions" referred to in the preceding quotation are explained. They include forecasts of population, employment, productivity, GNP, consumption of physical structure raw materials (materials other than for food or energy), and disposable personal income. Two sets of forecasts of assumed conditions, a lower and an upper set, are estimated. For the target date 1975 the two sets are little different, and only one (the lower, more conservative one) is used. For 2000, both the lower and the upper set are used. To illustrate, following are the assumptions regarding population (in millions) and GNP (in billion dollars):

| | |
|---|---|
| For 1975 (lower set): | |
| Population | 215 |
| GNP | 630 |
| For 2000: | |
| Lower set: | |
| Population | 275 |
| GNP | 1,200 |
| Upper set: | |
| Population | 360 |
| GNP | 1,450 |

By comparison, population at the date of reference (1952) was 157 million, and GNP was $354 billion.

Three levels of requirements estimates are then worked out. A "lower projection" and "medium projection" are developed for each target date from the lower set of assumed conditions. The lower projection is derived on the further assumption that timber products will show a substantially rising real-price trend and hence a consumption trend declining in relation to all physical-structure materials. The medium projection, on the other hand, assumes that timber products will hold their own in both price and consumption. Finally, an "upper projection" is developed from the upper set of assumed conditions (and thus only for 2000), with the same suppositions about price and consumption as for the medium projection.

The outcome is a set of goals which are the highest ever proposed. The medium projection is regarded as the basic estimate. The Forest Service believes that it "offers a reasonable and desirable objective as a matter of public policy." It is criticized by some as too high; by others, as too conservative for a truly normative goal. Such critics have the choice of the lower or upper projection, and they are given the advantage of knowing just what assumptions their choice would imply. Then there is still a third group of critics who regard the projections as neither too high nor too low but simply meaningless in view of their neglect of the cost-production relationship: their failure to investigate how much timber "the

Nation [to requote the report] can reasonably grow." The medium projection is summarized in Table 47, which also gives comparative figures for the date of reference, 1952. [How might you account for the fact that consumption exceeds production in every case?]

The TRR medium projection of requirements for the year 2000 represents an annual timber consumption of 82 cubic feet per capita, as against 78 in 1952. Thus the magnitude of the total figure stems primarily from

Table 47. Requirements for timber products in the United States as estimated in the TRR medium projection, expressed in terms of equivalent roundwood consumption and converted to terms of production (cut) of domestic standing timber— 1975 and 2000, and comparative data for 1952

| Date and species group | Consumption | Production | |
|---|---|---|---|
| | | All growing stock | Live saw timber |
| | Billion cubic feet | Billion cubic feet | Billion board feet |
| 1952: | | | |
| Softwood | 8.6 | 7.5 | 36.5 |
| Hardwood | 3.7 | 3.3 | 12.3 |
| All species | 12.3 | 10.8 | 48.8 |
| 1975: | | | |
| Softwood | 11.4 | 9.6 | 47.6 |
| Hardwood | 4.8 | 4.4 | 17.8 |
| All species | 16.2 | 14.0 | 65.4 |
| 2000: | | | |
| Softwood | 15.6 | 13.0 | 68.4 |
| Hardwood | 6.8 | 6.7 | 26.7 |
| All species | 22.4 | 19.7 | 95.1 |

SOURCE: U.S. Department of Agriculture, Forest Service: Timber Resources for America's Future, Forest Resource Report 14, 1958, table 280, p. 471.

the assumed growth in population. The medium projection for 2000 represents an average annual production of 40 cubic feet of all growing stock per acre of today's commercial forest land. Current production averages 22 cubic feet per acre.

## COMPARISON OF ESTIMATES

It is interesting to trace the series of requirements estimates that have been made over the years, comparing the figures one with another and with current actual consumption. Such a tracing is carried out in Table 48 for pulpwood, for which there has been the greatest number of requirements forecasts. Notice that you can compare the early estimates with actual consumption at the target date. [How do you think the later

Table 48. *Annual pulpwood requirements (consumption goals) in the United States: three decades of estimates*

| Report | Date of reference | Current annual consumption | Estimated annual requirements | Target date |
|---|---|---|---|---|
| | | *Million cords* | *Million cords* | |
| 1. Clapp-Boyce | 1922 | 9 | 15 | 1950 |
| 2. Copeland | 1930 | 13 | 25 | "Normal" |
| 3. Curran-Behre | 1930 | 13 | 25 | 1950 |
| 4. Marsh-Gibbons | 1938 | 15 | 25 | Indefinite |
| 5. Reappraisal | 1945 | 23 | 29 | 1950–1955 |
| Reappraisal | 1945 | 23 | 40 | 2000 |
| 6. Materials Policy Commission | 1950 | 34 | 51 | 1975 |
| 7. Stanford | 1952 | 35 | 61 | 1975 |
| 8. Timber Resource Review | 1952 | 35 | 72* | 1975 |
| Timber Resource Review | 1952 | 35 | 100* | 2000 |

* TRR goals are the medium projection.
SOURCE: Reports not previously identified are as follows: (1) Clapp, Earle H., and Charles W. Boyce: *How the United States Can Meet Its Present and Future Pulp-wood Requirements*, U.S. Department of Agriculture Bulletin 1241, 1924. (3) Curran, C. E., and C. Edward Behre: *National Pulp and Paper Requirements in Relation to Forest Conservation*, Senate Doc. 115, 74th Cong., 1st Sess., 1935. (4) Marsh, R. E., and William H. Gibbons: "Forest-resource Conservation," in *Farmers in a Changing World: The Yearbook of Agriculture, 1940*, U.S. Government Printing Office, Washington, pp. 458–488. (6) President's Materials Policy Commission: *Resources for Freedom*, U.S. Government Printing Office, Washington, 1952, vol. I, pp. 36–45. (7) Stanford Research Institute: *America's Demand for Wood 1929–1975*, Weyerhaeuser Timber Co., Tacoma, Wash., 1954.

estimates will compare? Observe the rising trend of the whole series. How do you explain this trend in a series of presumably normative forecasts?]

## REQUIREMENTS MODELS: SUPPLY AND DEMAND

Requirements estimates have come in for lively criticism over the years. The policy maker looks at the forestry programs and measures they imply and judges them too bold, or too timid, according to his lights and social philosophy. The technician attacks their method and assumptions. Let us look a little into the question of method.

In 1952, Professors Vaux and Zivnuska of the University of California published a criticism of the Forest Service approach, notably that taken in the Reappraisal.[18] Essentially, they found fault with the approach for

[18] Vaux and Zivnuska: Work cited.

its failure to meet certain standards that were listed earlier in this chapter as points 5, 6, and 7 in the ideal job of goal-setting (see p. 526). They proposed a model in which the quantity of timber requirements is determined at the intersection of price-demand and -supply curves such as our Figure 26 (p. 279) but which is "dynamic" in that both demand and supply are considered as changing over time in accordance with the principles of time jointness and time rivalry.

The Vaux-Zivnuska requirements model, calling for the simultaneous estimation of supply and demand schedules for an indefinite series of future dates, would present staggering difficulties in application, as the authors themselves point out. Furthermore, its use of price as the controlling variable opens the model to some question, at least on the supply side (compare Chap. 14). Nevertheless, the model gives requirements analysis a big push in the right direction by calling attention, first, to the fact that supply is not perfectly elastic with price and, second, to the dependency of supply, and of demand, in one period upon that in other periods.

Although we can cite no example where the whole Vaux-Zivnuska model was used to set timber goals, we do have a case where the static part of the model served to guide related planning. The case in point, worked out by Professor Vaux, concerns the best combination in sugar pine management, including blister-rust control.[19] A by-product of the study is a growth goal for this timber species. Let us trace the highlights of the study.

## SUPPLY AND DEMAND FOR SUGAR PINE

Sugar pine, one of the three principal soft pines in the United States, occurs commercially in northern and east central California and in southwestern Oregon. Its wood is useful for light construction and other general purposes but is particularly well suited to manufactures such as sash, doors, millwork, and patterns. The consumption of sugar pine stumpage has in the past been strongly correlated with price, GNP, and the quantitative position of California in the lumber industry. For the period 2010 to 2070, when most of today's young growth will become financially mature, the relation between consumption and price may be predicted on the basis of the past correlation, with the other two variables held constant at their most probable levels. The result is the demand curve that was reproduced in Figure 24b, page 270.

Sugar pine young growth occurs in patches of varying size, intermixed with other conifers in varying concentrations. To bring out its poten-

[19] Vaux, Henry J.: *Economics of the Young-growth Sugar Pine Resource*, California Agricultural Experiment Station Bulletin 738, Berkeley, 1954.

tialities will call for special management measures such as Ribes eradication for blister-rust control, thinning for the release of crop trees, and pruning to produce valuable clear lumber. By incurring such management costs, owners can increase their sugar pine yields in the period 2010 to 2070. The better the site, the greater the number of sugar pine crop trees per acre, and the easier the rust-control job—the lower the cost per thousand board feet of increasing the yield.

The commercial young-growth sugar pine land is, accordingly, classified into 280 classes according to site quality, stocking, age, and rust-control difficulty. For each class are estimated the acreage, the extra yield per acre obtainable by means of the special management measures, the total extra annual yield, and the extra, or marginal, cost per thousand board feet of obtaining the extra yield, in terms of the period 2010 to 2070. The land classes are then arrayed in a table in increasing order of marginal cost—that is, beginning with the classes that promise the greatest rewards from special management. Above these data, at the head of the table, is inserted the estimated total annual yield obtainable from the young growth without any special management measures. The first few entries in this long tabulation are reproduced in Table 49. The letters and figures in column 1 are the codes for site, age, stocking, and rust-control cost.

*Table 49. First few entries in the tabulation showing supplies of sugar pine obtainable from cutover land as special management measures are extended to areas of increasing cost per thousand board feet*

| Class of cutover land | Additional cost per thousand board feet of extra yield | Additional area | Average annual yield | |
|---|---|---|---|---|
| | | | Additional | Cumulative total |
| (1) | (2) | (3) | (4) | (5) |
| | *Dollars* | *Thousand acres* | *Million board feet* | *Million board feet* |
| All land without special management | 0.00 | — | — | 22.40 |
| A-31-3-0 | 7.05 | 0.2 | 0.10 | 22.50 |
| A-31-4-0 | 9.62 | 0.2 | 0.30 | 22.80 |
| A-51-4-2 | 10.16 | 0.1 | 0.06 | 22.86 |
| A-31-4-2 | 10.56 | 0.1 | 0.16 | 23.02 |
| A-11-4-0 | 10.69 | 2.1 | 2.71 | 25.73 |
| . . . | . . . | . . . | . . . | . . . |

SOURCE: Vaux, Henry J.: *Economics of the Young-growth Sugar Pine Resource*, California Agricultural Experiment Station Bulletin 738, Berkeley, 1954, table 10, p. 35.

If you will analyze columns 2 and 5 in Table 49, you will see that they represent a supply schedule. The cumulative total annual yields in column 5 are the amounts of stumpage that forest owners would make available at the prices in column 2, if these owners were to extend special management measures to just those areas that promised at least to defray the cost of the extra measures in the form of extra stumpage returns. If we were to curve the data in column 2 over those in column 5, the result would be a marginal cost, or supply, curve analogous to the ones we worked with in Part Two of this book. Professor Vaux does, in fact, draw the curve, after adding in an allowance for the extra yields of sugar pine from lands now bearing old growth. The upper end of his supply curve, together with the demand curve, we have already reproduced as Figure 29a (p. 287). The intersection at 155 million board feet estimates an annual growth goal for sugar pine for the period 2010 to 2070.

Two features of the sugar pine supply as derived by Professor Vaux are of special interest to us. Let us consider them in light of the arguments in Chapter 14. The first is the part of supply that is totally inelastic with price. This is mainly the stock supply. [What does the first entry in Table 49 mean to you? Does it mean literally that owners would grow 22.4 million board feet of stumpage per year even if they faced the prospect of giving it away? Why should they grow this amount—or any amount?]

The second feature of special interest is the part of supply that has positive price elasticity. This is the short-run supply. It is prominent in the sugar pine analysis because (1) the analysis is hinged upon using "special measures," such as rust control, to increase output, and (2) for these measures the costs analyzed are those of labor and of capital other than growing stock. The cost of holding growing stock, rust-controlled or otherwise, is not analyzed beyond the assumption that a 2½ per cent interest rate will set the financial maturity of sugar pine for any firm. [How would conclusions about supply be affected if the rate of interest were admitted as a variable? And if rust control were left out, as it would be for most forests?]

The sugar pine analysis concludes by offering a set of guides to forest owners for recognizing the stands where special management measures will pay. It stresses the tentative character of the estimated goal. It emphasizes that the best sugar pine management is not simply blister-rust control but a balanced program of complementary measures.

[Some years ago, in public planning for land management, a principle was sometimes advocated of working with the worst, or least promising, areas first, on the ground that the need there was greatest. What does the sugar pine analysis suggest to you about the validity of the "worst-first" principle?]

## SOME SPECULATION ABOUT MODELS

Now before leaving the subject of timber requirements, let us speculate a bit about some models other than the ones we have been looking at. No one has yet found the ideal model, and the hunting season is open. Perhaps it will be you who will bag this rare and valuable game.

Of course one needs to reflect that the requirements question is vastly complicated. A question of resource allocation, it comes down in the last analysis to the great social issue of ordering the public economic life. It may be too much to expect any one simple model to answer such a question, or for the answer to be found by approaching it from the forestry viewpoint.

What promise may there be in an absolute, rather than relativistic, solution to the timber-requirements problem? Nutritionists calculate standards for our daily intake of vitamins and minerals. Are there analogous standards to be found for our intake of forest products? Compare the reasoning of the Reappraisal report: [20]

In the case of residential construction, no attempt has been made to relate the estimate of lumber requirements directly to gross national product. There is clear evidence that the need for decent housing for all the people is coming to be recognized as one of the major social needs which cannot be left entirely to the free play of economic forces. Practicable methods are being sought to satisfy housing needs more adequately than has been done in the past. The estimates take this trend of national sentiment into account.

Here is represented a combining, and perhaps a desirable one, of relativistic and absolute approaches. But how shall we account for the cost of meeting absolute requirements?

On the other hand, if we are to follow a relativistic route, may there be more significant variables with which to replace or supplement price as a guide to requirements forecasting? How about using income as a variable? We know that demand is strongly related to income. The relationship has been used in the TRR and in other requirements estimates. But income is an index not only of consumers' position in the market but also of society's whole resource use and output. Perhaps, therefore, it can be taken as a variable on the supply side, too, of timber requirements. [How might you adapt the income-consumption relationship of Figure 24a (p. 270) as a requirements model?]

Or again, since timber requirements are a problem in conservation and since conservation is so largely determined by the rate of interest, or discount, why not make use of our models in Figure 20 (p. 217)? To do so would call for the very information that we as foresters are presumably

[20] *Potential Requirements for Timber Products*, p. 2.

most adept at furnishing: information on forest inputs and outputs. It is inconceivable that any valid estimate of United States timber requirements can be made without an inventory and classification of the nation's prospective forest lands. The classification would be worked out on the basis of timber productivity, measured in terms of production functions. The functions in question are of two kinds: First, there is the relation of timber outputs to growing stock, where the best combination is found through the marginal interest cost and the marginal value growth per cent: the interest-rate model. Second, there is the relation of outputs to cultural and administrative inputs, where the best combination is determined by the marginal cost of these inputs and their marginal value product: the price model.

In this approach, the interest-rate model would first be used to set basic goals for land classes, which would later be combined for regions and the nation. The interest rate could be varied with the region and the class of land ownership. It could be set at levels appropriate to the national propensity to conserve and thereby ensure a normative estimate. Thus the rate would measure the amount of public subsidy, if any, implied for fourth-stage programs (p. 515)—or alternatively it would measure any sacrifice to be demanded of individual owners in the public interest. Then the price model would be used to enlarge the basic goals for such special forestry measures as would be economical. In practice, the two models would be worked together, in successive approximations. The interest-rate model thus would serve to filter out any part of the enlarged goal that was unworkable as an act of saving. And as a whole the approach would escape the grave limitations of those requirements estimates that lean on a product-by-product projection. It is a much safer bet that timber will be in use in the far future than that any particular one of today's products will be, or that the field will not be dominated by new products of which we know little or nothing today.

[What do you think are the chief defects of such an approach? How might you remedy them? How would you allow for the influences of time rivalry and time jointness in a requirements forecast of this sort?]

*SUMMARY*

Among the forest products for which national or regional goals are estimated by means of program planning are recreation, water, and timber.

Planning of national goals for outdoor recreation is done by several Federal agencies, but notably the National Park Service. The Park Service's 1941 *A Study of the Park and Recreation Problem in the United States* considers, in effect, the demand for recreational services and lands, and the supply of such lands. It suggests criteria for balancing supply against demand and proposes national goals for outdoor recreational facilities in each of eight major categories.

Program planning in the area of water resources takes not a national approach but one by regions, river basins, or lesser areas. A great many agencies engage in planning. Some unifying and coordinating influence upon their work has been exerted by interagency committees and recent presidential commissions.

In national planning for timber production and consumption goals ("requirements"), the Federal Forest Service has taken the lead. This agency has made requirements studies periodically, beginning with the 1920 Capper Report and continuing through the 1958 report on the Timber Resource Review. No timber-planning job yet done meets all the standards for an ideal goal. Nine such standards may be recognized; they may be thought of collectively as a general model for requirements planning. A specific model centering on the use of price demand and supply has been employed in planning a growth goal for sugar pine timber. Other possible models emphasize the concept of absolute requirements, of consumption in relation to income, and of production in relation to interest rates and product prices.

Chapter 32

AREA

PLANNING

FOR FORESTRY

HERE WE have been talking about timber and about water resources and outdoor recreation almost as though each were sufficient unto itself. But of course we know very well that this is not the case. If we have learned anything at all from our review of the fundamentals of forestry economics, it is that single events and single resources can be explained and analyzed and understood only in relation to events and resources at large. The study of economics is like the study of ecology in teaching us to think of things always in their environment—in helping us to understand that the meaning of things is not intrinsic but is a product of their setting. In social planning, the obligation to interconnect events and resources is most sharp and demanding.

To be sure, this sort of thinking can be carried to foolish extremes. The ultimate plan is the one for the universe. To make it might well take a universe of talent and time—resources better devoted to other work, especially considering that it would be a little difficult to carry out the plan. In order to get on with his job, the social planner must accept something short of the conceptual ideal, some reasonable compromise in both geography and subject matter. Such a compromise may be found in area planning.

In our review of program planning in Chapter 31, you could see the inescapable tendency for the work to relate itself geographically—to the metropolitan region or the river basin or the nation or whatever. You could also observe how the planners were forced to look beyond the program at hand so as to take some account of the other industries with which theirs was interwoven. All economic planning must accommodate itself somehow to the five aspects of the economy that were pointed out in Chapter 2 (pp. 18–19): things, persons, places, time, and functions. Area planning is not sharply separated from program planning. Both not only recognize the five economic aspects, but may even represent identical scope in respect to each of them. Area planning is distinguished largely in the *explicit* attention it gives to more than one program or industry.

## SOUTHERN APPALACHIAN PROBLEMS

To learn something about area planning, let us study an example, an analysis made some years ago of a small group of communities in Breathitt County, in the eastern Kentucky hills.[1] The communities were named collectively the Quicksand area, after the settlement and post office situated near its center. The allusion, in the term, to the difficulties of planning was inadvertent.

The study of the Quicksand area was made at a time when the Southern Appalachian Highlands of the United States were much in the public eye as a scene of persistent problems. A heavily populated, heavily forested rural region, long settled, and long isolated from surrounding country by mountain and cultural barriers, the Southern Appalachians were (and still are) a territory of meager farming, scant industry, depleted woods, high birth rate, and low income. A flow of excess population from the region into the outside world—augmented in good times, checked and even reversed in bad—had called particular attention to the bonds between the Southern Appalachians and the rest of the country, to the national stake in the region's people and resources. At the end of World War II it was evident that old questions were again arising and calling to be answered.

What was the population outlook? How stood the inventory of land and industrial resources? What kind of land management would give the best incomes in the long run? Were there unseen potentialities in forestry that could bring more local prosperity? How develop such potentialities? What was the public interest in population trends and resource development? And how shape public policy to the public interest?

The study in the eastern-Kentucky portion of the Appalachians was sponsored by the Rockefeller Foundation in pursuit of its concern for social problems. The work was done by the Kentucky Agricultural Experiment Station, with help from the United States Forest Service. The Station chose the Quicksand area as a work center partly for administra-

[1] Duerr, William A., John H. Bondurant, W. D. Nicholls, Howard W. Beers, R. O. Gustafson, and John B. Roberts: *Farms and Forests of Eastern Kentucky in Relation to Population and Income: An Appraisal of Population and Land Resources and Their Potentials,* Kentucky Agricultural Experiment Station Bulletin 507, Lexington, 1947.

tive convenience and partly for the area's representativeness of Southern Highland conditions. The boundaries were set so as to include varied types of land and ownership in proportions typical of the region and so as to encompass whole communities, within which the people customarily came to common centers for their commerce and social life. Here we find the effort to set up a meaningful social unit for study. An effort was made also to hold the unit to workable size for detailed inventory and analysis. The result was a study area of 37,000 acres.

Six men were given major responsibilities in the study. The group included specialists in four fields: farm management, rural sociology, marketing, and forestry. Such an approach, using a team, or "task force," is commonly followed in the modern era of specialization where a research project calls for the use of varied disciplines. The approach has the obvious advantages of bringing all the relevant skills and points of view to bear on a complex problem, and thus is well suited to area planning. As a by-product of the collaboration, individual specialists on the team are helped, through their efforts to understand their colleagues, to broaden their outlook. Sometimes, weirdly, the coordination of the task force, like that of the Babel tower builders, breaks down for want of successful communication. The Quicksand team was fortunate in escaping this particular problem.

## QUICKSAND AREA

Now let us follow the Quicksand story as it was told by the research team. Their data for the second stage of the analysis (describing the current situation) related mainly to 1940 or thereabouts. To simplify our own talk, let us use the present tense in referring to that time. And remember that when we cite values, these are expressed in the dollars of that time.

The Quicksand unit is an ideal case for illustrating area planning because of the extreme simplicity of its economic life: "People; land, with its farms and forests; and a small industry and trade are the economic resources of the Quicksand area." Let us attempt to understand the character of each of these resources.

## PEOPLE

The people are the sixth-generation descendants of the first frontier settlers, most of whom had become established within the area by 1825. Their numbers grew rapidly, even despite heavy out migration. Growth was at least 20 per cent in every decade between the Civil War and 1910, and was close to that figure between 1930 and 1940. During the 1890s, at the height of the timbering boom, growth was 60 per cent. Now the population is just over 2,200 and comprises 414 families. As we might expect where numbers are expanding so fast, the proportion of young people is extraordinarily high: nearly 45 per cent under 15 years.

Originally the people were closely organized into a folk society built of clans and families, regulated by tradition, largely self-sufficient. The organization remained undisturbed until the 1870s. Then began a series of penetrations from the outside world that weakened the social structure, undermining its self-sufficiency but failing to offer workable, enduring alternatives. First came the timbering boom. It brought new employment, mills, money, and the railroad. When it was over, the people were left with depleted resources, with changed ways of life that now had to be abandoned, and with strong distrust for outside leadership. The coming of highways, the wars, radio, and government subsidy further eroded the folk society, leaving uncertainty and confusion.

Attitudes of the people are a product of their history. Reliance upon folk knowledge rather than formal education has caused the custom of school attendance to remain underdeveloped. About half of all persons twenty-five years old or older have had less than 6½ years of school. Alternative rates of return are high, planning horizons close, and resource-management attitudes generally exploitive. Seven farmers in ten report no farming plans for the year ahead; nine in ten, no plans for their woods. Forests are burned, hillsides permitted to wash away, fish dynamited—or rather, "pounded," by banging two rocks together under the water.

People still make their livelihood largely by producing their own requirements. Seventy per cent of employment is in subsistence farming; thirty per cent, in forestry, wood conversion, mining, trades, and services. The people pick berries and greens, shoot squirrels and birds, catch fish, harvest weeds for livestock fodder, gather firewood, and mine some coal from the farm hillside. Incomes are very small and principally in kind. A little cash comes from outside work, from gifts sent by family members who have migrated, and from relief, pensions, and other public sources. Workers possess the common skills but have little specialization.[2]

## LAND

The land of the Quicksand area is piled up into a scattering of steep little hills with sharp ridges and narrow, meandering and forking valleys. The climate is temperate and humid. The soils are highly variable, but mostly of low productivity.

[2] For more about the people, see the companion report by the rural sociologists Beers, Howard W., and Catherine P. Heflin: *People and Resources in Eastern Kentucky*, Kentucky Agricultural Experiment Station Bulletin 500, Lexington, 1947.

The best soils—and the only prime farming sites—are the bottomland ribbons that make up less than 5 per cent of the total land acreage (Table 50). Next in fertility are the coves that lie at the stream heads, fanning out into the hollows and merging with the hillsides. Because of their steepness and inaccessibility, the coves are little used for farming and thus are the prime forest sites. They occupy a sixth of the land area. The remainder of the land is hillside, of generally meager productivity, but varying significantly with slope and exposure. Nearly nine-tenths of the hillside acreage is classed as steep, with slopes ranging from 30 to 60

Table 50. *Types of land and their use in the Quicksand area, 1940*

| Land type | Crop-land | Build-ing lots | All cleared land | Forest | All land | |
|---|---|---|---|---|---|---|
| | *Acres* | *Acres* | *Acres* | *Acres* | *Acres* | *Per cent* |
| Bottomland | 1,570 | 110 | 1,680 | 90 | 1,770 | 4.8 |
| Cove | 350 | — | 350 | 5,820 | 6,170 | 16.7 |
| Sheltered slope: | | | | | | |
| Gentle | 610 | 50 | 660 | — | 660 | 1.8 |
| Steep | 6,960 | — | 6,960 | 8,200 | 15,160 | 41.0 |
| Very steep | 640 | — | 640 | 990 | 1,630 | 4.4 |
| Exposed slope: | | | | | | |
| Gentle | 360 | 30 | 390 | — | 390 | 1.1 |
| Steep | 790 | — | 790 | 9,890 | 10,680 | 28.9 |
| Very steep | 20 | — | 20 | 470 | 490 | 1.3 |
| All land types | 11,300 | 190 | 11,490 | 25,460 | 36,950 | 100.0 |
| | *Per cent* | *Per cent* | *Per cent* | *Per cent* | *Per cent* | |
| | 30.6 | 0.5 | 31.1 | 68.9 | 100.0 | |

SOURCE: *Farms and Forests of Eastern Kentucky*, Kentucky Agricultural Experiment Station Bulletin 507, Lexington, 1947, table 1, p. 9.

per cent. Hillside soils are thin and stony. Suffering the deficiencies of the sandstone and shale parent rock, they are markedly lacking in lime and phosphorus; they leach and erode severely when cleared. The sheltered slopes, those having a northerly to easterly aspect, are relatively moist and cool, and nearly half of them are cleared. Exposed slopes, on the other hand, along with the ridges, are hot and dry, and only occasionally has the effort been made to farm them.

More than 98 per cent of the land is privately owned; the small remainder is held by the state or county. Of the private land, roughly three-fourths is in farm properties averaging some 90 acres. One-fourth is owned by nonresident individuals and by companies (land, timber, and coal) for purposes other than farming.

## FARMS

The land units, or farms, operated by the area's 414 families average 4 acres of bottomland and 24 acres of other cleared land. They include also adjacent forest. The farms range in size from 1-acre house-and-garden plots of rural residents to more diversified units of several hundred acres. About half of the families own their units and half are renters or share-croppers.

Farms of the Quicksand area are almost all part-time, subsistence farms, producing chiefly garden crops, corn, and livestock products for home use. Centered upon a patch of bottomland along the stream, with fields extending up the steep, poor hillsides, the typical farm is small, crowded, worked by intensive hand methods, and unproductive in so far as any net cash income is concerned. The farm provides a place to live, a source of food, and a base of operations from which workers may go to earn a small income in outside occupations.

The crux of the farm situation rests in the use of labor.

Topography limits farm size; to extend farm fields would require mainly stretching them out along the stream bottom; the resulting unit would soon become unmanageable. The hillsides, which can be cultivated only on long rotations (a year in corn followed by several years of pasture or "resting") offer no substantial room for expansion. Farm topography and size also virtually rule out the use of machinery. Consequently, in order to produce the crop, the farm family must apply its labor intensively to the land, with the help only of simple tools and occasionally a horse or mule.

Although over the year as a whole the farm family has a great surplus of labor, its work is so largely concentrated in the corn-planting and harvest weeks, and is so time consuming, that the family is faced then with a critical labor shortage. All the members working together have as much as they can do to grow the 100 to 150 bushels of corn considered necessary to the yearly program, though outside the peak seasons, 2 or 3 man-hours per day suffice to run the farm. Here, then, is another factor that limits farm size.

Because soils are poor and crop yields low, because methods of culture are primitive, and because the layout of fields is inefficient, the farmer gets but a small reward for his work. When it takes 114 man-hours to produce 15 bushels of corn on a hillside acre, the return to labor is 5 to 10 cents per hour. With such low returns, derived largely in the form of subsistence, the farmer is severely pinched for cash and must follow those methods of management that permit minimum cash outlay. And so we find him refraining from the use of hired labor that might lighten the seasonal work load; skimping on seed, feed, and fertilizer; neglecting his pastures; and overemphasizing his corn enterprise.

But with all the cutting and skimping, the average farm family still finds itself laying out more cash than the farm will earn; the farm is not self-sustaining. To make up the deficit, members of the family find off-farm work, an average of 90 days per year, during the slack seasons. They use also their gifts and other gratuities to hold the farm together. The family's annual income statement turns out about as follows:[3]

| | | |
|---|---|---|
| Cash income: | | |
| Farm income (mostly calves, livestock products) | $107 | |
| Farm expense (mostly feed, seed, fertilizer) | 115 | |
| Net farm income (deficit) | −8 | |
| Off-farm earnings and gratuities | 236 | |
| Total net cash income | | $228 |
| Subsistence income: | | |
| Crop and livestock products used by family | $321 | |
| Forest products used by family | 26 | |
| Total subsistence income | | 347 |
| Total income | | $575 |

## FORESTS AND INDUSTRY

The forests of the Quicksand unit, despite their dominant place, area-wise, in land use, produce little revenue for the people. Their yield of fish and game is scant, their regulation of water insufficient to deter serious erosion and floods, their timber product a minor part of family livelihood. Of the $575 average income, $8 derives from timber sold and $26 from that used. Perhaps a tenth of off-farm work is in logging or milling. This failure of forest resources to fill the very part in the life of the area that they are needed for and solely qualified for is the consequence of their physical condition and of the economic barriers to timber conversion and marketing.

The heavy timbering operations that closed shortly after 1920 took the merchantable walnut, yellow-poplar, white oak, and other trees of value from the abundant hardwood forest. Today's timber cover is made up of residuals and second growth. Of the gross volume of saw-log-size trees, four-tenths is cull, principally the result of ground fires. Usable wood volume averages 1,700 board feet of saw timber and 580 cubic feet of smaller material per acre. Half of the saw timber is beech, hickory, and scarlet oak, species of low marketability. A tenth is walnut, yellow-poplar, and white oak. Much of the remainder is other oaks.

[3] Full details of the farm story are given by Nicholls, W. D., and John H. Bondurant: *Farm Management and Family Incomes in Eastern Kentucky*, Kentucky Agricultural Experiment Station Bulletin 491, Lexington, 1946.

Forest holdings are small, mostly less than 100 acres. Over half are less than 50 acres. Holdings change hands frequently: Half of them have been in their present ownership less than ten years, a third, for not more than five years. Such shifting occupancy is the outcome of the people's ceaseless milling about in search of something better. The tenants—who, you will recall, constitute half of the families—are the most restless: 50 per cent of them have been where they are for only a year; 80 per cent, for five years or less. Thus, though the people's attachment to the land in general is strong and enduring, their interest in a particular parcel is transitory. Forest management has little continuity, and its aims are of the very short term.

However, generally speaking, timber is not being overcut, except in the special sense that low-value trees are being allowed to accumulate disproportionately. The fact is that the present harvest, averaging less than 30 board feet of saw timber and 10 cubic feet of other wood per acre of forest, should be doubled or tripled immediately under the best management. Eventually it could be increased five to seven times. Thus timberlands have comparatively high potentialities. What stand in the way are such needs as heavy improvement cutting to start the management program, fire control, and the blazing of new paths of timber conversion and marketing that will lead to the outside world.[4]

Indeed, the timber industry, which has occasioned nearly all the manufacturing and trade that the Quicksand area has seen in its history, is now largely inactive. The forests, with their scarcity of choice trees, are economically difficult of access. Their scattered ownership, too, reduces their accessibility. The wooded hills and coves lie remote from the area's few, low-quality roads. The wood industry consists mainly of a scattering of small sawmills that make shoddy lumber for local use. The ties with outside markets are few and intermittent. In a word, we find the typical problems of the aftermath such as we discussed in Chapter 21 (pp. 345–351) and the need for an effective local system of concentration and manufacture that will put the area back in touch with its potential outlets and fill in the seasonal valleys of underemployment.[5]

## FACTORS IN LAND USE

Now quite evidently the life of the Quicksand area revolves around its land. Our interest centers upon the land economy: the production of farm

---

[4] The story of forest resources is told at greater length by Duerr, William A., and R. O. Gustafson: *Management of Forests in an Eastern Kentucky Area*, Kentucky Agricultural Experiment Station Bulletin 518, Lexington, 1948.

[5] See also Duerr, William A., John B. Roberts, and R. O. Gustafson: *Timber-products Marketing in Eastern Kentucky*, Kentucky Agricultural Experiment Station Bulletin 488, Lexington, 1946.

and forest commodities and their local use, transportation, processing, and marketing. The level of living, or income, of the people is linked to the intensity of land use—its use for forest or for crops or pasture and the application of labor and other inputs for these purposes. Therefore the planning for the area must be primarily land-use planning. Let us go over the main factors—physical, economic, and social—that condition land use, and then plan out some alternative land-use programs.

Among the physical factors in land use is the wide variation in productivity from one land type to another. Annual yields of corn on bottomland average 30 bushels per acre with present practices; on hill land, 16 bushels. The well-stocked hardwood forest will grow annually—again, under present practices—150 board feet to the acre in coves, 100 board feet on exposed slopes. Production functions for the different products on the different land types are essential data for planning. They must consider yields over a period of years, allowing, for instance, for the fact that corn fields are an impermanent use of hillsides, deteriorating the site and causing muddied streams and fluctuating water levels. Thus the production functions must be capable of revealing not only the relative returns from corn on different soils but also the comparative returns from corn and oak and the fact that the advantage of corn over oak diminishes on poorer and poorer ground. They must take into account, too, the rapidly rising inputs required to grow crops on more remote parts of the farm.

Economic factors in land use are the values of inputs and outputs that determine where, on the production functions, the best combinations may be found. For families who have no cash to buy food, the value of the year's minimum food requirement is immeasurably high. The land needed to meet this requirement is given over to it without much question. Beyond that, input values, especially of labor, carry increasing weight. The more plentiful the labor supply, the more land will be used in ways that can absorb a great deal of labor. This means, in general, more cropland and less forest. When off-farm employment is hard to find, the process of intensifying land use may be carried to the limit set by the worker's evaluation of leisure. However, if there are jobs to be had outside the land economy of the area, or other sources of cash income such as gifts and government allowances, then the intensity of land use at once is eased off. Such outside cash payments may be looked upon as subsidy to the land economy, allowing its practices to be extensified. The money that Johnnie sends from town keeps a hillside in forest on the home farm. Clearly, the local development of wood-using industry would have the same result.

As for the social factors that sway the use of land, tradition of course plays its customary role in opposition to change. The short-run mobility of workers and the closeness of family ties increase the subsidies to the land economy that extensify land use. The strength of families' long-term attachment to land works in the contrary direction. And above all, the size and rate of growth of the population and its labor characteristics affect the type and intensity of land use.

## FOUR ALTERNATIVES FOR FUTURE

In planning ahead, then, it seems evident that the future of the Quicksand area—the use of land and the level of living—will depend most directly upon two things: the population and the breadth of employment opportunity. That is to say, it will depend on the course followed by the area, whether toward greater isolation and an intensified subsistence economy or toward an economy based on fuller exchange of labor and of products with the outside world. In order to cover the broad range of possible alternative developments, the planners set up four different assumptions about the future and estimated what the population, employment, income, and land use would be under each assumption in the land economy of the Quicksand area. The purpose of this approach was to provide policy makers with a basis for deciding what trend of events would be most in the public interest and most worthy of their support. The four assumptions were as follows:

1. Intensified subsistence. Population will increase beyond the 1940 density, to the maximum foreseeable in the present century if past influences continue in force. Industrial activity and the manner of use of labor and capital in all production will remain as in 1940.

2. Modified subsistence. Population, industry, and production practices will be the same as they were in 1940. Land use will differ from that in 1940 only to the extent that it can be made more rational.

3. Modified exchange. Population will be less than in 1940, by the numbers that would be withdrawn through the force of continued prosperity on the outside. Production practices will be somewhat improved, and industry will be reorganized and slightly enlarged. Considerable part-time work will be available outside the land economy.

4. Full exchange. Population will be further reduced, to the level where workers will be receiving rates of return competitive with those on the outside. Farm and forest technology will be improved, and sufficient time will have elapsed to bring forests to full productivity. Industry will be at the maximum now foreseeable. Only those farm products will be produced for home use that can be produced more economically than purchased.

The salient features of the Quicksand land economy under each of the four assumptions are given in Table 51, where incomes are estimated in terms of 1940 dollars. Now let us see how the forecasts were made, beginning with those under the first assumption, the intensified subsistence economy.

Table 51. *Future land use, population, employment, and income in the Quicksand area under four different assumptions*

| Item | Intensified subsistence | Modified subsistence | Modified exchange | Full exchange |
|---|---|---|---|---|
| Cleared land: | | | | |
| Acres | 30,710 | 20,510 | 2,710 | 1,530 |
| Per cent | 83.1 | 55.5 | 7.3 | 4.2 |
| Forest land: | | | | |
| Acres | 6,240 | 16,440 | 34,240 | 35,260 |
| Per cent | 16.9 | 44.5 | 92.7 | 95.8 |
| Population: | | | | |
| Persons | 2,846 | 2,206 | 1,588 | 779 |
| Families | 593 | 414 | 338 | 173 |
| Annual employment, thousand man-hours | 1,060 | 598 | 488 | 572 |
| Annual income, dollars: | | | | |
| From land, per acre | 4.14 | 3.80 | 4.38 | 8.56 |
| From land, total | 153,010 | 140,340 | 161,720 | 314,860 |
| From subsidy | 128,070 | 97,700 | 152,030 | 0 |
| From all sources, total | 281,080 | 238,040 | 313,750 | 314,860 |
| All sources, per family | 474 | 575 | 928 | 1,820 |

SOURCE: *Farms and Forests of Eastern Kentucky,* Kentucky Agricultural Experiment Station Bulletin 507, Lexington, 1947, table 6, p. 53.

## INTENSIFIED SUBSISTENCE

The population of 2,846, comprising 593 families, was arrived at by projecting the 1920-to-1940 trend to 1980. Next, the planners described a hypothetical average farm of 62.3 acres (the study-unit total of 36,950 acres divided by 593 families), made up of the various land types in the same proportion as the whole study unit (see Table 50, last column). The management of this hypothetical average farm was then planned out by the budget method. In making the budget, the planners assumed that as much as possible of the family livelihood would be derived from the farm (including its forests), all open lands being cropped on as short a rotation as could be followed and still maintain their usefulness for three or four human generations. The rotations assumed ranged from annual cropping on bottomland to one year in twenty on very steep exposed slope. It was assumed that timber stands, too, would be harvested under a gradual depletion program.

Now the question of land use was studied. Two propositions were investigated: First, would any forest acre contribute more to net farm earnings than if it were cleared? Second, would any cropland acre contribute less to net earnings than if it were allowed to revert to forest?

On very steep exposed slopes, where the physical advantage of timber production over cultivation, hay production, and pasture is greatest, the unmanaged forest might conceivably make, in favorable instances, a contribution to net farm earnings amounting to $2.11 per year. This is the value of the maximum permissible harvest of products, assuming that timber is available locally to meet local requirements and assuming that the forest on this very steep exposed slope is as productive as the average of all types of forest, which would be a rare instance of high productivity. If an acre of such forest land is cleared, there is a loss in anticipated annual timber returns amounting $2.11. At the same time, there is a gain consisting of the value of timber products amassed at the time of clearing, some $42 worth, which, at the lowest rate of interest conceivably applicable in the present case—4 per cent—has an annual value of $1.68. There is also a gain consisting of the value of cultivated crops, livestock, and livestock products obtainable from the newly cleared land. On land of this poorest type, requiring long rotations and offering poor yields, the net value of these products is 62 cents per acre per year. The net effect upon annual farm earnings of clearing an acre of unmanaged timber on very steep exposed slope and using that acre to grow farm products is therefore as follows:

| | |
|---|---:|
| Gain from timber felled in clearing | $1.68 |
| Gain from crops, livestock, and livestock products | 0.62 |
| Total gain | 2.30 |
| Loss in anticipated timber returns | 2.11 |
| Net gain | $0.19 |

The second of the two propositions was similarly worked out, and the following answers found to the two: First, no forest acre would contribute more to net earnings than if it were cleared, so long as family labor were available for the clearing and cultivation. Second, no cropland acre that would yield an equivalent of at least 10 bushels of corn would contribute less to net earnings than if it were shifted to forest.

On the basis of the foregoing analysis, and with the data at hand on labor supply and requirements and corn yields, the best use of land was determined for the hypothetical average farm: about 83 per cent cleared land, as against 31 per cent in 1940. The cleared land would supply all the family's annual needs for food except an equivalent of 24 bushels of corn and certain other essentials, chiefly fats. These deficiencies and other elements of the family living requiring cash (assumed to be equal to the 1940 cash outlays) would have to be made up from subsidy. The resulting estimates for the average farm were multiplied by 593 so as to get area-wide totals. The summary is given in the first column of figures in Table 51.

Of the $281,080 total annual income in the intensified subsistence economy, 46 per cent is derived from subsidy—from work outside the land economy and from gratuities. The income from the land economy itself, $153,010, mainly in kind rather than cash, represents a return (to land, labor, and capital) of 14 cents per man-hour of work on cleared land, 29 cents per man-hour on forest land and its products. It is the need for food under the assumed subsistence conditions that forces such a lopsided intensification of cleared-land use. Although labor is intensively applied to resources, the poverty of the latter makes for high seasonal underemployment in the land economy: The total yearly employment of more than a million man-hours amounts to no more than 160 eight-hour days per worker.

## MODIFIED SUBSISTENCE

In order to forecast conditions in the modified subsistence economy, the planners studied a representative cross section of existing farms and drew up budgets for them. They estimated the use of land that would be required in order to produce the same incomes as were earned in 1940, but under a rational program that would minimize resource depletion. They found that the chief adjustments needed were in the direction of lengthening the crop rotations on hillsides, which were being cultivated too frequently. Their budgets consequently called for clearing more land on many farms—or, in terms of the whole Quicksand area, a cleared-land percentage of 55½: substantially more than in 1940, though much less than in the intensified subsistence economy. Forest lands, which were being underutilized in 1940, were slated for a corresponding reduction and more intensive utilization.

In the modified subsistence economy, family income is higher than under intensified subsistence. Income per acre of cleared land is also greater, and the return per man-hour on both cleared and forest land is substantially larger. However, income per acre of forest land is less under modified subsistence than under intensified, and employment per worker in the land economy is lower: 118 days per year as against 160. [Can you explain the difference?]

## MODIFIED EXCHANGE

To forecast what the modified exchange economy would be like, the planners followed roughly the same approach as for their first assumption. They estimated that the land economy would comprise 338 families working their farms part time primarily for products to be consumed at home, and employed during the rest of the year (actually to a total of about 8 full months) in local timber and milling operations and in jobs outside the area. On cleared land, the best farming practices would be followed. On forest land, a recommended management program would have been in effect about twenty years; the initial improvement cut would have been finished; and the timber harvest, all marketable, would be at the low point for the current rotation.

Again a hypothetical average farm is studied: 109 acres, or $\frac{1}{338}$ of the whole area. Because the family's employment alternatives now are favorable, the analysis of best land use gives farm crops and pasture the upper hand on only the bottomland and gentle slopes. Elsewhere, the forest use has the advantage. The outcome is a cleared-land percentage of 7.3 (see Table 51, third column of figures).

Total employment in the land economy, some 488,000 man-hours per year, is less than under either of the two previous assumptions, but employment per worker is greater than under modified subsistence, and far more productive than under either of the subsistence alternatives. The farm business, indeed, is self-supporting, requiring no subsidy to extensify land use. However, the land economy is heavily supplemented by off-the-area employment, and thus family income is enlarged to a yearly total of $928. Of the $480 of family income that is made within the land economy, 46 per cent comes from forest land and its products, a higher proportion than in previous cases.

## FULL EXCHANGE

Finally, for the fourth assumption, the case of full exchange, the population estimate is no longer a starting point. Rather, it is the outcome of forecasting the employment that the land economy would ultimately provide without subsidy, given full resource use, rational management, and competitive returns to labor. The land economy under full exchange includes two types of family: One is engaged primarily in commercial farming, with some woods or mill employment on the side to round out a full ten-month work year. The other is fully employed in timber industry, occupying the land only to the extent of a home site and garden space.

A study of the Quicksand area reveals that there is enough wide bottomland along major streams to provide the nucleus for thirty-eight commercial farms. The cleared-land requirements of these farms would include also a part of the adjacent gentle slopes. Sites for the garden farms, about 2 acres each, can be found aplenty on the minor bottoms. The remainder of the land, after an allowance for new roads and mill sites, is available for forest use. Assuming that forests are in full production and that all timber not used at home is processed locally before sale, the planners can estimate total employment, and from this the number of workers and the population. Including the commercial farm population, the result is 779 persons, or 173 families. By this standard, it looks as though the Quicksand area in 1940, with its comparatively depleted resources, was overpopulated more than threefold!

In the full exchange economy, forests occupy about 95 per cent of the land area. They are the main source of livelihood for eight persons out of ten, and a secondary source for the others. Income within the land economy amounts to about $315,000 per year in total, or $1,820 per family, both very much higher than under any of the other three assumptions.

## PHILOSOPHY OF SOCIAL PLANNING

Now let us stand back from all this figuring of alternative assumptions and see what it means and what, if anything, has been accomplished by it.

A group of technicians has gone into one of the problem areas of the United States, the Southern Appalachians, and selected a small study unit. The technicians have speculated about the future of the unit and made some projections of resource management, population, employment, and income. Apart from any question of the accuracy of specific projections, they have shown that, barring the unforeseen emergence of new kinds of resources or industry, there are two primary courses of development open to the area. One is toward the subsistence way of life: denser population, lower income, higher subsidy, more cleared farm land, and less forest. The other is toward exchange, with sparser population, higher income, less subsidy, and an increasing forest use of land.

We have attached the name of planning to this exercise in speculation, and yet actually no plan has been drawn. The four assumptions are not plans, but merely rough glimpses along the range of future possibilities. Is this disappointing? Would you rather see more specific alternative plans, or even the singling out of one particular plan, with the recommendation that it be chosen and followed?

Clearly, the procedure used in the Quicksand area reflects a certain philosophy about social planning. This is to the effect that the technician's role under democratic institutions is to present facts to the people—establish truth, and help to disseminate it. Then the people interpret the truth, perhaps variously, in terms of policy, and debate the policy, and come out with decisions about what they will do. They may reach decisions about far-reaching programs and then call the technicians back to help with the further planning. Or they may decide only on a few immediate steps that they believe are in the right direction in light of the facts.

And so in the Quicksand area, the planners' role was judged to be that of clearly establishing the implications of alternative policies—what they would mean in terms of resource use and output. Such knowledge is not easy for everyone to come by. It involves, as we have seen, technical input-output studies and a considering together of farming, forestry, and social data. Local leaders, agricultural extension people, state legislators, and others in a position of influence can take such knowledge and make decisions. If they favor the course toward an exchange economy, then they can take appropriate action or at least avoid the inappropriate. They can, for instance, work for the development of a stable timber industry[6] and discourage the use of subsidies that will keep more people on the land. If, on the other hand, they see advantages in holding the *status quo*, they will at least be informed of the disadvantages too.

[As concerns the problem of carrying out a plan, can you summarize the main points of similarity and difference between social planning and planning for the firm? How do political institutions bear upon the question?]

## SUMMARY

Area planning, though not sharply distinguished from program planning, differs from the latter in the explicit attention it gives to more than one program or industry. A simple example of area planning is a study made some years ago in a group of Southern Appalachian communities, the Quicksand area, where the principal industries are farming and forestry.

The Quicksand area is situated in a heavily populated hill country where farm resources are meager and overworked, forest resources are depleted, and the subsistence economy depends strongly upon outside subsidy for such income as it provides.

The planners, a team representing several disciplines, set up four different assumptions about the future of the Quicksand area. Under each assumption, they predicted population, employment, income, and resource use in the land economy. The assumptions cover the range of future possibilities in the development of the area. At one extreme lies intensified subsistence. At the other lies a full exchange economy, with relatively low population, high income, and great emphasis upon the forest use of land.

Such planning offers no prescription but merely states the most probable outcome of alternative policies. It offers facts and forecasts upon which the people and their leaders may base policy decisions.

[6] See Gustafson, R. O.: *Opportunities for Private Forest Enterprise in Eastern Kentucky*, Kentucky Agricultural Experiment Station Circular 60, Lexington, 1946.

I N CHAPTER 30 we described four stages of social planning, concerned respectively with the goal, the situation, the problem, and the measures for bending the situation toward the goal. Previously we had something to say on the subject of the situation. Subsequently we have talked about goals and measures. It remains for us, in closing our review of forestry-economics fundamentals, to give attention to the topic of problems. Let us do so with special reference to the forest economy of the United States.

Perhaps you are one of those persons who feel that problems are a dismal and cheerless study and who would rather think of opportunities. Then do so by all means. In any case, problems—or opportunities—are the gap between the goal and the reality.

We referred earlier to problem analysis as a necessary part of the political process of getting public action. In the United States forest economy, many comprehensive problem analyses have been drawn up for this purpose, most of them by the Federal agencies and most of them as a part of social planning for timber resources.

### REPORT UPON FORESTRY

An early example is the work of Dr. Franklin B. Hough, who was appointed in the Department of Agriculture in 1876 to make a study, specially authorized by Congress, of

. . . the annual amount of consumption, importation, and exportation of timber and other forest products; the probable supply for future wants; the

**556**

means best adapted to the preservation and renewal of forests; the influence of forests upon climate; and the measures that have been successfully applied in various countries for the preservation and restoration or planting of forests.

Dr. Hough, working against his day's crippling deficiencies of data, produced a comprehensive, detailed, loosely assembled report[1] addressed to the forestry problems of the time: the westward receding of the softwood timber industry from depleted forests of the Northeast; local timber shortages here and in the Middle West; the supposed disturbances of climate attending forest removal; the presumed need for artificial forest regeneration for protective and timber purposes; the heavy drain upon timber for export; the deficiences of national forestry policy in such matters as reserving public forest lands; the loss of timber to fire, insects, and disease; the lack of public education in forestry, and of a forestry profession in the United States.

## BUREAU OF CORPORATIONS STUDY

By the early years of the present century, the American Industrial Revolution, which had just been getting well under way in Dr. Hough's time, was gaining momentum and carrying the forest economy with it into new problem spheres. The great national wave of softwood timbering had passed across the Lake states, had entered the southern pine region, and was heading toward the Far West. Everyone could see that the fading of the old timber surpluses was no longer merely a local thing, but was taking on nationwide significance. The trend of lumber and timber prices, continuing to rise persistently, forced itself upon the attention of the country. The spread of industrial combines had penetrated the area of wood manufacture and forest ownership: The widely accepted prospect of continued timber depletion and inflation had encouraged—and Federal land-disposal policies had made possible—the concentration of much timberland in the hands of big operators and speculators. Against this background, the Congress passed resolutions requesting the Secretary of Commerce and Labor to find out why lumber prices were so high, and especially whether they were the result of any contracts, agreements, or combinations in restraint of trade.

Thus was organized the hunt for the timber barons. Begun under the colors of the antitrust movement, the chase was long continued, under various banners.

It was the Commerce and Labor Department's Bureau of Corporations that made the study called for in the congressional resolutions. The Bureau compiled cruise data and timber estimates of forest owners and

[1] Hough, Franklin B.: *Report upon Forestry*, U.S. Government Printing Office, Washington, 1878; vol. II, 1880.

produced one of the earliest nationwide inventories of the timber resource. It also carried out one of the first comprehensive studies of lumber production and distribution in this country. Its reports, published in 1913 and 1914,[2] brought out that although lumber manufacturing permitted of no such scale economies as were enjoyed in steelmaking and oil refining (exemplifying the great American trusts of the era), the industry had an avenue toward monopoly through the control of raw-material supplies. They revealed that the development of such concentration was far advanced, three firms owning more than a tenth of all the privately held standing timber in the United States and 195 firms, nearly four-tenths (compare Chap. 25, p. 428). They described the vast speculative purchase and holding of timberland by the big owners, far ahead of use. They pointed to the enormous increases in the value of standing timber and in lumber prices, and attributed them partly to the industry's concentration and its conspiracies to curtail output and push prices up.

If you will look again at Figure 34 on page 307, you will see in what an amazing price era these investigators were living, and you will appreciate their concern. The era began in 1897 and lasted until the great crash of 1920.

*CAPPER REPORT*

While the Bureau of Corporations was reporting its anxiety over the combination and concentration aspects of the forest problem, the Forest Service was viewing with equal alarm the aspect of timber depletion. It was felt that this aspect should not be permitted to suffer deemphasis but should be given at least equal attention by the American public. Accordingly Senator Arthur Capper of Kansas introduced a resolution calling upon the Forest Service to determine

1. The facts as to the depletion of timber, pulp wood, and other forest resources in the United States.
2. Whether, and to what extent, this affects the present high cost of materials.
3. Whether the export of lumber, especially of hardwoods, jeopardizes our domestic industries.
4. Whether this reported depletion tends to increase the concentration of ownership in timberlands and the manufacture of lumber, and to what extent; and if such concentration exists, how it affects or may affect the public welfare.

[2] U.S. Department of Commerce and Labor, Bureau of Corporations: *The Lumber Industry*, Part I, *Standing Timber*, 1913; Part II, *Concentration of Timber Ownership in Selected Important Regions*, 1914; Part III, *Land Holdings of Large Timber Owners (with Ownership Maps)*, 1914; Part IV, *Conditions in Production and Wholesale Distribution Including Wholesale Prices*, 1914.

In its report,[3] released only a few months before the timber market fell apart in 1920, the Forest Service held that forest depletion was indeed serious and that it was the fundamental problem underlying current scarcities and high prices, though the effects of depletion were admittedly heightened by short-term influences such as those connected with the war. The Forest Service found that lumber exports did contribute somewhat to scarcity, at least of the top grades. It reported that the concentration of forest ownership was about the same as when the Bureau of Corporations studied the problem but that tendencies toward bigger combinations in manufacturing and distribution could be observed. It pointed to concentration and combination as holding a greater threat to the public welfare, the further depletion should progress.


## COPELAND REPORT

By the time of the next comprehensive problem analysis in forestry, contained in the Forest Service's Copeland Report,[4] things looked a good deal different. The timber economy had moved out of sellers-market prosperity, through a decade of relatively low prices, high costs, and fervid liquidation, into the abyss of the Great Depression. The national mind was turning ever more strongly toward government action to solve the many problems, including those of forestry, against which private initiative was apparently defenseless. In the forest economy, attention was shifting from the issue of concentration versus dispersion of private resource ownership to that of public versus private ownership, though in the private category, big holdings were still considered to be the crux of the problem. Many specific forestry issues peculiar to depression time were being emphasized. The outlook upon all of them was deeply colored by the pervading stain of low income and wide unemployment.

The forestry problem, stated the Copeland Report, is the failure to realize forest potentialities. It consists in the depletion of most of our forests and in too extensive management of all, and it reaches also to the abandoned farm lands that ought to be in trees. It is one of the major problems of the United States, because forest land is more than a third of all the land, because timber and the various services of the forest are part of the foundations of our national life, and because solving the forest problem will give employment, create new income, and generally strengthen the American rural economy and therefore the economy at large.

[3] U.S. Department of Agriculture, Forest Service: *Timber Depletion, Lumber Prices, Lumber Exports, and Concentration of Timber Ownership*, 1920.

[4] U.S. Department of Agriculture, Forest Service: *A National Plan for American Forestry*, 1933.

Nearly all of the American forestry problem, the thesis continues, centers in, or has grown out of, private ownership. Nine-tenths of all lightly stocked or denuded timber land is privately owned. More than 99 per cent of the improvident cutting and 98 per cent of the burning is on private forests. At the same time, four-fifths of the timber-growing land, with nine-tenths of the growth capacity, is privately owned. Problems of taxation, of demoralized forest industry, of impoverished forest communities, of scanty timber growth in relation to drain and requirements, and of depleted watersheds and other nontimber resources have all, in the main, arisen from the mishandling of private lands.

You will recognize in this Copeland Report analysis, completed in the very trough of hard times, the low-water mark for private forestry in the United States. And you can readily see how the problems as then viewed by the Forest Service were logically interpreted as the need for public forest acquisition, for public controls over private practice, and for research and extension to further the public interest.

## REAPPRAISAL AND OTHER ANALYSES

Following the Copeland Report came more nationwide forestry problem analyses, at increasingly frequent intervals. Among them were Forest Service analyses of 1935[5] and 1940;[6] a 1941 study by a Joint Congressional Committee;[7] the Forest Service Reappraisal of 1948[8] and, of contrasting tone, the pair of reports released by the American Forestry Association in 1946[9] and 1951[10] as a part of its Appraisal; the work of the President's Materials Policy Commission, published in 1952;[11] and the Forest Service's Timber Resource Review, of which the final report appeared in 1958.[12] Let us have a look at the problem sections of the Reap-

[5] U.S. Department of Agriculture, Forest Service: *Forest Land Resources, Requirements, Problems, and Policy, Part VIII of the Supplementary Report of the Land Planning Committee to the National Resources Board*, 1935.

[6] Marsh, R. E., and W. H. Gibbons: "Forest-resource Conservation," in *Farmers in a Changing World: The Yearbook of Agriculture, 1940*, U.S. Government Printing Office, Washington, pp. 458–488.

[7] United States Congress, Joint Committee on Forestry: *Forest Lands of the United States*, Senate Doc. 32, 77th Cong., 1st Sess., 1941.

[8] U.S. Department of Agriculture, Forest Service: *Forests and National Prosperity*, U.S. Department of Agriculture Miscellaneous Publication 668, 1948.

[9] Woods, John B.: "Report of the Forest Resource Appraisal," *American Forests*, September, 1946, pp. 413–428.

[10] American Forestry Association: *The Progress of Forestry 1945 to 1950*, Washington, 1951.

[11] President's Materials Policy Commission: *Resources for Freedom*, U.S. Government Printing Office, Washington, 1952, vol. I, pp. 36–45; vol. V, pp. 33–46.

[12] U.S. Department of Agriculture, Forest Service: *Timber Resources for America's Future*, Forest Resource Report 14, 1958. See especially pp. 102–109 and 1–102.

praisal and Timber Resource Review, which represent the principal bench marks in the evolution of Forest Service thinking since Copeland Report days.

In the Reappraisal Report we find no longer the cautious pessimism of depression time but a new, adventurous optimism tuned to visions of postwar prosperity and abundance. What role are forests to perform in an abundant world? The need will not be to make jobs, as it was in the 1930s. Rather it will be to turn out a broad stream of goods and services, and to do so as efficiently as possible. The estimated high level of timber requirements is used as the starting point for the analysis: timber requirements to sustain American standards of living and to meet anticipated obligations abroad in a smaller, more peaceful, and more prosperous world.

Against the requirements forecasts, the problems of the United States timber economy are judged. There is plenty of forest land, but a scarcity of wood supplies, particularly in the preferred species, larger sizes, and higher grades. Forests are being operated in the red, with growth falling short not only of goals but also of current consumption by an industry pinched for supplies. It will take several decades to boost timber growth to the level of the goal. Meanwhile the United States cannot count on increasing its timber imports and faces a dilemma that must be solved, if at all, through more intensive utilization—of virgin forests, of public forests, and of all timber in the course of conversion.

Thus still, in the Reappraisal analysis, forest depletion is the basic problem. And still the problem centers on private lands, where both forest protection and timber-cutting practices are deficient. But progress is being made in private forestry. The big holdings—which, as we saw, were once the prime object of concern—are being handled the best. The nub of the problem is the predominantly exploitive practice on the small holdings—farm woodlands and other little tracts—that make up three-fourths of the privately owned commercial forest land (see Fig. 10, p. 153).

## TIMBER RESOURCE REVIEW

In the Timber Resource Review, we find the spirit of the Reappraisal largely sustained and heightened. There has been a decade's experience with nearly continuous postwar economic growth, with population and national product sweeping upward at a new, steep pitch. It seems not too daring to suppose that by the year 2000—now little more than four decades away, not long as forestry planning goes—the population of the United States may reach 275 million, and the gross national product 1,200 billion 1953 dollars. And with a decade's new and encouraging experience with the potentialities of both private and public forestry, it seems not too bold to propose timber goals in keeping with the bright economic prospects, and to point out the accompanying need for "an intensity of forestry practices that will startle many of us" and that will have to come soon to be effective within the planning period.

We find in the Timber Resource Review, even more than in the Reappraisal and far more than in any previous national forestry planning, the use of the timber-requirements forecast as the take-off point—truly "first stage," as we have called it (p. 515)—in the study of forestry conditions, deficiencies, and needs. We looked at the requirements estimates in Chapter 31. Let us look now at the problem analysis that flows from them in the TRR, emphasizing saw-log-size timber, which is expected to make up four-fifths of the total timber demand in 2000.

To meet future timber requirements, the United States will need to rely largely on its own resources. To produce our requirements at the level of the medium estimate will call for more than doubling the present growth of saw timber by the year 2000. The mere continuation of recent forestry trends, though they are in the right direction and have produced an upswing in growth rates, would not be nearly enough to turn the trick. It would be necessary for all 490 million acres of commercial forest land to be managed as intensively as today's better-managed lands. There is, therefore, no surplus of land.

Higher growth requires drastic adjustments of timber inventory, generally upward. A fourth of the commercial forest land is less than 40 per cent stocked with trees. In the East, which has three-fourths of the forest land, hardwood saw timber would need to be doubled by 2000 to meet the medium goal; softwood saw timber would need to be increased fourfold. In the West, which has two-thirds of the saw-timber volume, the inventory could stand a one-fourth reduction in the course of converting old growth to managed second growth. During the past decade, the long downward national trend in saw timber has apparently been arrested, the inventory standing constant at some 2,000 billion board feet. Furthermore, most eastern tree species now show favorable ratios of growth to cut. On the other hand, timber size and quality are still declining. And the proportion of softwoods, the critical segment of the inventory, continues to fall. Douglas-fir and southern pine alone are depended upon for half of the entire saw-timber harvest.

To adjust timber inventories and increase growth will necessitate some shift in the balance of industry and consumption from softwoods toward hardwoods as well as great enlargement of the forest economy in the East. It will also call for greatly intensified resource management. More than 50 million acres are in need of planting. Destructive agents, principally insects and disease, cause a loss of gross timber growth nearly equal to the 47 billion board feet of net annual growth itself. A fourth of the timber cut is unused. Management practices fall far short of the necessary mark.

The timber-management problem centers on the privately owned forests other than those held by wood-using industry. It is gravest on the small holdings, and particularly acute in the South.

## SOME ISSUES TO CONSIDER

Now before it's too late, we owe it to ourselves to stand aside for a while from others' problem analyses and form some judgments of our own upon the basis of such understanding as we may have of the United States forest economy. Below are itemized briefly some issues for you to consider. [Which of them would you include in your own list, and how would you explain and elaborate them? Which would you reject, and why? What others would you add?] Bear in mind that the economic problems of forestry are not the forest's problems, nor the mill's, nor those of the system: They are people's problems.

1. Ignorance. Too little is known about the basic psychological and physical determinants of the forest economy: consumers' preferences, forest owners' objectives, forestry inputs and outputs, and the potentialities of genetic and mechanical production. Too little is known about the quality of wood and other forest products and how to measure quality.

All the economic problems of forestry may be regarded as arising from ignorance. However, let us continue with the listing of a few issues that appear to deserve separate emphasis.

2. Achieving the public interest. How determine the public interest amidst the conflicting claims of influence centers? Is it possible, in a commercially oriented society, to give due weight to those goods and services of which the value is not readily measurable in money terms?

3. Multiple-purpose forest management. The idea of such management on individual properties and even on the same acres is widely accepted as a means for efficient resource use. But practice has yet to be developed and is held back by uncertainty about values, by interproduct conflicts, and by lack of leadership. Significantly, in the forestry colleges and the profession, and therefore among the public, the term *forest management* is generally used to mean timber management.

4. Resource exploitation. How may forest owners' choices between present and future be turned in the direction of the public interest? How may alternative rates of return be reduced, particularly in the case of the small, low-income owner? On the other hand, can a prosperous society practice conservation of its major resources?

5. Organization of the forestry firm. The great majority of firms that

control forest resources, such as the farms and other little holdings, are not organized for forest management. For such lands, workable types of organization have still to be discovered: the economic size of unit, its relation to other enterprises, the form of ownership, and the means for bringing technical knowledge to bear on planning and operation.

6. Inaccessibility of timber resources. At the same time that some forest areas and components are being overexploited, others are underused. Examples of the latter are the tropical hardwoods of the world, the back stretches of Western national forests, and the local leavings of logger and miller. The deficiencies are partly in transportation, but perhaps mostly in technical knowledge of materials and their extraction.

7. Lagging technology. Inaccessibility, scarcity, and high prices of timber products arise partly from the failure of technology in silviculture and conversion to keep pace with changes in the forest and changes in general productivity. A prime need is for more efficient methods of growing and handling wood.

8. Instability. Forest conservation thrives best in an equable economy and under consistent and continuing policies, where risks and discount rates are low. Cyclical ups and downs of the economy and instability of forest-land tenure, especially of the small holdings, are to be regarded as major problems.

9. Atoms versus aggregates. In the forest economy there still remain large elements of atomization and price competition, while in the general economy these elements have become minor. The small forest firm and the lumber industry are most markedly out of step with the world. How may the forest economy adapt itself to such a world?

10. Oversophistication of foresters. Forestry problems pertain not only to the consumer, landowner, and middleman, but also to the forester. Their gravity demands professional dedication—to the public interest as well as to that of immediate employers. Their long-term character calls for the exercise of vision. Their large noncommercial content requires the display of some militant idealism. Do we foresters think sufficiently of the failings of the forest economy as our problem, our fault, and our responsibility?

## SUMMARY

The economic problems of forestry in the United States have been analyzed in a series of national planning studies, mostly by Federal agencies and mostly emphasizing the timber resource.

Dr. Hough's 1878–1880 Report upon Forestry stresses local depletion and the need for developing forestry policy and practice. Scarcity and high prices of wood products are the subject of both the Bureau of

Corporations Report of 1913–1914 and the Capper Report of 1920, the former dwelling upon the effects of industrial land acquisition, the latter, of forest depletion. In the depression-time Copeland Report (1933), the big problems are associated with the private ownership of forests. On the other hand, the optimism of a great era of economic growth characterizes the Reappraisal Report of 1948 and the Timber Resource Review Report of 1958, both of which point to the problem of the small forest holding and the need for great intensification of forestry practice by all owners in light of high prospective national requirements for timber.

Our own study of forestry-economics fundamentals suggests additional problems or issues that merit thoughtful attention.

# INDEX

This index serves also as a glossary of special terms. Page references in **bold-face** type indicate definitions or explanations.

567